Terry Ackman

Applied Numerical Methods
for
Digital Computation
with FORTRAN

Applied Numerical Methods
for
Digital Computation
with FORTRAN

M. L. James

G. M. Smith   **J. C. Wolford**

Department of Engineering Mechanics
The University of Nebraska

International Textbook Company
Scranton, Pennsylvania

K-U-RC

Preface

Engineering methods and techniques have changed considerably during the past decade, as a result of the extensive use of high-speed computers in the solution of all sorts of problems encountered in design, research, and development. Therefore, it is essential for the modern engineer to be familiar with the numerical methods used in programming problems on the computer.

This text presents the principles and methods essential to the solution of engineering and scientific problems on the digital computer. The text is written with the philosophy that the most effective approach to learning numerical methods is to integrate the theoretical study with the actual solution of problems on the computer. In this manner the student is better able to appreciate and understand the power of numerical methods as a scientific tool when used in conjunction with modern high-speed digital computers.

To accomplish this end, the theoretical discussions of the numerical methods are complemented by the formulation of FORTRAN programs for the solution of typical engineering problems from the various disciplines.

The authors have included material of a scope intended to make the text adaptable for use at several course levels, since the level of the material which can be presented in a particular course depends upon the background of the students taking the course.

Chapter 1 presents basic FORTRAN—the most commonly used elements of the language. Most of the programs in the text can be understood after becoming familiar with the basic elements of FORTRAN II and IV presented in this chapter.

Chapter 2 presents additional FORTRAN for more advanced programming. It consists of those elements of FORTRAN IV not covered in Chapter 1.

Chapters 3 through 8 present many of the most commonly used numerical methods. An introduction to error analysis of numerical methods for integrating differential equations is included.

The authors wish to acknowledge the many individuals who have directly, or indirectly, contributed to this book. These contributions

v

from former teachers, colleagues, and students have occurred over many years, and it is impossible to acknowledge specifically each individual. The authors do wish especially to acknowledge the generosity of the IBM Corporation in furnishing **FORTRAN** specifications for their various computers. We are particularly grateful to our wives, Jane, Lois, and Joan, for their patience and understanding during the preparation of this text.

M. L. JAMES
G. M. SMITH
J. C. WOLFORD

Lincoln, Nebraska
October, 1967

Contents

part II   Digital-Computer Methods . . . 125

chapter 3   Roots of Algebraic and Transcendental Equations 127

chapter 4   Solution of Simultaneous Linear Algebraic Equations . . . 184

chapter 5   Numerical Integration and Differentiation 272

chapter 6   Numerical Integration of Ordinary Differential Equations: Initial-Value Problems 313

Applied Numerical Methods
for
Digital Computation
with FORTRAN

part I

The FORTRAN System

The material presented on the **FORTRAN** language in the first chapter is concerned with basic **FORTRAN**—the most commonly used elements of the language. Both **FORTRAN II** and **FORTRAN IV** will be discussed simultaneously, since the former is essentially a "subset" of the latter, the basic elements of both having a generally common language. The few differences which exist between the two versions, in the basic material covered in Chapter 1, will be called to the reader's attention as they appear. The majority of the programs in the text can be understood after becoming familiar with the basic **FORTRAN** material in this chapter.

Chapter 2 discusses additional **FORTRAN** for the more advanced programmer using the language of **FORTRAN IV**. Those elements in this chapter which are common to both **FORTRAN II** and **FORTRAN IV** will be pointed out to the reader as they appear.

chapter 1

Introduction to the Digital Computer and the FORTRAN System

1-1. Introduction

Primitive man did his counting and simple arithmetic with the aid of his fingers, pebbles, and sticks, by relating these objects to other objects such as sheep, goats, cattle, and so on. His pile of sticks or stones constituted the earliest primitive digital computer. The abacus, developed some 3000 years ago, represents the first great advance in digital computation.

In 1642 Blaise Pascal, a French religious philosopher, scientist, and mathematician, developed the first mechanical adding machine which was similar in principle to present-day machines. This machine is now on display in a French museum. In 1671 the German philosopher and mathematician Gottfried Wilhelm von Leibniz independently conceived a more-advanced mechanical calculator, which he completed in 1694.

Automatic mechanical calculators were suggested as early as the 18th century, but the technical knowledge required to build them was lacking. Joseph Jacquard, a French loom designer, perfected an automatic pattern loom in 1804 which contributed to the development of computers. The sequence of operations for the loom was controlled by punched cards, and the loom made intricate patterns as easily as other looms made plain cloth.

About 1833 the British mathematician Charles Babbage conceived and designed on paper the first automatic digital computer, which he called an "analytical engine." It had many features of modern computers. It was proposed to use a variation of the control mechanism of the Jacquard loom to control the sequence of arithmetic operations. These operations were to be specified, in advance, by means of punched cards. All calculations were to be done mechanically, and numbers were to be stored by the position of counter wheels. Unfortunately, this automatic computer was never built, owing to technical and financial difficulties, and an embittered Babbage died in 1871 without completing a working model, and with few people having even taken his work seriously.

It was not until the 1940's that computers, similar in principle to the one conceived by Babbage, were actually built. The first of these, known as the Automatic Sequence-Controlled Calculator, or Mark I, was designed by Howard Aiken of Harvard University, and was completed by the International Business Machine (IBM) Company in 1944. The Mark I was capable of performing a fixed sequence of operations controlled by punched tape. It consisted mainly of mechanical and electromechanical components and had a memory capable of storing 72 numbers of 24 digits each. World War II gave a definite impetus to the development of computers, and the Electronic Numerical Integrator and Calculator (ENIAC) was built under United States Army contract. It was completed in 1946 by engineers at the University of Pennsylvania, and was similar to the Mark I, except that it was predominantly electronic in operation and therefore performed its computations much more quickly. Its input and output were in the form of IBM punched cards.

A significant advance in computers was made in 1945 when John von Neumann, of the Princeton Institute for Advanced Study, and H. H. Goldstine, of the Army Ordnance Department, proposed storing in the computer memory the sequence of operations to be performed, along with the numbers which were to be operated on. This proposal was made in an Army Ordnance Department report, after an exchange of ideas with J. P. Eckert and John Mauchly of the Moore School of Electrical Engineering at the University of Pennsylvania. This feature enabled the computer to "branch"; that is, to follow either of two alternate sequences of steps, depending upon some condition existing at the time of execution of the branching instruction. It also made "looping" much easier; the repetitive execution of portions of the internally stored program of instructions could be easily accomplished. Thus, this important idea greatly increased the computing facility of the digital computer.

Digital-computer installations were constructed at only a moderate rate in the early 1950's, since it was felt that all the computing requirements of this country could be handled at a few large installations. However, the demand for computing facilities grew much faster than had been anticipated, and, at the present time, literally thousands of digital computers are being installed annually. It appears that this growth will surely continue, so it is imperative that most graduating engineers have some degree of familiarity with the programming and operation of digital computers.

Many equations in engineering problems, even though they can be solved analytically in closed form, require a great deal of tiresome and time-consuming work which can be eliminated by programming the equations to some type of computer. Other equations cannot be solved analytically, and, although their approximate solutions may be obtained by various numerical methods, these often involve large numbers of calculations which are time-consuming when performed manually. Furthermore, in some instances an engineer may wish to know the effect of changing certain design parameters on the behavior of a system, which necessitates the solving of the problem many times with different sets of data. A digital computer can be employed to perform the large number of calculations required, and, since they are executed at tremendous speeds, solutions are obtained quickly as well as accurately.

The digital computer performs arithmetic operations upon discrete numbers in a defined sequence of steps. Owing to modern developments in programming techniques, it is not necessary to be familiar with the details of the internal computing processes of a digital computer to be able to use one. It is helpful, however, to have a general concept of the operational characteristics of the computer, in order to understand its capabilities and limitations. Therefore, a brief discussion of the history of computers and of their components, functions, and operations is included here, although the primary topic of the chapter is the use of the FORTRAN compiler.

1-2. Digital-Computer Components

The modern electronic digital computer performs its functions by utilizing sequences of numerical operations performed upon discrete numbers. Five basic components are employed: 1) the *input* unit, which is used to provide data and instructions to the computer; 2) the *memory* or *storage* unit, in which data and instructions are stored; 3) the *arithmetic-logic* unit, which performs the arithmetic operations and provides the "decision-making" ability, or logic, of the computer; 4) the *control* unit, which controls and computer operations; and 5) the *output* unit, from which the computer results are obtained. The control unit and arithmetic-logic unit are often considered as a single unit, called the *central-processing* unit. The relationships of these components are shown symbolically in Fig. 1-1, where the lines indicate the flow of instructions and data or control information.

Input Unit. The input unit generally consists of one of the following devices: a card reader, a paper-tape reader, a magnetic-tape reader, a special typewriter, or a manual keyboard. The instructions, coded in machine language in the form of numbers or other characters, are transmitted by the input device to the memory unit of the computer before computation begins. Data may be transmitted by the input unit to the

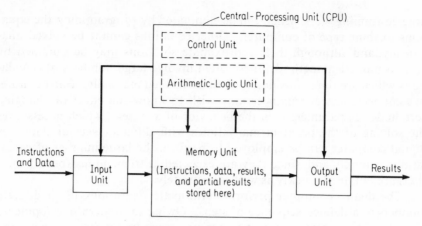

FIG. 1-1. Basic components of a digital computer.

memory unit before computation begins or may be "read in," as needed, during computation.

Memory or Storage Unit.   The memory unit must be capable of storing the numbers and other characters which represent instructions and data. Although many devices have been employed for storage, the use of magnetic cores for main memory is predominant, because of the rapidity with which the stored information can be located and transferred to another component. (The time required for such an operation is known as the *access time* of the computer.)   Magnetic cores are small rings of ferromagnetic material which can be magnetized with either polarity.   The numbers stored are in some form of the *binary*-number system.   Numbers can be represented in this system by just 2 digits (0 and 1), corresponding very conveniently to the two polarity states available in the computer. Although numbers are stored in pure binary form in many computers, they may also be stored in binary coded decimal form.   In the latter, each decimal digit of the number is stored in binary form, but the decimal sequence of the digits is maintained.   Numbers are thus represented in the computer by an array of polarities which the computer circuitry is designed to recognize.   Although it is not necessary for the engineer to understand the form of the binary-number system used in the computer, it is convenient if he is sufficiently familiar with the system to be able to read the contents of the computer registers, which are often displayed in some binary form.

The memory unit receives the instructions and data and stores them in separately assigned locations.   Each of these storage locations is designated by a numerical address, which identifies the location to the computer.   Once the data and instructions have been stored, they are subsequently always referred to by their numerical address.   In addition to storing data and instructions, the memory unit is utilized to store intermediate and final results for subsequent use or readout, or for comparison purposes. As mentioned above, the time it takes the computer to locate an instruction and transfer it to the control unit for interpretation, or the time it takes to locate a unit of data in memory and transfer it to the arithmetic unit for a computation, is known as the access time of the computer. Some modern high-speed computers have access times which are measured in *nanoseconds* (billionths of a second).

Arithmetic-Logic Unit. The arithmetic-logic units consists of all the electronic circuitry necessary for performing the various arithmetic operations and for supplying computer logic. The latter is usually accomplished by performing tests on certain conditions existing in the computer, to decide which of alternate sequences of steps will be followed.

Control Unit. The control unit consists of the circuitry required to take the instructions from memory, interpret them, and cause them to be executed. Normally, the instructions in memory are followed in sequential order, unless the control unit in instructed by the program to interrupt the sequence.

Output Unit. The results obtained as a consequence of the arithmetic operations performed by the computer must be communicated to the operator. This is accomplished by some type of output unit. Output units usually consist of one of the following devices: a tape punch, a magnetic-tape unit, a card punch, a special typewriter, a line printer, or a graphical plotter. Time is saved if the output data are punched on tape or cards or put on magnetic tape or in a disk file, and the results plotted or printed "off line," since the computer can often perform its operations faster than the results of the operations can be tabulated in final numerical form.

The functions of the various units will be described further as computer applications are discussed.

1-3. Preparing a Digital-Computer Program

The first phase in programming a problem to the digital computer is to decide on the approach or method to be used in obtaining the solution. Since the digital computer is capable of performing only arithmetic operations, problems which cannot be solved by arithmetic procedures, when in their usual form, must be put in a form consistent with such procedures. Obviously, a problem in addition can be solved per se, since its solution is inherently an arithmetic operation. However, the closed-form solution of a differential equation, for example, is not an arithmetic operation. An arithmetic procedure for solving such an equation must be developed. Such procedures are discussed in detail in subsequent chapters.

Once a method of solution has been selected, the problem must be programmed to the computer as a definite step-by-step procedure. This is called an *algorithm*. The second phase of programming is to establish a general outline of the steps involved in the algorithm. One method is to write the steps in a numbered sequence. More frequently, however, the algorithm is stated graphically by means of a *flow chart*, in which the steps are displayed in the form of a block diagram. A flow chart may show the required steps in considerable detail, or it may merely outline the general procedure necessary to obtain a computer solution to the problem. In general, excessively detailed procedures should be avoided in the flow chart, since its primary purpose is merely to outline the overall process, which will be implemented by the more specific steps appearing in the finished computer program. The use of a flow chart is illustrated in Example 1-1 (Fig. 1-3).

The computer must be instructed very specifically for it to perform its operations. In fact, each step must be initiated by an instruction. The instructions which the computer interprets and executes must be transmitted to it in a *coded* form which it can interpret. Thus, the third phase of programming is to write the *specific* program steps in coded form, following the outline provided by the flow chart. This procedure is called coding, and the resulting program is called a *machine-language* program.

Coding is a tedious task if the program is a long one, but, fortunately, it is no longer necessary to code the steps manually. The computer itself can be programmed to write the machine-language program. The desired program is first written in a less-detailed and much simpler language very similar to ordinary English and algebra. The simpler program is then translated into machine language by the computer. To accomplish this translation, the computer must first have a specially written machine-language program read into its memory. Such a special program is called a *translator*, a *processor*, or a *compiler*. The FORTRAN processor, or compiler, is an example of such a special program. It will be discussed in detail in later sections of this chapter.

If a compiler is not used and the machine-language program is written manually, it must next be transcribed to a suitable medium, such as tape or cards, so that it may be fed to the computer through the appropriate type of input unit.

If the machine-language program is compiled by the computer, it is stored on magnetic tape (or some other type of auxiliary storage facility), or is punched on cards or tape, as part of the compilation process. This completes the programming and translation phases of the computer routine, after which the execution phase, involving the actual computation, follows.

EXAMPLE 1-1

As an example of flow charting, let us consider the following problem. It is desired to find the first positive nonzero solution of the equation

$$1 + 5.25x - \sec\sqrt{0.68x} = 0$$

An approximate graph of the function $F(x) = 1 + 5.25x - \sec\sqrt{0.68x}$ is shown in Fig. 1-2. We must determine the first point at which the graph of the function crosses the x axis, as shown. For small values of x, the

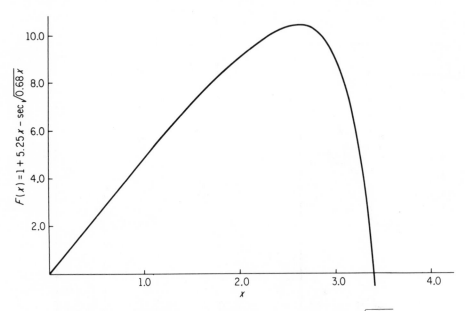

FIG. 1-2. Approximate graph of $F(x) = 1 + 5.25x - \sec\sqrt{0.68x}$.

function will be positive. The technique will consist of calculating $F(x)$ for successively larger values of x, starting at $x = \Delta x$, and incrementing x by successive values of $\Delta x = 0.1$, until the function becomes negative. We will then know that the x value for which the function will be zero has been exceeded. We then revert to the immediately preceding x value and again increase x, this time incrementing by a smaller amount, say one tenth of the previously used Δx. Incrementing continues until the function again becomes negative. Again, we revert to the immediately preceding value of x and begin to increase x with still-smaller increments. This procedure continues until the value of x which represents the first positive nonzero solution is obtained with the desired accuracy. The result is then printed.

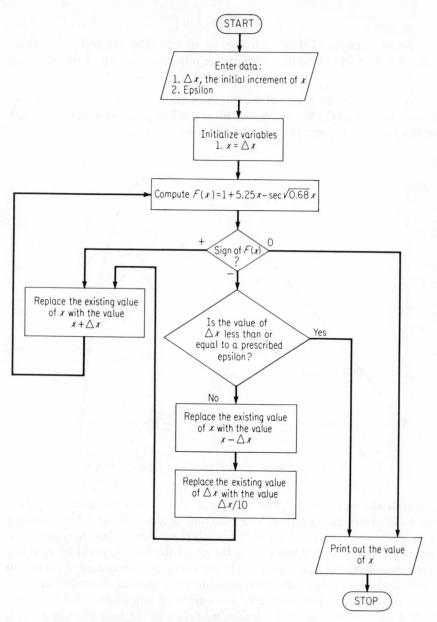

FIG. 1-3. Flow chart for Example 1-1.

As crude as this method may appear to be, a computer solution can rapidly be obtained by its use, since the computer performs the indicated operations so swiftly. Convergence to a solution can be obtained even more rapidly if we refine the preceding technique by writing a slightly more complicated program, using, for example, the Newton-Raphson method (illustrated in Sec. 3-4).

A flow chart for the foregoing solution is shown in Fig. 1-3. At this point, the reader should study the flow chart and correlate the notes in the blocks with the preceding problem discussion. Note that the flow chart merely outlines the general procedure to be followed. The actual program would be written by following this outline and detailing to the computer the specific instructions necessary to implement the procedures outlined in the blocks. The block symbols used for this flow chart, which will also be used in subsequent discussions in the text, are described in Fig. 1-4.

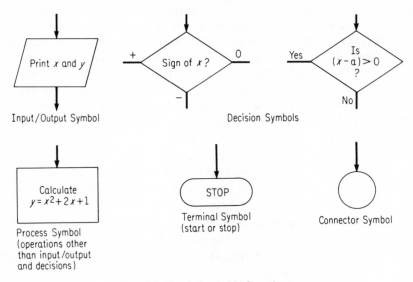

FIG. 1-4. Symbols used in flow charts.

1-4. Computer Sequence of Operations

If the computer is under *manual* control, the computer operating instructions, which are usually on cards or tape, are read into the computer by means of the input unit and then stored in the memory unit. These machine-language instructions may have been manually punched on cards or tape, or they may have been punched under computer control as the computer translated the compiler-language program, if a compiler program is being used.

If the computer is under *monitor* control (discussed at the end of this section), the machine-language instructions go into the main memory from an auxiliary storage device, such as a magnetic-tape unit or a disk file, where they have been stored as part of the translation process.

With the machine-language instructions in memory, computation begins with the control unit going to the location in memory in which the first instruction is stored and then interpreting the instruction it finds there. After interpretation, the computer executes the instruction, and the control unit returns to the memory unit for the next instruction. The above cycle is repeated over and over until the problem is finished and the computer is instructed to stop. One of the first instructions executed in most programs is for the computer to read data. The data values are stored in memory and are using during subsequent operations.

An instruction stored in memory may be a number in some binary form, as mentioned earlier. A typical instruction consists of an *operation code* defined by 2 digits, and 1 or 2 memory addresses, depending on whether a single- or double-address type of instruction is used. In some cases, data may be included as part of an instruction (IBM 1620 *immediate instructions*). Let us examine an example instruction used in an addition procedure. The coded instruction directs the computer to add the contents of the given address to the contents of the arithmetic-unit register and leave in the register the sum obtained. This instruction for a particular computer would look as follows:

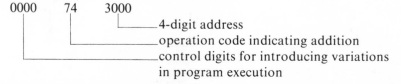

The number to be added to the contents of the arithmetic-unit register would be found in memory location 3000. The preceding is an example of a single-address system. A typical double-address instruction would be

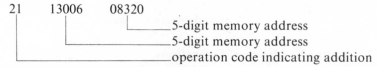

Here, the computer is instructed to add the number at the second address to the number at the first address and to replace the number at the first address by the sum computed.

As mentioned earlier, a cycle of operation consists of the control unit taking an instruction from memory, interpreting it, and causing its execution. It then returns to memory for another instruction. Unless instructed otherwise, the control unit takes instructions from memory sequentially. This sequence may be interrupted by certain instructions given to the computer: a *conditional branch* instruction and an *unconditional branch* instruction are examples. A conditional branch instruction involves computer *logic* or decision making, since the transfer depends upon some condition which the computer must test or check. For example, the instruction might tell the computer to go to a certain address in memory and sample the number therein. If the number is not zero, the computer is to interrupt the sequence and go to a specified address; if the number is zero, the computer is to continue the memory-address sequence. In this manner, various *branches* or paths are incorporated in the program, and the computer logic determines which path the computer will take. An unconditional branch instruction interrupts the memory-address sequence by arbitrarily instructing the computer to leave the sequence and go to a specified memory address.

The flow of information in the computer is illustrated by the chart of Fig. 1-5. The arrows indicate the flow of instructions and data or control information between the various units of the computer.

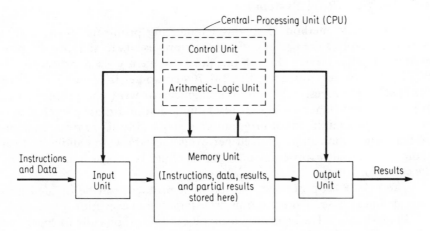

FIG. 1-5. Diagram illustrating communication between computer units.

Computer-System Monitors. As mentioned above, a computer system may be under either manual or monitor control. Most large computing centers have computers which operate under monitor control. The monitor program is a machine-language program which is put in computer memory and used to control the entire computer system. Little operator intervention is required. The various jobs, consisting of source programs, subroutines, data, and the required monitor cards, may be stacked in a card reader or transferred to magnetic tape. They are then processed by the computer, in rapid succession, with little idle time between jobs. The monitor program may be capable of calling on any of several different compilers for translation, depending upon the language in which the source program is written.

The translation is usually done in 2 steps. The source program is first translated into a machine-oriented language, which is still not executable and for which specific storage locations have not been assigned. The machine-oriented language instructions are next converted to machine-language instructions by a special program, called an *assembler*, which also assigns specific memory locations for the instructions.

After translation, the main program and any subprograms used are stored in main memory, and the control passes to the object program for execution. Execution is initiated immediately after translation, as described on page 16 for a "compile-and-go" operation. As soon as the execution of one job is complete, control reverts to the monitor program, which calls for the next job. If errors are detected in compiling a program, the object program is not loaded into main memory, the job is dumped, and the next job is called for.

1-5. The FORTRAN System

The modern method of solving engineering problems on the digital computer involves the use of compilers or processors to simplify the programming procedures. One of the most frequently used processors is FORTRAN, first developed for the IBM 704 computer in 1956. The use of the FORTRAN processor permits the engineer to write the problem program in a simple language closely resembling that of ordinary English and algebra, with a minimum of programming steps. In this process, as mentioned earlier, the computer itself performs the otherwise tedious task of coding the problem program into the machine language understood by the computer.

The FORTRAN-processor solution of a problem can be divided into three distinct phases—preparation, translation, and execution.

Preparation. The algorithm is first described graphically by means of a flow chart, as discussed in Sec. 1-3. Then, following the outline provided by the flow chart, the specific steps of the program are written in FORTRAN language. The resulting sequence of steps is called a *source* program. This program is next punched on cards or tape, and the resulting card deck or tape is known as a *source deck* or *source tape*. Data which are to be read in during the execution of the program are punched either on additional *data cards* or on separate tapes, known as data tapes, depending upon the type of input reader being used. This procedure usually completes the preparation phase.

Translation. The FORTRAN processor, which is on cards, on paper tape, or in some auxiliary storage device, and which is actually a program in itself, is next read into the memory of the computer. With this program in memory, the computer has the information and instructions necessary to interpret the FORTRAN statements of the source program. As the source program is read in, the computer translates the FORTRAN statements into its own machine language. The resulting program is known as the *object program*. As each statement is translated into machine language, it may be punched on cards or tape by the output unit, so that the object program is obtained in the form of an *object deck* or an *object tape*. If the computer is under monitor control, the object program is usually stored in auxiliary memory, where it is immediately available for execution.

The computer programs necessary to obtain the various mathematical functions commonly appearing in many problems are not programmed as part of the problem program each time they are needed. Instead, they are prepared in advance, as separate machine-language programs recorded on cards, paper tape, or magnetic tape, and thus they can be appropriately inserted in any problem program when needed. Such prepared programs are known as *subroutines* or *subprograms*. The FORTRAN language provides various classes of subprograms (discussed later in the text). They are usually introduced into the problem program in the process of compiling the object program, and they become a part of the object deck or tape if the object program is punched out. Sometimes the subroutines are read directly into memory at the time when the object program is read in; in this case, they do not become an integral part of the object deck or tape. Typical subroutines would include those for various trigonometric functions, square roots, exponential functions, absolute values, and so forth. The sequence and preparation of an object program for a system in which the subroutines are on cards or tape, and must be read into the computer via the input unit, are charted in Fig. 1-6.

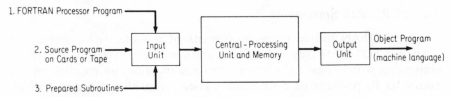

FIG. 1-6. Translation of the FORTRAN program into machine language.

Execution. Execution is the last phase of a computer solution. The machine-language object program, on cards or paper tape or in auxiliary storage, is brought into memory and stored at addresses assigned by the FORTRAN processor. If the subroutines are not part of the object program, they must be read into memory before execution begins. If the object program is brought into main memory from auxiliary storage immediately after compilation, and control is immediately transferred to the object program, the procedure is called a "compile-and-go" or a "load-and-go" operation. In a compile-and-go operation, an object deck or tape is not normally punched. In systems where a compile-and-go operation is not possible, the object program is punched on cards or tape and read into memory through the input unit. In either case, the computer now has the appropriate instructions for solving the given problem, stored in memory in the machine language with which its circuits are designed to work, and is ready to execute the program. At this time the data deck or tape must be in the input unit, ready to be read in. When execution is initiated, an instruction in the object program (placed there during compilation as the result of a statement in the source program) tells the computer to read cards or tape, and the data are read into memory. With this method of reading data into the computer, the same object program may be used, with many different combinations of data, merely by changing data decks or tapes. The data can be included in the source program rather than on separate cards, as just described, but this reduces the flexibility of the program, because the data cannot be varied without compiling a new object program. The execution phase for a system in which the object program is punched on cards or tape and read into memory via the input unit is shown in Fig. 1-7.

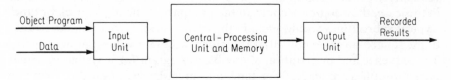

FIG. 1-7. Execution of the machine-language program.

1-6. FORTRAN Statements

A FORTRAN source program consists of a sequence of statements written in FORTRAN language. There are five general types of FORTRAN statements which convey the instructions and information required by the computer to perform its operations. They are arithmetic- and logical-assignment statements,[1] control statements, input and output statements, specification statements, and subprogram statements. In Chapter 1 we shall discuss only arithmetic-assignment statements, control statements, input and output statements, and specification statements. Before these statements can be explained in detail, the language in which they are written must be discussed. However, at this point we shall describe the func-

---

[1] In FORTRAN II, arithmetic-assignment statements are known simply as "arithmetic statements."

tions of the statements, returning to them in more detail after we have studied the elements of the FORTRAN language.

Arithmetic-Assignment Statements. These statements define the arithmetic operations which the computer is to perform in solving a problem, and they instruct the computer to perform them. These statements have the general appearance of ordinary algebraic formulas. For example, the FORTRAN statement

$$D = (B*B - 4.*A*C)**.5$$

instructs the computer to perform the arithmetic operations specified in the algebraic equation

$$D = (B^2 - 4AC)^{1/2}$$

The similarity in form of these expressions is evident.

Control Statements. Control statements are used principally to control the order in which the series of statements comprising the program are executed when there is to be a departure from the usual sequential execution. *Unconditional* and *conditional transfer* statements are examples of such control statements. The conditional transfer statement

$$IF(X-A)2,5,8$$

instructs the computer to check the magnitude of the quantity (X-A) and then to go to statement 2, statement 5, or statement 8, depending on whether the magnitude checked is less than zero, equal to zero, or greater than zero, respectively. Such a control statement is a method of providing computer logic.

Input and Output Statements. These are used to control the operation of the input and output units, respectively. A typical input statement such as

$$READ\ 3,X,Y,Z$$

would instruct the input unit to read in data corresponding to the quantities X, Y, and Z. The output statement

$$PRINT\ 6,Z$$

instructs the output unit to print the value of Z.

Specification Statements. Specification statements supply certain required information to the FORTRAN processor. These do not appear in the object program but are interpreted by the FORTRAN processor when the source tape or deck is read in. The DIMENSION statement is a typical specification statement. The dimension statement

$$DIMENSION\ A(10,10)$$

for example, reserves space for 100 subscripted variables in the computer memory.

Statement Length. The permissible length of FORTRAN statements (the number of characters in a statement) depends on the version of

FORTRAN used. In a version which does not permit *continuation* of statements on successive cards, 72 characters is the maximum permissible. Most versions permitting continuation cards allow at least 5 such cards, and many allow as much as 19 cards. A maximum of 72 FORTRAN characters (including blanks) is allowed per card. The FORTRAN statement

$$12 \ D = (B*B - 4.*A*C)**.5$$

for example, has 28 characters, including the blank spaces within the statement and three blank spaces preceding the statement. It would appear on a coding form as

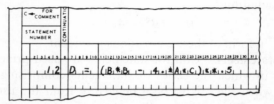

where the numbers across the coding form correspond to card columns. The format for writing FORTRAN statements will be discussed later in this chapter.

Numbering of Statements. Statements are normally not numbered unless they are to be referred to by a control or an input/output statement in the program. When a statement is designated by a number, the number precedes the statement proper, as illustrated by the number 12 in the statement shown in the preceding paragraph. The numbers assigned to such statements need not have any particular sequence, as long as an identifying number is not repeated. The number 0 is not permitted as a statement number.

Comments. Statements in the source program, which are included merely to provide information to the reader *about* the program, are called comments. Such statements do not appear in the object program but are interpreted as comments by the FORTRAN processor as the source program is read in. Comments are printed out along with the other statements of the source program in the listing during compilation. Comments are governed by slightly different rules in different versions of FORTRAN. In FORTRAN II and FORTRAN IV, if a C appears in the first column of a source-deck card, the following information on that card is treated as a comment. In some FORTRAN versions (IBM 1620 FORTRAN with FORMAT, for example) a statement beginning with a C and followed by 2 or more blanks is a comment. The following is a typical comment as it would appear printed in a source-program listing:

C   MISSILE PROGRAM

This comment would be used merely to identify, in the listing, the subject matter of the program. Comment statements are quite often used to identify the various parts of a program, and they are very helpful to the reader in understanding what the program is accomplishing. In some versions of FORTRAN, comments may occupy card columns 2 through 80, whereas in others the comments cannot extend past column 72. For longer comments, additional comment cards are used. The program listings beginning on pages 250 and 261 illustrate the use of comments.

1-7. The FORTRAN Source Program

Having studied the general types of FORTRAN statements and some examples of them, let us next consider in more detail how these statements are written and punched. Preferably, a FORTRAN source program is written on a *coding form* such as the one shown in Fig. 1-8. Coding-form columns 1 through 80 correspond to the 80 columns on a standard punch card. Each line of the coding form corresponds to 1 card.

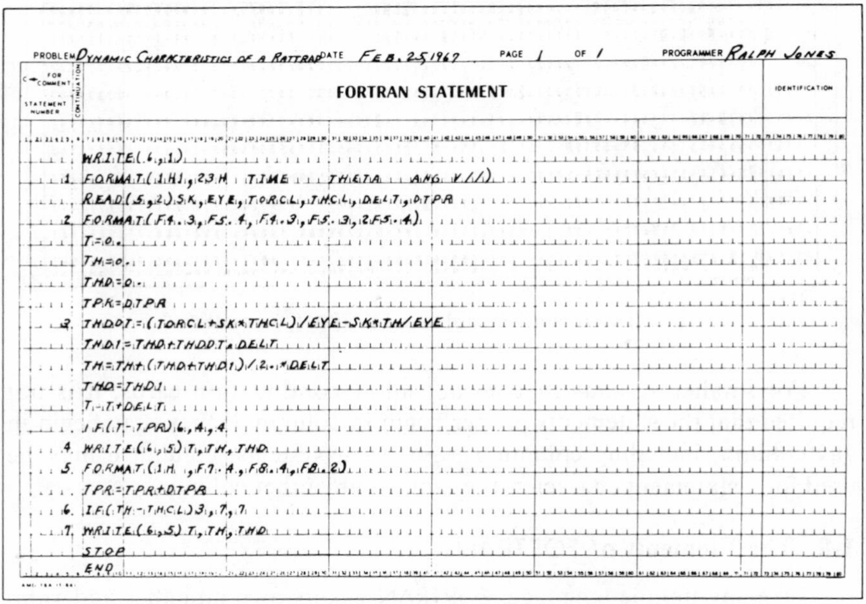

PROBLEM DYNAMIC CHARACTERISTICS OF A RATTRAP DATE FEB. 25 1967 PAGE 1 OF 1 PROGRAMMER RALPH JONES

FORTRAN STATEMENT

```
      WRITE(6,1)
    1 FORMAT(1H1,23H   TIME     THETA    ANG V//)
      READ(5,2)SK,EYE,TORCL,THCL,DELT,DTPR
    2 FORMAT(F4.3,F5.4,F4.3,F5.3,2F5.4)
      T=0.
      TH=0.
      THD=0.
      TPR=DTPR
    3 THDOT=(TORCL+SK*THCL)/EYE-SK*TH/EYE
      THD1=THD+THDOT*DELT
      TH=TH+(THD+THD1)/2.*DELT
      THD=THD1
      T=T+DELT
      IF(T-TPR)6,4,4
    4 WRITE(6,5)T,TH,THD
    5 FORMAT(1H ,F7.4,F8.4,F8.2)
      TPR=TPR+DTPR
    6 IF(TH-THCL)3,7,7
    7 WRITE(6,5)T,TH,THD
      STOP
      END
```

FIG. 1-8. A FORTRAN source program written on a FORTRAN coding form.

As previously mentioned, some statements must be numbered. The statement numbers are written in columns 1 through 5 of the coding form and, in most FORTRAN versions, consist of from 1 to 5 digits written without a decimal point. (Some FORTRAN versions for smaller systems permit a maximum of 4 digits for statement numbers.) The statements proper are written, 1 to a line, in columns 7 through 72. Blanks may be used, as desired, to increase readability, but they are ignored by the compiler. If a statement is too long to write on a single line, it may be continued on successive lines by placing any character (other than a blank or a zero) in column 6 of each continuation line. Columns 73 through 80 are ignored by the compiler and may be used for numbering the cards, identifying the program, miscellaneous information, and so forth.

In punching the source deck, the statements are punched in the cards exactly as they are written on the coding form. Each column of the coding form corresponds to a card column. A card, with a statement from the source program of Fig. 1-8 punched in it, is shown in Fig. 1-9. If a computer with a punched paper-tape input is used, the tape is punched by typing the statements just as they are written on the coding form.

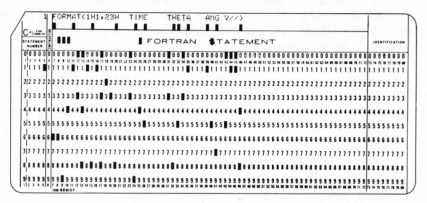

Fig. 1-9. A punched card for a FORTRAN source deck.

For smaller systems that do not allow continuation cards, it is not required that the statements proper begin in column 7; they may begin in any column, including column 1. For such systems, column 6 may be used for a statement character, the same as any other column.

1-8. The Elements of FORTRAN

Like any unique language, FORTRAN has its own alphabet and rules of grammar and punctuation. The alphabet of FORTRAN consists of the *capital* letters of the English alphabet. Various combinations of these letters, ordinary numbers, and the special characters of FORTRAN are arranged and punctuated according to well-defined rules to make up the FORTRAN statements already introduced.

Before discussing FORTRAN statements in greater detail, we must consider the *elements* used to form such statements. These include *constants, variables, subscripted variables, operation symbols, expressions,* and *mathe-*

erent forms—the
13.62, for exam-

will discuss these elements
oration into FORTRAN state-

n for that form,
nich the number
ositive power of
the power of 10
e of a plus sign,
negative power
oer 113.62 may

ants. The FORTRAN language
1 real (floating-point) constants.
napter 2) also includes double-
its. Familiarity with the latter
anding of the programs shown in
omitted, in an introductory study

ut decimal points and can, thus, be
stant may be positive, negative, or
integers is optional, but a negative
integers. The maximum number of
computer used and may vary from
nvolving integer constants, the result
the next lowest whole number if the
nstants are therefore usually used for
ent numbers, subscripts, tallying opera-

in real form,
often contain
ns (which may
not tolerable.
real constants
nputers. The
varies greatly
ORTRANs ac-
usually used
he following
exponential

nts are sometimes referred to as "book-
ssion will become clear in subsequent
ures are discussed. The following are
its:

$$-216$$

$$4295$$

write the last constant (above) as 4,295,
in writing constants.

ers written with a decimal point, whether or
The integer constants illustrated in the pre-
pear as real constants if they were written as

ogram, or
gram, the
digits and
e quanti-
Since the
n integer

0.　　　−216.

42.　　　4295.

esponding integer and real constants represents
ney would be stored in different forms in the

complex,
oductory
always

lown, in FORTRAN II, as fixed-point constants, because the
dered to be in a fixed position—to the right of the lowest-

nstants are known as floating-point constants.

Real constants may be written in either of two dif usual decimal form or *exponential form*. The number ple, can be written as

$$113.62 \quad \text{or as} \quad 1.1362E+2$$

In the exponential form, the E is the FORTRAN designati and the integer following the E is the power of 10 by w preceding the E is multiplied. The plus sign indicates a p 10. When a real constant is written in exponential form, must always be an integer. If the power is positive, the us as shown above, is optional. However, when using a of 10, the minus sign must be used. For example, the num also be written as

$$11362.E-2$$

in equally valid form.

Numbers in arithmetic statements are usually written since the numbers appearing in engineering calculations fractional parts and since the previously described truncatio occur in operations involving integer constants) are usually The number of significant digits that can be used in writing varies with computers, but it is usually at least 7 for most co magnitude range of the numbers a computer can deal with with the FORTRANs written for different machines, some F cepting numbers as great as 10^{616}. The exponential form is when either very large or very small numbers are involved. T examples of valid real constants including several acceptable forms:

$$36. \qquad 8.0E+03$$
$$0.0002 \qquad 712.2E-35$$
$$6.E3 \qquad 6.E+3$$

1-10. Variables

When a quantity is to be assigned different values in a pr when it assumes different values during the execution of the pr quantity is referred to as a *variable* and is given a *name*. Only alphabetic characters may be used in forming names for variab ties, and the name must begin with an alphabetic character. variable may have a value in either integer or real mode, bot *variables* and *real variables* are possible.

Complete FORTRAN IV also provides for double-precision, and logical variables, but these will not be considered in this intr study. (They are discussed in Chapter 2.) Integer variables mus have a name starting with one of the letters I, J, K, L, M, or N.   Real variables may have a name starting with any *other* letter of the alphabet. (These requirements do not hold when Type statements are used, as will be discussed in Chapter 2.)

The FORTRAN processor attaches no special significance to the name assigned to a variable, except for the first character, which establishes the mode. To the computer, the name is merely a location in memory where the value corresponding to that name is stored.   The names chosen are usually made as similar to the common name of the variable as possible, in order to make the program easier to follow.   For example, if the velocity of an accelerating aircraft were to be computed after various time intervals, in real mode, the velocity of the aircraft might be referred to, in the computer program, as VELOC or as ACVEL.   If a continuous inventory of the number of shear pins available daily in stockroom 3 were to be reviewed for the last month (an integer variable could be used here), the variable might be assigned the name INVS3, INPIN, NPI, or perhaps just I. The maximum number of characters permissible in a name varies with different FORTRAN versions, but it is 6 for most computers using FORTRAN II and FORTRAN IV. The minimum length is 1 *alphabetic* character.

1-11. Subscripted Variables

When it is desired to identify a number of different quantities by the same name, *subscripted-variable names* must be used.   For example, it might be found convenient to give the temperatures, at a series of stations along a rod, a common name such as TEMP.   To identify which station along the rod TEMP referred to, the name would be given subscripts such as TEMP(1), TEMP(2), TEMP(3), and so on.   The name used may be either an integer name or a real name, but in many versions of FORTRAN the subscripts must be integer constants, integer variables, or certain permissible combinations of the two.   The following are examples of permissible subscripted-variable names:

PALM(3)	CAT(1,2)	NAB(K,3)
PALM(L)	CAT(N,M)	NAB(K,J)
PALM(M)	CAT(N,2)	NAB(4,I)

Note that both 1 and 2 subscripts are shown with the names.   Some versions of FORTRAN provide for 3 or more subscripts.

It is often convenient to use an integer-variable subscript which can assume different numerical values during the execution of the program. For example, the variable subscript I in TEMP(I) might have the value 1 during the first execution of a portion of a program, the value 2 when the same portion is repeated, the value 3 on the third run, and so on.   Such a repetitive process is often called *looping* and is a common procedure in digital-computer solutions. As will be seen later, the DO statement is convenient for use in looping, and subscripted variables are very commonly used in conjunction with DO statements.

The example in which 1 subscript was employed would refer to a *1-dimensional array*, but 2-dimensional arrays and, in many FORTRAN versions, 3-dimensional arrays, are permitted. In several versions, including IBM 360 FORTRAN IV, 7-dimensional arrays are possible. The elements of a matrix such as

$$
\begin{matrix}
A_{1,1} & A_{1,2} & A_{1,3} & \cdots & A_{1,n} \\
A_{2,1} & A_{2,2} & A_{2,3} & \cdots & A_{2,n} \\
A_{3,1} & A_{3,2} & A_{3,3} & \cdots & A_{3,n} \\
\vdots & & & & \vdots \\
A_{m,1} & & \cdots & & A_{m,n}
\end{matrix}
$$

form a 2-dimensional array which could be represented in FORTRAN by the subscripted variable A(I, J), with the variable subscripts I and J assuming the various combinations of values shown in the matrix. Computer techniques utilizing subscripted variables will be illustrated in Chapters 3 through 8.

In most systems, subscripts may have any one of the following forms:

Symbolic Form	FORTRAN Form
v	JMAX
c	3
$v + c$	I + 1
$v - c$	J − 1

where v represents an unsigned, nonsubscripted, integer variable, and c represents an unsigned integer constant. Many systems also permit the following forms:

Symbolic Form	FORTRAN Form
$c*v$	3*JOBNO
$c*v + c'$	6*I+7
$c*v - c'$	4*N−2

where c' represents a positive integer constant, and v and c are as stated before. In most FORTRANs the subscript values must be positive and nonzero.

In IBM 360 FORTRAN IV considerably more freedom is allowed in the choice of subscript forms. Function names, subscripted variables, and all of the arithmetic operators may appear in expressions used as subscripts. It is also permissible to mix real and integer modes in subscript expressions. Such expressions are real in mode, and the values of *all real* expressions used as subscripts are converted to integer form after being evaluated. The values must be such that the integer form is always greater than zero (the values must always be ≥ 1). The following subscripted variables, for example, are valid in IBM 360 FORTRAN IV:

$$A(I/2, 2*B(K,L))$$
$$MATR(A + 1, C*K**2/4)$$

1-12. Operation Symbols and Arithmetic Expressions

The operation symbols of FORTRAN define the arithmetic operations which the computer is to perform. These symbols are as follows:

Symbol	Operation
+	Addition
−	Subtraction
*	Multiplication
/	Division
**	Exponentiation (involution)

These symbols are used in various combinations in the arithmetic expressions appearing in FORTRAN statements, primarily in arithmetic statements. A FORTRAN *expression* is simply a combination of constants, variables, and functions (the latter will be discussed later) which are separated by operation symbols and parentheses to form the FORTRAN equivalent of a mathematical expression. The term *expression*, in the broadest sense, is used to include a single constant, a single variable, or a single function, but most often consists of a combination of these elements, as illustrated in the examples which follow. Blanks are disregarded, by the compiler, in a FORTRAN expression, so they may be used arbitrarily to improve the appearance of the expression for readability.

In writing FORTRAN expressions, operation symbols cannot appear consecutively; that is,

$$A*-B$$

is not a valid expression. It should be written as

$$A*(-B)$$

the operation symbols being separated by a parenthesis symbol.

In most FORTRAN versions, integer and real quantities *cannot be mixed* in a FORTRAN expression. In these versions, the expression

$$(2*A)/(I + 3.1416)$$

is not valid, since it contains a real variable, an integer variable, an integer constant, and a real constant. A correct method of writing the expression would be

$$(2.*A)/(EYE + 3.1416)$$

in which only real quantities are used. One exception to the rule on mixing modes in an expression is that a real quantity may be raised to an integer power. For example,

$$(A + B)**(I + 1)$$

$$Y**J$$

and

$$X**2$$

are acceptable expressions. However, it is not permissible to raise an integer quantity to a real power. If the exponent is in real mode, the quantity being exponentiated must be real. Most versions permit the raising of an integer quantity to an integer power, but a few do not allow any exponentiation of integer quantities. Exceptions to the rules prohibiting mixing of modes occur in IBM 360 FORTRAN IV in which almost complete mixing of modes is permissible. See Figs. 2-1b and 2-2b in Chapter 2. It is not permissible to raise a negative value to a real power or to raise zero to the zero power.

When several operation symbols appear in a FORTRAN statement, it is necessary to control the order in which the operations are to be performed. One method of establishing the order of operations is by another FORTRAN symbol, the parenthesis.

Parentheses are used in a FORTRAN expression to form groupings, much the same as in ordinary mathematical usage. When more than one set of parentheses is used in a FORTRAN expression, the order of operations indicated is from the inside parentheses outward. This can best be explained by an example. Suppose we wish to write the FORTRAN equivalent of the algebraic expression

$$\frac{(A + B)C - D}{F}$$

It might appear in FORTRAN form as

$$(((A + B)*C) - D)/F$$

Operating from the inside parentheses outward, the computer would first add A and B, then multiply this sum by C, then subtract D from the product, and finally divide by F.

If parentheses are not used in an expression to control the order of operations, the FORTRAN processor causes the computer to perform the indicated operations in the following order: exponentiation, multiplication *or* division, and addition *or* subtraction. For example, the FORTRAN expression

$$(A + B)/(C + D)$$

instructs the computer to divide the quantity (A + B) by the quantity (C + D). If the same expression were written without parentheses as

$$A + B/C + D$$

the computer would first divide B by C, then add A to this quotient, and finally add D to the resulting sum. Obviously, the results would differ.

In the natural FORTRAN operational sequence explained in the preceding paragraph, it was indicated that multiplication has the same order of preference in the sequence as division, and that addition has the same order of preference as subtraction. When several operations which have the same order of preference appear in an unparenthesized FORTRAN expression, the operations proceed from *left to right* within each preference level.   (An exception occurs in IBM 360 FORTRAN IV, in which a series of exponentiations is evaluated from *right to left*.) For example, consider the FORTRAN expression

$$A/B - C*D + E/F$$

The order of operations would be as follows: the computer would divide A by B, multiply C by D, divide E by F, subtract the product C*D from A/B, and add the quantity E/F to the result of (A/B) − C*D.

As another example, consider the algebraic expression

$$(A^B)C + D$$

Using parentheses to control the order of operations, an equivalent FORTRAN expression would be

$$((A**B)*C) + D$$

Taking advantage of the natural FORTRAN operational sequence, the same expression could be written in FORTRAN as

$$A**B*C + D$$

which, in this case, gives a slightly simpler expression. Since expressions are intrinsic to arithmetic-assignment statements, further examples of their use will appear in Sec. 1-14.

1-13. Mathematical-Function Subroutines

The operations required to evaluate certain commonly used mathematical functions, such as the square root of a number, the sine of an angle, the natural logarithm of a number, and so on, are not programmed each time they are required as part of a computer solution. Such functions are preprogrammed, and the programs are recorded on tape or cards which are available as part of the FORTRAN system.

Each mathematical function has a FORTRAN name. A mathematical function is expressed in a standard arithmetic expression by writing the name of the function, followed by an expression enclosed in parentheses which is the argument of the function. The compiler then arranges for the use of the prewritten instructions in computing the desired function during execution.

The mathematical-function subroutines required in a program are usually introduced into the object program as part of the compiling process. In some systems they may be read directly into memory, along with the object program, as part of the execution phase. In either case, the subroutines are available to instruct the computer in the operations necessary to evaluate the desired functions during the execution phase. Some of the common mathematical-function subroutines, supplied with almost all FORTRAN compilers, are listed below, with their respective FORTRAN names and an example of each.

Function	FORTRAN Name	Example
Square root of an argument	SQRT	SQRT(B*B − 4.*A*C)
Exponential (e^x)	EXP	EXP(X)
Sine of an angle, in radians	SIN	SIN(THETA)
Cosine of an angle, in radians	COS	COS(THETA)
Arc tangent (computed value of an angle, in radians)	ATAN	ATAN(B/A)
Natural logarithm of a number in many systems	ALOG	ALOG(C*D)
Natural logarithm of a number in some systems	LOG	LOG(C*D)
Absolute value of a number	ABS	ABS(Y)

A complete list of supplied function subroutines depends upon the particular FORTRAN version being used. In FORTRAN II the FORTRAN function names must end in F, as SQRTF, COSF, and so forth. In some FORTRAN versions the use of the F is optional.

In the source program the name of the function is followed by the argument which is specified in the parentheses by a real (floating-point) expression. For example, if THETA were the FORTRAN name assigned to a variable angle (specified in radians) appearing in a problem, and the sine of the angle were required in the computer calculations, the appearance of SIN(THETA) in the source program would call for the sine subroutine during the execution phase of the solution. The subroutine would, at that time, calculate the sine of the angle represented by the name THETA.

Subroutines are not limited to the common trigonometric and algebraic mathematical functions in the more complete versions of FORTRAN. Complete FORTRAN IV, for example, provides for 4 classes of subroutines or subprograms: arithmetic statement functions, built-in functions, function subprograms, and subroutine subprograms. However, for the present we shall be concerned only with the common mathematical functions supplied with the compiler, and a detailed discussion of the major features of the 4 classes of subprograms will be postponed until Chapter 2. At that time we shall find that the common mathematical functions, discussed in this section, fall, for the most part, under the classification of function subprograms. We shall also learn how a programmer, needing a function or any set of commonly used operations such as a particular matrix routine that is not supplied with the compiler, can write the routine himself with FORTRAN statements and use it as a function subprogram or as a subroutine subprogram.

1-14. Arithmetic-Assignment Statements

Arithmetic-assignment statements define the calculations to be performed by the computer. An arithmetic-assignment statement consists of a single variable (without a sign) which is set equal to an expression of some kind, such as a single variable, a constant, a function, or a combination of variables, constants, and functions.

The following is a typical arithmetic-assignment statement:

$$X = (-B + SQRT(B*B - 4.*A*C))/(2.*A)$$

The right-hand side should be recognized as the FORTRAN equivalent of an expression for 1 root of a quadratic equation. Such a statement instructs the computer to calculate the value of the expression on the right of the equals sign and then to assign that calculated value to the variable name on the left. If X has a value prior to the execution of the arithmetic statement, this value will be *replaced* by the value calculated during the execution.

In FORTRAN language the equality sign does not have its customary mathematical meaning of "is equal to." Instead, it means "is to be replaced by." For example, the FORTRAN statement

$$I = I + 1$$

is a perfectly valid arithmetic-assignment statement with the FORTRAN interpretation of the equality sign given above. This statement instructs the computer to add 1 to the existing value of I and then to replace the existing value of I by the sum obtained.

The statements

$$X*(2.*A) = -B + SQRT(B*B - 4.*A*C)$$

and

$$I - 1 = I$$

are *invalid* because they do not observe the rule of having only a single variable on the left of the equality sign.

As mentioned previously, most arithmetic-assignment statements are written in real (floating-point) form or mode, since the use of decimal fractions is often necessary, and also since the results of calculations in integer (fixed-point) arithmetic are truncated if they are not whole numbers. In integer arithmetic, if the result of each calculation is not a whole number, the number is truncated to the next *lowest* whole number. Therefore, as discussed in Sec. 1-9, the use of integer arithmetic is usually reserved for special purposes such as subscripting variables, tallying, and so forth. It is sometimes necessary or convenient to use different modes on both sides of an equality sign, and such a procedure is valid. That is, the expression on the right side of the equality sign need not be in the same mode as the variable on the left side. For example, if we have the statement

$$A = I + 1$$

the value of the expression I + 1 will be calculated in integer mode, and this value will then be stored in the location referred to by the variable name A in real mode. In the statement

$$J = X**2 - B$$

the expression on the right is evaluated in real mode, and the result is then truncated to the next lowest integer value and stored in integer mode in the location referred to by the variable name J.

EXAMPLE 1-2

Let us program a problem for solution on the digital computer. Consider the electric circuit shown in Fig. 1-10. The equation

$$I = \frac{E}{\sqrt{R^2 + \left(2\pi f L - \dfrac{1}{2\pi f C}\right)^2}}$$

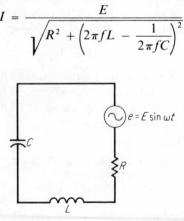

FIG. 1-10. Electric circuit for Example 1-2.

defines the current I in the circuit for various combinations of values of the other parameters, which are

E = voltage, 120 volts

R = resistance, 20 ohms

L = inductance, 0.1 henry

C = capacitance, 0.000025 farad

f = frequency, 2000 cycles per second

Suppose it is desired to find the value of I, when the other problem parameters have the values shown. Such a simple problem does not really require a flow chart, but we shall employ one to become more familiar with their use. The flow chart is shown in Fig. 1-11.

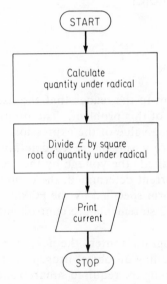

FIG. 1-11. Flow chart for Example 1-2.

In writing the source program, names may be assigned to the parameters. Let us use the following real names:

AMP = current

VOL = voltage

R = resistance

HENRY = inductance

C = capacitance

FREQ = frequency

It will be recalled that data may be specified either in the source program or, in a more flexible manner, by using separate data cards or a data tape. Utilizing the former method in this example, and following the outline provided by the flow chart of Fig. 1-11, the source program may be written as

```
    VOL = 120.
    R = 20.
    HENRY = .1
    C = .000025
    FREQ = 2000.
    RADIC = R*R + (6.2832*FREQ*HENRY — 1./(6.2832*FREQ*C))**2
    AMP = VOL/SQRT(RADIC)
2   FORMAT(E14.8)
    PRINT 2,AMP
    STOP
    END
```

It should be apparent to the reader that the use of the real mode is required in the solution of this problem. The program first instructs the computer to determine the value of the expression under the radical sign, then to utilize a square root subroutine to determine the square root of this value, and then to divide the voltage by the result of the subroutine. With the value of the current determined, the computer is next instructed to print this value in a form specified by the FORMAT statement shown in the program. The final 2 statements are control statements which will be discussed later.

With the source program written, the next step would be to use the source program in compiling an object program. The machine-language instructions for determining the required square root would appear in the object program as one of the subroutines introduced during the compilation. With the object program stored in an auxiliary memory device or punched out on cards or paper tape, it would then be ready to be placed in main computer memory for obtaining a solution.

1-15. Control Statements

Introduction. Control statements perform a variety of functions in FORTRAN programming. Several types of control statements are used to interrupt the usual sequential execution of program statements, to provide computer logic by selecting alternate sequences of operation within a program, to repeat sequences of steps within a program, and to halt temporarily the execution of a program. The various control statements which perform these functions will now be discussed.

Unconditional GO TO Statement. This statement, referred to as an unconditional branch or transfer statement, is used to interrupt the usual sequential execution of statements by an unconditional transfer of control to a specified *numbered* statement. For example, the statement

GO TO 16

instructs the computer to execute immediately the statement numbered 16, regardless of the position of the statement in the program sequence.

Computed GO TO Statement. This statement is a conditional branch or transfer type of control statement, since the transfer of control depends on the value of an integer variable which is a part of the computed GO TO statement. For example, the statement

GO TO(3,8,11,24),J

will transfer control to statement 3 if the value of J is 1, to statement 8 if J is 2, and so on. Any number of statements to which control can be transferred is permissible. The integer variable J cannot be given a value greater than the number of statements referred to in the parentheses of the GO TO statement.

Arithmetic IF Statement. The IF statement is also a conditional type of control statement. It provides computer logic by allowing transfer of control to any one of 3 numbered statements, depending on the value of the expression enclosed in parentheses which is part of the IF statement. For example, the statement

IF(X − A)14,13,7

transfers control to statement 14 if the quantity (X − A) is *negative*, to statement 13 if (X − A) is equal to *zero*, and to statement 7 if (X − A) is *positive*. The parenthetical portion of the IF statement may contain any legitimate arithmetic expression other than a complex expression (complex expressions are discussed in Chapter 2), including a single variable name.

The *logical* IF statement is another type of IF statement which may be used.[4] This statement tests logical expressions and executes different statements depending on whether the logical expression is true or false. (This statement is discussed in Chapter 2.)

EXAMPLE 1-3

As a simple illustration of the use of conditional and unconditional transfer or branching statements, let us find the value of *y* for values of *x* in increments of 0.1 over a range of *x* from 0 to 5 for the curve shown in

---

[4]Not available in FORTRAN II.

Fig. 1-12. The curve shown is a composite of portions of 2 curves, the equations of which are

$$y = \frac{x}{3} + 2 \qquad\qquad 0 \le x \le 3$$

$$y = \frac{x^2}{3} - \frac{5}{3}x + 5 \qquad 3 < x \le 5$$

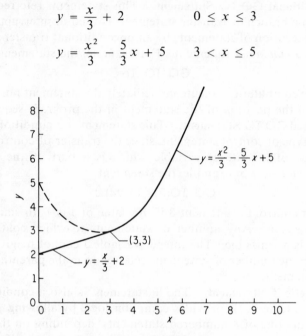

FIG. 1-12. Graph for Example 1-3.

In performing the specified operations, the computer must make 2 logical decisions: which equation it should solve for a particular value of x, and when it should stop calculating. With these requirements in mind, the flow chart (Fig. 1-13) is sketched. The reader should note the two branching points in the flow chart and trace the resulting alternate paths.

With the flow chart as an outline, the following source program may be written:

```
      X = 0.
  2   IF(X - 3.)3,3,4
  3   Y = X/3. + 2.
      GO TO 5
  4   Y = X*X/3. - 5./3.*X + 5.
  5   PRINT 6,X,Y
  6   FORMAT(F4.1,F8.3)
      IF(X - 5.)7,8,8
```

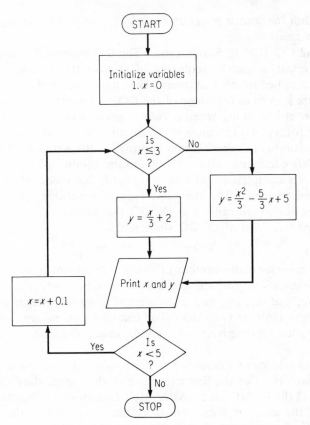

FIG. 1-13. Flow chart for Example 1-3.

```
7 X = X + .1
  GO TO 2
8 STOP
  END
```

At this point the reader should follow the sequence of control in the source program, referring, when necessary, to the previous discussions of control statements. The computer is a very finicky slave; it will perform its tasks correctly only if it is perfectly instructed. To be sure that we are giving correct instructions to the computer, we must begin by writing a flawless source program. Not only must the logic be correct, but every statement written must be perfect in form, content, and punctuation. Most FORTRAN processors have routines which inform the operator of errors of the latter type, but errors in logic may go undetected. Therefore, it is important that a flow chart be sketched for the more complex problems and that the source program be in agreement with the logic planned in the flow chart.

DO and CONTINUE Statements.   The DO statement causes the computer to repeat a specific sequence of statements, within a given program, a prescribed number of times. The statements in the sequence to be repeated are known as the *range* of the DO statement. This type of statement is convenient to use when a known number of repetitions, or loops, is required for a given sequence of statements. It may also be used when a maximum number of repetitions is specified, with a transfer from the DO loop *possibly* occurring before the maximum number of repetitions specified has been completed. The IF statement, discussed previously, may also be used to accomplish the same type of repetitive operation, but it generally is not so convenient as the DO statement.

The general form of the DO statement is

$$\text{DO n i} = m_1, m_2, m_3$$

in which n represents the number of the last statement in the range of the DO, i represents a nonsubscripted integer variable known as the *index* or DO *variable*, and m_1, m_2, and m_3 represent unsigned integer constants or nonsubscripted integer variables called *indexing parameters*. Individually, they are called, respectively, the *initial value*, the *test value*, and the *increment*.

The DO statement causes the statements within the range to be executed repeatedly. For the first execution of the range, the index has the value of m_1, the initial value. After each execution of the statements in the range, the index is incremented by the value of m_3, the increment. The index is then compared with the value of m_2, the test value. If it is less than or equal to the test value, execution of the statements in the range is carried out again. If the index value exceeds the test value, the execution of the DO loop ceases, and control passes to the first statement following the end of the range of the DO. The DO statement is then said to be satisfied, and the exit from the DO loop is known as a *normal exit*.

Let us consider the DO statement

$$\text{DO 6I} = 1,100,2$$

as an example. The number 6 identifies statement number 6 as the last statement of the group of statements which are to be executed repeatedly. The integer variable I is the index in this example. The index may be used in statements within the range for any purpose for which any other integer variable would be permissible. It is most commonly used as a subscript for a subscripted variable. However, it is not necessary that the index be used in any of the statements in the range. If it is not, it merely serves as a counter and is incremented by the value of m_3 after each execution of the range. The index in this example would have a value of 1 during the first execution. Following each execution of the loop, the index would be incremented by the value of 2. When the value of the index reached 99, an additional execution of the loop would be made. The index would then assume a value of 101. This value would then be compared with the test value of 100, and, since it exceeds the test value, execution of the DO loop would cease.

After a normal exit, the integer variable assigned as the index may or may not be defined and available for use in a subsequent portion of the program, depending upon the version of FORTRAN being used. Usually, it is not. If control is transferred from a statement in the DO loop to a statement outside the DO loop before the DO statement is satisfied (a transfer of this type is permitted at any time), the index remains defined and may be used, as so defined, in a subsequent portion of the program. In most versions of FORTRAN, it is not permissible to transfer control from a statement outside a DO loop to a statement within a DO loop.

If the constant or variable defining the increment is omitted (along with the comma which would precede it) from the DO statement, the index will be incremented by 1 after each execution. Thus, the statement

$$\text{DO} \quad 4J = 2,50$$

would assign a value of 2 to the index J for the first execution of the DO loop. The index would subsequently be incremented by 1, following each execution of the loop, and, after 49 executions (the index during the last loop would be equal to 50), control would pass to the statement immediately following the DO loop.

Certain restrictions, placed on the statements in the range of the DO, must be observed. They are:

1. No statement within the range of the DO can redefine the index or any of the indexing parameters.

2. The last statement in the range of the DO cannot be an arithmetic IF or a GO TO type of statement, a PAUSE statement, a STOP statement, or a nonexecutable statement. (An executable statement is one which is translated into machine-language instructions for execution, as opposed to one which simply gives information to the compiler.)

3. In some versions of FORTRAN, the first statement in the range must be an executable statement.

Referring to the second restriction, the last statement in the range may be a logical IF statement; its use in this regard will be discussed in Sec. 2-9. For situations in which it would be desirable to use a transfer-of-control statement as the last statement in the range, the CONTINUE statement is provided. CONTINUE is a dummy statement that is not translated into any executable instructions. Its use will be illustrated in Example 1-4.

It is permissible to use 1 or more DO statements within the range of another DO statement. Such arrangements are known as *nested* DO's. Their use will be discussed subsequently.

EXAMPLE 1-4

Frequently, it is necessary to determine the largest or smallest element of a number of elements stored in computer memory. One such application occurs in the solution of simultaneous algebraic equations in which it is desirable to determine the coefficient, in the set of equations, having the largest absolute value, for use as the pivot element in a calculation involved in the solution of the set of equations.

Let us assume that the 100 coefficients of a set of simultaneous equations are stored in computer memory as the 100 elements of a 1-dimensional array A(I), A_1 through A_{100}. It is desired to find the element having the largest absolute value, and to store this value in memory in a location referred to by the variable name BIG. The subscript of this particular element is to be given the variable name N. After the computer has determined the values of the variables BIG and N, it is to continue with another portion of the program (not shown in the example). Figure 1-14 is a flow chart for the portion of the program referred to above. In this program the index of the DO is used as a subscript in the range of the DO.

Using an IF statement as the branching device, and letting the fixed-point variable I be both the subscript designation for the elements and the index of the DO statement, the following program is evolved from the outline provided by the flow chart:

```
          . . . . . . . . . . . . . . . .
          N = 1
          BIG = ABS(A(1))
          DO 4I = 2,100
          IF(BIG — ABS(A(I)))3,4,4
       3  BIG = ABS(A(I))
          N = I
       4  CONTINUE
          . . . . . . . . . . . . . . . .
```

Note that, in writing the source program, BIG was given an initial value of the absolute value of A(1). This provides a comparison value for the first execution of the IF statement in which the absolute values of A(1) and A(2) are compared. If the element A_2 has an absolute value greater than that of BIG in the first comparison made by the IF statement, control passes to statement 3, which assigns the name BIG to the absolute value of

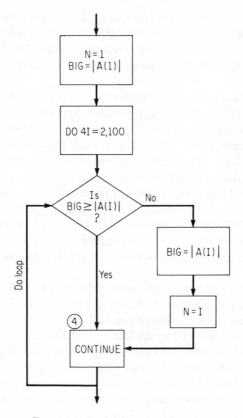

FIG. 1-14. Partial flow chart for Example 1-4.

A_2. The name N is then assigned the value of the subscript of A_2. Control then reverts through statement 4 to the first statement in the DO range, and the absolute value of A_2 is compared with the absolute value of A_3. If the absolute value of A_3 is greater than the absolute value of A_2 (the current value of BIG), the sequence of steps outlined above is repeated, and the absolute value of A_3 is assigned to the name BIG. If the absolute value of A_3 is smaller than or equal to the absolute value of A_2, the IF statement bypasses statement 3 and the statement following it, by transferring control to statement 4. Statement 4 then allows control to transfer back to the first statement in the DO loop, and the value of A_4 is next compared with the current value of BIG.

Ninety-nine cycles of the DO loop are executed, the sequence of steps within the loop being one or the other of the two outlined above, depending on the relative magnitudes of the compared quantities. During the 99th execution of the DO loop, the index I will have a value of 100, meaning that the last element of the array, A_{100}, is under comparison. After this execution the index is incremented to 101 (which exceeds the test value of the DO statement), a normal exit is made from the DO loop to the statement which follows the last statement in the DO loop, and the program continues.

The partial source program under discussion also illustrates the use of the CONTINUE statement. If A(I) is not bigger than the value of BIG in the IF statement, statement 3 and the statement following it must be bypassed. To increment the index, control must pass to the last statement in the range of the DO. We might be tempted to use a GO TO statement as this last statement, to transfer control back to the first statement in the range of the DO However, this is not permissible, so a CONTINUE statement is used as the last statement in the range. When control is transferred to the CONTINUE statement, the index I is incremented by 1, and either the execution of the range is repeated, or a normal exit is made from the DO loop, depending upon whether or not the DO statement has been satisfied.

Nested DO's. When 1 or more DO statements are placed in the range of another DO statement, the set of DO loops is referred to as nested DO's. If the range of a DO statement includes another DO statement, the former is called the *outer* or *major* DO, and the latter is called the *inner* or *minor* DO. All the statements in the range of an inner DO must also be in the range of the outer DO. This rule allows the inner and outer DO loops to end with a statement common to each loop, if this is desired. A set of nested DO's, as a portion of an overall program, might appear as follows:

```
    . . . . .
    READ 2,M
  2 FORMAT (I4)
    N = M + 1
    DO 9 I = 2,M
    DO 9 J = 2,N
    L = J − 1
    SUM = 0.
    DO 8 K = 1,L
  8 SUM = SUM + B(I,K)*T(K,J)
  9 B(I,J) = A(I,J) − SUM
    . . . . .
    . . . . .
```

The rules governing the use of single DO loops apply also to nested DO loops. It is permissible to transfer at any time, by means of a transfer-of-control statement, from an inner DO loop to an outer DO loop. In most versions of FORTRAN, however, it is not permissible to transfer from an outer DO loop into an inner DO loop by a transfer-of-control statement, since this violates the rule against transferring into a DO loop from outside its range.

In the normal sequence of operations of a set of nested DO's, control is first passed to the outer DO from another part of the program. The statements in the outer DO range preceding the inner DO statement are then executed in some type of sequence until that sequence arrives at the inner DO statement, to which control then passes. After the inner DO is satisfied, or after exit from it occurs by a transfer, any remaining statements in the outer DO are executed, completing the first cycle of the outer DO. Unless exit occurs from an inner DO by a transfer, it cycles the specified number of times and is satisfied for each separate execution of the range of the outer DO.

To illustrate such a sequence a little more specifically, let us trace 1 cycle through the outer DO loop of the example. Control passes from the general program to the outer DO statement. On the first cycle the index I is equal to 2, as specified in the DO statement. Control immediately passes to the inner DO, with its index J having an initial value of 2. The arithmetic statements $L = J - 1$ and SUM = 0. are executed, and control passes to the DO statement which is within the first inner DO loop. The statement SUM = SUM + B(I,K)*T(K,J) is executed repeatedly until the second inner DO is satisfied. Then the statement B(I,J) = A(I,J) − SUM is executed, completing the first cycle of the first inner DO. After the first inner DO cycles the specified number of times and is satisfied, 1 cycle of the outer DO is complete. Looping through the outer DO continues until it is satisfied.

Problems in which a number of parameters are to be varied over definite ranges can usually be programmed with nested DO's. In such problems the use of nested DO's is a very powerful programming tool. They are also especially convenient in programming problems involving 2- and 3-dimensional arrays, since the indexes of the DO statements correspond very nicely to the subscripts of the elements of the array.

The ranges of the DO loops, in the case just discussed, are marked with brackets to show the range of each DO statement. The configuration of the DO loops of the example might be illustrated as follows:

This is a permissible configuration. The following configuration *is not* permissible, since not all the statements in the inner DO are in the range of the outer DO.

Using the same schematic representation of DO loop configurations, with arrows added to represent transfers of control, the following diagrams show valid and invalid transfers.

Valid   *Invalid*

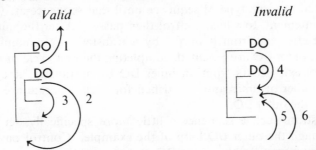

Transfers 1 and 2 are valid, since transfer of control from inside the range of a DO to outside its range is permitted at any time, provided the transfer is not into the range of another DO from outside its range. Transfer 3 is permissible, since it is a transfer from an inner DO into an outer DO. Note that such a transfer does not violate the rule against transferring into a DO loop from outside its range. Transfers 4, 5, and 6 illustrate transfers into a DO loop from outside its range—an invalid procedure in most versions of FORTRAN. Note that a transfer from an outer DO into an inner DO is included in invalid transfers. The use of nested DO loops will be further illustrated in subsequent chapters.

PAUSE, STOP, and END Statements. These control statements perform the functions which their names indicate. The PAUSE statement instructs the computer to halt temporarily the execution sequence in order to allow time for checking intermediate results, adjusting control switches, and so forth. When the computer is restarted, the sequence of execution begins where it left off at the PAUSE instruction. The statement has the general form

PAUSE

or

PAUSE n

where n represents an unsigned integer constant in the last form. For example, in most versions of FORTRAN, the statement

PAUSE 2

would cause the computer to halt temporarily and print out PAUSE 00002 on the printer. If n were not specified, the printout would be PAUSE 00000. There may be several PAUSE statements in a program, and the printing out of the number of the PAUSE tells the programmer which statements have just been executed. Normally, the PAUSE statement is not used when the computer is under monitor control.

The STOP statement instructs the computer to halt execution permanently. This statement consists simply of the word STOP. If the computer operation is under monitor control, control reverts to the monitor program after the execution of a stop. Some FORTRAN compilers permit the use of numbered STOP statements similar to numbered PAUSE statements, utilizing an unsigned integer constant.

The END statement is the last statement in all FORTRAN programs and subprograms, since its purpose is to notify the compiler of the end of the source program. This statement is not translated into machine language.

1-16. Input and Output Statements

The input/output (I/O) statements control the transmission of information between the computer and the input/output devices used, such as card readers, card punches, paper-tape readers, paper-tape punches, printers, typewriters, and magnetic-tape units. In most versions of FORTRAN, I/O statements include those which fall into the following categories:

1. General I/O statements cause the values of a *list* of variables, included in the statement, to be transmitted from core storage to an output device, or from an input device to core storage. They include the statements READ, WRITE, ACCEPT, ACCEPT TAPE, PRINT, PUNCH, and so forth, in the various FORTRAN versions.

2. FORMAT statements are nonexecutable statements that specify the arrangement and form of the data to be transmitted. For example, a FORMAT statement associated with a data input statement informs the compiler of the number of spaces or columns used for each value, the mode of each value, the form of each real value, and the location of the decimal point in real quantities if it is not explicitly given with the value. A FORMAT statement associated with an output statement informs the compiler of the number of spaces or columns to be allocated for each output unit, the mode of each quantity, the output form of each real value, and the number of digits to be shown after the decimal point of each real value. FORMAT statements are sometimes classified as specification statements, but they are described in this section since they are always used with the general I/O statements listed in category 1.

3. Manipulative I/O statements include the statements END FILE, REWIND, and BACKSPACE, which are used to manipulate magnetic tapes.

Input Statements. Input statements provide the means of reading numerical data into a program by specifying the variable names which represent memory locations in which the corresponding numerical values are to be stored. In most newer versions of FORTRAN (the various FORTRAN IV versions), the READ statement can be used to transfer information from *any* input device to the computer storage; older FORTRAN versions provide different types of statements for different types of input or output devices. For example, the input statement ACCEPT TAPE is used for paper-tape input in the various versions for the IBM 1620 computer, and the ACCEPT statement is used for typewriter input in the same FORTRAN versions. The reader should familiarize himself with the input statements associated with the version of FORTRAN he is using, since variations do exist. The information which follows is typical of FORTRAN IV.

The READ statement has the following general form:

$$\text{READ n, list}^5$$

or

$$\text{READ (i,n)list}$$

The former is used for on-line card input only, whereas the latter ιn be used for input from any device. In the general form of these statements, i represents an unsigned integer constant or a nonsubscripted integer variable that specifies a symbolic unit to be used for input data. For example, the constant 5 might be the symbolic-unit number (referred to in IBM 360 FORTRAN IV as the *data set reference number*), associated with the card reader, or the constant 2 might be the symbolic-unit number associated with a particular magnetic-tape unit. The symbolic-unit-number assignments may be obtained by the user from his computer center.

The n, in the general forms shown, represents the statement number of the FORMAT statement describing the data being transmitted. The *list* denotes a list of variable names separated by commas. The simplest type of list, in which all the variables are named explicitly, indicates the number of items of data which are to be read in, as well as the order in which they are to be read in. The data values entering into computer memory via the input unit are assigned to the variable names in the order in which the variables appear in the list.

The statement

$$\text{READ 3,A,B,C}$$

would cause a card, or cards, to be read from the on-line card reader. Each time the READ statement was executed, 3 values would be read in and assigned to the variable names A, B, and C, respectively. The number 3 in the statement is the number of the FORMAT statement associated with the READ statement.

Execution of the statement

$$\text{READ(5,8)A,B,I}$$

[5]Also used in FORTRAN II.

would cause the reading of 3 data values from the input device associated with the number 5. As in the preceding example, the 3 values read in would be assigned to the variables A, B, and I, respectively. The number 8 is the number of the FORMAT statement associated with this READ statement.

Assuming an appropriate FORMAT statement, the 3 data values to be read in might all be on 1 card. If there were more than 3 data values on the card, only 3 values would be read in, and the remaining quantities would be ignored, since only as many data values as are specified in the list are transmitted.

The statements

$$DO\ 2I\ =\ 1,10$$

$$2\ READ(5,7)A(I)$$

used in conjunction would cause 10 values to be read in via the input device associated with the number 5. They would be assigned to the variable names $A(1), A(2), A(3), \ldots, A(10)$. Assuming the input device to be a card reader, each item would be read from a separate card. In most versions of FORTRAN, variables within an input or output list can be indexed and incremented without the use of the DO statement, as illustrated above, using what is known as an *implied* DO in the list. The use of the implied DO is not discussed in this introductory study of FORTRAN, but it will be described in Chapter 2.

Output Statements.   Output statements provide a means of translating the results of computer calculations into printed, punched, or other output form. The output statements for FORTRAN IV have the following general forms:

$$PUNCH\ n,\ list[6]$$

$$PRINT\ n,\ list[6]$$

$$WRITE\ (i,n)\ list$$

In these general forms, the i represents an unsigned integer constant or a nonsubscripted integer variable which specifies the output device by which the output data are to be transmitted. The n represents the FORMAT-statement number associated with the output statement. The *list* denotes the variable names, separated by commas, whose values are to appear as output.

The PUNCH statement may be used to obtain output data punched on cards, using an on-line punch. The word PRINT specifies the printing of output data on an on-line printer. However, all output may be specified with the use of the WRITE statement, in FORTRAN IV, by specifying, in the statement, the appropriate output device.

[6]Also used in FORTRAN II.

The statement

WRITE(6,2)VEL,ACCEL

for example, would cause the values of the variables VEL and ACCEL to appear as output on the device associated with the number 6. The FORMAT statement associated with this WRITE statement would be numbered 2.

The statement

WRITE(6,3)

in the absence of a list, would specify that the information to appear as output would be contained in FORMAT statement 3. An example of the use of this statement will be given later, in the discussion of *Hollerith* specifications.

FORMAT Statements. As mentioned previously, FORMAT statements are associated with both input and output statements. The compiler must know the form in which the data have been prepared for read-in and the form they should have as output. FORMAT statements are not executed and, in most versions of FORTRAN, can be placed anywhere in the source program except where a nonexecutable statement is prohibited (as the last statement in the range of a DO, for example).

The general form of a FORMAT statement is

$$n \text{ FORMAT}(s_1, s_2, \ldots, s_m)$$

where n is the FORMAT-statement number, and $s_1, s_2, \ldots, s_m$ are *format* or *field specifications*. In this chapter we will discuss three general kinds of field specifications for numerical data. They are known as I-type, F-type, and E-type specifications. The Hollerith and Literal specifications, which are associated with alphameric input and output, and the Blank Field specification will also be described. Since the details of FORMAT statements may vary slightly with different versions of FORTRAN, the reader is advised to refer to a FORTRAN reference manual or FORTRAN specifications for the particular version being used.

I-Type Specification (*I-conversion*). This kind of specification is used for the input and output of *integer* quantities. The specification consists of the letter I, sometimes called the *control character* of the field, and an integer constant whose value specifies the *field width* (the number of spaces required to represent the datum value and its sign). There must be a field specification of some type in the FORMAT statement for each quantity read in or out, although there will not always necessarily be a 1-to-1 correspondence between the number of field specifications and the number of variables; that is, 1 field specification may be used for several variables.

To introduce the general concept of a field specification, suppose that the input statement

READ(5,2)NR, LP,MO

or

READ 2,NR,LP,MO

appears in a source program associated with the FORMAT statement

2 FORMAT(I3,I5,I4)

The field specifications within the parentheses of the FORMAT statement apply to 1 *record* of data. A record is the information contained on 1 card or 1 printed line.   Thus, the specifications with the parentheses of the above FORMAT statement specify that a total of 12 card columns will be used on 1 card, as shown in Fig. 1-15.   The field specification I3 means

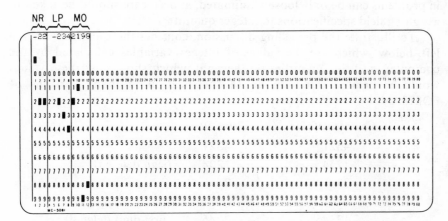

FIG. 1-15. Example of a data card for one of the given input statements.

that 3 card columns will be used for the numerical value of the variable named NR when the data cards are punched. The next specification means that 5 card columns will be used for the numerical value of the variable named LP, and so forth. Figure 1-15 shows a data card as it would be punched to be read in by one of the input statements above. The vertical lines shown here are not actually on the card; they are added to separate the 3 data fields corresponding to the variables NR, LP, and MO.

If the FORMAT statement

2 FORMAT(I3,I5,I4)

were associated with an output statement such as

PRINT 2,NAB,MOP,KOB

or

WRITE(6,2)NAB,MOP,KOB

the field specification I5 would inform the compiler that 5 spaces should be allocated for the printout of the numerical value of the variable named MOP (including its sign, if one is printed). If the numerical value of MOP were of small enough magnitude so that 5 spaces were not required for the printout, the numerical value would be printed out in the right-hand portion of the field, leaving a corresponding number of blank spaces to the left to conform to the specification. If the numerical value of MOP were such that more than 5 spaces were required for its printout, the 5 right-hand digits would be printed out, but any excess digits in front of these would be lopped off. For example, if the numerical value of MOP were calculated as 3456789, the printout would appear as 56789 with the above specification. Thus, it is possible to specify too small a field and obtain an erroneous result. Since the magnitudes of many quantities in problems can be only loosely estimated, at best, care should be taken in assigning field specifications to integer quantities.

To illustrate the preceding discussion, consider the quantities on the left, below, which are the values of integer variables calculated by the computer, and the quantities on the right, which show how these values would be printed out with an I4 specification in many versions of FORTRAN.

Calculated Value	Printout	
4321	4321	
−1234	1234	(sign deleted)
−34	−34	
6	6	
12345	2345	(first digit deleted)
0	0	
−1	−1	

Since the specifications given in the FORMAT statement

2 FORMAT(I3,I5,I4)

apply to 1 record of output information, all 3 output data values would be printed on a single line. The FORMAT statement

2 FORMAT(I5)

associated with the output statement

PRINT 2,NAB,MOP,KOB

would result in the field specification I5 being used 3 times, but each datum value would be printed out as a separate record; that is, on separate lines.

F-*Type Specification* (F-*conversion*).   This specification is used whenever a *real* value in ordinary decimal form is to be read in as data, or when a real quantity in computer memory is to be read out in ordinary decimal form. The field specification consists of the letter F, sometimes called the *control character* of the specification, followed by 2 integer constants which are separated by a decimal point. The first number after the control character indicates the *field width*, and the second number indicates the

number of digits of the real value which appear *after the decimal point.*
For example, if the FORMAT statement

3 FORMAT(F10.4,F6.3)

were used in association with an input statement, the first field specification shown would specify that 10 card columns be used in punching the
numerical value of the real variable associated with that specification.
(The sign of the number and the decimal point are included in the field-
width count.) It would further specify that 4 digits appear after the decimal point. If no decimal point were punched on the data card, the number would be considered to have a value corresponding to a decimal point
preceding the last 4 digits.

If the decimal point is punched on the card and is not located in agreement with the specification, the punched location of the decimal point
takes precedence. For this reason, many programmers use the specification Fw.0 (w is the field width) if the decimal point is to be punched on
the card.

If the FORMAT statement

3 FORMAT(F10.4,F6.3)

were used with an output statement, the first field specification shown
would tell the processor to allocate 10 spaces for the printout of the
numerical value of the corresponding real variable, and that 4 digits were
to appear after the decimal point. The second field specification would
tell the processor to allocate 6 spaces for the printout of the next corresponding variable, and that 3 digits were to appear after the decimal
point.

As in the I-type specification, care must be exercised in assigning a
field specification to a variable which is to be calculated by the computer
and printed as output. If the field specification specifies a field width
larger than required by the magnitude of the quantity, no error is introduced, since the numerical value will be printed out in the right-hand
portion of the field, leaving blank spaces to the left to fill out the specified
field width. However, if the field width is specified too small, the complete
numerical result cannot be placed in the specified field, and either an
erroneous result will be printed out, there will be no numerical printout
at all, or, in some versions of FORTRAN, a printout in exponent form
may occur. In the latter instance a correct value will be given, but the
exponent form may upset the planned page format. If it is practically
impossible to estimate the magnitude of the real variables which are to
appear as output, the programmer may use an E-type specification (the
next type of specification to be discussed). The column on the left, below,
shows the value of several real variables calculated by the computer, and
the column to the right shows how these quantities would print out, with
the specification F6.2, in many FORTRAN versions.

Calculated Value	*Printout*	
116.21	116.21	
−303.11	303.11	(sign deleted)
6.1234	6.12	(2 significant digits deleted)
3152.69	152.69	(first digit deleted)

As stated above, the second and fourth quantities would be printed out in exponent form in some versions of FORTRAN.

E-*Type Specification* (E-*conversion*). This specification is similar to the F-type specification but is used with real quantities which are expressed in exponent form. The specification consists of the letter E as the *control character*, and 2 integer constants separated by a decimal point. The first integer constant after the control character specifies the field width associated with the real value, and the second indicates the number of digits appearing after the decimal point. With the FORMAT statement

6 FORMAT(E14.7,E10.6)

associated with an input statement, the field specification E14.7 specifies that a real quantity, in exponent form, with a field width of 14 card columns and having 7 digits after the decimal point, is to be read in first. In this specification the field width includes the exponent designation and its sign, as well as the sign and decimal point of the number. For example, the quantity −1346.762, written in exponent form as −.1346762E+4, might be given a field specification of E12.7 when used for input. The same quantity, written in exponent form as −13.46762E+2, could be given a field specification of E12.5 for input.

If the location of the decimal point in the input data is not in agreement with the specification, the computer stores the value punched on the card; that is, the actual location of the decimal point overrides the specification. If no decimal point is punched, the computer stores the number with the decimal point located according to the specification.

When data are used in exponent form so that an E-type specification is used, several different forms are permissible for expressing the exponent. For example, the desired exponent might be expressed in the form of E+05. It could also appear in the following equivalent forms: E05, E+5, E5, E 05, or +5. In other words, it is not necessary to use 4 card columns to express the exponent unless it is so desired. If the exponent wanted were E−05, a minimum of 2 card columns would be required, with the exponent expressed as −5.

When output is specified in exponent form, the exact form in which the number is printed out varies with different FORTRAN versions. With some compilers the number will print out in the form

±0.nnnnn ... E±ee

with the decimal point placed to the left of the leading significant digit. For example, if the result of a calculation in the computer were -1378.2230, and the field specification E12.5 were used for the printout of this result, the printout would appear as $-0.13782E+04$. In other versions the zero preceding the decimal point prints only in the case of a positive number, and the signs print only if the number or the exponent is negative. Such a version would print out in the following general forms:

$$0.\text{nnnnn}\ldots E\quad ee$$
$$0.\text{nnnnn}\ldots E-ee$$
$$-.\text{nnnnn}\ldots E\quad ee$$
$$-.\text{nnnnn}\ldots E-ee$$

A major deviation from the preceding occurs with the use of 1620 FORTRAN with FORMAT, in which the processor causes as many significant digits to be placed to the left of the decimal point as is consistent with the field specification used. In this version the number -1378.2230 calculated by the computer, with a field specification of E12.5, would be printed out as $-1.37822E+03$. The columns below show several examples of how calculated values would appear printed out, with an E11.3 specification, in many versions of FORTRAN,

Calculated Value	Printout
$-.0005$	$^{bb}-.500E-03$
$.000003261$	$^{bb}\ 0.326E-05$
-219.51	$^{bb}-.219E\ \ 03$
$5321.$	$^{bb}\ 0.532E\ \ 04$

where the b's indicate blanks.

Since different versions of FORTRAN have slightly different printout forms, the reader is again reminded to become familiar with the characteristics of the particular FORTRAN version he is using. Input variations also exist in various compilers. For example, in using compilers which have so-called "free-form" input (1620 UTO and PDQ FORTRANS), the field width of numbers being used as input data need not be in agreement with the field-width specification. In these versions, the numbers need not even be expressed in exponent form when an E-type specification is used.

To conclude our discussion of FORMAT statements for numerical data, several remarks are in order which are applicable to all the types of field specifications thus far described. A field specification can be repeated by preceding the specification with an unsigned integer constant. Thus, the FORMAT statement

2 FORMAT(4F10.2)

is equivalent to

2 FORMAT(F10.2,F10.2,F10.2,F10.2)

Groups of field specifications can be repeated by the use of parentheses. The FORMAT statement

2 FORMAT(I3,2(E14.8,F6.2,F8.1))

is equivalent to

2 FORMAT(I3,E14.8,F6.2,F8.1,E14.8,F6.2,F8.1)

The I-type, F-type, and E-type specifications are shown below in a typical example of a WRITE statement with its associated FORMAT statement:

WRITE(6,10)N,X,Y

10 FORMAT(I5,F6.2,E14.6)

The resulting printout might appear as

$-392^b 19.32^{bb} - .378492E^b 04$

where the b's indicate blanks.

The following is a typical READ statement, with its associated FORMAT statement, containing all three types of field specifications:

READ(5,3)X,Y,XDOT,YDOT,N

3 FORMAT(F3.0,F4.1,E8.3,E10.4,I3)

Figure 1-16 shows a data card as it might be punched for read-in by the above READ statement. The vertical lines would not actually appear on the card; they have been added to identify clearly the various fields.

When the line printer is operating in program-control mode, the first character of an output record is not actually printed but is used for carriage control of the line printer. This control character is commonly specified with a Hollerith specification.

Hollerith Specification (*H-conversion*). The Hollerith, or H-type, specification is used for printing out alphameric text. Titles, names, dates,

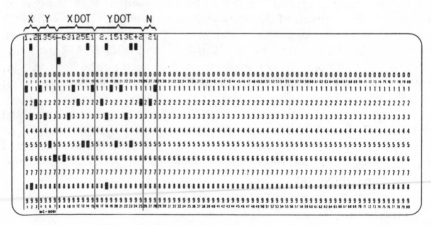

FIG. 1-16. Data card for given input statements.

an example, the statements

```
        WRITE(6,2)
    2 FORMAT(1H1,17HROCKET VELOCITIES)
```

buld cause the heading ROCKET VELOCITIES to be printed at the top of a
w page starting at the left margin. The statements

```
        WRITE(6,3)DISPL,VEL
    3 FORMAT(1H ,2F8.2)
```

when executed a number of times, would cause a series of values of the
variables DISPL and VEL to be printed out with normal single spacing.

The use of the Hollerith specification on input is illustrated by the
following example. Let us assume the two statements

```
        READ(5,33)
    33 FORMAT(16Hᵇ USERSᵇ NAMEᵇ HERE)
```

appear in a source program and that the symbolic unit number (data set
reference number) 5 is associated with the card reader. These statements
would cause 16 characters to be read from a card. They would replace, in
storage, the 16 characters, arbitrarily selected in the FORMAT statement,
following the H. (An appropriate number of blanks or other characters
could be used in the source program FORMAT statement instead of the
characters shown above.) As an example, suppose that the 16 characters
read from the card are

ᵇ WILLIAMᵇ BROWNᵇᵇ

A subsequent statement

```
        WRITE(6,33)
```

in the source program, where symbolic unit number 6 is associated with
the line printer, would cause printout of the user's name, William Brown.
The first blank in the field read in is for carriage control of the line printer,
which is assumed to be operating in program control mode.

The Literal Specification. Some versions of FORTRAN IV provide a
literal-data FORMAT specification for input or output of alphameric characters, in addition to the Hollerith specification. The literal specification
may be used in place of the Hollerith specification, and it has the advantage that the number of characters in the field need not be counted, in
making the specification. The text, or *literal data,* as it is called in using
this specification, is simply enclosed in single quotation marks. The
statements

```
        WRITE(6,4)
    4 FORMAT(' DYNAMIC CHARACTERISTICS OF A ROCKET')
```

column headings, and so forth, are often printed o
tion. It may also be used for input of alphameric cha
less commonly used for this purpose. The H-type
general form wH, in which w is an integer constant
number of alphameric characters in the message to
field width). This message, usually referred to as *Hol*
the letter H. Any desired blank spaces in the text are inc
width count. The statement

WRITE(6,2)

2 FORMAT(34HSOLUTION OF SIMULTANEOUS E

appearing in a source program would result in a printe
shown following the letter H.

Hollerith text can also be printed along with the nume
variables in the printed output. This is best illustrated b
such as

WRITE(6,3)DISPL,VEL,ACCEL

3 FORMAT(F8.2,4H^{b}FT.,F9.2,9H^{b}FT./SEC.,F7.2,14H^{b}FT./S

where the b's again indicate blank spaces. The first 8 spaces i
out are allocated for the numerical value of the variable DISPL
2 spaces after the decimal point. Following the printout of thi
the 4 Hollerith text characters, including the blank, appear as
The next 9 spaces are allocated for the printout of the numerica
the variable VEL, followed by 9 characters of Hollerith text, and
The printed output might appear as

^{b}1326.25 ^{b}FT.^{bbb}165.21 ^{b}FT./SEC.^{bb}28.61 ^{b}FT./SEC./SEC.

where the brackets are added to indicate the conformance of the n
cal printout to the field specifications shown in the FORMAT state

As previously mentioned, when the line printer is operati
program-control mode, the first character of an output record is not
ally printed but is used for vertical carriage control of the line pri
This first character can be conveniently indicated by a Hollerith speci
tion. The following tabulation shows some normally used control char
ters, the corresponding Hollerith specification which makes each charac
the first character in the output record, and the control function pe
formed by each:

Character	Hollerith Specification	Control Function
Blank	1H^b	Single spacing
0 (zero)	1H0	Double spacing
1	1H1	Brings up a new page

for example, would result in the printout

DYNAMIC CHARACTERISTICS OF A ROCKET

with the symbolic unit 6 denoting the line printer. The blank space preceding the letter D is for carriage control of the printer. It would not appear in the printout.

If the literal specification appears in a FORMAT statement which is used with an input statement, a number of characters, equal to the number of characters between the apostrophes of the FORMAT statement, will be read in from the designated input device. The desired characters replace, in storage, the arbitrary characters specified between the apostrophes of the FORMAT statement in writing the statement.

Thus, the statements

> READ(5,33)
> 33 FORMAT(' USERS NAME HERE')

appearing in a source program would cause 16 characters to be read from the input unit associated with the symbolic unit number 5. If the 16 characters read in are

$$^b\text{ROBERT}^b\text{STEWART}^b$$

a subsequent statement

> WRITE(6,33)

in the source program would cause output of the user's name, Robert Stewart, on the unit associated with symbolic unit number 6.

Blank Fields—The X Specification. When it is wished to leave blank spaces (not blank lines) in the printout, or when card columns are to be ignored during read-in, they may be called for by the use of the X specification in the FORMAT statement. Suppose, for example, that the values of time, displacement, velocity, and acceleration of a rocket are to be printed out for specified time increments over a specified time interval, and that all 4 values at each time increment are to be printed on a single line. A more readable printout would be obtained if a number of blank spaces were used to separate the various columns of figures and their headings.

The X specification has the general form wX, where w is an integer constant specifying the number of blank spaces to be provided in the output record. As an example, the FORMAT statement

> 3 FORMAT(5X,F6.2,6X,F5.1)

associated with a WRITE statement listing 2 variables, might cause printout as

$$\underbrace{^{bbbbb}-34.6}\underbrace{^{bbbbbb}}^b89.1$$

where the fields are indicated by the brackets shown.

The specification 1X can be used as the first specification in an output FORMAT statement in place of the Hollerith specification $1H^b$ previously suggested for use in making the first character in the output record a blank for line-printer carriage control. The statements

WRITE(6,3)DISPL,VEL

3 FORMAT(1X,2F8.2)

would cause the values of DISPL and VEL to be printed out with normal single spacing. The FORMAT statement

3 FORMAT(8X,2F8.2)

would provide normal vertical single spacing and would leave 7 blank spaces preceding the fields for the values of DISPL and VEL.

Used for input, the blank-field specification 20X would cause 20 card columns to be skipped. Such a specification could be used where it was not desired to read some of the data on the card, or where the columns to be skipped contained information other than data.

The Use of Slashes and the Multiple Use of Field Specifications. In a FORMAT statement, a slash (/) can be used to indicate the end of 1 record of input or output data. A slash is used to separate field specifications in a FORMAT statement when the FORMAT statement is associated with a READ or WRITE statement which is to read in or print out more than 1 record of data. Thus, if the FORMAT statement

3 FORMAT(F9.2/F10.4)

were associated with a WRITE statement having 2 variables in its list, the values of these variables would be printed out on separate lines. If this FORMAT statement were associated with a READ statement listing 2 variables, the 2 values to be read in would be punched on separate cards.

Suppose that the FORMAT statement

9 FORMAT(2F6.2,3E14.8/I5)

were used with an input or output statement which was to be executed a number of times. This FORMAT statement would then be used over and over for the input or output of a number of records. It would specify a format of (2F6.2,3E14.8) for the first and succeeding odd-numbered records, and a format of (I5) for the second and succeeding even-numbered records.

Scale Factors. In discussing the output of the values of real variables for which E-type field specifications are used, it was shown that the value always (with a few rare exceptions) had the form of a number between 0.1 and 1.0 multiplied by some power of 10. If it is desired that the value have the form of a number between 1.0 and 10 multiplied by a power of 10, a 1P is added in front of the E specification. The 1 preceding the P is called the *scale factor.* If it is desired that the value have the form of a number between 10 and 100 multiplied by a power of 10, a 2P precedes the E specification. For example, the statements

WRITE(6,2)A,B

2 FORMAT(1P2E13.6)

might cause the following printout:

$$-3.123456E-01^b7.543212E\ 06$$

A positive scale factor multiplies the number by $(10)^{\text{scale factor}}$ and decreases the exponent a corresponding amount. The scale factor applies to all E and F field specifications which follow it within the FORMAT statement. This applies to multiple-record formats as well as single-record formats. To change back to a zero scale factor for a subsequent and following specifications in the FORMAT statement, a 0P (zero followed by P) may be used preceding the specification.

Scale factors have no effect on I-type specifications. With output, a scale factor will cause data values with F-type specifications to be multiplied by $(10)^{\text{scale factor}}$. Such multiplication is generally not desirable, although it is conceivable that it might be desired to convert units such as amperes to milliamperes or meters to centimeters, and so forth, by this method. For example, a value, with the units of amperes, stored in memory could be printed out as the value in milliamperes by using a scale factor of 3.

With input, scale factors may be used only with the F-type specification. The scale factor is then defined as follows:

$$(\text{External quantity})(10)^{-\text{scale factor}} = (\text{internal quantity})$$

For example, if the FORMAT statement

2 FORMAT(2PF6.2)

were used in conjunction with a READ statement, the datum value 312.24 would be read into the computer and stored as 3.1224.

Manipulative Input/Output Statements. Three manipulative statements are used with magnetic tape. The statement

BACKSPACE 2

would cause tape unit 2 to backspace 1 record. The statement

REWIND 3

would cause tape 3 to be rewound back to its beginning. The statement

END FILE 4

would cause an end-of-file mark to be written on the tape in unit 4. This would mark the end of the data stored on that tape.

1-17. DIMENSION Statements

The DIMENSION statement is a specification statement used in conjunction with subscripted variables. (A discussion of other specification statements will be given in Chapter 2.) The DIMENSION statement must precede the first use of the subscripted variables in the source program, so most programmers make a practice of placing all DIMENSION statements near the beginning of the program. They are used to give information to the FORTRAN compiler pertinent to the allocation of storage for the subscripted-variable values while the object program is being compiled. For example, if a 2-dimensional array of subscripted elements T(I, J) were to be used in a program in which I and J had maximum values of 10 and 20, respectively, the statement

DIMENSION T(10,20)

in the source program would allocate 200 locations in memory for the 200 elements in the array.

A single DIMENSION statement may be used for as many subscripted variables as desired. When more than 1 subscripted variable appears in a DIMENSION statement, they are separated by commas. As an example, the DIMENSION statement

DIMENSION A(15,16),B(15,15),T(15,16),X(15)

would provide memory locations for the subscripted variables A(I, J), B(L,M), T(K,N), and X(I), respectively. A total of 720 memory locations would be allocated.

Problems

1-1. Listed below are some FORTRAN real constants. Rewrite these constants in ordinary form.

.07E$-$3	$-$3.21E$-$02	.00E5
$+$.9E$+$04	.0002E$-$5	$-$10.E$-$10
$-$10.E$-$1	.9999E9	$+$10.E0
.86E5	.1111E1	1234.E$-$03

1-2. Listed below are several numbers written in ordinary form. Rewrite these numbers as real constants in E form.

1,000,000	$3.67(10)^{-2}$
10^{15}	8.04
$10(10)^{-3}$	$32.61(10)^{2}$
1	9.54602
.000001	10

1-3. For each of the names listed below, indicate whether the name is an acceptable real-variable name, an acceptable integer-variable name, or an invalid name. Base your determination upon the FORTRAN version which you are using. For the names which are invalid, state why.

Y	MIN$S	JOHN	AB
(Y)	22B4	ABLE	B(B)
12	XCUBED	BAKER	VALUE
I.1	1MORE	CHARLIE	ACCELER
KKG	VELOC	−TEN	JERK
B707	STRESS	A*B	E*EPSI

1-4. Write the following mathematical expressions as FORTRAN expressions:

$$\frac{(A + B)C}{D}$$

$$\frac{AB}{CD}$$

$$(A + B)^2$$

$$A - B + C$$

$$A^{(B^C)}$$

$$\frac{X + Y}{W + Z}$$

$$\frac{X}{Y + \dfrac{A}{B}}$$

$$A + B^2$$

$$A + \frac{BC}{D}$$

$$(A + B)/(C/D)$$

$$-3A + (B - C)$$

$$\frac{A}{B}(10)^{-2}$$

1-5. Each FORTRAN expression below is written to represent the equivalent mathematical expression shown on the left. Point out the errors, if any, in each case and write the correct FORTRAN expression.

Mathematical Expression	FORTRAN *Expression*
$A + \dfrac{BC}{D} + F^E - G$	(A + B)*C/D+F**E−G
$\dfrac{A}{BC}$	A/B*C
$(A + B)C$	A + B*C
$(A + I)^2$	(A + I)**2
$X^2 + 3X + 4$	X*X+3.(X)+4.
$\dfrac{EHC}{AB}$	E*H/A/B/C
πR^2	(3.1416*(R**2)
I^A	I**A

1-6. Some of the arithmetic statements listed below contain errors. Rewrite the invalid statements in correct form.

A − B = C + D	A*B = C/D
N = (X + Y)	X(2 + I,3) = −2.*(A − B)
Z = I + J − 2.	6. = R
−X = −(A + B)	J(A) = A − 10.
X(I,3) = I3	A(J) = 10. − A

1-7. Write a source program for calculating the amplitude of a forced vibration. The amplitude is given by

$$A = \frac{Q/K}{\sqrt{\left(1 - \frac{\omega^2}{\omega_n^2}\right)^2 + \left(\frac{C^2\omega^2}{K^2}\right)}}$$

where

A = amplitude
Q = maximum value of periodic disturbing force
K = spring constant
ω = 2π times the forcing frequency
ω_n = 2π times the natural frequency
C = damping coefficient

The values of Q, K, ω, ω_n, and C are to be read from data cards. The value of the amplitude is to be printed as output.

1-8. Write a program for determining the acceleration of the slider of a slider-crank mechanism. The formula for the acceleration is

$$a = r\omega^2 \left[\cos\theta + \frac{c\cos 2\theta + c^3 \sin^4\theta}{(1 - c^2 \sin^2\theta)^{3/2}}\right]$$

where

a = acceleration of slider
c = ratio of crank length to connecting-rod length
ω = angular velocity of crank
r = crank length
θ = angle of crank from a line through the fixed pivot of the crank and the joint connecting the slider and connecting rod

The values for c, ω, r, and θ are to be read from data cards. The value of the acceleration and angle θ are to be printed as output.

1-9. Write a FORTRAN source program for calculating the radius of gyration of a rectangular hollow beam about a horizontal axis. The equation for the radius of gyration is

$$k = \sqrt{\frac{b_1 d_1^3 - b_2 d_2^3}{12(b_1 d_1 - b_2 d_2)}}$$

The dimensions b_1 and d_1 are the outside width and depth of the section, respectively, and b_2 and d_2 are the corresponding inside dimensions, all in inches. The numerical value of these dimensions are to be read in from cards, and all dimensions and the corresponding radius of gyration are to be printed out.

In the Probs. 1-10 through 1-13, a partial flow chart is to be made for each problem, and the FORTRAN statements which accomplish the given requirements are to be written as partial source programs.

1-10. The algebraically smallest of the 3 variables A, B, and C is to be given the name SMALL. The algebraically largest of the same variables is to be given the name BIG.

1-11. If $X > Y$ and $W > Z$, N is to be given the value 1. If $X \leq Y$ and $W \leq Z$, N is to be given the value of Z; otherwise, set $N = 3$.

1-12. If $E \leq 100$ and either $F \leq 10$ or $G \leq 1$ or both, set $N = 1$; otherwise, set $N = 2$.

1-13. Give the smallest of the 3 variables A, B, and C the name SMALL, using only 2 IF statements.

1-14. Draw a flow chart and write a complete FORTRAN source program for calculating the theoretical adiabatic horsepower of a quantity of gas (the horsepower necessary to compress Q cubic feet of gas per second from p_1 to p_2). The formula is

$$\text{Hp} = \frac{144k}{500(k - 1)} p_1 Q \left[\left(\frac{p_2}{p_1} \right)^{\frac{k-1}{k}} - 1 \right]$$

where

Q = quantity of gas, cu ft/sec
p_1 = initial pressure of gas, lb/in.^{2}
p_2 = final pressure of gas, lb/in.^{2}
k = ratio of specific heat at constant pressure to specific heat at constant volume

The values of k, p_1, p_2, and Q are to be entered as data from cards, and the ratio of p_2/p_1 is to vary from 1.5 to 10, in increments of 0.5.

1-15. Write a complete FORTRAN source program for determining the acceleration of the slider of a slider-crank mechanism (see Prob. 1-8) for a number of different proportions of the linkage and over 180° of crank rotation. Let the ratio of crank length to connecting-rod length vary from 0.1 to 0.9, in increments of 0.1. Both the angular velocity of the crank and the crank length are to be entered as data, using cards. Print out the acceleration for every 5° of crank rotation for each value of crank-to-connecting-rod ratio.

1-16. One hundred numbers, X(1) through X(100), are available for use from a previous portion of a program. Continue the program by writing the statements required to find the *mean* of the value of these numbers (the sum of the numbers divided by their number). Store the result in AVG.

1-17. Two hundred numbers, X(1) through X(100) and F(1) through F(100), are stored in memory. Write the statements necessary to find

$$\frac{1}{100} \sum_{I=1}^{100} [X(I)][F(I)]$$

and store the result in COFG.

1-18. The values of X(1) through X(50) are available from a previous portion of a program. Write the statements necessary to calculate

$$\sum_{I=1}^{50} \left(X(I) - \frac{1}{50} \sum_{J=1}^{50} X(J) \right)^2$$

and store the result in a location SMIN.

1-19. The elements of a square matrix A(I,J) of order n have been read in as data. The order n has also been read in as data. Write the statements necessary to calculate the trace of the matrix $(A_{11} + A_{22} + A_{33} + \cdots + A_{nn})$ and store the result in a location defined by the name TRACE.

1-20.   The elements of a square matrix B(I, J) of order n have been read in as data. The value of n has also been entered as data. There are available, from the previous portion of the program, n values of X(J), from X(1) through X(N). Write the statements necessary to compute the n elements of a new array, named A(I), whose elements are given by

$$A(I) = \sum_{j=1}^{n} (B(I,J))(X(J))$$

chapter 2

Additional FORTRAN

2-1. Introduction

Chapter 1 presented the basic and most-often-used elements of the FORTRAN language. The material consisted, for the most part, of both FORTRAN II and FORTRAN IV. In the topics covered in Chapter 1, the differences between the two FORTRAN versions were minor.

In Chapter 2 we shall study additional FORTRAN for more advanced programming techniques. Some of the material will consist of both FORTRAN II and FORTRAN IV, as in the use of subprograms, for example. Other material will present features which are unique to FORTRAN IV, such as *logical*, *double-precision*, and *complex* constants; *logical*, *double-precision*, and *complex* variables; the *logical* IF statement; and *relational* and *logical* operators. Features which are available in FORTRAN II as well as in FORTRAN IV will be pointed out as they appear.

2-2. Double-Precision Constants

FORTRAN IV incorporates the use of double-precision constants to minimize the cumulative effect of roundoff errors in the numerous arithmetic operations performed in a sequence of calculations. As will be seen later, in Chapter 4, some methods for handling simultaneous algebraic equations are limited, by the effects of roundoff error, to the solution of approximately 15 to 20 equations, if reasonable engineering accuracy is to be expected in the results. The use of double-precision constants permits the solution of a greater number of simultaneous equations by a given method and with greater accuracy.

Double-precision constants are numbers, written with a decimal point, which are precise to approximately twice the number of decimal digits given by real constants; that is, they can be written with up to approximately 14 to 29 decimal digits (typically about 16) depending upon the particular computer being used. The constants may be written in ordinary decimal form or in exponent form. If they are written in ordinary decimal form, such as

$$236.1392176549821$$

they are double-precision by virtue of the fact that they contain more digits than are valid for real constants. When written in exponent form, a D is used instead of an E, as before. For example,

92.137D+4	is	$(92.137)10^4$
7.1D0	is	$(7.1)10^0$
.12397654321D−07	is	$(.12397654321)10^{-7}$

are valid double-precision constants. In the first two examples, no more digits are specified than could have been legitimately specified in writing the numbers as real constants, and, in a binary-coded decimal computer, they would be no more accurate when written as double-precision constants than they would when written as real constants. However, in a pure binary computer many decimal fractions cannot be expressed exactly in pure binary form, no matter how many binary digits are used, and in this type of computer more accuracy would be obtained by using double-precision constants even if the number of decimal digits did not exceed the permissible number for real constants. For example, with a pure binary computer, a number written in double-precision form as

$$7.2D0$$

in a program will be represented more accurately in the computer than if it is written in real form as 7.2.

2-3. Complex Constants

Complex numbers are often used in problems from various engineering areas. FORTRAN IV provides for arithmetic operations involving complex quantities. Complex constants are represented by an *ordered pair* of *real* constants. The pair of real constants is enclosed in parentheses and separated by a comma. For example,

(5.71,−2.95)	represents	5.71 − 2.95i
(+3.91,0.)	represents	3.91
(.196,.251E−2)	represents	.196 + .00251i

where $i = \sqrt{-1}$. A plus sign is permitted with any of the real constants expressing the real and imaginary portions of complex constants when the quantity is positive, as in the second example above, but plus signs are not required.

2-4. Logical Constants

Subsequent portions of this chapter will discuss the use of relational and logical expressions which are either *true* or *false*. Variables set equal to such expressions take on the value "true" or "false." Such variables are called *logical variables*, and the values "true" and "false" are the two *logical constants*. Logical constants appearing in a source program are written as

.TRUE.

.FALSE.

where the periods are required.

2-5. Double-Precision, Complex, and Logical Variables

In Chapter 1 two types of variables were discussed—the real (floating-point) variable and the integer (fixed-point) variable. It may be recalled that each of these types is *implicitly* specified by the first character used in the variable name. FORTRAN IV provides for the use of three more kinds of variables—*double-precision, complex*, and *logical*.

For most computers, FORTRAN IV variable names for all these types of variables consist of 1 to 6 alphameric characters, with the requirement that the first character be alphabetic. Double-precision, complex, and logical variables cannot be specified implicitly as to type but must be explicitly specified by listing them in Type statements. Type statements come under the general classification of specification statements but are discussed here because of their close association with variables. Other specification statements are discussed in Secs. 2-11 and 2-13. Real and integer variables may be specified *either* implicitly or explicitly, but an explicit specification will override the type implied by the first character of the name.

A Type statement must precede the first appearance of any of the listed variable names in executable statements in a program. (Executable statements include the arithmetic-assignment statement, the DO, GO TO, computed GO TO, IF, PAUSE, PRINT, PUNCH, and READ statements, the CONTINUE statement, and the CALL and RETURN statements.) Variables are explicitly specified, as shown by the following examples of Type statements:

REAL I,MASS,FORCE

INTEGER X,Y,Z,A(15,15)

DOUBLE PRECISION A,B

COMPLEX AMP,VOLT

LOGICAL LOG1, LOG2

As many variables as necessary may be included in a single Type statement. Note that, in the first statement, the real variable FORCE would not need to be included, since it is implicitly specified as a real variable by the first character of the name. However, it is permissible to include it as shown.

The subscripted variable A is dimensioned in the second Type statement shown. A variable dimensioned in a Type statement may not be dimensioned elsewhere (such as in a DIMENSION statement).

Another Type statement, the EXTERNAL statement, is not included with the examples given. Names appearing in EXTERNAL statements are subprogram names that are arguments of other subprograms; this kind of statement will be discussed in Sec. 2-15, following the description of subprograms.

The FORTRAN IV Type statements just discussed are all accepted by the IBM 360 version of FORTRAN IV. However, this particular version also includes additional Type statements which are capable of providing considerably more specifications than the Type statements discussed in the preceding paragraphs.

The IBM 360 computer memory consists of magnetic cores capable of storing the binary digits(bits) 0 and 1. The magnetic cores themselves are often referred to as bits. To represent various characters uniquely, groups of bits must be handled by the computer. In the IBM 360 computer eight-bit groups are used, each such group being referred to as a *byte*. A byte is then the addressable unit, and is referred to as an address or memory location in this version.

In all versions of FORTRAN a *standard* number of memory locations is reserved for the values assigned to each type of variable available in that version. However, an IBM 360 FORTRAN IV Type statement may specify that a number of locations, different than the standard number, be reserved for any of the different types of variables available in that version. The following table shows each type of variable, the associated standard number, and the optional number of memory locations which may be specified.

Variable Type	Standard Number of Memory Locations	Optional Number of Memory Locations
INTEGER	4	2
REAL	4	8 (double-precision)
COMPLEX	8	16 (double-precision complex)
LOGICAL	4	1

In IBM 360 FORTRAN IV variable types may be specified in any one of 3 ways. They are the *predefined* specification, the *explicit* specification, and the IMPLICIT specification.

The Predefined Specification. This is the familiar convention used in all FORTRAN versions in which integer and real variables are specified by the first letter of the variable name. The initial letters I, J, K, L, M, and N are used to specify integer variables, while any other initial letter specifies a real variable. In most versions of FORTRAN such a method of specifying the type of variable is known as *implicit* specification. However, in IBM

360 FORTRAN IV this kind of specification is referred to as a predefined specification, since an IMPLICIT Type statement, which will be discussed subsequently, is included in this version.

The Explicit Specification. As discussed previously, for other versions of FORTRAN IV, the explicit Type statement specifies the type of each variable in the statement list by preceding the listed variables by REAL, INTEGER, DOUBLE PRECISION, COMPLEX, or LOGICAL as the case may be, and also provides for dimensioning variables in the list. IBM 360 FORTRAN IV explicit Type statements, in addition to the above, can also be used to specify the standard or optional number of memory locations for each variable and, if desired, can be used to specify the initial values of variables.

For example, the Type statement

REAL*8 DBL1, DBL2, DBL3

specifies the listed variables as real, double-precision variables since the *8 following REAL specifies that 8 memory locations are to be reserved for each variable, rather than the standard 4 locations. If the *8 were deleted from the above statement, the absence of this length specification would provide the standard number of memory locations for each variable.

The Type statement

REAL INV, JOB

would specify the listed variables as real variables, overriding the predefined convention, and 4 memory locations would be provided for each variable.

If some real variables in a list are to be double-precision, while others are not, a Type statement such as

REAL*8A,B,NUM*4,MATR(10,10)

might be used. The variables A, B, and MATR are specified as real, double-precision variables since 8 memory locations are specified. The variable NUM is specified a real, single-precision variable since the standard 4 memory locations are specified for it.

When a length specification is associated with the type specification, it applies to each variable in the list, unless a length specification is associated with a particular variable, in which case the former length specification is overridden. For example, in the last Type statement shown above, the length specification *4 associated with the variable NUM overrides the length specification *8, and specifies NUM as a single-precision variable. If *4 were deleted from the above statement, NUM would be specified as double-precision.

If it is known that the magnitudes of certain integer variables will never exceed $32,767(2^{15} - 1)$, memory space can be saved by specifying that these variables are to occupy only 2 locations in memory. The statement

INTEGER*2I,J,LL,JOB*4(10,10)

will reserve 2 storage locations for the values of the variables I, J, and LL. The elements of the array JOB, however, will each have 4 storage locations reserved. Note that the array JOB is dimensioned as part of the Type statement. Since 100 elements are indicated in this array, 400 memory locations will be reserved for the array values.

The following statements illustrate the assignation of initial values to variables in IBM 360 FORTRAN IV Type statements:

COMPLEX*16D,TAU/(3.92,1.54)/,CC*8

REAL A(10,10)/90*0.0,10*1.0/,B*8/1.1E6/,C(5)/5*0.0/,G/32.17/

In the first statement, D and TAU are specified as complex, double-precision variables, with 16 memory locations specified for each. The variable TAU is also assigned the initial value (3.92, 1.54) as shown. The variable CC is specified as single-precision complex, with 8 memory locations reserved, 4 for the real part and 4 for the imaginary part.

In the second statement, the first 90 values of the 100 element array A are assigned initial values of 0.0, while the last 10 elements are initialized as 1.0. (The order of the array elements in memory are A(1,1), A(2,1), A(3,1),..., A(1,2), A(2,2), A(3,2),..., A(1,3), A(2,3), A(3,3),..., and so forth, up to A(10,10), with the first subscript varying the fastest.) The variable B is specified as double-precision, and has the initial value 1.1E6. Array C will have space reserved for 5 elements, each occupying the standard 4 locations, and the initial value of all 5 elements will be 0.0. The variable G has the standard memory locations reserved, and an initial value of 32.17.

The IMPLICIT Type Statement.   This IBM 360 FORTRAN IV statement allows the programmer to specify types of variables in a manner similar to the predefined convention discussed earlier. However, it is a more flexible specification, since it allows the programmer to select which initial letters are to specify a particular type of variable. It can also be used to specify all types of variable, whereas the predefined convention is limited to integer and real variables. In addition, the IMPLICIT Type statement can specify the number of storage locations for variables of all types and precisions. For example, the statement

IMPLICIT REAL*8(A − K, O − Z)

specifies that all variables in the program beginning with the letters A through K and O through Z are real, double-precision variables. The statement

IMPLICIT INTEGER*2(I,J,K)

specifies that all variables beginning with the letters I, J, and K are integer variables, occupying only 2 memory locations each. The last statement above might also have been written as

IMPLICIT INTEGER*2(I − K)

Several different type specifications can be included in a single IMPLICIT statement, and if a length specification is not included with the type of variable, the standard length is specified. For example, the statement

IMPLICIT INTEGER(A,B,D−F),REAL*8(G−K),COMPLEX(C),LOGICAL(L−N)

specifies that all variables beginning with the letters A, B, and D through F are integer variables with a standard number of memory locations for each; that all variables beginning with the letters G through K are real, double-precision variables with 8 memory locations reserved for each; that all variables beginning with the letter C are complex with a standard number of 8 memory locations for each; and that all variables beginning with the letters L through N are logical variables with a standard number of memory locations reserved. All initial letters not included in the IMPLICIT statement follow the predefined convention.

Each of the kinds of specification statements just discussed must precede the first appearance of any of the specified variables in executable statements in a program. An IMPLICIT Type statement overrides the predefined convention, while an explicit Type statement overrides both the predefined convention and the IMPLICIT Type statement.

2-6. Expressions and Statements Containing Double-Precision and Complex Quantities

FORTRAN IV provides for *arithmetic* and *logical* expressions. Chapter 1 discussed arithmetic expressions containing real and integer quantities. In this section we shall consider arithmetic expressions and statements containing double-precision and complex quantities. *Logical* expressions will be taken up in the next section.

The operation symbols used in double-precision and complex expressions are the same as those used in real and integer expressions, and similar rules apply in writing these expressions. The types of constants, variables, and functions which can be combined to give various kinds of arithmetic expressions are shown in Fig. 2-1(a). The intersection of a particular row and column shows the validity or invalidity of the combination represented by the row and column headings, the resulting type of expression for the combination being shown in parentheses if the result is a valid combination. IBM 360 FORTRAN IV and a few other versions per-

Operations +, −, *, /	Integer	Real	Double−Precision	Complex
Integer	Valid (integer)	Invalid	Invalid	Invalid
Real	Invalid	Valid (real)	Valid (DP)	Valid (complex)
Double−Precision	Invalid	Valid (DP)	Valid (DP)	Invalid
Complex	Invalid	Valid (complex)	Invalid	Valid (complex)

(a) Valid and invalid combinations in expressions in most versions of FORTRAN IV.

Operations +, −, *, /	Integer (2)	Integer (4)	Real (4)	Real (8)	Complex (8)	Complex (16)
Integer (2)	Integer (2)	Integer (4)	Real (4)	Real (8)	Complex (8)	Complex (16)
Integer (4)	Integer (4)	Integer (4)	Real (4)	Real (8)	Complex (8)	Complex (16)
Real (4)	Real (4)	Real (4)	Real (4)	Real (8)	Complex (8)	Complex (16)
Real (8)	Real (8)	Real (8)	Real (8)	Real (8)	Complex (16)	Complex (16)
Complex (8)	Complex (8)	Complex (8)	Complex (8)	Complex (16)	Complex (8)	Complex (16)
Complex (16)	Complex (16)	Complex (16)	Complex (16)	Complex (16)	Complex (16)	Complex (16)

(b) Modes of expressions containing mixed types of operands in IBM 360 FORTRAN IV.

FIG. 2-1. Combinations of modes in FORTRAN IV expressions. (Operations +, −, *, /).

mit almost complete mixing of modes in arithmetic expressions. Figure 2-1(b) shows resulting types of expressions for combinations of various types of operands in IBM 360 FORTRAN IV. Figure 2-1 is valid only for the operations denoted by +, −, *, and /.

As an illustration, Fig. 2-1 reveals that real and double-precision quantities can be mixed, the result being a double-precision quantity. Thus, if X (in the statement below) is real and DX and DPX are double-precision variables, the expression on the right side of the statement

DPX = 5.25*X/DX + 2.1D0*DX

is a valid double-precision expression and would be stored as a double-precision quantity having the name DPX. As discussed before, DPX and DX would have to be explicitly specified as double-precision type in a Type statement.

Valid combinations of constants, variables, and functions with respect to the operator ** are shown in Fig. 2-2, where the intersection of a particular row and column shows the validity or invalidity of the combination, with the resulting type of expression shown in parentheses for valid combinations.

For example, if COM and C are complex variables and have been

Type of Exponent

Operation **	Integer	Real	Double-Precision	Complex
Integer	Valid (integer)	Invalid	Invalid	Invalid
Real	Valid (real)	Valid (real)	Valid (DP)	Invalid
Double-Precision	Valid (DP)	Valid (DP)	Valid (DP)	Invalid
Complex	Valid (complex)	Invalid	Invalid	Invalid

Type of Base is the row label for this table.

(a) Valid and invalid combinations in most versions of FORTRAN IV.

Kind of Exponent (either length)

Operation (**)	Integer	Real	Complex
Integer	Valid (integer)	Valid (real)	Invalid
Real	Valid (real)	Valid (real)	Invalid
Complex	Valid (complex)	Invalid	Invalid

Type of Base (either length) is the row label for this table.

(b) Valid and invalid combinations in IBM 360 FORTRAN IV.

FIG. 2-2. Valid combinations in **FORTRAN IV** expressions
with respect to the operator **.

properly named in a Type statement, and if J is an integer variable, the
expression on the right side of the arithmetic-assignment statement

$$COM = C**J$$

is valid, and the result is complex. It is stored as a complex quantity
having the name **COM**. It is not permissible to mix integer, real, complex,
or double-precision quantities with logical constants or variables.

It is permissible to mix modes across the equal sign of an arithmetic-
assignment statement for a number of combinations of mode. The mode
of any valid arithmetic expression can be established by reference to Figs.
2-1 and 2-2. All the arithmetic is done in this mode. The result is then
stored in memory in the mode of the variable on the *left* of the equal sign.
Valid and invalid combinations of variables on the left, and corresponding
expressions on the right, are given by the intersections of appropriate
rows and columns in Fig. 2-3. Thus, if DP is a double-precision variable

Expression on Right

	Integer	Real	Double-Precision	Complex
Integer	Valid	Valid	Valid	Invalid*
Real	Valid	Valid	Valid	Invalid*
Double-Precision	Valid	Valid	Valid	Invalid*
Complex	Invalid	Valid	Invalid	Valid*

Variable on Left is the row label for this table.

*Valid in IBM 360 FORTRAN IV.

FIG. 2-3. Valid and invalid combinations of mixed mode
across equals sign.

and A and B are real variables, the statement

$$B = 2.0*DP*A - 7.2D0$$

would cause the expression on the right to be calculated in double-precision form, and then the most significant part of the result would be stored as a real quantity with the name B.

2-7. Logical Expressions

A logical expression always has the value .TRUE. or .FALSE.. The simplest form of a logical expression is a single logical constant, a single logical variable, or a single logical function. Another logical expression is known as a *relational* expression. A relational expression simply makes a declaration regarding the relative magnitudes of 2 arithmetic expressions. For example, it might state that A + B is greater than C * D. In FORTRAN IV this is stated by writing the 2 arithmetic expressions separated by the relational operator .GT., giving

$$A + B .GT. C * D$$

The relational operators available in FORTRAN IV are as follows:

Relational Operator	Definition
.GT.	Greater than
.GE.	Greater than or equal to
.EQ.	Equal to
.NE.	Not equal to
.LT.	Less than
.LE.	Less than or equal to

The types of expressions which can be combined by relational operators to form valid relational expressions are shown by the intersections of the appropriate rows and columns in Fig. 2-4. The relational expression

$$Y * A/B .NE. 3 + I$$

for example, is not valid in many FORTRAN versions, since the expression on the left of the operator is real, whereas that on the right is an integer expression. Complex and logical quantities are not included in Fig. 2-4, since they cannot be used in relational expressions.

Other logical expressions can be formed by combining relational expressions, logical constants, and logical variables with the logical operators .AND., .OR., and .NOT.. Such expressions will always have the value .TRUE. or .FALSE.. The operator .NOT. must always be followed by a logical expression. The expression

$$.NOT. A .GT. B$$

Arithmetic Expression on Right

		Integer	Real	Double−Precision
Arithmetic Expression on Left	Integer	Valid	Invalid*	Invalid*
	Real	Invalid*	Valid	Valid
	Double−Precision	Invalid*	Valid	Valid

*Valid in IBM 360 FORTRAN IV.

FIG. 2-4. Valid combinations of expressions separated by relational operators.

would have the value .TRUE. if A .GT. B is .FALSE., or the value .FALSE. if A .GT. B is .TRUE.. The logical operators .AND. and .OR. must be *preceded and followed* by logical expressions. For example,

A .GT. B .AND. X .LE. Y

is a valid logical expression. It has the value .TRUE. only if A .GT. B and X .LE. Y are both .TRUE.. Otherwise, the expression has the value .FALSE.. Likewise,

(D .GE. E) .OR. (F .NE. 0.)

is a valid logical expression having the value .TRUE. if either of the expressions D .GE. E or F .NE. 0. is .TRUE.. It has the value .FALSE. if both the relational expressions are .FALSE.. Any logical expression may be enclosed in parentheses, as shown above, for the relational expressions with the .OR. operator. A logical expression following a .NOT. must be enclosed in parentheses if it contains 2 or more quantities, since the operator .NOT. has a higher priority than .AND. or .OR.. Thus, the parentheses in the expression

.NOT.(A .GT. B .AND. X .LE. Y)

are required, or the expression would be interpreted as

(.NOT. A .GT. B) .AND. (X .LE. Y)

The hierarchy of operations for the logical operators is

Operator	*Priority*
.NOT.	Highest
.AND.	Second
.OR.	Lowest

Thus,

A .GT. B .AND. X .LT. Y .OR. C .EQ. D .AND.

.NOT. I .EQ. N .AND. J .LT. 10

would be interpreted as

$$((A.GT.B).AND.(X.LT.Y)).OR.((C.EQ.D).AND.$$

$$(.NOT.I.EQ.N).AND.(J.LT.10))$$

It is permissible for the operator .NOT. to follow an .AND. or .OR. directly, but otherwise no 2 logical operators may appear in sequence.

2-8. Logical-Assignment Statements

Statements consisting of a logical variable on the left side of an equals sign and a logical expression on the right side are sometimes classified as arithmetic-assignment statements, although they are preferably classified as "*logical-assignment*" statements. The expression on the right is evaluated as either .TRUE. or .FALSE., and this value is then assigned to the variable on the left. The following are examples of valid logical-assignment statements where the variables on the left are logical variables:

$$LV1 = .TRUE.$$
$$LV2 = X .GT. Y$$
$$LV3 = LV2$$
$$LV4 = A .GT. B .AND. C .EQ. D$$
$$LV5 = .NOT. LV4$$

It is not permissible to mix modes across the equals sign when logical quantities are involved. For example, if RV, A, and B are real variables, the statements

$$LV1 = A + B$$

and

$$RV = .TRUE.$$

are invalid.

2-9. Control Statements

Chapter 1 discussed a number of control statements which were sufficient to enable the programmer to control the flow of a program and to stop the computer upon the completion of the program. The control statements discussed included the unconditional GO TO, computed GO TO, arithmetic IF, DO, CONTINUE, PAUSE, STOP, and END statements. FORTRAN IV includes additional control statements which, in certain instances, provide added convenience for the programmer. Such statements will be discussed in the paragraphs to follow.

The Assigned GO TO and ASSIGN Statements. The general form of the assigned GO TO statement is

$$GO\ TO\ i,(n_1, n_2, n_3, \ldots, n_m)$$

where i represents an integer variable (nonsubscripted) and the n's are *statement numbers.* The integer variable must have appeared previously in an ASSIGN statement having the general form

ASSIGN n to i

where n represents a statement number and i represents the integer variable which appears subsequently in the assigned GO TO statement. Thus, the appearance in a program of the statements

ASSIGN 10 TO INT

GO TO INT,(5,10,36,42)

would cause transfer of control to statement 10 listed in the assigned GO TO statement. The number assigned to the integer variable in the ASSIGN statement must always be one of the statement numbers listed in the assigned GO TO statement, or the combination of the 2 statements will be invalid.

The Logical IF Statement.   The logical IF statement is somewhat more versatile than the arithmetic IF statement. It has the general form

IF(e)s

where e represents a *logical expression* and s represents any executable FORTRAN statement except a DO or another logical IF. For example, if A and B are real variables and LV1, LV2, and LV3 are logical variables, the following are valid logical IF statements:

IF(A .GT. B)GO TO 16

IF(LV1)Y = A/B

IF(LV2 .AND. A .LE. B)LV3 = .TRUE.

If the logical expression in parentheses (symbolized by e in the general expression) is .TRUE., the statement following (symbolized by s) is executed. The statement following the logical IF statement is then executed unless statement s is a transfer-of-control statement. In the latter instance, control is transferred as specified by statement s. If the logical expression e is .FALSE., control passes to the next statement in the program following the logical IF statement. In the first of the examples of valid logical IF statements shown above, control would be transferred to statement 16 if A were greater than B. If A were not greater than B, control would transfer to the statement in the program following the logical IF statement.

It was pointed out, in Chapter 1, that an arithmetic IF statement cannot be used as the last statement in the range of a DO. However it is permissible to use a logical IF statement as the last statement in the range, providing the statement symbolized by s is not a transfer-of-control statement.

2-10. Input and Output

The input and output features not included in the introductory study of FORTRAN (in Chapter 1) will now be described. These features include the transmission of entire arrays, the indexing of input/output lists, various additional field specifications, and the input and output of the logical, double-precision, and complex quantities available in FORTRAN IV.

Input and Output of Entire Arrays. An entire array or a part of an array can be transmitted (read into memory or printed out from memory) by using a double DO loop. For example, the appearance in a program of the statements

$$47 \quad \text{FORMAT(F10.2)}$$
$$\text{DO } 6J = 1,N$$
$$\text{DO } 6I = J,N$$
$$6 \quad \text{WRITE(6,47) A(I,J)}$$

would cause the printout of the elements

$$a_{11}$$
$$a_{21} \quad a_{22}$$
$$a_{31} \quad a_{32} \quad a_{33}$$
$$\vdots \qquad \vdots$$
$$a_{n1} \cdots\cdots\cdots a_{n4} \cdots a_{nn}$$

of an array. These elements would not appear in the form shown above but would be printed out, 1 element to a line, in 1 long column, their order being $a_{11}, a_{21}, a_{31}, \ldots, a_{n1}, a_{22}, a_{32}, \ldots, a_{n2}, a_{33}, a_{43}, \ldots, a_{n3}$, and so forth. If the entire array were to be printed out, instead of just the elements shown, the statements referred to could be used by simply changing the initial value (first indexing parameter), in the second DO statement, from a J to a 1.

Another method of printing an entire array is by using a set of statements such as

$$\text{DIMENSION B(10)}$$
$$49 \quad \text{FORMAT(F10.2)}$$
$$\text{WRITE(6,49)B}$$

in which the array name B appears in the list in nonsubscripted form.[1] In printing the 1-dimensional array B, all 10 elements would be printed consecutively in a column, with 1 element to a line. By changing statement 49 to FORMAT(10F10.2), all 10 elements of the array would be

---

[1]Transmission of entire arrays may be effected in this manner in both FORTRAN II and FORTRAN IV. In FORTRAN II, PRINT 49,B would replace the WRITE statement.

printed out consecutively on a single line. The input of an entire array may be handled in a similar manner.

If the array to be handled is 2-dimensional or greater, a set of statements, such as those in the preceding paragraph, will read in or print out the elements in an order in which the *first* subscript progresses most rapidly, the second subscript progresses the next most rapidly, and so forth. For example, the elements of a 3-by-3-by-3, 3-dimensional array would print out as $a_{111}, a_{211}, a_{311}, a_{121}, a_{221}, a_{321}, a_{131}, a_{231}, a_{331}, a_{112}, a_{212}, a_{312}, a_{122}, a_{222}, a_{322}$, and so forth.

Indexing Within an Input or Output List.[2] Subscripted variables in an input or output list may be indexed and incremented without the use of DO statements. For example, the statements

$$27 \ \ FORMAT(10F7.1)$$

$$READ(5,27)(A(I),I = 1,10)$$

would cause the reading of 10 quantities, from symbolic unit 5, which would be assigned to A(1), A(2), ..., A(10), respectively. This indexing of subscripted variables within an input or output list is referred to as an *implied* DO. It has the advantage over the explicit use of the DO statement such as

$$27 \ \ FORMAT(F7.1)$$

$$DO \ 7I = 1,10$$

$$7 \ \ READ(5,27)A(I)$$

in that, in the explicit use of the DO, each input value must be in a separate input record (be punched on a separate card). Changing the FORMAT specification to 10F7.1, for example, would not alter this requirement. Only the first F7.1 specification would be used each time the READ statement was executed. On the other hand, in the implied DO example shown, all 10 values would be in the same input record (be punched on a single card).

Implied DO's may also be nested. For example, the statements

$$51 \ \ FORMAT(10F7.1)$$

$$WRITE(6,49)((A(I,J),J = 1,10),I = 1,10)$$

would cause the printout of the a_{ij} array in the form

$$a_{11} \quad a_{12} \quad a_{13} \cdots \cdot a_{10}$$
$$a_{21} \quad a_{22} \quad a_{23} \qquad \cdot$$
$$a_{31} \qquad\qquad\qquad\quad \cdot$$
$$\vdots \qquad\qquad\qquad\quad \cdot$$
$$a_{10, 1} \quad a_{10, 2} \cdots\cdots\cdot a_{10, 10}$$

[2]This feature is available in **FORTRAN II** as well as **FORTRAN IV**.

This form is obtained since the subscript J progresses the fastest because it is in the inner implied DO in the WRITE statement shown. Note that this is not the order in which the elements would print out if the array were transmitted by using the array name in the list in nonsubscripted form, as discussed several paragraphs previously.

In the examples thus far, the increment of the index has been assumed to be 1, but it can be given any other value by using a third indexing parameter, just as in the DO statement. The statements

29 FORMAT(5F9.2)

WRITE(6,29)(A(I),I = 2,10,2)

would cause the values of A(2), A(4), A(6), A(8), and A(10) to be printed out on 1 line.

Input and Output of Double-Precision Quantities (D-Conversion). The input and output of double-precision quantities is very similar to E-conversion. The general form of the FORMAT specification for D-conversion is

Dw.d

where w symbolizes an integer constant which specifies the total field width, and d symbolizes an integer constant which specifies the number of digits to the right of the decimal point. The variable associated with a D specification must be defined as a double-precision variable in a Type statement. When the value of a double-precision variable is printed out, it will appear with a D preceding the power of 10 by which the number is to be multiplied. Similarly, upon input, in punching the value of the variables on cards, D is used preceding the exponent (the D may be omitted if space is critical or greater punching speed is desired, provided a sign is punched preceding the exponent). A maximum of approximately 14 to 29 (typically about 16) significant digits may be read in or printed out for the value of a double-precision variable, depending upon the computer used.

Input and Output of Complex Quantities. As discussed previously, a complex constant is represented by an ordered pair of real constants. The first real constant is the real part of the complex number and the second is the imaginary part. The input and output of complex quantities requires a field specification for each of the real numbers representing the real and imaginary parts of the complex number. For example, if COMP is a complex variable, the statements

WRITE(6,12)COMP

12 FORMAT(F8.3,F9.2)

might be used for output. The specification F8.3 would be used for the real part of COMP and the specification F9.2 for the imaginary part. As another example, if COMP1, COMP2, and COMP3 are complex variables, and A is a real variable, the statements

WRITE(6,17)COMP1,COMP2,COMP3,A

17 FORMAT(E10.4,E12.4,2(E13.5,F9.2),F7.1)

might be used for output. The specifications E10.4 and E12.4 would be associated with the real and imaginary parts, respectively, of COMP1. The specifications E13.5 and F9.2 would be associated with the real and imaginary parts, respectively, of COMP2 and COMP3, and the specification F7.1 would be associated with the real variable A.

Input and Output of Logical Quantities (L-Conversion). The general form of the specification for a logical quantity is

Lw

where w represents an integer constant which specifies the data field width. For example, the input specification

L5

would indicate that 5 card columns should be read as the value of a logical variable. If the first nonblank character of the card field is a T, a value of .TRUE. is stored for the logical variable. If the first nonblank character is an F, a value of .FALSE. is stored. If the field is entirely blank, a value of .FALSE. is stored. For output a specification of L4 would allot 4 spaces for the value of the logical variable to be written. If the value of the logical variable were .TRUE., a T would be written in the farthest right portion of the field. If the value of the logical variable were .FALSE., an F would be written in the farthest right portion of the field. A specification of L1 would obviously suffice, but larger field widths might be desired for spacing and for the appearance of the data.

Alphameric Input and Output (A-Conversion).[3] Both the Hollerith field (H-conversion) and the literal data FORMAT specification have been discussed previously in connection with the input and output of alphameric characters. The A field specification may also be used for the input and output of alphameric characters. It differs from H-conversion in that the characters transmitted by A-conversion are given variable names, either real or integer. The A field is used instead of the H field when the alphameric data in storage are to be modified by the program. It can also be used to store FORMAT information which is read in at the time that a program is executed. The latter use will be discussed later in the section where its use is applicable.

The general form of the A specification is

Aw

[3] The A field specification is available in FORTRAN II as well as FORTRAN IV.

where w is an integer constant specifying the number of characters to be read into or written from the memory location or locations associated with a particular variable name. Corresponding to each variable name, some maximum number of characters m can be stored. The value of m ranges from 4 to 16 for most computers, but it is variable for others which do not have a fixed word length. Normally, w will not exceed m for input, but, if it does, only the m characters the farthest to the right in the input field of width w will be read in. If w is less than m, the storage location will be filled with blanks *following* the w characters. For output, if w exceeds m, only m characters will be written. These characters will be preceded by w − m blanks. If w is less than m, the first w characters in the storage location (the w characters farthest to the left) will be written.

If the alphameric data to be stored contain more characters than can be assigned to 1 variable name (more than m characters), several successive A fields can be specified in the usual manner of specifying successive fields having the same format. That is, the specification 10A6 would indicate 10 successive A fields, each with a field width of 6 spaces, and 10 variable names would be required to refer to the storage locations in which the alphameric characters were stored. A subscripted-variable name could be conveniently used for this purpose. Thus, the 10 groups of characters might be stored in locations referred to by the names C(1), C(2), . . . , C(10). The statements

20 FORMAT(10A6)

READ(5,20)(C(I),I = 1,10)

could then be used to read the 60 alphameric characters to be stored as the values of the 10 variables C(I).

Suppose that one wished to print out the contents of just the storage locations referred to by the variable names C(5) through C(10). This could be accomplished with the use of the statements

16 FORMAT(1H^b,6A6)

WRITE(6,16)(C(I)I = 5,10)

The T Specification. One version of FORTRAN IV (IBM 360) includes the T specification. It is not a field specification but is used with output to indicate the position, in a FORTRAN record, at which the transfer of data is to begin. It has the general form

Tw

where w specifies the record position. If the output is being *printed*, the print position will be w − 1, since the first character of the output record is used for carriage control of the printer. For example, used in conjunction with a literal specification (discussed in Chapter 1), the statements

17 FORMAT(T1,ᵇDISPLACEMENT',T38,'ACCELERATION',T21,'VELOCITY')
    WRITE(6,17)

would cause the following printout:

DISPLACEMENT ᵇᵇᵇᵇᵇᵇ VELOCITY ᵇᵇᵇᵇᵇᵇᵇᵇ ACCELERATION

└─print position 1   └─print   └─print position 37
                        position 20

In this example the literal specification causing the printout of **VELOCITY**
follows the literal specification for **ACCELERATION** in the **FORMAT** statement. However, printout begins in the position specified, less 1. **DIS-
PLACEMENT** begins in position 1, because the first character of the literal
specification is a blank for carriage control of the printer.

   With input, the T specification can be used to indicate at which card
column the reading will begin for the following field. Thus, the statements

READ(5,29)A,B

29 FORMAT(T15,E17.8,T1,E12.0)

would cause the reading of a 17-character field containing the value of A,
beginning in card column 15. Beginning in column 1, a 12-character field
containing the value of B would be read.

   Reading in FORMAT Statements at Object Time.   Many programs are
general in nature and are not written just for a specific set of input data.
The magnitude of the variable values read in as data, and the number of
significant digits required for these values, may vary considerably from
one program application to another. The same may be true of variable
values which are to be printed out. It may not be practical to write
FORMAT statements in a program which are suitable for all possible applications to which the program may be put. FORTRAN IV handles this problem by making it possible to read FORMAT statements directly into
memory at object time (at the time the program is executed) using the
A field specification. The word FORMAT and the statement number are
omitted in this process. Only the FORMAT specifications and the left and
right parentheses enclosing them are read into memory. This alphameric
information is stored in locations referred to by a subscripted variable.
The READ or WRITE statement then uses the array name in place of a
FORMAT-statement number. Thus, instead of writing

READ(5,64)A,B,C

with the FORMAT information given in statement **64**, the statements

DIMENSION SPC(4)

2 FORMAT(4A6)

READ(5,2)(SPC(I),I = 1,4)

READ(5,SPC)A,B,C

could be used. The first READ statement reads in 4 fields, of 6 alphameric characters each, and stores them in locations referred to by the names SPC(1), SPC(2), ..., SPC(4). (The assumption is made here that the computer being used can store 6 alphameric characters per storage location.) The alphameric characters must be the desired FORMAT specifications for the second READ statement and must include the left and right parentheses. Then the array name SPC is used in place of a FORMAT-statement number in the second READ statement. The array name may be chosen arbitrarily, and it must appear in a DIMENSION statement even if there is only 1 element in the array.

2-11. Additional Specification Statements

Specification statements of FORTRAN IV include DIMENSION, COMMON, EQUIVALENCE, Type, and DATA statements. The DIMENSION statement has already been discussed in Chapter 1, the Type statements in Sec. 2-5. The COMMON statement, and additional material having to do with the DIMENSION statement using variables as dimensions of an array in a subprogram, will be described following the discussion of subprograms later in this chapter.

EQUIVALENCE Statement.[4]   In most programs, the values of variables are normally assigned to unique locations in memory. In a large program, where there is often a shortage of memory space, it frequently is desirable, where feasible, to let different variables share locations in memory. With the use of the EQUIVALENCE statement, such an arrangement is possible. Since the storage of large arrays is a common source of memory shortage, subscripted variables are more frequently equivalenced (made to share memory locations) than are nonsubscripted variables.

To take advantage of such a technique, the program must obviously be such that it is never necessary for the values of different variables, which share the same locations, to be stored in memory at the same time. For example, if 1 subscripted variable is used only in the early portion of a program, and another subscripted variable is used only in a later part of the same program, the 2 arrays could be stored in the same locations in memory but at different times. However, if values from both arrays must be available in memory throughout the program, they obviously cannot share the same memory space, unless they happen to have identical values.

The general form of the EQUIVALENCE statement is

$$\text{EQUIVALENCE}(a, b, \ldots), (e, f, \ldots), (x, y, \ldots)$$

In this general form the characters in the parentheses represent a series of variables which are equivalenced; that is, the variable values within a set

---

[4]Available in FORTRAN II as well as FORTRAN IV.

of parentheses will be stored in the same location in memory but at different times. The order of the variables is not important. Any required number of equivalences (sets of parentheses) may be used. For example, the statement

EQUIVALENCE(A,B,C),(X,Y),(I,N)

would cause the values of A, B, and C to be stored in a single location in memory at different times, the values of X and Y would share another memory location in the same manner, and the values of I and N would share yet another location.

Equivalence variables may be nonsubscripted, as in the above example, but, as mentioned earlier, subscripted variables are most often necessarily equivalenced. When the latter are equivalenced, they must be single-subscripted variables or else the number of subscripts must equal the number of dimensions of the array in which the variables appear. Some FORTRAN versions *require* that a single subscript be used. In this case the double-subscripted array

B(1,1), B(2,1), B(3,1), B(1,2), B(2,2), B(3,2), B(1,3), B(2,3), B(3,3)

which is shown in what is termed its *usual order* (with the first subscript progressing the fastest), would be single-subscripted by taking advantage of the order in which the elements appear in the *usual order*. For example, the element B(3,2), shown above, would be listed in the equivalence statement as B(6), since it is the 6th element in the order shown above. Such a procedure allows the identification of the elements of a higher-subscripted array by the use of single subscripts. Using this technique, the statements

DIMENSION A(5,5),B(10)
. . . .
EQUIVALENCE(A(21),B(1))

would cause the values of A(1,5) and B(1) to share the same memory location. (The former is the 21st element of the 5-by-5 array *in its usual order*, and the latter is the 1st element of the 1-dimensional array B.) It would also cause the values of A(2,5) and B(2), A(3,5) and B(3), and so forth (through the 25th element of the A array and the 5th element of the B array) to share memory locations. Thus, the 2 arrays would be stored in memory in the following staggered form

A(1,1)

A(2,1)

A(3,1)

:
:

A(3,4)

A(4,4)

A(5,4)

A(1,5)	B(1)
A(2,5)	B(2)
A(3,5)	B(3)
A(4,5)	B(4)
A(5,5)	B(5)
	B(6)
	⋮
	B(10)

where only the 5 matching elements shown would share memory space.

Most versions of FORTRAN permit the EQUIVALENCE statement to appear anywhere in the source program, but some require that it precede all executable statements and DATA statements.

The DATA Statement. In many programs, variables are assigned values which do not vary throughout the execution of the program. Thus, the value of the acceleration of gravity, 32.17 ft/sec^2, might be assigned the name G. The variable G, rather than the larger constant 32.17, would then be used in any calculation involving the acceleration of gravity. Other variables in a program may have values which vary during the execution but which always have the same value at the start of execution each time the program is run. These variables, whose values are either invariant throughout the program or at the start of every run of the program, are usually not assigned values which are read in as data; instead, arithmetic-assignment statements of the form

$$G = 32.17$$
$$\text{TERM} = 160.$$
$$T = 0.$$
$$X = 0.$$
$$Y = 0.$$
$$YD = 125.$$

are used.

The DATA statement of FORTRAN IV provides an alternate method of assigning values to the sort of variables just discussed. It may also be used to assign alphameric characters to variable names without reading A fields from cards. The DATA statement is a nonexecutable statement having the general form

$$\text{DATA } v_1, v_2, \ldots, v_n/d_1, d_2, \ldots, d_n/, \; v_a, v_b, \ldots, v_i/d_a, d_b, \ldots, d_i/, \ldots$$

in which the v's represent variable names and the d's are their respective values. Since the d's are not always *numerical* values, they are more properly referred to as *information literals.* There is a 1-to-1 correspondence between the variables in a list and the information literals which follow between a given pair of slashes.

As a simple example, let us enter the data (previously shown as being entered by arithmetic-assignment statements) by the use of a DATA statement. This statement might appear as

DATA G,TERM,T,X,Y,YD/32.17,160.0,0.0,0.0,0.0,125.0/

The following 2 statements are alternate DATA statements which could be used to enter the same information:

DATA G/32.17/,TERM/160./,T/0./,X/0./,Y/0./,YD/125./

or

DATA G,TERM/32.17,160./, T,X/0.,0./, Y,YD/0.,125./

In using DATA statements, the assigned values are stored in memory upon loading the object program. The variables listed in a DATA statement may subsequently take on other values as the execution proceeds, but control cannot revert to the DATA statement for reassigning the original values, since the DATA statement is not an executable statement.

Any of the variables in the list of a DATA statement may be subscripted with integer constants, or an array name may be used without subscripts where the values of all the elements of the array must be listed. For example, in the statements

DIMENSION B(4),C(9)

. . . .

DATA C(4),B/8.4,3.2,6.7,5.3,9.7/

only the value of the particular element C(4) of the C array would be listed (8.4), but all 4 values of the B array would have to be listed as shown. Some versions of FORTRAN IV permit the use of the implied DO in the list to specify particular elements of an array.

Each information literal may be a double-precision, integer, complex, or logical constant, or it may consist of alphameric characters. In DATA statements, logical constants may be written as .TRUE. and .FALSE. or as T and F. Some FORTRAN IV versions use Hollerith text for the alphameric characters, whereas others use literal data. Both methods will be illustrated later.

An information literal may have the form

k * d

where k is an integer constant and d is an information literal. This means that k consecutive-list variables are to be assigned the particular value d.

For example, the statement

DATA X,Y,YD/3*0.0/

would cause zero values to be stored for the variables X, Y, and YD.

The following example illustrates the use of the implied DO in the list of a DATA statement and the use of Hollerith texts as information literals:

DATA(CODE(I), I = 1,4)/1H*,1H.,1H−,1H+/

Using this statement, an asterisk would be stored in a location referred to by the name CODE(1). It would be stored in a memory location such that, on printout of the contents of the memory location, the asterisk would be on the left, followed by blanks. A period would be stored in the location referred to by the name CODE(2), and so forth.

Each Hollerith text, in the above example, contains a single character. Several characters (perhaps 6 or 8, the exact number depending upon the computer used) may be stored in each memory location. Suppose that, for a particular computer, 8 alphameric characters form a word (fill 1 memory location). If a particular Hollerith text contained 16 characters, 2 variable names would have to be used to refer to that information. If it contained 21 characters, 3 variable names would be required, with 2 memory locations being filled completely with alphameric text and the third location containing 3 alphameric characters and filled out with 3 blanks. For example, the statements

DIMENSION TITLE(3)

DATA TITLE/21HACCELERATION ANALYSIS/

would cause the Hollerith text to be stored in locations referred to by the names TITLE(1), TITLE(2), and TITLE(3). The statements

DIMENSION TITLE(3)

DATA TITLE/'ACCELERATION ANALYSIS'/

could be used for the same purpose in versions in which literal data are permitted.

2-12. Subprograms or Subroutines

FORTRAN language provides for the use of several kinds of subprograms or subroutines. Some are supplied as part of the FORTRAN system, some may be added to the function library of a particular computer installation by the personnel of the installation, and still others may be written by the individual programmer. In Chapter 1 the use of some common mathematical-function subroutines was discussed. The subroutines for calculating the functions mentioned there are supplied as part of nearly all FORTRAN systems. It may be recalled that, in order to use these functions, it is necessary only to write the function name in the expression in which it is required and to supply an expression for the argument. (The expression may be as simple as a single variable or it may be a more complicated form.)

In this section we shall consider all *classes* of subprograms available to the FORTRAN programmer. Most of the discussion will be applicable to both FORTRAN II and FORTRAN IV, but the portions which are unique to one or the other will be identified as such.

There are 4 main classes of subprograms, identified as follows:
1. Arithmetic Statement Functions
2. Built-in Functions
3. Function Subprograms
   a) Predefined functions in the function library and automatically available to the compiler
   b) Functions written by the programmer
4. Subroutine Subprograms
   a) Subprograms provided by FORTRAN
   b) Subprograms written by the programmer

The mathematical functions studied in Chapter 1 come under classification 3a, as function subprograms which are part of the function library.

Arithmetic Statement Functions. The arithmetic statement function (also known as the statement function) is the simplest type of subprogram. It consists of a single statement defining a function which can subsequently be used in an arithmetic statement anywhere in the program. The general form is

$$n(a, b, \ldots) = e$$

in which n represents the function name, the letters a, b, ... represent the arguments of the function, and e represents an arithmetic or logical expression which is a function of the arguments a, b, ...

The same rules apply in choosing a function name n as in choosing variable names;[5] that is, the name must consist of 1 to 6 alphabetic and numeric characters, the first of which must be alphabetic. If the name begins with any of the letters I through N, the function is integer. If it begins with any other alphabetic character, the function is real. Type declarations for function names may also be made with Type statements, just as for variable names.

In the definition of the function, the arguments of the function a, b, ... are merely dummy variables which are replaced by the desired quantities (variables, constants, or expressions) when the function is used later in the program in an arithmetic statement. For example, the statement

DRAG(S,V) = COEFF * RHO * S * V**2/2.

[5] In FORTRAN II the name must be 4 to 7 characters in length and must end in F. If the function is to be fixed-point (integer), it must begin with X. A floating-point (real) function will have a name beginning with any letter other than X.

might appear in a source program to define a function with the name
DRAG. (All such definition statements must precede the first executable
statement of the source program.) The variables in the expression on the
right, which are in addition to the arguments S and V, are known as
parameters of the function. During compilation, the FORTRAN compiler
sets up the necessary machine-language instructions to calculate the value
of the function DRAG. These instructions are then used whenever the
function is called for later in the program in an arithmetic statement,
using the values of whatever quantities are supplied for the dummy arguments S and V. For example, the arithmetic statement

$$F = FP - D1 - DRAG(AREA,VEL)$$

might appear later in the source program. The value of DRAG would be
calculated by using the current values of the arguments AREA and VEL for
the dummy arguments S and V, respectively, in the function definition.
The variables COEFF and RHO also appear in the definition, and their current values are used in the calculation. This value of DRAG would then
be included in the calculation of F.

The dummy arguments S and V in the statement definition can be used
in more than 1 arithmetic statement function, and can also be used elsewhere in the program, as names for other variables, if desired. No relationship will exist between the latter and the dummy arguments. The
dummy arguments cannot be subscripted, since the expression on the right
side of the function definition cannot validly contain any subscripted variables. However, when the function is called for in an arithmetic statement, the arguments used at that time may contain subscripted variables.
For example, the arithmetic statement

$$D2 = DRAG(A(2),VEL + 100.)$$

would constitute a valid use of the previously defined function DRAG,
where A(2) and VEL + 100. are the arguments corresponding to the
dummy arguments S and V in the function definition. The expressions
used as arguments, when the function appears in an arithmetic statement,
should be of the same type as the dummy arguments used in the definition.

It is possible for the dummy arguments in the statement definition to
be the same as the arguments used when the function appears in an arithmetic statement. For example, the function RATE might be defined as

$$RATE(C,D) = ACC/C + D$$

and might appear later in an arithmetic statement

$$TEL = 4.8782/RATE(C,D) + AMP2$$

where the current values of C and D would be used to calculate the value
of RATE.

Built-in Functions. Built-in functions (also called intrinsic functions) are subprograms that are supplied as part of the FORTRAN system. They differ from supplied function subprograms in that a set of machine-language instructions for calculating the value of a function is placed in the object program each time the function name is used in the source program. Usually, only a few instructions are required. Built-in functions are often referred to as *open* subprograms or subroutines. Function subprograms, on the other hand, are referred to as *closed* subprograms, since they use just a single set of instructions to calculate the value of a particular function each time the function name is used.

The common built-in functions available in FORTRAN IV are:

Function Name	Number of Arguments	Function Type	Argument Type	Description
ABS IABS DABS	1 1 1	Real Integer Double*	Real Integer Double	Finds absolute value of the argument
AINT INT IDINT	1 1 1	Real Integer Integer	Real Real Double	Truncates argument to largest integer having an absolute value less than or equal to argument; sign same as sign of argument
AMOD MOD	2 2	Real Integer	Real Integer	$MOD(a_1, a_2)$ defined as $a_1 - [a_1/a_2]a_2$ where $[a_1 a_2]$ is truncated value of the quotient (the a's represent arguments in all definitions here and following)
AMAX0 AMAX1 MAX0 MAX1 DMAX1	≥ 2	Real Real Integer Integer Double	Integer Real Integer Real Double	$AMAX1\ (a_1, a_2, a_3, \ldots)$ chooses the largest of the arguments a_i
AMIN0 AMIN1 MIN0 MIN1 DMIN1	≥ 2	Real Real Integer Integer Double	Integer Real Integer Real Double	$AMIN1\ (a_1, a_2, a_3, \ldots)$ chooses the smallest of the arguments a_i
FLOAT	1	Real	Integer	FLOAT (i) has the value of the argument i converted to real
IFIX	1	Integer	Real	IFIX (a) has a value equal to that of the argument a converted to integer (with truncation)
SIGN ISIGN DSIGN	2	Real Integer Double	Real Integer Double	$SIGN\ (a_1, a_2)$ has a value equal to the magnitude of a_1 with the sign of a_2 (often called Transfer of Sign Function)
DIM IDIM	2	Real Integer	Real Integer	For arguments a_1 and a_2 the function DIM determines $a_1 - \text{Min} (a_1, a_2)$ (called Positive Difference Function)

Function Name	Number of Arguments	Function Type	Argument Type	Description
SNGL	1	Real	Double	Obtains the most significant part of a double-precision argument
REAL	1	Real	Complex	Obtains the real part of a complex argument
AIMAG	1	Real	Complex	Obtains the imaginary part of a complex argument
DBLE	1	Double	Real	Expresses a single-precision argument in double-precision form
CMPLX	2	Complex	Real	Expresses 2 real arguments in complex form
CONJG	1	Complex	Complex	Obtains the conjugate of a complex argument

*Double-precision type.

Function Subprograms. Function subprograms form two groups: 1) the so-called library functions consisting of subprograms supplied by the computer manufacturer and library subprograms written by the programmers at a computer installation, and 2) the subprograms written by individual programmers which do not become a part of the system library. To employ functions from the system library, the programmer need use only the function name, with suitable arguments, in an arithmetic expression in his source program. (Chapter 1 discussed the use of some commonly supplied library functions—mathematical functions such as sine, cosine, arc tangent, and so forth.)

Function subprograms are *closed* subroutines, since only 1 set of instructions is used to calculate the value of a function each time the function name is used in the calling program (the program in which the function is used). Function subprograms are also called *external* functions, since they may be named in an EXTERNAL statement which permits their use as an argument in another subprogram calling statement. (This will become clearer later, when the EXTERNAL statement is discussed.) Built-in functions (discussed earlier) may not be named in an EXTERNAL statement.

Let us first consider those function subprograms which may be written by an individual programmer and which do not become a part of the system library. (Subsequent use of the term function subprogram will imply this type, unless otherwise stated.)

The arithmetic statement function is limited to functions that can be defined in a single statement. Function subprograms are used for defining functions whose definitions require more than a single statement. A function subprogram can be compiled at the same time the main program and other subprograms are being compiled, but it has a distinct advantage in that it can also be compiled and checked out independently of all the main programs or other subprograms with which it might be used. A short calling program is written for purposes of the check-out. In a sense, a function subprogram is an independent program, since its variable names are independent of the variable names in the main program or other subprograms. However, it must always be used with a calling program.

A function subprogram is *called* in a program in the same manner as are statement functions and mathematical functions—by simply writing the name of the function subprogram in an arithmetic statement, with appropriate expressions as arguments. When the value of the function is calculated, these arguments replace the dummy arguments used in the function *definition*. A function subprogram is defined by a separate set of statements which begins with a FUNCTION statement and ends with an END statement. The general form is

$$\text{FUNCTION } n \ (a_1, a_2, a_3, \ldots, a_m)$$
$$\cdot \ \cdot \ \cdot \ \cdot$$
$$\text{(FORTRAN defining statements)}$$
$$\cdot \ \cdot \ \cdot \ \cdot$$
$$n \ = \ \text{(an arithmetic statement)}$$
$$\cdot \ \cdot \ \cdot \ \cdot$$
$$\cdot \ \cdot \ \cdot \ \cdot$$

RETURN

END

The FUNCTION statement consists of the word FUNCTION followed by the function name, symbolized in the general form above by the letter n, and a list of dummy arguments, symbolically shown above as $a_1, a_2, \ldots, a_m$. The function name n may be chosen by the programmer, using the same rules as apply to choosing names for variables. (In FORTRAN II the last letter of the function name *cannot* be the letter F if the name consists of more than 3 characters.) In FORTRAN IV, if it is desired to override the type specification for the function implied by the first letter, or if the type is something other than integer or real, the type may be explicitly specified by preceding the word FUNCTION, in the FUNCTION statement, with the appropriate type (INTEGER, REAL, and so forth). The function name must appear in at least 1 of the FORTRAN defining statements which define the function, so that the function can be given a value by the subprogram. The function may get its value by appearing in a READ statement or as an argument in a CALL statement, but it usually gets its value by appearing as a variable on the left of an equals sign, as shown in the general form of the subprogram above. A function subprogram always returns a single value to the calling program.

The dummy arguments $a_1, a_2, a_3, \ldots, a_m$ are nonsubscripted variables, array names, or dummy names of subroutine subprograms or other function subprograms. (See Sec. 2-15 for the use of subprogram names as arguments.) The actual arguments in the function reference must correspond in number, order, and type to the corresponding dummy arguments in the FUNCTION statement. If one of the dummy arguments is an array name, a suitable DIMENSION statement must be used *in the subprogram*. The corresponding actual argument in the function reference must also be an array name and must be dimensioned *in the calling program*. Both the dummy and the actual arrays must be given the same size in their respective DIMENSION statements except when *adjustable dimensions* are used (Sec. 2-14). Dummy arguments may not be equivalenced in a subprogram, and they must not be redefined in the subprogram; that is, they cannot appear on the left of the equals sign in arithmetic statements.

The FORTRAN statements of the subprogram which follow the FUNCTION statement and which define the function may not contain another FUNCTION statement or a SUBROUTINE statement. However, they may *call* on other subprograms, library functions, and so forth, but a subprogram obviously cannot call on itself. If one subprogram calls another subprogram, the called subprogram cannot call the calling subroutine.

The defining statements are followed by the RETURN statement which causes a return of control to the calling program at the point from which the subprogram was called. More than one RETURN statement may appear if branching in the subprogram results in the function value being determined at one of several possible places in the subprogram. An END statement is always the last statement of a subprogram.

Let us look at an example of the use of a function subprogram called by a main program. Only the pertinent statements of the main program are shown.

Calling Program	*Function Subprogram*
. . . . .	FUNCTION PRESS(T,D)
. . . . .	RATIO = T/D
STR = PRESS(THICK,DI)	IF(RATIO .LE. .023)GO TO 3
*D/(4. * THICK)	PRESS = 86670. * RATIO − 1386.
. . . . .	RETURN
. . . . .	3 RAD = 1. − 1600. * RATIO**2
P = PRESS(.025,1.25)	PRESS = 1000. *(1. − SQRT(RAD))
. . . . .	RETURN
. . . . .	END

The function PRESS is called 2 times, in the calling program, by writing the function name and listing the actual arguments to be used in evaluating the function. When the value of the function PRESS is calculated the first time, the value of the variable THICK would be used where T appears in the defining statements, and the value of the variable DI would be used where D appears. For the second calculation of the value of PRESS,

.025 would be used for T and 1.25 for D. Using a function name in a calling program is referred to as referencing the function. When a function is referenced, the actual arguments must agree in number and mode with the dummy arguments used in the FUNCTION statement (T and D in this example). Note that in the first reference the actual arguments are variables, but in the second they are constants. Any suitable real expressions would be valid arguments in this example. Their mode would have to be real, since T and D are real. Note that the function subprogram PRESS calls on the library function SQRT.

Having learned how a programmer can write his own function subprograms, let us next consider function subprograms supplied as part of a FORTRAN IV system. A fairly complete list of those functions supplied with most systems is shown at the end of this paragraph. Most of these are also included in FORTRAN II, except those which are complex or double-precision and the real function CABS which has a complex argument. The names of all supplied mathematical functions for FORTRAN II systems, however, end in F (SQRTF, SINF, and so forth).

Function Name	Number of Arguments	Function Type	Argument Type	Definition
EXP	1	Real	Real	e^a
DEXP	1	Double*	Double	(a is the argument in all definitions
CEXP	1	Complex	Complex	here and following)
ALOG	1	Real	Real	
DLOG	1	Double	Double	$\log_e(a)$
CLOG	1	Complex	Complex	
ALOG10	1	Real	Real	$\log_{10}(a)$
DLOG10	1	Double	Double	
ATAN	1	Real	Real	arc tan (a)
ATAN2	2	Real	Real	arc tan (a_1/a_2)
DATAN	1	Double	Double	arc tan (a)
DATAN2	2	Double	Double	arc tan (a_1/a_2)
SIN	1	Real	Real	
DSIN	1	Double	Double	sin(a) (a in radians)
CSIN	1	Complex	Complex	
COS	1	Real	Real	
DCOS	1	Double	Double	cos(a) (a in radians)
CCOS	1	Complex	Complex	
SQRT	1	Real	Real	
DSQRT	1	Double	Double	$\sqrt{a}$
CSQRT	1	Complex	Complex	
TANH	1	Real	Real	tanh(a)
DTANH	1	Double	Double	
CABS	1	Real	Complex	Finds the modulus of a complex number; that is, $\sqrt{a^2 + b^2}$ for a + ib.

*Double-precision type.

Subroutine Subprograms. Subroutine subprograms differ from function subprograms in three respects: First, function subprograms always return just 1 value to the calling program; this is the value of the function for the arguments listed in the function reference. Subroutine subprograms, on the other hand, may return any number of values or no values at all. The values returned to the calling program, called the output of the subprogram, are the result of calculations in the subprogram for some of the argument values. That is, values may be assigned to some of the subprogram arguments by the subprogram itself, and these values are returned to the calling program. The name of the subprogram does not receive a value, as in the case of function subprograms. Second, the subprogram is called differently for the two types of subprograms. The subroutine subprogram cannot be called by simply listing its name in an arithmetic expression, as a function subprogram can, since it has no value. A special **CALL** statement (discussed subsequently) is used. Third, since the subroutine subprogram name has no value associated with it, it cannot be of a particular type, such as integer or real. The output of a subroutine subprogram results from the values given to arguments, some of which may be real and some of which may be integer. Therefore, the first letter of the name in a subroutine subprogram has no special significance.

The subroutine subprogram begins with a **SUBROUTINE** statement and ends with an **END** statement. The general form is

SUBROUTINE n $(a_1, a_2, a_3, \ldots, a_m)$

. . . . .

(FORTRAN statements)

. . . . .

RETURN

END

where n represents the subprogram name and the a's represent dummy variables which correspond to the actual variables listed in the **CALL** statement.

The **CALL** statement, used to call a subroutine subprogram, has the general form

CALL n $(x_1, x_2, x_3, \ldots, x_m)$

where n represents the subprogram name. The x's are the actual arguments and each may be either an arithmetic expression (which includes, and most often would be, a single constant or a single-subscripted or nonsubscripted variable) or a subprogram name. Some of the arguments may appear as input to the subprogram, whereas others may receive values in the subprogram. For example, one of the arguments in the **CALL** statement might be a variable which has a value in the calling program. This value is assigned to the corresponding dummy variable in the subprogram as an input to the subprogram. Another argument might be a variable which has no value in the calling program. It would be assigned a value as a result of calculations done in the subprogram. The assigning of values to such variables constitutes the output of the subprogram. Arguments which return values to a calling program must appear on the left side of an arithmetic statement or in an input list in the subprogram.

In many respects a subroutine subprogram is similar to a function subprogram, with the exceptions noted above. The rules for choosing names are the same except that no convention is attached to the first letter of the name of a subroutine subprogram. Both types of subprograms consist of a set of commonly used statements, and both return control to the calling program (by use of a RETURN statement) and end with an END statement. The dummy arguments of a subroutine subprogram, like those of a function subprogram, are nonsubscripted variables, array names, or dummy names of subroutine or function subprograms. The dummy arguments may not be equivalenced in the subprogram, and the actual arguments must agree in number, order, and type with the dummy arguments. If arrays are used as arguments, they must be dimensioned in both the calling program and the subprogram with the same dimensions. Neither function subprograms nor subroutine subprograms may contain a FUNCTION statement or a SUBROUTINE statement within the body of the subprogram (after the first statement).

To illustrate the operation of a subroutine subprogram, let us consider the following simple example. Suppose that the addition of 2 n-by-m matrices is a very common operation in some particular program, and it is desired to use a subprogram to perform this operation each time it is required. The following might be used:

Calling Program

. . . .

DIMENSION X(15,15), Y(15,15), Z(15,15)

. . . .

CALL ADD(X,Y,Z,K,L)

. . . .

Subroutine Subprogram
```
   SUBROUTINE ADD(A,B,C,N,M)
   DIMENSION A(15,15), B(15,15), C(15,15)
   DO 7 I = 1,N
   DO 7 J = 1,M
 7 C(I,J) = A(I,J) + B(I,J)
   RETURN
   END
```

Arrays X and Y are available in the calling program. They have K rows and L columns. The values of the X and Y array elements replace the elements of A and B in the subprogram, and the values of K and L replace N and M, respectively. The values of array C are calculated in the subprogram and are stored in memory, where they are available to the calling program by use of the variable name Z. These values of Z are available after the CALL statement has brought the subprogram into operation. Control returns from the subprogram to the statement following the CALL statement in the calling program.

A subroutine subprogram need not return any values to the calling program, as mentioned previously. If there also were no input to the subprogram, no arguments would be listed in the CALL or SUBROUTINE statements. Such a subprogram might be used, for example, to print out column headings at the top of each page for a program having many pages of output data.

2-13. The COMMON Statement

The COMMON statement is most often used in linking a main program with its subprograms, without using arguments in the CALL and SUBROUTINE statements. Before discussing the applications of the COMMON statement, let us first consider the statement itself. It has the general form

COMMON a, b, c, d, . . .

where a, b, c, d, . . . are variables, including array names that may be dimensioned. (In FORTRAN II the general form of the statement is as shown, but the list is enclosed by parentheses.)

As an example, consider the statement

COMMON DISPL, VEL, ACCEL, N

appearing in a source program. The values of the variables listed would be stored in memory in the sequence in which they appear in the list in the statement. The block of memory in which these variables would be stored is referred to as a COMMON *block*. COMMON blocks can be labeled with names assigned by the programmer, but, in the example above, no name is assigned, and the block is known as a *blank* COMMON. The blank COMMON block is used more frequently, so it will be discussed first.

It is impossible for 2 variables listed in a COMMON statement to be equivalenced, since the variables listed could not have their values stored sequentially in separate locations and, at the same time, have 2 of them share the same location. This would be somewhat like attempting to equivalence 2 elements of an array, which is also invalid. It is also invalid to equivalence 2 variables in different COMMON blocks.

The size of a COMMON block, indicated by the number of variables listed in the COMMON statement, can be increased when an EQUIVA-LENCE statement is used in the following manner:

DIMENSION A(4)

. . . . . .

COMMON X,Y,Z

EQUIVALENCE(Z,A(1))

The variable values would occupy storage locations as shown below, with X in the lowest numbered location and Z and A(1) sharing the same location in memory:

X, Y, Z

A(1), A(2), A(3), A(4)

In this case the COMMON block has been extended to higher locations and includes 6 memory locations instead of 3. An extension cannot be made to lower locations. For example, the statements

DIMENSION A(4)

COMMON X,Y,Z

EQUIVALENCE (X,A(4))

would be invalid.

If a blank COMMON statement appears in both a main program and a subprogram or subprograms, the variables in these COMMON statements share the same COMMON block in memory. For example, if the statement

COMMON E,F,G,N

appears in a main program, and the statement

COMMON P,Q,R,I

appears in a subprogram of the main program, the values of E and P, F and Q and so forth, share locations in memory. (The variable names E and P, F and Q, and so forth, refer to the same memory locations.) If the statement

CALL SUB(E,F,G,N)

appears in a main program, and the statement

SUBROUTINE SUB(P,Q,R,I)

appears in a subprogram of the main program, the variables, in some FORTRAN versions, again share locations in memory, as just described. (In IBM 360 FORTRAN IV, the *values* of the actual arguments rather than their addresses are brought from the calling program to the subprogram, unless the arguments are each enclosed in slashes.) Thus, in both instances, the effect of equivalencing is obtained, but without the use of the EQUIVALENCE statement. The same effect could not be obtained by equivalencing E and P, F and Q, and so forth, with the use of the EQUIV-ALENCE statement, since only variables appearing in the *same* program or subprogram can be equivalenced.

Using the statements shown in either of the last two examples, if E is a variable which has been defined in the main program, the appearance of P in the subprogram will cause the value stored as E to be used in the subprogram calculation, since the variable names E and P refer to the same memory location. Similarly, if the value of R is defined in the subprogram, this value will be stored in memory and will be available for use in the main program by using the name G. Since both sets of statements in the last two examples accomplish the same result, the use of 2 COMMON statements in a main program and a subprogram, respectively, allows the omission of the lists of arguments in the CALL and SUBROUTINE statements. Such a use of the COMMON statements results in a more efficient object program.

Another advantage of using COMMON statements is in dimensioning array names while linking elements between programs. For example, if the statement

COMMON A,B,C(50)

appears in a main program, and the statement

COMMON X,Y,Z(50)

appears in a subprogram of the main program, the values of A and X and of B and Y share memory locations, as described before, and the values of C(1) through C(50) share memory locations with Z(1) through Z(50), respectively. When the COMMON statement is used for dimensioning, the arrays dimensioned in it must *not* be listed in a DIMENSION statement or a Type statement containing dimension information.

Common statements are often used when a long program is written in segments consisting of a main program and a number of subprograms, so that the individual segments can be checked independently. In this instance a variable defined in 1 segment may be required for use in 1 or more other segments. The variable would not be automatically available in different segments, since the variables used in a main program and in individual subprograms are independent of each other, even if the same variable names are used in the different programs. The variables can be made available, where required, by using the COMMON statement or by proper use of the CALL and SUBROUTINE statements. Let us consider the latter method first.

A program consists of 4 segments—a main program and 3 subprograms. The variables A, B, C, and D are defined and are required in the various segments, as indicated in the following:

Main Program

Variable A defined;
variables A, B, C, and D
required

```
. . .
A = . . .
. . .
CALL SUB1(A,B)
. . .
CALL SUB2(A,B,C)
. . .
CALL SUB3(A,B,C,D)
. . .
BEAR = D + A/B − C*A
. . .
```

Subprogram SUB1

Variable B defined;
variable A required

```
SUBROUTINE SUB1(A,B)
. . .
DARE = A + . . .
. . .
B = . . .
. . .
RETURN
END
```

Subprogram SUB2

Variable C defined;
variables A and B required

```
SUBROUTINE SUB2(A,B,C)
. . .
TOT = A * B + . . .
. . .
C = . . .
. . .
RETURN
END
```

Subprogram SUB3

Variable D defined;
variables A, B, and C
required

```
SUBROUTINE SUB3(A,B,C,D)
. . .
VAR = A * B/C + . . .
. . .
D = . . .
. . .
RETURN
END
```

The CALL and SUBROUTINE statements, as written, assure that the variable C, for example, which is defined in SUBROUTINE SUB2, is available for use in SUBROUTINE SUB3, where it is required, and so forth.

Another method of assuring that a particular variable is available in any subprogram where it might be required is to list all the variables of the program in a COMMON statement and put this same statement in the main program and in each subprogram. In this case the arguments are omitted in the CALL and SUBROUTINE statements. Identical cards containing the COMMON statement can be used in each segment of the overall program, thus avoiding the chance of errors which might arise in writing and punching CALL and SUBROUTINE statements with arguments.

To avoid listing all the variables of a program in the COMMON statement of each subprogram, when any particular subprogram does not require the use of all the variables, a number of COMMON blocks may be set up in memory, each with its own name and each containing certain variables appropriate to the requirements for using the variables in the various subprograms. Such blocks are known as *labeled* COMMON blocks. Before illustrating the preceding discussion, let us consider the statements used to set up labeled COMMON blocks. The statement has the general form

$$\text{COMMON} \; / \; n \; / \; a_1, a_2, \ldots, a_m / \; n_1 / \; b_1, b_2, \ldots, b_m \ldots$$

where the n's represent names assigned to the block of variables following them. These block names should consist of 1 to 6 alphameric characters, the first of which is alphabetic. The a's and b's are the variables listed for each block, and they appear in the block in the order given in the list.

To illustrate the labeled COMMON block and its use in avoiding the listing of all program variables in each subprogram, let us consider the following:

Main Program   . . . .

Variables A, C, and E	COMMON/NAMA/A,B/NAMB/C,D/NAMC/E,F
defined;	. . . .
variables B, D, and F	A = · · · ·
required	CALL SUB1
	· · · ·
	C = · · · ·
	CALL SUB2
	· · · ·
	E = · · · ·
	CALL SUB3
	· · · ·
	TILT = B*D/F
	· · · ·

First Subprogram	SUBROUTINE SUB1
Variable A required;	COMMON/NAMA/A,B
variable B defined	. . . .
	B = A + ...
	RETURN
	. . . .
	B = 2.*A + ...
	RETURN
	END
Second Subprogram	SUBROUTINE SUB2
Variable C required;	COMMON/NAMB/C,D
variable D defined	. . . .
	D = C**2 + . . .
	RETURN
	. . . .
	D = C**3 + . . .
	RETURN
	END
Third Subprogram	SUBROUTINE SUB3
Variable E required;	COMMON/NAMC/E,F
variable F defined	
	F = 5.*E + . . .
	RETURN
	. . . .
	F = 10.*E + . . .
	RETURN
	END

The COMMON statement in the main program would cause 3 blocks to be set up in memory, having the names NAMA, NAMB, and NAMC. The labeled COMMON statements in each subprogram contain only the variables whose values are required or calculated in that subprogram. For example, the first subprogram uses the value of the variable A, as defined in the main program, and calculates a value of the variable B which is used, in turn, to calculate the value of TILT in the main program.

The COMMON statement in the first subprogram lists only variables A and B. Thus, by using labeled COMMON blocks, certain variables of a main program might share a certain block of memory with the same variables in 1 or more subprograms, variables common to several subprograms might share a block, and so forth. As should be evident, there is more chance of introducing an error in using the labeled COMMON in this manner than in using identical blank COMMON statements in each segment. Usually, only professional programmers make extensive use of the labeled COMMON.

2-14. Adjustable Dimensions

It has been pointed out previously that the arguments of both function subprograms and subroutine subprograms may contain array names. These arrays must be dimensioned in both the calling program and the subprograms. In FORTRAN IV an array used in a subprogram can have adjustable dimensions. The purpose of such a feature is to allow a subprogram to be used with different-sized arrays without having to reserve space for the largest array that might conceivably ever be used in the subprogram.

To give adjustable dimensions to an array appearing in a subprogram, integer variables are used in place of integer constants in the DIMENSION statement of the subprogram. When the subprogram is called, the integer variables which specify the array dimensions of the subprogram array receive values from the calling program. This is accomplished by placing the integer variables in the argument list of the SUBROUTINE statement in the subprogram, and specifying values for these variables in the CALL statement of the calling program.

As an example, consider the following:

Calling Program	*Subprogram*
	SUBROUTINE MATI(...,XS,I,J,...)
...	
DIMENSION X(10,10)	DIMENSION XS(I,J)
CALL MATI(...,X,5,5,...)	...
...	...
	RETURN
	END

With the dimensions of the array which is to be used in the subprogram known, these dimensions are specified in the CALL statement of the calling program, as shown above. The dimensions specified in the DIMENSION statement of the calling program must then be equal to, or larger than, the dimensions specified for the subprogram array. The array XS of the subprogram corresponds to the array X of the calling program. Each of the variables I and J in the subprogram receives the value of 5 from the calling program, specifying the size of the array which is to be used in the subprogram.

Adjustable dimensions cannot be altered within a subprogram, and arrays listed in a COMMON statement may not have adjustable dimensions.

2-15. Subprogram Names as Arguments of Other Subprograms—the EXTERNAL Statement

It has been mentioned before that, in FORTRAN IV, a function subprogram or subroutine subprogram name can be used as an argument of another subprogram. To distinguish a subprogram name in an argument list from an ordinary variable name, it must appear in an EXTERNAL statement. This statement has the general form

EXTERNAL a, b, c, . . .

where a, b, c, . . . represent the names of subprograms used as arguments of other subprograms. In the statements below, for example, the function name COS would be listed in an EXTERNAL statement to distinguish it as a subprogram name in the CALL statement shown.

EXTERNAL COS
CALL SUBX(E,COS,G)
. . . . .

To illustrate the use of a function name as an argument, consider the following:

Calling Program

```
. . .
EXTERNAL FUNC
CALL CALC(X,FUNC,Y,Z)
. . .
```

First Subprogram

```
SUBROUTINE CALC(A,F,C,D)
G = F(C,D)
. . . .
A = · · ·
. . . .
RETURN
END
```

Second Subprogram

```
FUNCTION FUNC(G,H)
IF(G − H)1,1,2
1 FUNC = 2.* G * H
RETURN
2 FUNC = 5. * G/H
RETURN
END
```

The function name FUNC replaces the dummy variable F in the first subprogram. The values of the variables Y and Z are used as the arguments of the function FUNC in the calculation of its value in the second subprogram. The function FUNC is shown in this example as a function subprogram with 2 arguments, written by the programmer. The supplied function subprograms (mathematical functions) EXP,ALOG, ALOG10,SIN, COS, TANH, SQRT, ATAN, CABS, and so forth may also be used as arguments of other subprograms if they are listed in an EXTERNAL statement. The built-in functions cannot be used as arguments of subprograms.

2-16. Examples of the Use of Additional FORTRAN

EXAMPLE 2-1

To illustrate an application of complex quantities in a FORTRAN program, let us consider a typical transfer function describing a process control system.[6] Such a transfer function might appear as

$$\frac{O}{I} = \frac{G_o(1 + \tau_4 D)}{(1 + \tau_2 D)(1 + \tau_3 D)(1 + \tau_4 D) + G_o} \tag{2-1}$$

where:

O = output of system

I = input to system

G_o = overall system gain

τ_2, τ_3, τ_4 = time constants of various system components

$D = \dfrac{d}{dt}$ (differential operator)

Equation 2-1 can be put in the form of a third-order differential equation by performing the multiplications indicated in the equation, and collecting terms. The solution of this differential equation will yield the response characteristics of the system in the time domain (displacement versus time curves, for example).

Another approach to the system analysis is to transform Eq. 2-1 from the time domain to the frequency domain. This method is very effective when the input to the system is *sinusoidal* in form, since, in this case, the amplitude of the steady-state response may be obtained without actually determining a solution of the differential equation.

When the input to the system is sinusoidal, the operator D, in Eq. 2-1, may be replaced by $i\omega$, with the latter providing the same results as would be obtained by the application of the replaced operator ($i = \sqrt{-1}$ and ω = frequency of system input, radians/sec). The validity of such a

[6]James, M. L., Smith, G. M., and Wolford, J. C. *Analog Computer Simulation of Engineering Systems.* Scranton, Pa.: International Textbook Company, 1966, p. 223.

substitution may be illustrated as follows: Let

$$y = \sin \omega t$$
$$Dy = \omega \cos \omega t$$
$$D^2 y = -\omega^2 \sin \omega t = -\omega^2 y$$

and observe that the result of D^2 operating on y is identical to the result obtained by replacing D by $i\omega$.

Utilizing this relationship, Eq. 2-1 may be written in the complex form

$$\frac{O}{I}(i\omega) = \frac{G_o(1 + i\omega\tau_4)}{(1 + i\omega\tau_2)(1 + i\omega\tau_3)(1 + i\omega\tau_4) + G_o} \qquad (2\text{-}2)$$

Performing the multiplications indicated in the denominator of Eq. 2-2 yields a complex quantity of the general form

$$a + ib$$

for the denominator. Equation 2-2 then has the general form

$$\frac{O}{I}(i\omega) = \frac{c + id}{a + ib} \qquad (2\text{-}3)$$

Upon multiplying both the numerator and denominator of Eq. 2-3 by the conjugate $(a - ib)$, the equation reduces to the general form

$$\frac{O}{I}(i\omega) = A + iB = M e^{i\theta} \qquad (2\text{-}4)$$

where M is the *magnitude* of the transfer function which characterizes the steady-state response of the system. Referring to Fig. 2-5, it can be

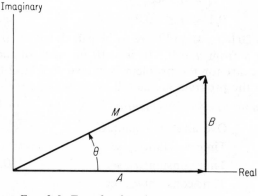

FIG. 2-5. Transfer function represented in complex plane.

seen that the magnitude of M is the square root of the sum of the squares of the real and imaginary parts of the transfer function. Thus,

$$M = \sqrt{A^2 + B^2} \qquad (2\text{-}5)$$

and

$$\theta = \tan^{-1} \frac{B}{A}$$

where the phase angle θ indicates the lag between the output and input.

If the quantities $20 \log_{10} M$ and θ are plotted against a nondimensional frequency u, we obtain what is known as a *Bode diagram*.[7] The nondimensional parameter u may be formed in terms of any one of the time constants τ_2, τ_3, or τ_4. If

$$u = \omega \tau_3$$

Eq. 2-2 would have the form

$$\frac{O}{I}(i\omega) = \frac{G_o\left(1 + i\frac{\tau_4}{\tau_3}u\right)}{\left(1 + i\frac{\tau_2}{\tau_3}u\right)(1 + iu)\left(1 + i\frac{\tau_4}{\tau_3}u\right) + G_o} \tag{2-6}$$

The computer can be used to determine the quantities necessary for constructing a Bode diagram from Eq. 2-6 utilizing, in general, the procedure described in Eqs. 2-2 through 2-5. To see specifically how the computer accomplishes this, let us write a **FORTRAN** program for obtaining the necessary quantities.

The pertinent system data are as follows:

$$G_o = 10$$
$$\tau_2 = 2 \text{ sec}$$
$$\tau_3 = 10 \text{ sec}, 7 \text{ sec}, 5 \text{ sec}, \text{ and } 2 \text{ sec}$$
$$\tau_4 = 0.5 \text{ sec}$$
$$0.1 \leq u \leq 10.0$$

The quantities $20 \log_{10} M$ and θ are to be calculated for 0.1 increments of the parameter u from $u = 0.1$ to $u = 10$ for each of the values for τ_3.

The flow chart for the problem is shown in Fig. 2-6. The variable names used in the program are as follows:

Variable Name	Quantity	Value Used
G	Overall system gain, G_o	10.
TAU2	Time constant τ_2, sec	2.
TAU3	Time constant τ_3, sec	10., 7., 5., and 2.
TAU4	Time constant τ_4, sec	0.5
U	Nondimensional parameter, $\omega \tau_3$	$0.1 \leq u \leq 10.$
UT10	U times 10	$1.0 \leq 10u \leq 100.$
UMIN10	Minimum U value times 10	1.0
UMAX10	Maximum U value times 10	100.

[7] The quantity $20 \log_{10} M$ is in decibels and θ is in degrees.

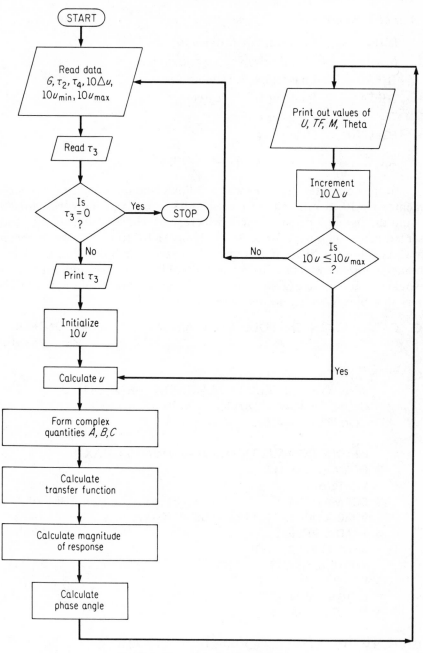

FIG. 2-6. Flow chart for Example 2-1.

Variable Name	Quantity	Value Used
DUT10	Increment of U times 10	1.
M	Magnitude of transfer function	
THRAD	Phase angle θ, radians	
THETA	Phase angle, θ, degrees	
TF	Transfer function	
LGMT20	$20 \log_{10} M$	
A,B,C,	$\left(1 + i\dfrac{\tau_4}{\tau_3}u\right), \left(1 + i\dfrac{\tau_2}{\tau_3}u\right), (1 + iu)$	

In the computer program which follows, the quantity $10u$ was incremented by $10\Delta u$ rather than incrementing u by Δu. This was done to avoid the use of a decimal-fraction increment which could not be represented exactly in binary form. Multiplying Δu by 10 makes the increment a whole number which can be represented exactly in binary form. (A pure binary computer was used to solve the problem, and 0.1 added 100 times would not add up to exactly 10.0.) Such a procedure would not be necessary in a binary-coded decimal computer.

```
C   CALCULATION OF BODE DIAGRAM DATA FOR A CONTROL
                                             SYSTEM
C
C   TYPE STATEMENTS
        REAL  G,TAU2,TAU3,TAU4,M,THETA,THRAD,UT10,U,
       .UMIN10,UMAX10,DUT10,LGMT20
        COMPLEX  TF,A,B,C
C
        READ(5,2)G,TAU2,TAU4,DUT10,UMIN10,UMAX10
      2 FORMAT(6F5.1)
        WRITE(6,3)
      3 FORMAT(1H1,7H    TAU3,5X,1HU,6X,9HMAGNITUDE,6X,
       .8H20 LOG M,5X,11HPHASE ANGLE/)
      4 READ(5,2)TAU3
        IF(TAU3.EQ.0.)STOP
        WRITE(6,5)TAU3
      5 FORMAT(1H ,F7.1)
        UT10=UMIN10
      6 U=UT10/10.
C
C   FORM THE COMPLEX QUANTITIES A,B, AND C
C   OF THE TRANSFER FUNCTION EQUATION
        A=CMPLX(1.,TAU4/TAU3*U)
        B=CMPLX(1.,TAU2/TAU3*U)
        C=CMPLX(1.,U)
```

```
C
C   CALCULATE TRANSFER FUNCTION
        TF = G*A/(B*C*A+G)
C
C   CALCULATE MAGNITUDE M OF TRANSFER FUNCTION AND
C   PHASE ANGLE IN DEGREES
        M = CABS(TF)
        LGMT20 = 20.*ALOG10(M)
        THRAD = ATAN2(AIMAG(TF),REAL(TF))
        THETA = THRAD*180./3.1415927
C
        WRITE(6,7)U,M,LGMT20,THETA
      7 FORMAT(1H ,7X,F7.1,3E15.4)
        UT10 = UT10+DUT10
        IF(UT10 .LE. UMAX10) GO TO 6
        GO TO 4
        END
```

Following is a portion of the printout obtained from the above program:

TAU3	U	MAGNITUDE	20 LOG M	PHASE ANGLE
10.0				
	0.1	0.9093E 00	-0.8263E 00	-0.3647E 00
	0.2	0.9098E 00	-0.8214E 00	-0.7298E 00
	0.3	0.9106E 00	-0.8134E 00	-0.1096E 01
	0.4	0.9118E 00	-0.8022E 00	-0.1463E 01
	0.5	0.9133E 00	-0.7878E 00	-0.1833E 01
	0.6	0.9152E 00	-0.7701E 00	-0.2204E 01
	0.7	0.9174E 00	-0.7492E 00	-0.2579E 01
	0.8	0.9199E 00	-0.7250E 00	-0.2956E 01
	0.9	0.9228E 00	-0.6975E 00	-0.3338E 01
	1.0	0.9261E 00	-0.6668E 00	-0.3724E 01
	1.1	0.9298E 00	-0.6327E 00	-0.4114E 01
	1.2	0.9338E 00	-0.5952E 00	-0.4510E 01
	1.3	0.9382E 00	-0.5544E 00	-0.4912E 01
	1.4	0.9430E 00	-0.5102E 00	-0.5321E 01
	1.5	0.9481E 00	-0.4625E 00	-0.5736E 01
	1.6	0.9537E 00	-0.4113E 00	-0.6160E 01
	1.7	0.9598E 00	-0.3566E 00	-0.6592E 01
	1.8	0.9662E 00	-0.2984E 00	-0.7033E 01
	1.9	0.9731E 00	-0.2366E 00	-0.7484E 01
	2.0	0.9805E 00	-0.1711E 00	-0.7946E 01
	2.1	0.9883E 00	-0.1019E 00	-0.8419E 01

2.2	0.9967E 00	−0.2895E−01	−0.8905E 01
2.3	0.1006E 01	0.4779E−01	−0.9404E 01
2.4	0.1015E 01	0.1284E 00	−0.9918E 01
2.5	0.1025E 01	0.2129E 00	−0.1045E 02
2.6	0.1035E 01	0.3014E 00	−0.1099E 02
2.7	0.1046E 01	0.3939E 00	−0.1155E 02
2.8	0.1058E 01	0.4905E 00	−0.1214E 02
2.9	0.1070E 01	0.5912E 00	−0.1274E 02
3.0	0.1083E 01	0.6962E 00	−0.1336E 02
3.1	0.1097E 01	0.8054E 00	−0.1401E 02
3.2	0.1112E 01	0.9189E 00	−0.1468E 02
3.3	0.1127E 01	0.1037E 01	−0.1538E 02
3.4	0.1143E 01	0.1159E 01	−0.1611E 02
3.5	0.1160E 01	0.1286E 01	−0.1687E 02
3.6	0.1177E 01	0.1417E 01	−0.1766E 02
3.7	0.1196E 01	0.1553E 01	−0.1848E 02
3.8	0.1215E 01	0.1694E 01	−0.1935E 02
3.9	0.1236E 01	0.1839E 01	−0.2025E 02
4.0	0.1257E 01	0.1988E 01	−0.2120E 02
4.1	0.1280E 01	0.2142E 01	−0.2220E 02
4.2	0.1303E 01	0.2301E 01	−0.2325E 02
4.3	0.1328E 01	0.2464E 01	−0.2435E 02
4.4	0.1354E 01	0.2631E 01	−0.2551E 02
4.5	0.1381E 01	0.2802E 01	−0.2674E 02
4.6	0.1409E 01	0.2977E 01	−0.2803E 02
4.7	0.1438E 01	0.3156E 01	−0.2939E 02
4.8	0.1468E 01	0.3337E 01	−0.3084E 02
..	. . . .	. . . .	. . . .
..	. . . .	. . . .	. . . .

The Bode diagram obtained from the computer program is shown in Fig. 2-7a and b. The amplitude ratio for the various values of τ_3 indicates the range of u over which the system has a flat response frequency. For example, with $\tau_3 = 10$, the response of the system is essentially independent of the frequency up to $u = 1.0$. It should be noted that the phase lag between the output and input is essentially zero for the frequency range up to $u = 2.0$.

EXAMPLE 2-2

To illustrate the use of logical quantities and other FORTRAN, let us consider the number systems used in digital computers. Essentially, all digital computers employ some form of the binary-number system, since binary devices have proved to be advantageous from the standpoints

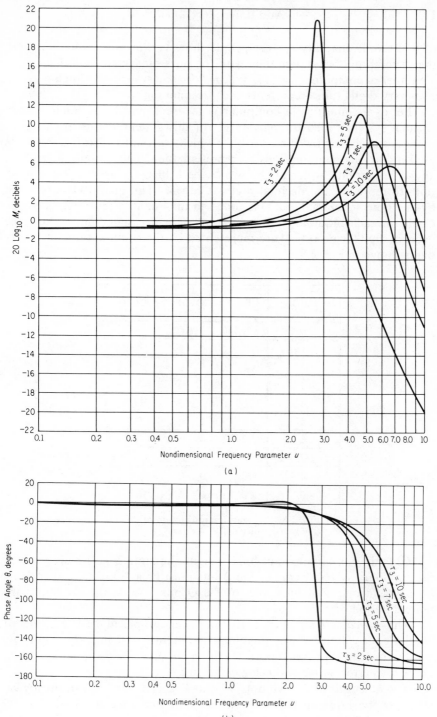

(a)

(b)

Fig. 2-7. Bode diagram.

of speed and reliability. Most people, however, are more familiar with the decimal-number system than with the pure binary system. Therefore, a number of computers use *binary-coded decimal* systems in which a group of binary digits (bits) represents each decimal digit.

Let us assume that a computer is to use a particular binary-coded decimal system called the *biquinary*. In this system, 7 bits are used to represent each decimal digit: 5 bits, which we shall call the Q bits, are used in various combinations to represent the decimal digits 0, 1, 2, 3, and 4; 2 other bits, which are known as the B bits, are used in 2 combinations to represent the decimal digits 0 and 5. The quantity represented by the B bits (either a 0 or a 5) is added to the quantity represented by the Q bits in each biquinary representation of a decimal digit. Thus, the decimal digits from 0 to 9 are represented by the combinations of binary digits shown in Fig. 2-8.

Decimal Digits	B0	B5	Q0	Q1	Q2	Q3	Q4
0	1	0	1	0	0	0	0
1	1	0	0	1	0	0	0
2	1	0	0	0	1	0	0
3	1	0	0	0	0	1	0
4	1	0	0	0	0	0	1
5	0	1	1	0	0	0	0
6	0	1	0	1	0	0	0
7	0	1	0	0	1	0	0
8	0	1	0	0	0	1	0
9	0	1	0	0	0	0	1

Fig. 2-8. Biquinary representation of the decimal digits.

Only the combinations of binary digits shown in Fig. 2-8 are valid in the biquinary system. One of the B bits must be a 1 and the other must be a 0, and one, and only one, of the Q bits is a 1, in any biquinary representation of a decimal digit.

The *logical circuit* (Fig. 2-10) has been proposed as a method of checking the validity of any possible combination of 7 bits. Our purpose will be to write a program which will enable us to use the computer to check the performance of this logical circuit.

The functions of the symbols used in Fig. 2-10 for the various logical elements are shown in Fig. 2-9. In the computer program, logical statements are used to simulate the action of the various logical devices. The

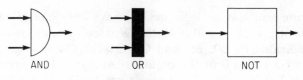

FIG. 2-9. Symbol designations.

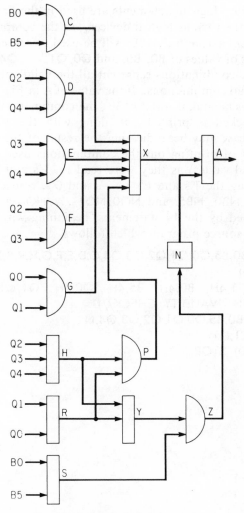

FIG. 2-10. Logical circuit used to check the validity of 7 bit combinations in the biquinary binary-coded decimal system.

signals entering and leaving logic devices have only one of two values, such as ON or OFF, + or −, and so forth. Whatever the physical nature of the inputs indicated by B0, B5, and Q0, Q1, . . . , Q4 in Fig. 2-10, each represents only a 1 or a 0 of the biquinary system. The signal from an AND device is 1 if, and only if, all inputs are 1. The signal from an OR device is 1 if any input is 1. The signal from a NOT device is the negative of the input; that is, the output would be 1 for a 0 input and 0 for a 1 input.

As stated earlier, logical statements are used in the program to simulate the action of the various logical devices. In the computer .TRUE. will be used to represent a 1, and .FALSE. will be used to represent a 0. Various combinations of values of B0, B5, and Q0, Q1, . . . , Q4 are to be read in as data. These combinations represent all the valid combinations and a number of invalid combinations. If the value of A in Fig. 2-10 is .TRUE., the combination is invalid; if A is .FALSE., the combination is valid. Each combination checked is printed out along with the word VALID or INVALID, as the case may be, indicating the result of the validity check. However, instead of printing out the combinations used in the form of T's and F's (logical values) as they were read in, 1's and 0's are printed out. In converting the T's and F's to 1's and 0's, respectively, the new integer variables NB0, NB5, and NQ0, NQ1, . . . , NQ4 are used. Their values are assigned by the 14 statements, beginning with the statement NB0 = 0, in the source program which follows.

```
      LOGICAL B0,B5,Q0,Q1,Q2,Q3,Q4,C,D,E,F,G,H,R,S,X,P,Y,Z,A
      WRITE(6,30)
   30 FORMAT(1H1,4H  B0,4H  B5,4H  Q0,4H  Q1,4H  Q2,4HQ3,
     .4H  Q4,17H  VALIDITY CHECK//)
    2 READ(5,20)B0,B5,Q0,Q1,Q2,Q3,Q4,N
   20 FORMAT(7L1,I1)
      IF(N .EQ. 0) STOP
      NB0=0
      NB5=0
      NQ0=0
      NQ1=0
      NQ2=0
      NQ3=0
      NQ4=0
      IF(B0)NB0=1
      IF(B5)NB5=1
      IF(Q0)NQ0=1
      IF(Q1)NQ1=1
      IF(Q2)NQ2=1
      IF(Q3)NQ3=1
```

```
     IF(Q4)NQ4=1
     C=B0 .AND. B5
     D=Q2 .AND. Q4
     E=Q3 .AND. Q4
     F=Q2 .AND. Q3
     G=Q0 .AND. Q1
     H=Q2 .OR. Q3 .OR. Q4
     R=Q1 .OR. Q0
     S=B0 .OR. B5
     P=H .AND. R
     X=C .OR. D .OR. E .OR. F .OR. G .OR. P
     Y=H .OR. R
     Z=Y .AND. S
     A=X .OR. .NOT. Z
     IF(A) GO TO 3
     WRITE(6,40)NB0,NB5,NQ0,NQ1,NQ2,NQ3,NQ4
  40 FORMAT(1H0,7I4,7X,5HVALID)
     GO TO 2
   3 WRITE(6,50)NB0,NB5,NQ0,NQ1,NQ2,NQ3,NQ4
  50 FORMAT(1H0,7I4,6X,7HINVALID)
     GO TO 2
     END
```

The computer printout obtained from the program is as follows:

B0	B5	Q0	Q1	Q2	Q3	Q4	VALIDITY CHECK
1	0	1	0	0	0	0	VALID
1	0	0	1	0	0	0	VALID
1	0	0	0	1	0	0	VALID
1	0	0	0	0	1	0	VALID
1	0	0	0	0	0	1	VALID
0	1	1	0	0	0	0	VALID
0	1	0	1	0	0	0	VALID
0	1	0	0	1	0	0	VALID
0	1	0	0	0	1	0	VALID
0	1	0	0	0	0	1	VALID
1	1	1	0	0	0	0	INVALID
1	0	1	1	0	0	0	INVALID
1	0	1	0	1	0	0	INVALID
1	0	1	0	0	1	0	INVALID

1	0	1	0	0	0	1	INVALID
1	1	0	1	0	0	0	INVALID
0	0	1	1	0	0	0	INVALID
0	0	0	1	1	0	0	INVALID
0	0	0	0	1	1	0	INVALID
0	0	0	0	0	1	1	INVALID

Problems

2-1. Listed below are some FORTRAN double-precision constants. Rewrite these in ordinary engineering form.

$-.09D+1$ 3408655.1392

$+10.1D0$ .00363D2

$.2D-03$ 1.D+25

$.1928374654389D+09$ 5.D02

2-2. Listed below are several numbers written in ordinary engineering form. Rewrite these as FORTRAN double-precision constants.

$-.003$ .1

5,921,364.559 $+10$

10^{10} .0000001

$-10(10)^{-7}$ 2.5900283171

2-3. Write the quantities below as FORTRAN complex constants.

$\sqrt{-169} + 12$ $-95.2 - \sqrt{-49}$

$-\sqrt{169}$ $9 + 6i$

$10^{13} + (7.21)^9 \sqrt{-1}$ 35.127

$136.2i$ $3 + 4i$

2-4. The type statements

DOUBLE PRECISION DBL1, DBL2,N

COMPLEX COMP1, COMP2,X

appear in a program in which the expressions containing double-precision and complex quantities (shown below) are used. Indicate the validity or invalidity of each expression. If the expression is invalid, state why.

N + 1

(A + .14159D0)*DIAM

N/DBL1 + 3.

COMP1 *2.2

DBL2 + COMP1 − 6.75D+08

.314159D+01 * LRAD**2

COMP2/(.153, .43E−2)

DBL2 − .74328D−4

X*(3,4)

X**2

(DBL1 − N)**X

I**J

24.4151 **2.D1

COMP1**X

2-5. Determine the value of each of the following logical expressions, assuming that A > B, LG1 = .TRUE., LG2 = .TRUE., LG3 = .FALSE., and LG4 = .FALSE..

  a) A .EQ. B .AND. LG2

  b) LG1 .AND. .NOT. A .LT. B

  c) A .EQ. B .OR. LG3

  d) A .LT. B .OR. LG4

  e) .NOT. A .LT. B .AND. LG3

  f) .NOT.(A .LT. B .AND. LG3)

  g) .NOT. (A .LT. B .OR. LG1)

  h) LG3 .AND. LG2 .OR. LG1

  i) .NOT. B .LE. A .OR. LG1 .AND. LG4

2-6. Indicate the validity or invalidity of each of the statements listed below. If invalid, state why. Assume that COMP1, COMP2, COMP3, and COMP4 have been declared to be complex variables in a Type statement. Also assume that DBL1, DBL2, and DBL3 have been declared to be double-precision variables in a Type statement, and that LG1, LG2, LG3, and LG4 have been declared logical variables in a Type statement.

COMP1 = A + COMP2

B = COMP1 + (6.5, .0)

COMP3 = 2.51D+5 + A + B

DBL1 = A/B + C*D

I = C + C + COMP1

J = DBL1 + F/H

X = DBL1 * 3.7154981668

DBL2 = J

DBL3 = COMP1/3.1416 + 2.99

COMP4 = J

COMP2 = A * B/C + F/G

LG1 = DBL2 .GT. DBL3

LG2 = COMP1 .NE. COMP2

A = I .LT. X

LG3 = LG1 .EQ. .TRUE.

X = C + (3.,4.)

COMP4 = X/Y

LG1 = X *C/D .LE. I + J

2-7. Making use of the logical IF statement, write a statement or statements to carry out the requirements of parts a through h, below. Assume that each statement you write is part of a complete program in which all variables have been assigned values. a) If THETA − THETA1 < 360., transfer to statement 5. Otherwise, continue in sequence. b) If X > Y, set A = X/2. Otherwise, set A = X. c) If GAMMA + PHI > 180., transfer to statement 28. Otherwise, transfer to statement 53. d) If Y is an even number, go to statement 10. Otherwise, continue in sequence. e) If X − XMAX is < 0, go to statement 55. Otherwise, stop. f) If | PTH1 − CTH1 | < EPSI, go to statement 69. Otherwise, continue in sequence. g) If A > 0., and if B > 10. or C < 20., let X = (C + B)/A. h) If A is the largest of the variables A, B, and C, set BIGEST equal to A and then go to statement 15. Otherwise, go directly to statement 15.

2-8. A 1-dimensional array $A(N)$ is to be read into computer memory. The array has a maximum of 50 elements. Write a portion of a **FORTRAN** program which will read in the array. Assume that the value of each element will be on a separate card in the first 10 card columns. Assume that the decimal points are punched and that no exponents are used. The cards will be in order, with the value of A(1) on the card which is read in first.

2-9. A 1-dimensional array $A(N)$ is to be read into computer memory. The array has a maximum of 50 elements. Write a portion of a **FORTRAN** program which will read in the array. Assume that the cards will not be in any particular order, so that the first 2 card columns will be used to identify the element, with the next 10 card columns used for the value of the element. Also assume that the decimal points are punched and that no exponents are used. Devise a method of indicating to the program that the last card of the array has been read.

2-10. Write a portion of a **FORTRAN** program using an implied **DO** for reading the elements of a triangular matrix into computer memory. The matrix has the form

$$
\begin{array}{cccc}
a_{11} & a_{12} \cdots \cdots \cdots & a_{1n} \\
 & a_{22} & a_{23} \cdots \cdots & a_{2n} \\
 & & a_{33} \cdots \cdots & a_{3n} \\
 & & & \vdots \\
 & & & a_{nn}
\end{array}
$$

where the value of n is to be read in as data.

2-11. Write a portion of a **FORTRAN** program for printing out the temperature values at the mesh points on a square plate. The temperature values are stored as the values of the elements of an 11-by-11 array $T(I, J)$, where I is the value of the row number of the mesh points, and J is the value of the column number. The temperature values are to be printed on the page in the same positions as those occupied by the mesh points on the plate; that is, there will be 11 values in 1 row on the paper, and there will be 11 rows. All temperatures will lie between 100 C and 0 C. One digit after the decimal point will provide a sufficiently accurate printout. The line printer is under program control.

2-12. Write statements defining the following arithmetic statement functions:

a) $f(x, y) = \sqrt{x^2 + y^2}$
b) $f(x) = a + bx + cx^2 + dx^3 + ex^4$
c) $f(x, a, b, c, d) = a + bx + cx^2 + dx^3$
d) $f(x, a, b, c, d) = a + b \cos x + c \cos^2 x + d \cos^3 x$

2-13. Write a statement defining the statement function FORCE as given by

$$\text{FORCE} = H\left(\frac{7.64}{\tau_2} - \frac{7.95}{\tau_1}\right)$$

Let τ_1 and τ_2 be arguments of the function, and let H be a parameter.

2-14. Write a statement defining the statement function RADGYN given by

$$\text{RADGYN} = R\sqrt{\frac{\alpha + \sin \alpha \cos \alpha - 2 \sin^2 \alpha/\alpha}{2\alpha}}$$

Let α and R be arguments of the function.

2-15. Write a statement defining the statement function RADIUS as given by

$$\text{RADIUS} = 0.721 \sqrt[3]{(P)(D)\left[\frac{1 - \nu_1^2}{E_1} + \frac{1 - \nu_2^2}{E_2}\right]}$$

Let P and D be the arguments of the function, and let ν_1, ν_2, and E_1 and E_2 be parameters.

2-16. Write a statement defining the statement function WEIGHT as given by

$$\text{WEIGHT} = 0.4722A\sqrt{\frac{P_1}{v_s}\left(\frac{1 - \dfrac{1}{x^2}}{N + \log_e x}\right)}$$

Let P_1, x, and v_s be the arguments of the function, and let A and N be parameters.

2-17. Write a statement defining the statement function THICK as given by

$$\text{THICK} = \frac{1}{2}D[\sqrt{(S + 0.4p)/(S - 1.3p)} - 1]$$

Let D and p be arguments of the function, and let S be a parameter.

2-18. Write a statement defining the statement function VOLUM as given by

$$\text{VOLUM} = \frac{1}{4}\pi d^2 \sqrt{\left(\frac{gd}{4fl}\right)\frac{1}{wp_1}(p_1^2 - p_2^2)}$$

where $g = 32.2$, and $f = 0.0028(1.0 + 3.6/d)$. Let p_1, p_2, and w be arguments of the function, and let d and l be parameters.

2-19. Write a FUNCTION subprogram defining the function CRTICL where

$$CRTICL = \frac{0.669b^3d\sqrt{(1 - 0.63b/d)EG}}{l^2}\left[1 - \frac{a}{2l}\sqrt{\frac{E}{G(1 - 0.63b/d)}}\right]$$

Let a, b, d, l, E, and G be the function arguments.

2-20. Write a FUNCTION subprogram defining the function FOFY as given by

$$FOFY = R_1\cos x - R_2\cos y + R_3 - \cos(x - y)$$

where

$R_1 = D/C,$

$R_2 = D/A,$

$R_3 = \dfrac{D^2 + A^2 - B^2 + C^2}{2CA}.$

The function arguments are A, B, C, D, x, and y.

2-21. Write a FUNCTION subprogram defining the complex function ROOT. If the roots are real, the subprogram is to determine the algebraically largest root of the quadratic equation

$$ax^2 + bx + c = 0$$

and the function is to take on the value of this root. If the roots are complex, the value of the function is to take on the complex value

$$-\frac{b}{2a} + \sqrt{-(b^2 - 4ac)}\,i$$

2-22. Write a FUNCTION subprogram defining a function PROD which is assigned the value of the product of the elements on the main diagonal of an n-by-n matrix.

2-23. Write a FUNCTION subprogram defining a function ONES which is assigned a value by the subprogram equal to the number of 1's in an m-by-n matrix whose elements all have the value 0 or 1.

2-24. Write a FUNCTION subprogram defining a function MAXA which is assigned the value of the largest element in an m-by-n array

$$\begin{matrix} a_{11} & a_{12} & a_{13} & \cdots & a_{1n} \\ a_{21} & a_{22} & & & \\ a_{31} & a_{32} & & & \\ \vdots & \vdots & & & \vdots \\ a_{m1} & a_{m2} & & \cdots & a_{mn} \end{matrix}$$

2-25. Write a SUBROUTINE subprogram for finding the largest element in an m-by-n array such as that shown in Prob. 2-24. The largest element value is to be returned to the calling program as the value of an argument.

2-26. Write a SUBROUTINE subprogram which determines the number of 0's, 1's, and 2's in any m-by-n matrix, all of whose elements are known to be 0's, 1's, or 2's.

2-27. Write a SUBROUTINE subprogram which will interchange row k and row l of an m-by-n matrix a_{ij}.

2-28. Write a SUBROUTINE subprogram for finding the product of 2 matrices a_{ij} and b_{jk}, where the former is an m-by-n matrix, and the latter is a matrix having n rows and j columns.

2-29. Write a SUBROUTINE subprogram for determining the largest element of a 1-dimensional array $a_1, a_2, a_3, \ldots, a_n$.

2-30. Write a SUBROUTINE subprogram which will sort the elements of an array $a_1, a_2, \ldots, a_n$ into ascending order. That is, a_1 will be the name associated with the smallest element, a_2 will be the name associated with the next-to-the-smallest element, and so forth. Do the sorting by interchanging array elements a_i and a_{i+1} if a_i is greater than a_{i+1}, for $i = 1, 2, \ldots, k$, where k is initially equal to $n - 1$. This procedure will assign the largest value of the array to a_n. Then reduce k by 1 and repeat. This will assign the next-to-the-largest value in the array to a_{n-1}. Continue interchanging in this manner until and including $k = 2$.

2-31. The vibration isolation of instruments and machines is an important application of vibration theory. The spring-and-mass system in the accompanying figure represents schematically an instrument or machine in which the motion of the base structure is sinusoidal. If the parameters of the supporting mounts

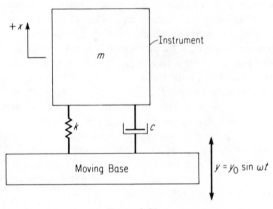

PROB. 2-31

(the spring constant k and the dashpot constant c) are properly selected with respect to the mass m and the exciting frequency ω, the displacement x of the instrument can be reduced to a small fraction of the displacement y of the base. Such vibration isolation results in small ratios of X/y_o where X is the amplitude of vibration of the instrument and y_o is the amplitude of the moving base.

The differential equation of motion of the mass m is

$$m\ddot{x} + c\dot{x} + kx = ky + c\dot{y}$$

This equation yields the transfer function in the frequency domain as

$$\frac{x}{y}(i\omega) = \frac{1 + i(2\lambda u)}{(1 - u^2) + i(2\lambda u)}$$

where

$u = \omega/p$, a nondimensional frequency parameter

$p = \sqrt{k/m}$, the natural undamped circular frequency of the system

$\lambda = c/2mp$, a damping parameter ($c/2m = p$ for critical damping)

Write a **FORTRAN** program for obtaining the quantities necessary for a Bode diagram for the values

$$\lambda = 0.2, 0.4, 0.6, 0.8, \text{ and } 1.0 \, (0.1 \leq u \leq 5.0)$$

It should be noted that the magnitude M of the transfer function is

$$M = X/y_0$$

where X and y_o are as defined above.

2-32. The accompanying illustration shows a single-degree-of-freedom gyro and servo system for maintaining zero torque about the x axis of a stable platform in an inertial-guidance system. In general, a stable platform is supported by two gimbal frames (not shown) which permit 3 degrees of freedom in rotation for the platform. The disturbing torques (friction and so forth) about the x, y, and z axes can be eliminated by the use of a system of 3 servomotors, each of which is actuated by a single-degree-of-freedom gyro. The 3 gyros are oriented in such a manner that they sense the rotations due to the disturbing torques.

For the system shown, the rotation ϕ_x, which is due to a disturbing torque T_x, subjects the gyro to a moment which, in turn, causes the gyro to rotate about the y axis through an angle θ. The rotation θ is sensed electrically, and a signal is fed to the servomotor through an amplifier. The servomotor, in turn, applies a torque T_s to the platform about the x axis. This correcting torque is opposite in sense to the disturbing torque T_x. Therefore, if $T_s = T_x$ in magnitude, and if T_s does not lag T_x, the space platform will be kept from rotating about the x axis and will provide a fixed frame of reference with respect to this axis.

This platform, gyro, and servo system constitutes a feedback system which may be described by the block diagram shown in the figure. In this diagram, Y_1, Y_2, Y_3, and Y_4 are the transfer functions of the respective components. The transfer functions Y_1 and Y_2 of the platform and gyro, respectively, are obtained from the angular-momentum relationship

$$\mathbf{M}_o = \frac{d\mathbf{H}_o}{dt} = \frac{d}{dt} \left(I_x \dot{\phi}_x \mathbf{i} + I_y \dot{\theta} \mathbf{j} + h\mathbf{k} \right) \tag{a}$$

where

i, j, and k are unit vectors

I_x = moment of inertia of the platform and gyro assembly about the x axis

I_y = moment of inertia of the gyro and gimbal about the y axis

$h = I\omega$ = angular momentum of the gyro due to the spin velocity ω

I = moment of inertia of the rotating element of the gyro about the spin axis

From Eq. a, we obtain

$$M_x = T_x - T_s = I_x D^2 \phi_x + hD\theta \tag{b}$$

$$M_y = 0 = I_y D^2 \theta - hD\phi_x = I_y D\dot{\theta} - h\phi_x \tag{c}$$

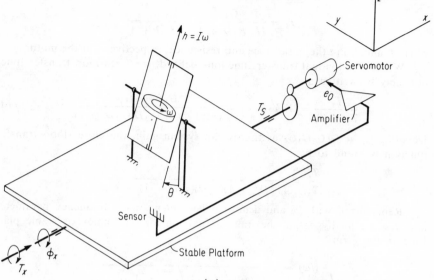

(a)

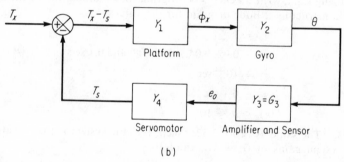

(b)

PROB. 2-32

where the derivatives are shown in operator notation. These equations yield the transfer functions

$$Y_1 = \frac{\phi_x}{T_x - T_s} = \frac{I_y/h^2}{(I_x I_y/h^2)D^2 + 1} = \frac{G_1}{\tau_1^2 D^2 + 1}$$

and

$$Y_2 = \frac{\theta}{\phi_x} = \frac{1}{(I_y/h)D} = \frac{G_2}{\tau_2 D}$$

where the component gains are $G_1 = I_y/h^2$ and $G_2 = 1$. Assuming zero time lag for the amplifier and sensor as a unit,

$$Y_3 = G_3$$

The transfer function for the d-c motor is

$$Y_4 = \frac{G_4}{(L/R)D + 1} = \frac{G_4}{\tau_3 D + 1}$$

where L and R are the inductance and resistance, respectively, of the motor.

With the individual transfer functions defined, the open-loop transfer function may be written as

$$\frac{T_s}{T_x - T_s} = Y_1 Y_2 Y_3 Y_4 = \frac{G_1 G_2 G_3 G_4}{(\tau_1^2 D^2 + 1)(\tau_2 D)(\tau_3 D + 1)} \qquad (d)$$

Denoting $G_o = G_1 G_2 G_3 G_4$ as the overall system gain, the closed-loop transfer function is found to be

$$\frac{T_s}{T_x} = \frac{G_o}{(\tau_1^2 D^2 + 1)(\tau_2 D)(\tau_3 D + 1) + G_o} \qquad (e)$$

Replacing D with $i\omega$ and denoting the dimensionless frequency parameter $u = \tau_1 \omega$, we finally obtain the transfer function for the single-axis stable platform in the form

$$\frac{T_s}{T_x}(i\omega) = \frac{G_o}{(1 - u^2)\left(i\,\dfrac{\tau_2}{\tau_1}\,u\right)\left(1 + i\,\dfrac{\tau_3}{\tau_1}\,u\right) + G_o} \qquad (f)$$

Utilizing Eq. f, write a **FORTRAN** program for obtaining the quantities necessary for constructing a Bode diagram for the values

$$G_o = 1$$

$$\tau_1 = 0.02, 0.04, 0.06, 0.08, \text{ and } 0.1 \text{ sec}$$

$$\tau_2 = 10^{-4} \text{ sec}$$

$$\tau_3 = 0.1 \text{ sec}$$

$$0.1 \le u \le 10$$

2-33. The same as Prob. 2-32, except that the system is to be evaluated for overall system gains of $G_o = 1, 5,$ and 10.

part **II**

Digital-Computer Methods

Since the digital computer is capable of performing only arithmetic operations, the engineer must be familiar with various numerical methods that can be utilized to efficiently solve diverse types of problems. Certain kinds of equations encountered are inherently adaptable to solution by arithmetic procedures, whereas others cannot be solved directly by arithmetic methods. For the latter, approximate methods of solution have been developed which utilize arithmetic procedures.

This chapter and the following ones present some of the most commonly used numerical methods for solving engineering problems. The reader will find it helpful, in learning the techniques of programming, to study carefully the flow charts and programs appearing in the examples which illustrate the various numerical methods. The function of each statement appearing in a program should be correlated with the overall objective of the program, and the various sequences of operations should be traced in order to develop a "feel" for computer logic.

chapter 3

Roots of Algebraic and Transcendental Equations

3-1. Introduction

A problem commonly encountered in engineering is that of determining the roots of an equation of the form

$$f(x) = 0 \tag{3-1}$$

In this chapter we shall consider four methods of finding the *real* roots of such algebraic and transcendental equations: 1) the trial-and-error method, 2) the linear-interpolation method, 3) the Newton-Raphson method, and 4) Newton's second-order method.

If $f(x)$ is a polynomial in x with real coefficients, there are several ways to find both the *real* and the *complex* roots of the polynomial, among them Graeffe's root-squaring method which will also be presented here.

3-2. Trial-and-Error Method

In the trial-and-error approach we determine values of $f(x)$ for successive values of x until a sign change occurs for $f(x)$. The sign change indicates that the root has been passed. A closer approximation to the value of the root may then be obtained by reverting to the last x value preceding the sign change and, beginning with this x value, again determining values of $f(x)$ for successive values of x, using a smaller increment than was used initially, until the sign of $f(x)$ changes again. This procedure is repeated with progressively smaller increments of x until a sufficiently accurate value of the root is obtained. If additional roots are desired, the incrementation of x can be continued until the next root is approximately located by another sign change of $f(x)$, and so on.

Care must be exercised in selecting the initial value by which x is to be incremented, so that a root is not bypassed in an instance when 2 roots are close together in value. This is usually not troublesome, if fairly small increments are used in the initial sequence. Provision may have to be made to prevent the computer from stopping because of overflow, if the

127

value of the function tends to become infinitely large for certain values of x. Since the method chosen to accomplish this, if it is necessary, depends on the computer being used, no attempt to discuss such a provision will be made here. The following example will illustrate the use of the trial-and-error procedure.

EXAMPLE 3-1

It is desired to determine the first positive nonzero root of the equation

$$1 + 5.25x - \sec \sqrt{0.68x} = 0 \tag{3-2}$$

by a trial-and-error method. A plot of the function is shown in Fig. 3-1. The first step is to sketch a flow chart outlining the general procedure (Fig. 3-2).

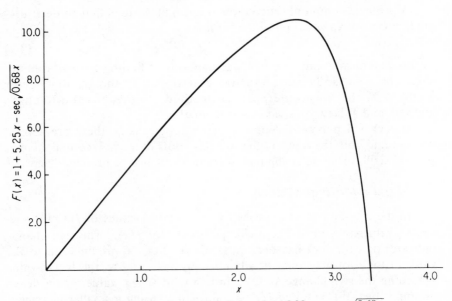

FIG. 3-1. Approximate graph of $f(x) = 1 + 5.25x - \sec \sqrt{0.68x}$.

The flow chart shows that a printout of the value of x and $f(x)$ is specified after each calculation of $f(x)$. Such a printout is superfluous to the solution, but it is included here to illustrate more clearly the operations of the computer, since the computer solution is shown at the end of the example. Note that the initial value of Δx is entered on cards rather than being specified in the source program. In this manner the magnitude of the increment may be varied, if it is found to be too large or too small, without necessitating the compilation of a new object program. In the

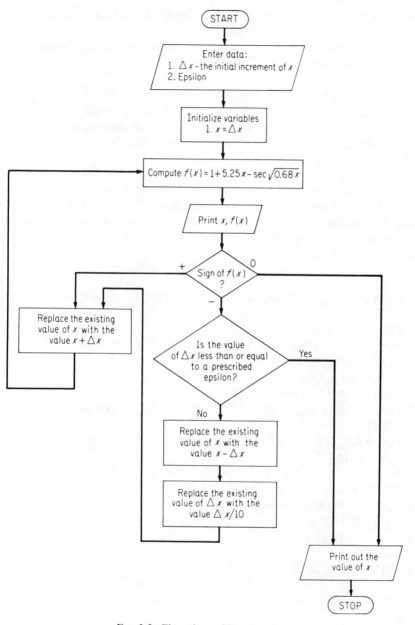

FIG. 3-2. Flow chart of Example 3-1.

computer program which follows, the initial value of Δx was selected as 0.10.

In writing the source program, the following variable names were selected for the corresponding quantities:

Variable Name	Quantity	Remarks
X	x	In locating a root, Δx is con-
Y	$f(x)$	tinuously decreased until it is
DELTX	Δx	less than or equal to ϵ.
EPSI	ϵ	

A FORTRAN program for the IBM 1620 with card input is shown below, followed by the printed computer output. A résumé of the computer operations involved in determining the approximation of the root is revealed in the sequence of values shown preceding the value of the root.

```
   PRINT 2
 2 FORMAT(23X,39HTRIAL AND ERROR DETERMINATION OF A
                                              ROOT)
   PRINT 3
 3 FORMAT(29X,28HOF A TRANSCENDENTAL EQUATION//)
   READ 4,DELTX,EPSI
 4 FORMAT(F5.2,F8.6)
   PRINT 5,DELTX,EPSI
 5 FORMAT(27X,8HDELTX = ,F5.2,7X,7HEPSI = ,F8.6)
   PRINT 6
 6 FORMAT(//4X,1HX,9X,1HY/)
   X = DELTX
 7 Y = 1. + 5.25*X−1./COS(SQRT(.68*X))
   PRINT 8,X,Y
 8 FORMAT(F7.4,3X,F9.4)
   IF(Y) 10,12,9
 9 X = X+DELTX
   GO TO 7
10 IF(DELTX−EPSI) 12,12,11
11 X=X−DELTX
   DELTX=DELTX/10.
   GO TO 9
12 PRINT 13,X
13 FORMAT(//7HROOT IS,F7.4)
   STOP
   END
```

TRIAL-AND-ERROR DETERMINATION OF A ROOT OF A TRANSCENDENTAL EQUATION

DELTX = .10   EPSI = .000100

X	Y
.1000	.4900
.2000	.9779
.3000	1.4635
.4000	1.9466
.5000	2.4270
.6000	2.9044
.7000	3.3784
.8000	3.8488
.9000	4.3151
1.0000	4.7768
1.1000	5.2335
1.2000	5.6844
1.3000	6.1289
1.4000	6.5661
1.5000	6.9949
1.6000	7.4141
1.7000	7.8222
1.8000	8.2175
1.9000	8.5975
2.0000	8.9597
2.1000	9.3003
2.2000	9.6150
2.3000	9.8979
2.4000	10.1411
2.5000	10.3341
2.6000	10.4624
2.7000	10.5050
2.8000	10.4308
2.9000	10.1917
3.0000	9.7091
3.1000	8.8447
3.2000	7.3313
3.3000	4.5761
3.4000	−1.0509
3.3100	4.1873
3.3200	3.7698
3.3300	3.3209
3.3400	2.8371

TRIAL-AND-ERROR DETERMINATION OF A ROOT OF A
TRANSCENDENTAL EQUATION

DELTX = .10   EPSI = .000100

X	Y
3.3500	2.3149
3.3600	1.7499
3.3700	1.1370
3.3800	.4706
3.3900	−.2560
3.3810	.4008
3.3820	.3303
3.3830	.2593
3.3840	.1876
3.3850	.1153
3.3860	.0423
3.3870	−.0312
3.3861	.0350
3.3862	.0276
3.3863	.0203
3.3864	.0129
3.3865	.0056
3.3866	−.0017

ROOT IS 3.3866
STOP

EXAMPLE 3-2

As another example of the trial-and-error method, let us consider the
solution of the transcendental equation

$$x^2(1 - \cos x \cosh x) - \gamma \sin x \sinh x = 0 \qquad (3\text{-}3)$$

which is associated with the flexural vibrations of a missile subjected to a
thrust T, as shown in Fig. 3-3. The derivation of Eq. 3-3 will not be given
here, since it involves theory normally covered in a course in vibrations,
which is beyond the scope of this text. However, it serves to illustrate the
fact that such equations do arise in the analysis of engineering problems,
and it provides a practical example of the solution of transcendental
equations.

The thrust T is directly related to the parameter γ (gamma) appearing
in Eq. 3-3, and the positive roots of the equation determine the configurations and natural frequencies of oscillation of a missile in flight. This
information is pertinent to the design of guidance and control systems for
such missiles.

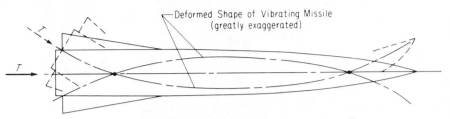

FIG. 3-3. Configuration for first mode of vibrating missile.

To gain experience in the use of *logic* in programming, let us formulate a computer program to determine the roots of Eq. 3-3. In developing this program, we will consider the following:

1. The solution will be limited to the determination of the first 3 non-zero roots. (Actually, there is an infinite number of such roots for this equation.)

2. Solutions will be obtained for a range of γ specified by $0.1 \le \gamma \le 3.0$.

3. Increments of 0.1 will be used for γ until $\gamma = 1.0$, after which increments of 0.5 will be used until the limiting value of $\gamma = 3.0$ is reached.

Preparatory to developing a flow chart for the solution, let us consider the curves shown in Fig. 3-4 which, in a general way, might represent a plot of the left side of Eq. 3-3 versus x for two different values of γ. The general shape of these curves reveals that each of the several roots can be approximately located by the sign change which occurs as the root is passed.

Starting with an initial value of $\gamma = 0.1$, the first 3 roots of the equation are determined by incrementing x, as explained in detail in Example 1-1. Since the root $x = 0$ is obvious from an inspection of the equation,

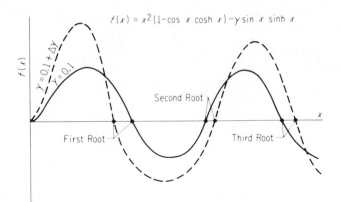

FIG. 3-4. General $f(x)$ curves.

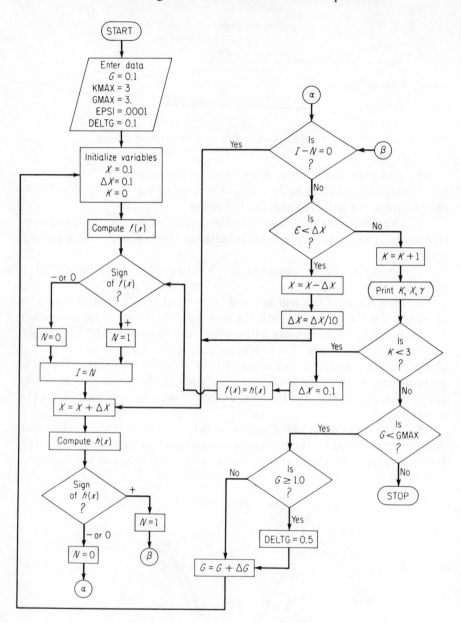

FIG. 3-5. Flow chart of Example 3-2.

an initial value of $x = 0.1$ may be used to start the calculations. After the 3 roots have been determined to the desired degree of accuracy, γ is incremented, and the procedure is repeated to determine the 3 roots associated with the new γ value. The process is continued until solutions have been obtained for all of the specified values of γ.

The FORTRAN variable names used, and their corresponding quantities, are as follows:

Variable Name	Quantity	Values Used
X	x	
FX	$f(x)$	
HX	$f(x)$	
DELTX	Δx	
GMAX	Maximum value of γ	3.0
G	Thrust parameter γ	
EPSI	Accuracy-check value ϵ	0.0001
DELTG	Increment of γ	$\left\{\begin{matrix} 0.1 \text{ for } \gamma \leq 1.0 \\ 0.5 \text{ for } \gamma > 1.0 \end{matrix}\right\}$
K	Root number	First root, $K = 1$
KMAX	Maximum value of K	3
W	Cosh x	
U	Sinh x	

A flow chart is shown in Fig. 3-5. In following the program outline provided by the flow chart, it should be noted that the sign change of $f(x)$, which indicates the approximate location of a root, is determined when $I - N \neq 0$. It should also be noted that when the thrust parameter γ (G) exceeds a value of 1.0, the increment of γ (DELTG) is increased to 0.5.

The FORTRAN source program is shown below.

```
1 FORMAT(15X,36HEIGENVALUES FOR VARIABLE MASS ROCKET/)
  PRINT 1
  READ 2, G, KMAX,GMAX, EPSI, DELTG
2 FORMAT(F4.1,I2,F5.1,F6.4,F4.1)
4 X=.1
  DELTX=.1
  K=0
  Y=EXP(X)
  Z=EXP(-X)
  W=(Y+Z)/2.
```

```
     U=(Y−Z)/2.
     FX=X*X*(1.−COS(X)*W)−G*SIN(X)*U
  6  IF(FX)8,8,10
  8  N=0
     I=N
     GO TO 12
 10  N=1
     I=N
 12  X=X+DELTX
     Y=EXP(X)
     Z=EXP(−X)
     W=(Y+Z)/2.
     U=(Y−Z)/2.
     HX=X*X*(1.−COS(X)*W)−G*SIN(X)*U
     IF(HX)16,16,18
 16  N=0
     GO TO 20
 18  N=1
 20  IF(I−N)22,12,22
 22  IF(EPSI−DELTX)24,28,28
 24  X  =  X−DELTX
     DELTX=DELTX/10.
     GO TO 12
 28  K=K+1
 30  PRINT 32,K,X,G
 32  FORMAT(9X,11HMODE NO. = ,I2,9X,7HROOT = ,F9.4,9X,
                                  8HGAMMA = ,F6.1)
     IF(K−3)34,36,36
 34  DELTX  =  0.1
     FX=HX
     GO TO 6
 36  IF(G−GMAX)38,44,44
 38  IF(G−1.0)40,42,42
 40  G  =  G+DELTG
     GO TO 4
 42  DELTG  =  0.5
     G  =  G+DELTG
     GO TO 4
 44  STOP
     END
```

The computer printout, giving the roots for the various values of γ, is as follows:

EIGENVALUES FOR VARIABLE MASS ROCKET

MODE NO. =	1	ROOT =	.8790	GAMMA =	.1
MODE NO. =	2	ROOT =	4.7345	GAMMA =	.1
MODE NO. =	3	ROOT =	7.8549	GAMMA =	.1
MODE NO. =	1	ROOT =	1.0440	GAMMA =	.2
MODE NO. =	2	ROOT =	4.7388	GAMMA =	.2
MODE NO. =	3	ROOT =	7.8565	GAMMA =	.2
MODE NO. =	1	ROOT =	1.1538	GAMMA =	.3
MODE NO. =	2	ROOT =	4.7432	GAMMA =	.3
MODE NO. =	3	ROOT =	7.8581	GAMMA =	.3
MODE NO. =	1	ROOT =	1.2383	GAMMA =	.4
MODE NO. =	2	ROOT =	4.7475	GAMMA =	.4
MODE NO. =	3	ROOT =	7.8597	GAMMA =	.4
MODE NO. =	1	ROOT =	1.3076	GAMMA =	.5
MODE NO. =	2	ROOT =	4.7518	GAMMA =	.5
MODE NO. =	3	ROOT =	7.8614	GAMMA =	.5
MODE NO. =	1	ROOT =	1.3668	GAMMA =	.6
MODE NO. =	2	ROOT =	4.7561	GAMMA =	.6
MODE NO. =	3	ROOT =	7.8630	GAMMA =	.6
MODE NO. =	1	ROOT =	1.4187	GAMMA =	.7
MODE NO. =	2	ROOT =	4.7604	GAMMA =	.7
MODE NO. =	3	ROOT =	7.8646	GAMMA =	.7
MODE NO. =	1	ROOT =	1.4650	GAMMA =	.8
MODE NO. =	2	ROOT =	4.7647	GAMMA =	.8
MODE NO. =	3	ROOT =	7.8662	GAMMA =	.8
MODE NO. =	1	ROOT =	1.5069	GAMMA =	.9
MODE NO. =	2	ROOT =	4.7690	GAMMA =	.9
MODE NO. =	3	ROOT =	7.8678	GAMMA =	.9
MODE NO. =	1	ROOT =	1.5451	GAMMA =	1.0
MODE NO. =	2	ROOT =	4.7732	GAMMA =	1.0
MODE NO. =	3	ROOT =	7.8694	GAMMA =	1.0
MODE NO. =	1	ROOT =	1.6993	GAMMA =	1.5
MODE NO. =	2	ROOT =	4.7941	GAMMA =	1.5
MODE NO. =	3	ROOT =	7.8774	GAMMA =	1.5
MODE NO. =	1	ROOT =	1.8148	GAMMA =	2.0
MODE NO. =	2	ROOT =	4.8147	GAMMA =	2.0
MODE NO. =	3	ROOT =	7.8854	GAMMA =	2.0
MODE NO. =	1	ROOT =	1.9073	GAMMA =	2.5
MODE NO. =	2	ROOT =	4.8348	GAMMA =	2.5
MODE NO. =	3	ROOT =	7.8934	GAMMA =	2.5
MODE NO. =	1	ROOT =	1.9844	GAMMA =	3.0
MODE NO. =	2	ROOT =	4.8545	GAMMA =	3.0
MODE NO. =	3	ROOT =	7.9013	GAMMA =	3.0

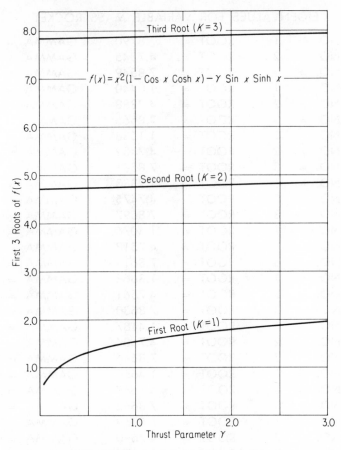

FIG. 3-6. Roots of $f(x)$ for Example 3-2.

The first 3 roots as functions of γ are shown graphically in Fig. 3-6. It is of interest to note that the first-root curve varies considerably with the thrust parameter γ, whereas the other curves are relatively unaffected.

3-3. Linear-Interpolation Method

This method may be used with the computer to obtain the roots of an equation, to a specified degree of accuracy, with fewer computer calculations than are involved in trial and error. The first 2 approximations of the root value are obtained by the trial-and-error method, after which a linear interpolation between 2 points, such as P_1 and P_2, is used, as illustrated in Fig. 3-7.

Let us assume that the values y_1 and y_2 have been obtained for $f(x_1)$ and $f(x_2)$ by the trial-and-error method. Since y_1 and y_2 are of opposite

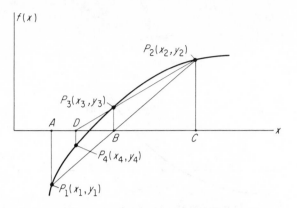

FIG. 3-7. Root determination by linear interpolation.

sign, as shown, a root is known to lie between the corresponding values of x_1 and x_2. From similar triangles we may write the relationship

$$\frac{y_2 - y_1}{x_2 - x_1} = \frac{0 - y_1}{x_3 - x_1}$$

in which x_3 is a closer approximation of the root, as can be seen from the figure. Rearranging the above expression shows that

$$x_3 = \frac{x_1 y_2 - x_2 y_1}{y_2 - y_1} \qquad (3\text{-}4)$$

The value of x_3 can be determined from Eq. 3-4, since all the values on the right-hand side are known. The determined value of x_3 is then substituted into the function to determine the value of y_3. This is followed by an interpolation between points P_2 and P_3, from which the value of x_4, which is an even closer approximation, is obtained. The process is repeated with successive pairs of points until an approximation of the desired accuracy is reached. When two successive values of x differ by less than an accuracy-check value ϵ, the desired accuracy has been attained.

It is suggested that the reader sketch a flow chart and write a program for determining the first nonzero root of Eq. 3-2, using the linear-interpolation method.

3-4. Newton-Raphson Method

This method is very useful for improving a first approximation to a root of an equation of the form $f(x) = 0$, which might have been obtained by trial and error, by an approximate graph of the function, or by some other means.

Consider the graph of $f(x)$ versus x, shown in Fig. 3-8, and assume that x_n is a first approximation of a root. If we draw a tangent line to the

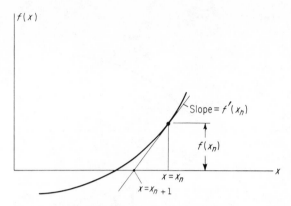

FIG. 3-8. Newton-Raphson method.

curve at $x = x_n$, the tangent line will intersect the x axis at a value x_{n+1}, which is an improved approximation to the root. It can be seen (Fig. 3-8) that the slope of the tangent line is

$$f'(x_n) = \frac{f(x_n)}{x_n - x_{n+1}} \tag{3-5}$$

from which

$$x_{n+1} = x_n - \frac{f(x_n)}{f'(x_n)} \tag{3-6}$$

The value of the function and the value of the derivative of the function are determined at $x = x_n$, and the new approximation to the root, x_{n+1}, is obtained by using Eq. 3-6. The same procedure is repeated, with the new approximation, to get a still-better approximation to the root. This continues until successive values of the approximate root differ by less than a prescribed small epsilon which controls the allowable error in the root.

EXAMPLE 3-3

Let us consider the rattrap shown in Fig. 3-9. The trap consists of a movable jaw, trip arm, torsion spring, and trip pan. Upon release of the trip arm owing to a slight disturbance of the trip pan, the torque of the torsion spring closes the movable jaw and annihilates the rat.

The relationship giving the angular displacement of the jaw as a function of time can be determined as[1]

$$\theta = \frac{T_0}{k}\left(1 - \cos\sqrt{\frac{k}{I_o}}\, t\right) \tag{3-7}$$

[1] The derivation is shown in Sec. 6-3.

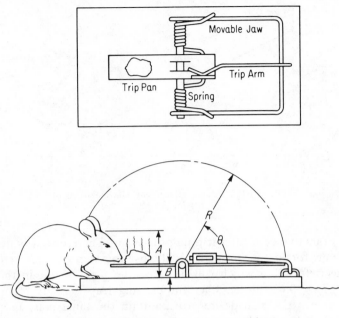

FIG. 3-9. Rattrap shown in open position.

where

θ = angular displacement of jaw from "set" position, radians
T_0 = torque exerted by spring on jaw at $\theta = 0$, lb-ft
k = torsional spring constant, lb-ft/radian
I_o = mass moment of inertia of jaw about axis of rotation, lb-ft-sec^2
t = time, sec

With the following trap dimensions ($A = 1.125$ in, $B = 0.5$ in., and $R = 3.75$ in.), we can determine that

θ_k = 2.97 radians or 170.4° (angular displacement of jaw upon contact with the rat)

θ_c = 3.27 radians or 187.7° (angular displacement of jaw in the closed position)

The torque T_0 is related to the spring constant by the relationship

$$T_0 = T_c + 3.27k \qquad (3\text{-}8)$$

as indicated in Fig. 3-10 where T_c is the torque when the jaw is in the unset or closed position ($\theta = 3.27$ radians).

The manufacturer of the trap has received complaints that the trap he is marketing closes too slowly (0.0382 sec to strike the rat) and allows

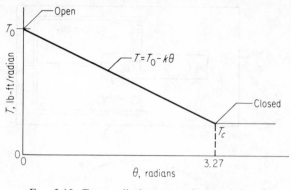

FIG. 3-10. Torque-displacement characteristic of
torsion spring.

too many rats to escape after tripping the trap. Therefore, it is desired to
install a new torsion spring which will close the trap on the rat twice as
quickly as before, but which will still have the same torque in the closed
position (T_c = 0.625 lb-ft), since the existing trap is easily set with this
initial torque. It is also desired to maintain the same mass moment of
inertia (0.0006 lb-ft-sec²) for the jaw, so that increased energy will also be
available in the new trap for killing the rat. The value of the new spring
constant is to be determined.

Observing these design requirements and utilizing the fact that θ =
2.97 radians when t = 0.0191 sec, Eq 3-7 can be put in the following form:

$$\frac{0.625 + 0.30k}{0.625 + 3.27k} - \cos \sqrt{\frac{k}{0.0006}} \, (0.0191) = 0 \qquad (3\text{-}9)$$

A value of k = 0 is obviously a root of this equation, but it yields a trivial
solution with no physical significance. The solution we desire is that given
by the first positive nonzero root.

Examination of Eq. 3-9 reveals that the function on the left-hand side
will initially be negative as the value of k increases from zero. Our method
of solution will involve increasing the value of k, in small increments, until
the function becomes positive, so that an approximate value of the root is
obtained, and then applying the Newton-Raphson method to get a more
accurate approximation.

The flow chart for this approach is shown in Fig. 3-11. A printout of
k and $f(k)$ is specified after each calculation of $f(k)$ merely to enable the
reader to follow the calculations in the computer printout of the solution,
shown at the end of this example. The FORTRAN variable names represent the problem quantities shown below.

Variable Name	Quantity	Data Values
SK	Spring constant k	
DELSK	Δk	0.2 lb-ft/radian
EPSI	Accuracy-check value	0.0001 lb-ft/radian
FOFK	$f(k)$ and $f(k_{n+1})$	
SK1	Improved value of spring constant	
A	Part of $f'(k)$	
B	Remaining part of $f'(k)$	
DFOFK	$f'(k)$	

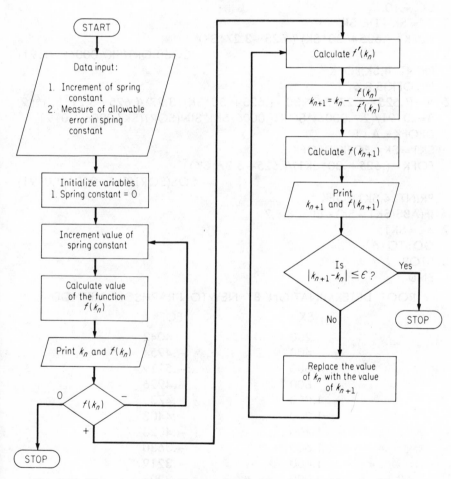

FIG. 3-11. Flow chart for half-time solution of rattrap problem by Newton-Raphson method.

The following **FORTRAN** program was used in obtaining the data output shown at the end of this example.

```
1 FORMAT(5X,43HROOT  DETERMINATION  BY  NEWTON-RAPHSON
                                            METHOD//)
2 FORMAT(4X,2HSK,5X,4HFOFK/)
3 FORMAT(F4.1,F7.4)
4 FORMAT(F7.3,F9.4)
  PRINT 1
  PRINT 2
  READ  3,DELSK,EPSI
  SK  =  0.
5 SK = SK + DELSK
  FOFK = (.625 + .30*SK)/(.625 + 3.27*SK)
                          - COS(SQRT(SK/.0006)*.0191)
  PRINT 4,SK,FOFK
  IF(FOFK)5,8,6
6 A = ((.625 + 3.27*SK)*.30 - (.625 + .30*SK)*3.27)/(.625 + 3.27*SK)**2
  B = .0191/(2.*.0006)*SQRT(.0006/SK)*SIN(SQRT(SK/.0006)*.0191)
  DFOFK = A + B
  SK1 = SK - FOFK/DFOFK
  FOFK = (.625 + .30*SK1)/(.625 + 3.27*SK1)
                          - COS(SQRT(SK1/.0006)*.0191)
  PRINT 4,SK1,FOFK
  IF(ABS(SK1 - SK) - EPSI)8,8,7
7 SK = SK1
  GO TO 6
8 STOP
  END
```

ROOT DETERMINATION BY NEWTON-RAPHSON METHOD

SK	FOFK
.200	−.4042
.400	−.4954
.600	−.5119
.800	−.4996
1.000	−.4736
1.200	−.4403
1.400	−.4028
1.600	−.3630
1.800	−.3219
2.000	−.2801
2.200	−.2381
2.400	−.1961

2.600	−.1544
2.800	−.1131
3.000	−.0723
3.200	−.0320
3.400	.0074
3.361	−.0000
3.361	.0000
STOP 0000	

The computer printout reveals how quickly the program converges to the desired solution after the initial approximation has been obtained, at which time the Newton-Raphson method is introduced. The desired spring constant is shown to have a value of 3.361 lb-ft/radian.

EXAMPLE 3-4

As another example of the Newton-Raphson method, let us consider the problem of relating the input and output crank angles of a 4-bar mechanism. These angles, θ and ϕ, respectively, are measured from the line of the fixed pivots, as shown in Fig. 3-12. The moving links are a, b, and c, and the fixed link is d. Considering the links as vectors, as indicated by the arrows shown in the figure, it follows that their vector sum must always be equal to zero, since they constitute a closed polygon. Setting the sum of the x components and the y components equal to zero, respectively, yields the following equations:

$$b \cos \beta - c \cos \phi + d + a \cos \theta = 0 \qquad (3\text{-}10)$$

$$b \sin \beta - c \sin \phi + a \sin \theta = 0 \qquad (3\text{-}11)$$

Solving Eqs. 3-10 and 3-11 for $b \cos \beta$ and $b \sin \beta$, respectively, and squaring both sides of the resulting equations yields

$$b^2 \cos^2 \beta = (c \cos \phi - d - a \cos \theta)^2 \qquad (3\text{-}12)$$

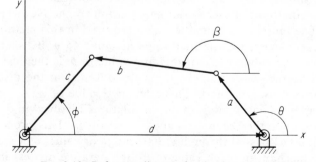

FIG. 3-12. Reference diagram for development of the relation between input and output crank angles of a 4-bar mechanism.

$$b^2 \sin^2 \beta = (c \sin \phi - a \sin \theta)^2 \qquad (3\text{-}13)$$

Adding Eqs. 3-12 and 3-13 gives

$$b^2 = c^2 + d^2 + a^2 - 2dc \cos \phi - 2ca \cos \phi \cos \theta$$
$$- 2ca \sin \phi \sin \theta + 2da \cos \theta \qquad (3\text{-}14)$$

Dividing both sides of Eq. 3-14 by $2ca$ and letting

$$R_1 = d/c$$
$$R_2 = d/a$$
$$R_3 = (d^2 + a^2 - b^2 + c^2)/2ca$$

we can write Eq. 3-14 in simpler form as

$$R_1 \cos \theta - R_2 \cos \phi + R_3 - \cos(\theta - \phi) = 0 \qquad (3\text{-}15)$$

This, known as *Freudenstein's* equation, is probably the most useful form of the relation between input and output crank angles of a 4-bar mechanism. It should be noted that this equation cannot be readily solved directly for ϕ as a single-valued function of θ.

Let us select a particular 4-bar mechanism so that R_1, R_2, and R_3 are defined, and program a computer solution of Eq. 3-15 which will yield the output angle ϕ for each corresponding input angle θ over the full range of motion of the mechanism, using successive values of θ varying by increments of 5°. If we select the following linkage dimensions,

$$a = \text{length of input crank} = 1 \text{ in.}$$
$$b = \text{length of coupler link} = 2 \text{ in.}$$
$$c = \text{length of output crank} = 2 \text{ in.}$$
$$d = \text{length of fixed link} = 2 \text{ in.}$$

the proportions of these dimensions define a *crank-and-lever* mechanism in which the input crank has 360° of motion while the output lever oscillates.

Our approach to the problem will consist of substituting successive values of θ into Eq. 3-15 and determining the root (the value of ϕ which satisfies the equation) of each resulting equation by the Newton-Raphson method. The initial approximation of ϕ required in this method may be obtained graphically, for the first value assigned to θ, by sketching the mechanism. The value of ϕ, for this first value of θ, is then calculated to the desired degree of accuracy by the steps outlined in the discussion of the Newton-Raphson method. This calculated value of ϕ_1 is then used as the initial approximation of ϕ_2 in the calculations involved in determining the value of ϕ for the second assigned value of θ. This procedure continues until θ has passed through a 360° range of values. For each position of the mechanism (each value of θ), the iterative process involved in converging on the root value continues until two successive values of ϕ

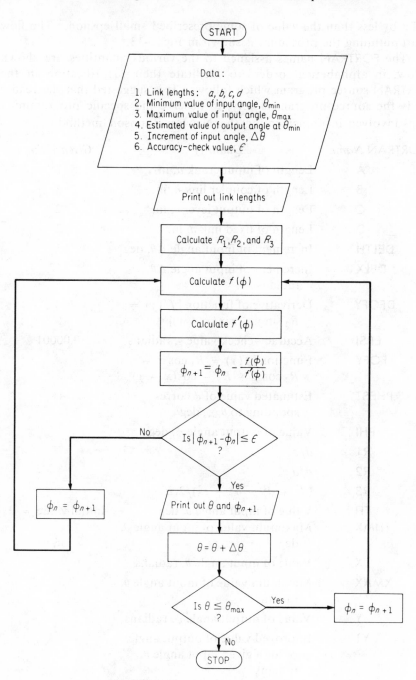

Fɪɢ. 3-13. Flow chart for Example 3-4.

differ by less than the value of some prescribed small epsilon. The flow chart outlining the procedure is shown in Fig. 3-13.

The FORTRAN names assigned to the various quantities are shown below, in alphabetical order, to facilitate their identification in the FORTRAN source program which follows. It is suggested that the reader study the source program closely, to observe the specific programming steps involved in implementing the Newton-Raphson method.

FORTRAN *Name*	*Quantity*	*Given Value*
A	Length of input crank a, in.	1
B	Length of coupler link b, in.	2
C	Length of output lever c, in.	2
D	Length of fixed link d, in.	2
DELTH	Increment of input angle $\Delta\theta$, deg	5
DELX	Increment of input angle $\Delta\theta$, radians	
DFOFY	Derivative of function $[f'(y) = R_2 \sin y - \sin(x - y)]$	
EPSI	Accuracy-check value ϵ, radians	0.00001
FOFY	Function $[f(y) = R_1 \cos x - R_2 \cos y + R_3 - \cos(x - y)]$	
PHEST	Estimated value of ϕ corresponding to θ_{min}, deg	41
PHI	Value of output angle ϕ, deg	
R1	d/c	
R2	d/a	
R3	$(d^2 + a^2 - b^2 + c^2)/2ca$	
TH	Value of input angle θ, deg	Initial value = 0
THMX	Maximum value of input angle θ, deg	360
X	Value of input angle θ, radians	
XMAX	Maximum value of input angle θ, radians	
Y	Value of output angle ϕ, radians	
Y1	Improved value of output angle ϕ, for a given input angle θ, radians	

```
   PRINT 1
 1 FORMAT (27X,26H4-BAR LINKAGE INPUT-OUTPUT//)
   PRINT 2
 2 FORMAT (24X,32HNEWTON-RAPHSON METHOD APPLIED TO)
   PRINT 3
 3 FORMAT (29X,21HFREUDENSTEIN EQUATION//)
   READ 4,A,B,C,D
 4 FORMAT (4F8.4)
   PRINT 5
 5 FORMAT (33X,13HLINK LENGTHS,)
   PRINT 6,A,B,C,D
 6 FORMAT (7X,4HA = ,F8.4,7X,4HB = ,F8.4,7X,4HC = ,F8.4,
                                       7X,3HD =,F8.4//)
   PRINT 7
 7 FORMAT (3X,5HTHETA,11X,3HPHI/)
   READ 28,TH,THMX,PHEST,DELTH,EPSI
28 FORMAT (2F6.1,F5.0,F5.1,F7.5)
   R1=D/C
   R2=D/A
   R3=(D*D+A*A−B*B+C*C)/(2.*C*A)
   XMAX=THMX*.0174533
   X=TH*.0174533
   Y=PHEST*.0174533
 8 FOFY=R1*COS(X)−R2*COS(Y)+R3−COS(X−Y)
   DFOFY=R2*SIN(Y)−SIN(X−Y)
   Y1=Y−FOFY/DFOFY
   IF(ABS(Y1−Y)−EPSI)10,10,9
 9 Y=Y1
   GO TO 8
10 TH=X/.0174533
   PHI=Y1/.0174533
   PRINT 11,TH,PHI
11 FORMAT (F10.5,5X,F10.5)
   DELX=DELTH*.0174533
   X=X+DELX
   IF(X−XMAX),12,12,13
12 Y=Y1
   GO TO 8
13 STOP
   END
```

4-BAR LINKAGE INPUT-OUTPUT
NEWTON-RAPHSON METHOD APPLIED TO
FREUDENSTEIN EQUATION
LINK LENGTHS,

A = +1.0000   B = +2.0000   C = +2.0000   D = +2.0000

THETA	PHI
.00000	41.40960
5.00000	43.13073
10.00000	44.95839
15.00000	46.88826
20.00000	48.91502
25.00000	51.03237
30.00000	53.23319
35.00000	55.50952
40.00000	57.85265
45.00000	60.25324
50.00000	62.70130
55.00000	65.18627
60.00000	67.69696
65.00000	70.22153
70.00000	72.74739
75.00000	75.26107
80.00000	77.74807
85.00000	80.19257
90.00000	82.57719
95.00000	84.88255
100.00000	87.08691
105.00000	89.16552
110.00000	91.09008
115.00000	92.82789
120.00000	94.34107
125.00000	95.58561
130.00000	96.51062
135.00000	97.05763
140.00000	97.16077
145.00000	96.74805
150.00000	95.74503
155.00000	94.08195
160.00000	91.70564
165.00000	88.59613
170.00000	84.78555
175.00000	80.37247
180.00000	75.52237

THETA	PHI
185.00000	70.44790
190.00000	65.37257
195.00000	60.49229
200.00000	55.94964
205.00000	51.82744
210.00000	48.15704
215.00000	44.93330
220.00000	42.12925
225.00000	39.70751
230.00000	37.62767
235.00000	35.85069
240.00000	34.34104
245.00000	33.06757
250.00000	32.00357
255.00000	31.12658
260.00000	30.41791
265.00000	29.86223
270.00000	29.44708
275.00000	29.16250
280.00000	29.00067
285.00000	28.95563
290.00000	29.02296
295.00000	29.19963
300.00000	29.48377
305.00000	29.87444
310.00000	30.37156
315.00000	30.97564
320.00000	31.68769
325.00000	32.50902
330.00000	33.44104
335.00000	34.48516
340.00000	35.64251
345.00000	36.91383
350.00000	38.29931
355.00000	39.79838
360.00000	41.40965
STOP 0000	

3-5. Newton's Second-Order Method

When it is necessary to determine very accurately the value of a root of an equation, Newton's second-order method has the advantage of converging rapidly to a solution, and an extremely close approximation of the value of the root may be obtained with a minimum of calculations. However, this method is limited, in a practical sense, to use on equations which have fairly simple higher-order derivatives (second-order, at least), since the time consumed in obtaining and programming involved derivatives outweighs the advantage of rapid convergence. This will be understood more clearly after the following discussion.

Consider, once again, an equation of the form

$$f(x) = 0$$

A graph of the function plotted against x is shown in Fig. 3-14. Suppose that an approximate value of the root, $x = x_n$, has been determined by

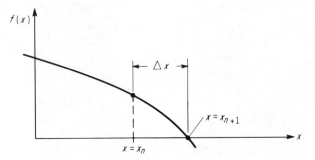

FIG. 3-14. Newton's second-order method.

some method such as a graphical approximation. Expanding $f(x)$ in a Taylor series about $x = x_n$ gives

$$f(x_{n+1}) = f(x_n) + f'(x_n)(\Delta x) + \frac{f''(x_n)(\Delta x)^2}{2!}$$
$$+ \frac{f'''(x_n)(\Delta x)^3}{3!} + \cdots \qquad (3\text{-}16)$$

If Δx were the particular increment of x which, added to x_n, would result in a zero value for the series, then the quantity $(x_n + \Delta x)$ would be the exact root. Since we are interested in a practical means of determining a value of Δx which will make the series sum to zero, let us set the right side of Eq. 3-16 equal to zero, using just 3 terms of the series. We obtain the approximate equality

$$f(x_n) + \Delta x \left[f'(x_n) + \frac{f''(x_n)(\Delta x)}{2} \right] = 0 \qquad (3\text{-}17)$$

A value of Δx determined from Eq. 3-17, when added to x_n, will not yield the exact value of the root, since only 3 terms of an infinite series were utilized in evaluating Δx. However, a much closer approximation to the value of the root will be obtained. Inspection reveals that Eq. 3-17 is a quadratic in Δx and can be solved as such. However, such a solution involves the problem of determining which root is the correct one. This can be avoided, at the cost of slightly slower convergence, by substituting the following expression (from Eq. 3-5) for the Δx ($\Delta x = x_{n+1} - x_n$) within the brackets of Eq. 3-17,

$$\Delta x = -\frac{f(x_n)}{f'(x_n)}$$

and writing Eq. 3-17 in the new form

$$f(x_n) + \Delta x\left[f'(x_n) - \frac{f''(x_n)f(x_n)}{2f'(x_n)}\right] = 0 \qquad (3\text{-}18)$$

Solving Eq. 3-18 for Δx, we obtain

$$\Delta x = -\left[\frac{f(x_n)}{f'(x_n) - \left(\dfrac{f''(x_n)f(x_n)}{2f'(x_n)}\right)}\right] \qquad (3\text{-}19)$$

Since $\Delta x = x_{n+1} - x_n$, we may rewrite Eq. 3-19 as

$$x_{n+1} = x_n - \left[\frac{f(x_n)}{f'(x_n) - \left(\dfrac{f''(x_n)f(x_n)}{2f'(x_n)}\right)}\right] \qquad (3\text{-}20)$$

which may be used to obtain successively closer approximations to a root by successive applications.

EXAMPLE 3-5

Let us determine the positive real root of the equation

$$2 \cos x - e^x = 0 \qquad (3\text{-}21)$$

Inspection of Eq. 3-21 reveals that it has an infinite number of negative real roots but only 1 positive real root. This can best be seen by sketching separately the graphs of $y_1 = 2 \cos x$ and $y_2 = e^x$, as shown in Fig. 3-15, and noting the intersection of the curves. The positive real root lies between $x = 0.5$ and $x = 0.6$. To demonstrate the rapidity of convergence of this method, even when the initial approximation is not too close, we will take $x = 0.4$ as a first approximation, and apply Eq. 3-20 successively until we obtain a solution of the desired accuracy. The results, calculated to 3 decimal places, are shown herewith.

x	$f(x) = 2\cos x - e^x$	$f'(x) = -2\sin x - e^x$	$f''(x) = -2\cos x - e^x$	$FR*$
$x_n = 0.4$	0.350	-2.270	-3.334	-0.139
$x_{n+1} = 0.539$	0.003	-2.741	-3.433	-0.001
$x_{n+2} = 0.540$	0.000			

*FR is the bracketed expression in Eq. 3-20.

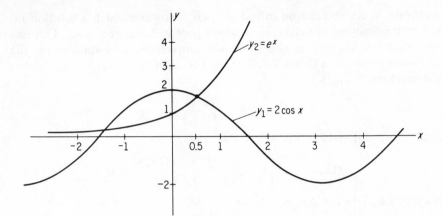

FIG. 3-15. Approximate location of the positive real root of the transcendental equation $2\cos x - e^x = 0$.

3-6. Graeffe's Root-Squaring Method

The analysis of certain types of physical systems involves the solution of polynomial equations of various degrees. The roots of second-degree polynomials are readily determined by the use of the quadratic formula. The roots of higher-degree polynomials are not so easily obtained. Various formulas exist for determining the roots of third- and fourth-degree polynomials, but, in general, they are difficult to apply. Graeffe's root-squaring method provides a general procedure for finding both real and complex roots of higher-degree polynomials.

To establish a background for the discussion of this method, let us review the general characteristics of the nth-degree polynomial

$$x^n + a_1 x^{n-1} + a_2 x^{n-2} + a_3 x^{n-3} + \cdots + a_n = 0 \qquad (3\text{-}22)$$

where the coefficients $a_1, a_2, \ldots, a_n$ are real numbers. For such a polynomial, the following facts apply:

1. There will be n roots.

2. There will always be at least 1 real root if n is an odd integer.

3. Descarte's rule states that the number of positive roots is equal to the number of sign changes of the coefficients *or* is less than this number by an *even* integer.

4. It is possible that equal roots exist.

5. When complex roots exist, they occur in conjugate pairs.

Graeffe's method for determining the roots of a polynomial is based upon the formation of a new polynomial, of the same degree as the original polynomial but having roots which are some large *even* power m of the roots of the original polynomial. The new polynomial will have relationships between its coefficients and its roots which may be solved to obtain the values of the roots. The roots of the original polynomial are then obtained by utilizing the exponential relationships existing between the roots of the *original* polynomial and the *derived* polynomial.

In developing Graeffe's method, let us first discuss a root-squaring procedure for obtaining a derived polynomial whose roots are the *negative* of some *even* power of the roots of the original polynomial. For the sake of simplicity, let us at present consider the third-degree polynomial

$$f(x) = 0 = x^3 + a_1 x^2 + a_2 x + a_3 \tag{3-23}$$

having the roots x_1, x_2, and x_3. A polynomial having the roots $-x_1$, $-x_2$, and $-x_3$ would be

$$f(-x) = 0 = -x^3 + a_1 x^2 - a_2 x + a_3 \tag{3-24}$$

Multiplying Eq. 3-23 by Eq. 3-24 yields

$$f(x)f(-x) = 0 = -x^6 + (a_1^2 - 2a_2)x^4 + (-a_2^2 + 2a_1 a_3)x^2 + a_3^2 \tag{3-25}$$

Letting $y = -x^2$, Eq. 3-25 may be written as

$$y^3 + (a_1^2 - 2a_2)y^2 + (a_2^2 - 2a_1 a_3)y + a_3^2 = 0 \tag{3-26}$$

Equation 3-26 is a *derived* polynomial of the same degree as the *original* polynomial of Eq. 3-23, and it has roots which are the *negative* of the squares of the roots of the original polynomial ($-x_1^2$, $-x_2^2$, and $-x_3^2$). If this root-squaring procedure is again applied, beginning with the derived polynomial of Eq. 3-26, another third-degree polynomial will be obtained whose roots will be the negative of the squares of the roots of the derived polynomial of Eq. 3-26 and, at the same time, the negative of the *fourth powers* of the roots of the original polynomial. Successive applications of the root-squaring process will thus yield successive derived polynomials having roots which are the negative of successively higher even powers m of the roots of the original polynomial.

If the root-squaring process is applied to an nth-degree polynomial, the derived polynomials will have the general form of

$$y^n + (a_1^2 - 2a_2)y^{n-1} + (a_2^2 - 2a_1 a_3 + 2a_4)y^{n-2}$$
$$+ (a_3^2 - 2a_2 a_4 + 2a_1 a_5 - 2a_6)y^{n-3} + \cdots + a_n^2 = 0 \quad \text{(a)}$$

or

$$y^n + \left\{ \begin{array}{l} a_1^2 \\ -2a_2 \end{array} \right\} y^{n-1} + \left\{ \begin{array}{l} a_2^2 \\ -2a_1 a_3 \\ +2a_4 \end{array} \right\} y^{n-2} + \left\{ \begin{array}{l} a_3^2 \\ -2a_2 a_4 \\ +2a_1 a_5 \\ -2a_6 \end{array} \right\} y^{n-3}$$
$$+ \cdots + a_n^2 = 0 \quad \text{(b)} \tag{3-27}$$

Inspection of Eq. 3-27 reveals that each coefficient of the polynomial being formed consists of the sum of the square of the corresponding coefficient in the preceding polynomial and twice each product which can be formed by multiplying coefficients that are symmetrically located on each side of the corresponding coefficient in the preceding polynomial. The signs of the product terms are alternately negative and positive.

Thus, when the coefficients of a given polynomial are substituted into Eq. 3-27, a new polynomial, having new coefficients and roots which are the negatives of the squares of the original polynomial, is obtained. If the coefficients of the derived polynomial are then, in turn, substituted into Eq. 3-27, still another derived polynomial, having roots which are the negatives of the squares of the roots of the polynomial from which it was derived, is obtained. These roots are, at the same time, the negatives of the fourth powers of the roots of the original polynomial, and so on. Each successive derived polynomial will have roots which are further and further apart in magnitude. This may be seen, for example, by considering an original polynomial with the roots 1, -2, and 4. After just 3 applications of Eq. 3-27, the last derived polynomial would have roots of -1, -256, and $-65,536$. The root-squaring process is terminated, in Graeffe's method, when the roots of the last derived polynomial are very widely separated. The separation necessary can be determined from the relationships observed between the values of corresponding coefficients in successively derived polynomials obtained in the root-squaring process. Such relationships, for various types of roots, will be studied later in this section.

Having now discussed the root-squaring process, which is an integral part of Graeffe's method, let us go on to the method itself. Three kinds of polynomials will be considered individually: 1) those having only real and distinct roots, 2) those whose real roots include equal roots, and 3) those whose roots include conjugate pairs of complex roots. Examples of third-degree polynomials having each type of roots are shown in Fig. 3-16.

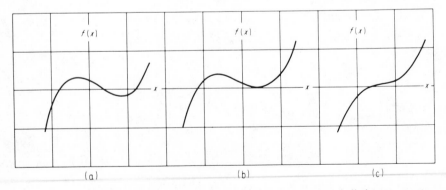

FIG. 3-16. Examples of third-degree polynomials. a) Real and distinct roots. b) Real and equal roots. c) Real and complex roots.

Real and Distinct Roots. Consider again the general third-degree polynomial

$$x^3 + a_1 x^2 + a_2 x + a_3 = 0 \tag{3-28}$$

which has the roots x_1, x_2, and x_3. Equation 3-28 may be expressed in factored form as

$$f(x) = 0 = (x - x_1)(x - x_2)(x - x_3)$$

Carrying out the multiplication indicated in the latter expression yields

$$x^3 - (x_1 + x_2 + x_3)x^2 + (x_1 x_2 + x_1 x_3 + x_2 x_3)x - x_1 x_2 x_3 = 0 \tag{3-29}$$

Comparing Eqs. 3-28 and 3-29, we obtain the following relationships between the coefficients and the roots of the polynomial:

$$
\begin{aligned}
a_1 &= -(x_1 + x_2 + x_3) \\
a_2 &= x_1 x_2 + x_1 x_3 + x_2 x_3 \\
a_3 &= -x_1 x_2 x_3
\end{aligned}
\tag{3-30}
$$

At this point, let us introduce the *Enke* roots of Eq. 3-28. The Enke roots of a polynomial are the *negatives* of the roots of the polynomial. Thus, letting r be the designation for an Enke root, we may write

$$
\begin{aligned}
x_1 &= -r_1 \\
x_2 &= -r_2 \\
&\cdots \\
x_n &= -r_n
\end{aligned}
$$

If these relationships are substituted into Eq. 3-30, the following relationships are obtained between the coefficients of the polynomial and its *Enke* roots:

$$
\begin{aligned}
a_1 &= r_1 + r_2 + r_3 \\
a_2 &= r_1 r_2 + r_1 r_3 + r_2 r_3 \\
a_3 &= r_1 r_2 r_3
\end{aligned}
\tag{3-31}
$$

Inspection of Eq. 3-31 reveals that all the relationships between the coefficients and the Enke roots are positive. Remembering that, in the root-squaring process, the derived polynomials have roots which are the *negatives* of even powers of the roots of the original polynomial ($-x_1^m$, $-x_2^m, \ldots, -x_n^m$), we see that the Enke roots of the derived polynomials will be $r_1^m, r_2^m, \ldots, r_n^m$, so that positive relationships will also exist between the coefficients and the Enke roots of the derived polynomials. Thus, the coefficients b_i, determined for successive derived polynomials in the root-squaring process, will always be positive (with one significant exception which will be discussed when complex roots are considered).

Let us return now to a consideration of the relationships given by Eq. 3-31. This set of simultaneous nonlinear algebraic equations would be difficult to solve. To avoid working with this set of equations, let us now consider the application of the root-squaring process in Graeffe's method. Applying the process to the original polynomial of Eq. 3-28 by repeated applications of Eq. 3-27, we determine a final derived polynomial

$$y^3 + b_1 y^2 + b_2 y + b_3 = 0 \qquad (3\text{-}32)$$

having the Enke roots r_1^m, r_2^m, and r_3^m. As pointed out, the derived polynomials have the same relationships between their roots and coefficients as those given for the original polynomial in Eq. 3-31, so that

$$
\begin{aligned}
b_1 &= r_1^m + r_2^m + r_3^m \\
b_2 &= r_1^m r_2^m + r_1^m r_3^m + r_2^m r_3^m \\
b_3 &= r_1^m r_2^m r_3^m
\end{aligned}
\qquad (3\text{-}33)
$$

For purposes of derivation, the *absolute* values of the roots of the original polynomial are considered to be related so that the Enke roots will have the relationship $|r_1| > |r_2| > |r_3|$. After sufficient applications of the root-squaring process, the Enke roots of the last derived polynomial will then be related by $r_1^m \gg r_2^m \gg r_3^m$. With the roots thus widely separated in magnitude, only the dominant terms of Eq. 3-33 need be retained, and we may write

$$
\begin{aligned}
b_1 &\cong r_1^m \\
b_2 &\cong r_1^m r_2^m \\
b_3 &= r_1^m r_2^m r_3^m
\end{aligned}
\qquad (3\text{-}34)
$$

where the approximations will be very close with m sufficiently large.

The expressions of Eq. 3-34 are easily solved for the Enke roots r_i^m. The roots of the original polynomial may then be obtained as

$$x_i = \pm (r_i^m)^{1/m}$$

The correct signs of the roots must be determined by substituting each possibility into the original polynomial and selecting the respective signs which allow the equation to be satisfied.

To determine the point at which the root-squaring process may be terminated, again consider Eq. 3-34. As stated earlier, these relationships between the coefficients and the roots of a derived polynomial exist only when the root-squaring process has been applied a sufficient number of times (when m has become large enough to develop dominant terms). The coefficients b_i shown are then the coefficients of the last derived polynomial which it is necessary to obtain. To determine when this point has been reached, consider *one more* application of the root-squaring process. Using the coefficients of Eq. 3-34 and applying Eq. 3-27, the coefficients

b'_i of the new polynomial will be

$$b'_1 = r_1^{2m} - 2r_1^m r_2^m$$
$$b'_2 = r_1^{2m} r_2^{2m} - 2r_1^{2m} r_2^m r_3^m \qquad (3\text{-}35)$$
$$b'_3 = r_1^{2m} r_2^{2m} r_3^{2m}$$

Considering the dominant terms of each of the new coefficients,

$$b'_1 \cong r_1^{2m}$$
$$b'_2 \cong r_1^{2m} r_2^{2m} \qquad (3\text{-}36)$$
$$b'_3 = r_1^{2m} r_2^{2m} r_3^{2m}$$

Comparing Eqs. 3-34 and 3-36, it can be seen that each new coefficient is essentially the square of the corresponding preceding coefficient. Thus, when m is sufficiently large to develop dominant terms, consecutive applications of the root-squaring process will yield coefficients with values such that *each* new coefficient obtained is essentially the square of the corresponding preceding coefficient, and the process may then be terminated. The relationship between consecutive values of a coefficient, just described, is known as a *regular* relationship and will be referred to as such subsequently.

The coefficient relationships just discussed provide not only the criteria for stopping the root-squaring process but also the information necessary to determine the type of roots to expect when solving a given polynomial. Sometimes the physical problem, from which the polynomial stems, will indicate the kind of roots contained in the root system of the polynomial. However, when little is known about what sorts of roots to expect from the polynomial being solved, the numerical relationships existing between the consecutive coefficients obtained in the root-squaring process will indicate what type, or types, of roots comprise the root system of the polynomial. In fact, as will be seen later, the relationships between consecutive coefficient values must be analyzed to determine each kind of root present before the root values can be determined. For example, if *all* the coefficients assume a regular relationship at the end of the root-squaring process, the polynomial being solved will be found to have all real and distinct roots, as was indicated by the relationships between Eqs. 3-34 and 3-36. However, when the root system of the polynomial being solved contains equal roots, complex roots, or combinations of all three types of roots, not all the coefficient relationships will be regular. The relationships which do exist will be discussed when the solutions of polynomials having such roots are taken up later.

In a manner similar to that detailed earlier for the specific case of a third-degree polynomial, it can be demonstrated that, for an nth-degree polymomial, the coefficients and Enke roots of the derived polynomials are related by[2]

$$b_1 = r_1^m + r_2^m + r_3^m + \cdots + r_n^m \qquad \text{(a)}$$

$$b_2 = (r_1 r_2)^m + (r_1 r_3)^m + \cdots + (r_1 r_n)^m + (r_2 r_3)^m$$
$$+ (r_2 r_4)^m + \cdots + (r_2 r_n)^m + \cdots + (r_{n-1} r_n)^m \qquad \text{(b)}$$

$$b_3 = (r_1 r_2 r_3)^m + (r_1 r_2 r_4)^m + \cdots + (r_1 r_2 r_n)^m$$
$$+ (r_2 r_3 r_4)^m + (r_2 r_3 r_5)^m + \cdots + (r_2 r_3 r_n)^m$$
$$+ \cdots + (r_{n-2} r_{n-1} r_n)^m \qquad \text{(c)}$$

$$\vdots$$

$$b_n = (r_1 r_2 r_3 \cdots r_n)^m \qquad \text{(d)}$$

$$(3\text{-}37)$$

After repeated applications of the root-squaring process, so that m is large enough to provide dominant terms, we may write (from Eq. 3-37), for polynomials having only real and distinct roots,

$$b_1 \cong r_1^m$$
$$b_2 \cong (r_1 r_2)^m$$
$$b_3 \cong (r_1 r_2 r_3)^m$$
$$b_4 \cong (r_1 r_2 r_3 r_4)^m$$
$$\cdots \cdots$$
$$b_n = (r_1 r_2 r_3 r_4 \cdots r_n)^m$$

$$(3\text{-}38)$$

Inspection of Eqs. 3-37 and 3-38 indicates that the coefficients of the derived polynomials will always be positive, since m is always an even power. (A significant exception occurs when complex roots are present, as will be seen later.)

From Eq. 3-38 we may write

$$r_1^m \cong b_1 \qquad\qquad r_1 \cong (b_1)^{1/m}$$

$$r_2^m \cong \frac{b_2}{b_1} \qquad\qquad r_2 \cong \left(\frac{b_2}{b_1}\right)^{1/m}$$

$$r_3^m \cong \frac{b_3}{b_2} \quad \text{or} \quad r_3 \cong \left(\frac{b_3}{b_2}\right)^{1/m}$$

$$\cdots \cdots \qquad\qquad \cdots \cdots$$

$$r_n^m \cong \frac{b_n}{b_{n-1}} \qquad\qquad r_n \cong \left(\frac{b_n}{b_{n-1}}\right)^{1/m}$$

$$(3\text{-}39)$$

The form of Eq. 3-39 is well suited for applying Graeffe's method on a digital computer, but logarithms are often used when the calculations are made on a slide rule, as will be seen in the following example.

[2]a) Sum of all Enke roots; b) all possible combinations of products of 2 Enke roots; c) all possible combinations of products of 3 Enke roots; ... d) product of all Enke roots.

EXAMPLE 3-6

In determining the roots of a polynomial having only real and distinct roots, let us consider the fourth-degree polynomial

$$x^4 - 6x^3 + 8x^2 + 2x - 1 = 0 \qquad (3\text{-}40)$$

To obtain a feeling for the root-squaring process, before reducing it to a computer routine, let us apply the procedure manually, utilizing a slide

	a_0^2	a_1^2 $-2a_2$	a_2^2 $-2a_1a_3$ $+2a_4$	a_3^2 $-2a_2a_4$	a_4^2
m	x^4	a_1x^3	a_2x^2	a_3x	a_4x^0
1	1	-6	8	2	-1
	1	36	64	4	1
		-16	24	16	
			-2		
2	1	20	86	20	1
	1	400	7396	400	1
		-172	-800	-172	
			2		
4	1	228	6598	228	1
	1	$5.20(10)^4$	$4360(10)^4$	$5.20(10)^4$	1
		$-1.32(10)^4$	$-10(10)^4$	$-1.32(10)^4$	
			2		
8	1	$3.88(10)^4$	$4352(10)^4$	$3.88(10)^4$	1
	1	$15.05(10)^8$	$18.95(10)^{14}$	$15.05(10)^8$	1
		$0.87(10)^8$	$----$	$0.87(10)^8$	
			$----$		
16	1	$14.18(10)^8$	$18.95(10)^{14}$	$14.18(10)^8$	1
	1	$2.05(10)^{18}$	$3.59(10)^{30}$	$2.05(10)^{18}$	1
		$----$	$----$	$----$	
			$----$		
32	1	$2.05(10)^{18}$	$3.59(10)^{30}$	$2.05(10)^{18}$	1

FIG. 3-17. Root-squaring table for Example 3-6.

rule for the computation. Equation 3-27 is applied to determine the coefficients of the successively derived polynomials.

To establish an orderly procedure, a table such as the one in Fig. 3-17 is prepared. At the top of the table the pertinent terms of Eq. 3-27, for the given polynomial, are listed for easy reference. The coefficients of the original polynomial are shown in the first row of the table under the appropriate powers of x. These coefficients are then used in Eq. 3-27 to determine the coefficients of a new polynomial having roots which are the negatives of the squares of the roots of the original polynomial ($m = 2$). These new coefficients are then used, in turn, to determine the coefficients of yet another derived polynomial ($m = 4$), and so on. The numerical values of the squared and product terms used to determine the new coefficients are displayed in that order in the respective columns immediately above the values of the new coefficients.

As shown in Fig. 3-17, the root-squaring process was terminated when $m = 32$, since, at this point, each new coefficient obtained was essentially the square of the corresponding preceding coefficient. Since *each* coefficient has a regular relationship, the root-squaring process indicates that all the roots are real and distinct. The coefficients of the last derived polynomial are thus

$$b_1 = 2.05(10)^{18}$$
$$b_2 = 3.59(10)^{30}$$
$$b_3 = 2.05(10)^{18}$$
$$b_4 = 1$$

From Eq. 3-39 we may write

$$\log r_1 = \frac{1}{m} \log b_1 = \frac{1}{32} [\log 2.05(10)^{18}] = 0.572$$

$$r_1 = \pm 3.73$$

Similarly,

$$\log r_2 = \frac{1}{m} [\log b_2 - \log b_1]$$

$$= \frac{1}{32} [\log 3.59(10)^{30} - \log 2.05(10)^{18}] = 0.383$$

$$r_2 = \pm 2.415$$

$$\log r_3 = \frac{1}{m} [\log b_3 - \log b_2]$$

$$= \frac{1}{32} [\log 2.05(10)^{18} - \log 3.59(10)^{30}] = -0.383$$

$$r_3 = \pm 0.413$$

$$\log r_4 = \frac{1}{m} [\log b_4 - \log b_3] = \frac{1}{32} [\log 1 - \log 2.05(10)^{18}] = -0.573$$

$$r_4 = \pm 0.268$$

Substituting the plus and minus values of each root into the original polynomial of Eq. 3-40, we find that the roots are

$$x_1 = 3.73$$
$$x_2 = 2.415$$
$$x_3 = -0.413$$
$$x_4 = 0.268$$

Descarte's rule, when applied to Eq. 3-40, predicts 1 or 3 positive roots, owing to the 3 sign changes in the equation. Note that 3 positive roots were obtained.

Real and Equal Roots.   In the preceding discussion it was found that, when all the roots of a polynomial are real and distinct, *all* the coefficients determined in the root-squaring process assume regular relationships. However, when 2 or more real and equal roots are part of the root system of a polynomial, the coefficient relationships obtained in the root-squaring process are not all regular. (Equal roots, in Graeffe's method, are considered to be roots which are equal in *absolute* value.)

To find the kind of relationships that do exist, let us again consider a third-degree polynomial—this one having all real roots, 2 of which are equal. The general relationships between the coefficients and the Enke roots of third-degree derived polynomials are given by Eq. 3-33 and are repeated here for convenience.

$$b_1 = r_1^m + r_2^m + r_3^m$$
$$b_2 = r_1^m r_2^m + r_1^m r_3^m + r_2^m r_3^m \qquad (3\text{-}41)$$
$$b_3 = r_1^m r_2^m r_3^m$$

If $|r_2| = |r_3|$ and the Enke roots are defined as being related by $|r_1| > |r_2| = |r_3|$, Eq. 3-41 becomes

$$b_1 = r_1^m + 2r_2^m$$
$$b_2 = 2r_1^m r_2^m + r_2^{2m} \qquad (3\text{-}42)$$
$$b_3 = r_1^m r_2^{2m}$$

When the root-squaring process has been repeated enough times so that dominant terms exist ($r_1^m \gg r_2^m = r_3^m$), a consideration of the dominant terms of Eq. 3-42 yields the following relationships:

$$b_1 \cong r_1^m$$
$$b_2 \cong 2r_1^m r_2^m \qquad (3\text{-}43)$$
$$b_3 = r_1^m r_2^{2m}$$

where the coefficients b_i are the coefficients of the last derived polynomial which it is necessary to obtain.

If we now consider *one more* application of the root-squaring process, using the coefficients of Eq. 3-43 and applying Eq. 3-27, we obtain the new coefficients

$$b_1' = r_1^{2m} - 4r_1^m r_2^m$$
$$b_2' = 4r_1^{2m} r_2^{2m} - 2r_1^{2m} r_2^{2m} \tag{3-44}$$
$$b_3' = r_1^{2m} r_2^{4m}$$

Considering only the dominant terms, we obtain

$$b_1' = r_1^{2m}$$
$$b_2' = 2r_1^{2m} r_2^{2m} \tag{3-45}$$
$$b_3' = r_1^{2m} r_2^{4m}$$

Comparing Eqs. 3-43 and 3-45, it can be seen that, when the root-squaring process terminates, 2 of the new coefficients (b_1' and b_3') are essentially the square of the corresponding preceding coefficients b_1 and b_3, whereas the new coefficient b_2' is essentially *one half* the square of b_2.

Thus, when the root-squaring process terminates, the presence of a coefficient whose final value is essentially one half the square of its preceding value indicates that the polynomial has 2 equal roots. Note that, with $|r_2| = |r_3|$ as initially assumed, the coefficient b_2 assumes the *half-squared* relationship just discussed.

If it had been assumed initially that $|r_1| = |r_2|$ in the preceding development, with $|r_1| = |r_2| > |r_3|$, the following relationships would have been obtained instead of those shown in Eq. 3-43:

$$b_1 = 2r_1^m$$
$$b_2 \cong r_1^{2m} \tag{3-46}$$
$$b_3 = r_1^{2m} r_3^m$$

In this case, one more application of the root-squaring process would show that the coefficient b_1 is the one which has a final value essentially equal to one half the square of its preceding value. Thus, in general, if the coefficient b_i has the half-squared relationship, the roots r_i and r_{i+1} will be the equal roots.

If a polynomial has 3 real and equal roots, the procedure used for the case of 2 equal roots will show that 2 of the coefficients will approach final values such that the last derived coefficients are *one third* of the square of the preceding ones, and that, if b_i and b_{i+1} are these coefficients, the roots r_i, r_{i+1}, and r_{i+2} will be the equal roots.

EXAMPLE 3-7

To solve a polynomial which has a pair of equal roots, let us consider the third-degree polynomial

$$x^3 + 3x^2 - 4 = 0 \qquad (3\text{-}47)$$

Utilizing Eq. 3-27 in the root-squaring process, the coefficient table of Fig. 3-18 is obtained. For convenience, the pertinent terms of Eq. 3-27 are listed at the top of the table. The first row shows the coefficients of the original polynomial, and the last row gives the coefficient values of the last derived polynomial with $m = 32$, at which point the root-squaring process was terminated.

Inspection of the table reveals that the coefficient b_1 terminates in a half-squared relationship, the last value of $88(10)^8$ being essentially one

	a_0^2	a_1^2 $-2a_2$	a_2^2 $-2a_1a_3$	a_3^2
m	x^3	a_1x^2	a_2x	a_3x^0
1	1	3	0	-4
	1	9	0	16
		0	24	
2	1	9	24	16
	1	81	576	256
		-48	-288	
4	1	33	288	256
	1	1089	$8.30(10)^4$	$6.56(10)^4$
		-576	$-1.69(10)^4$	
8	1	513	$6.61(10)^4$	$6.56(10)^4$
	1	$26.4(10)^4$	$43.7(10)^8$	$43(10)^8$
		$-13.2(10)^4$	$-0.7(10)^8$	
16	1	$13.2(10)^4$	$43.0(10)^8$	$43(10)^8$
	1	$174(10)^8$	$1850(10)^{16}$	$1850(10)^{16}$
		$-86(10)^8$	$----$	
32	1	$88(10)^8$	$1850(10)^{16}$	$1850(10)^{16}$

FIG. 3-18. Root-squaring table for Example 3-7.

half of the square of the preceding value of $13.2(10)^4$. This indicates that the roots r_1 and r_2 are the equal roots. The other 2 coefficients terminate in a regular relationship, indicating that the third root of the polynomial is real and distinct. Knowing that $|r_1| = |r_2|$ and that r_3 is real, we refer to the general coefficient-root relationships, given by Eq. 3-37, and substitute the fact that $r_1 = r_2$ into the given expressions. Considering only the dominant terms of the resulting expressions (by convention, we assume that $r_1^m = r_2^m \gg r_3^m$), we find that

$$b_1 \cong 2r_1^m$$
$$b_2 \cong r_1^{2m} \tag{3-48}$$
$$b_3 \cong r_1^{2m} r_3^m$$

Utilizing Eq. 3-48 and the coefficient values shown in Fig. 3-18, we find that

$$b_1 = (2r_1)^{32} \qquad = 88(10)^8$$
$$b_2 = (r_1)^{64} \qquad = 1850(10)^{16}$$
$$b_3 = (r_1)^{64}(r_3)^{32} = 1850(10)^{16}$$

The value of r_1 may be determined from the above relationship involving *either* b_1 or b_2, after which the value of r_3 is determined. These values are found to be

$$r_1 = r_2 = \pm 2$$
$$r_3 = \pm 1$$

Substituting the plus and minus values into the given polynomial of Eq. 3-47 determines that the roots of the polynomial are

$$x_1 = x_2 = -2$$
$$x_3 = 1$$

Complex Roots. When the root system of a polynomial contains complex roots, they occur in conjugate pairs. The presence of complex roots is indicated, in the root-squaring process, when the signs of 1 or more of the coefficients fluctuate during the calculations (1 coefficient will fluctuate in sign for each distinct conjugate pair present).

To investigate the procedure for determining the complex roots of a polynomial, let us consider a fourth-degree polynomial having 2 real and distinct roots x_1 and x_2, and a conjugate pair x_3 and x_4. Assuming that the roots of the complex pair have a magnitude of R, they may be expressed as

$$x_3 = Re^{i\theta} = R(\cos \theta + i \sin \theta) = u + iv$$
$$x_4 = Re^{-i\theta} = R(\cos \theta - i \sin \theta) = u - iv \tag{3-49}$$

where $i = \sqrt{-1}$ and $R = \sqrt{u^2 + v^2}$.

Referring to Eq. 3-37, we may write the following relationships between the coefficients and the Enke roots of the derived polynomials:

$$b_1 = r_1^m + r_2^m + R^m(e^{i\theta m} + e^{-i\theta m})$$

$$b_2 = (r_1 r_2)^m + (r_1 Re^{i\theta})^m + (r_1 Re^{-i\theta})^m + (r_2 Re^{i\theta})^m$$
$$+ (r_2 Re^{-i\theta})^m + R^{2m} \qquad (3\text{-}50)$$

$$b_3 = (r_1 r_2 Re^{i\theta})^m + (r_1 r_2 Re^{-i\theta})^m + (r_1 R^2)^m + (r_2 R^2)^m$$

$$b_4 = (r_1 r_2 R^2)^m$$

Utilizing the trigonometric relationships of Eq. 3-49 and simplifying, we may express Eq. 3-50 as

$$b_1 = r_1^m + r_2^m + 2R^m \cos m\theta$$

$$b_2 = (r_1 r_2)^m + 2R^m(r_1^m + r_2^m) \cos m\theta + R^{2m}$$

$$b_3 = 2(r_1 r_2 R)^m \cos m\theta + R^{2m}(r_1^m + r_2^m) \qquad (3\text{-}51)$$

$$b_4 = (r_1 r_2 R^2)^m$$

Again assuming that $|r_1| > |r_2| > |R|$, the root-squaring process will result in $r_1^m \gg r_2^m \gg R^m$, and only the dominant terms of Eq. 3-51 need be considered. This establishes the following relationships:

$$b_1 \cong r_1^m$$

$$b_2 \cong (r_1 r_2)^m$$

$$b_3 \cong 2(r_1 r_2 R)^m \cos m\theta \qquad (3\text{-}52)$$

$$b_4 = (r_1 r_2 R^2)^m$$

It is apparent, from the relationships of Eq. 3-52, that the sign of the coefficient b_3 will fluctuate owing to the trigonometric function $\cos m\theta$, since m is doubled each time a new coefficient value is determined in the root-squaring process. The sign fluctuations will not occur in a regular pattern, since successive values of $m\theta$ are not necessarily separated by π. However, sign fluctuations of successive values of a coefficient b_i occur *only* when complex roots exist, so the fluctuations, per se, are significant.

If b_3 is a coefficient with a fluctuating sign, the Enke roots r_3 and r_4 constitute a conjugate pair of complex roots. If the sign of b_2 fluctuates, the roots r_2 and r_3 comprise a complex pair. In general, then, if the sign of the coefficient b_i fluctuates, the roots r_i and r_{i+1} constitute a conjugate pair of complex roots.

Example 3-8

To solve a polynomial having a root system containing complex roots, let us consider the fourth-degree polynomial

$$x^4 + x^3 - 6x^2 - 14x - 12 = 0 \qquad (3\text{-}53)$$

Utilizing Eq. 3-27 in the root-squaring process, the table of Fig. 3-19 is obtained. For convenience, the pertinent terms of Eq. 3-27 are given at the top of the table. The first row shows the coefficients of the original polynomial, and the last row gives the coefficient values of the last derived polynomial with $m = 64$. The sign fluctuations evident in the column of b_3 values indicate that the roots r_3 and r_4 are complex. The regular relationships observed for the coefficients b_1 and b_2 indicate that the roots r_1 and r_2 are real and distinct.

To determine the magnitudes of the roots, we first consider the real and distinct roots r_1 and r_2. From Eq. 3-52 and the coefficient values in Fig. 3-19, we find that

$$r_1^{64} = b_1 = 3.42(10)^{30}$$

$$r_2^{64} = \frac{b_2}{b_1} = \frac{65.5(10)^{48}}{3.42(10)^{30}}$$

The magnitude or modulus of the complex roots is next determined as

$$R^{128} = \frac{b_4}{b_2} = \frac{11.3(10)^{68}}{65.5(10)^{48}}$$

Solving the preceding expressions, we find that

$$r_1 = \pm 3$$
$$r_2 = \pm 2$$
$$R = \pm 1.414 = \pm\sqrt{2}$$

Substituting the plus and minus values of r_1 and r_2 into the original polynomial determines that the real and distinct roots are

$$x_1 = 3 \quad \text{and} \quad x_2 = -2$$

We next determine the real part of each of the complex roots. Referring to Eq. 3-30, which illustrates the relationships between the coefficients and the roots of the original polynomial, we extend the first of these relationships to a fourth-degree polynomial and write

$$a_1 = -(x_1 + x_2 + x_3 + x_4) \tag{3-54}$$

With the roots x_1 and x_2 determined, the value of a_1 given in Eq. 3-53, and Eq. 3-49 showing that the sum of the roots x_3 and x_4 is $2u$, Eq. 3-54 may be written as

$$1 = -(3 - 2 + 2u)$$

from which

$$u = -1$$

The imaginary parts of the complex roots x_3 and x_4 may now be determined from the relationship

$$R^2 = u^2 + v^2$$

	a_0^2	a_1^2 $-2a_2$	a_2^2 $-2a_1a_3$ $+2a_4$	a_3^2 $-2a_2a_4$	a_4^2
m	x^4	$a_1 x^3$	$a_2 x^2$	$a_3 x$	$a_4 x^0$
1	1	1	-6	-14	-12
	1	1	36	196	144
		12	28	-144	
			-24		
2	1	13	40	52	144
	1	169	$16(10)^2$	$27.1(10)^2$	$2.07(10)^4$
		-80	$-13.5(10)^2$	$-115.2(10)^2$	
			$2.9(10)^2$		
4	1	89	$5.4(10)^2$	$-88.1(10)^2$	$2.07(10)^4$
	1	$79.2(10)^2$	$29.2(10)^4$	$77.7(10)^6$	$4.28(10)^8$
		$-10.8(10)^2$	$157.0(10)^4$	$22.3(10)^6$	
			$4.1(10)^4$		
8	1	$68.4(10)^2$	$190.3(10)^4$	$55.4(10)^6$	$4.28(10)^8$
	1	$46.8(10)^6$	$3.62(10)^{12}$	$30.7(10)^{14}$	$18.3(10)^{16}$
		$-3.8(10)^6$	$-0.76(10)^{12}$	$-16.3(10)^{14}$	
			$----$		
16	1	$43.0(10)^6$	$2.86(10)^{12}$	$14.4(10)^{14}$	$18.3(10)^{16}$
	1	$18.5(10)^{14}$	$8.2(10)^{24}$	$20.8(10)^{29}$	$3.36(10)^{34}$
		$----$	$-0.1(10)^{24}$	$-10.5(10)^{29}$	
			$----$		
32	1	$18.5(10)^{14}$	$8.1(10)^{24}$	$10.3(10)^{29}$	$3.36(10)^{34}$
	1	$3.42(10)^{30}$	$65.5(10)^{48}$	$106(10)^{58}$	$11.3(10)^{68}$
		$----$	$----$	$-54(10)^{58}$	
				$----$	
64	1	$3.42(10)^{30}$	$65.5(10)^{48}$	$52(10)^{58}$	$11.3(10)^{68}$

FIG. 3-19. Root-squaring table for Example 3-8.

so that

$$v = \sqrt{2 - 1} = 1$$

Thus, the roots of Eq. 3-53 are

$$x_1 = \quad 3$$
$$x_2 = -2$$
$$x_3 = -1 + i$$
$$x_4 = -1 - i$$

We have now found that the relationships between successive derived coefficient values, in the root-squaring process, indicate the type of roots composing the root system of the polynomial being solved and that, furthermore, the coefficient b_i having a particular relationship indicates which of the roots $r_i, r_{i+1}, \ldots, r_n$ are of the kind associated with that relationship.

Recalling how the coefficient relationships were developed for various types of roots, and realizing that many different combinations of root types are possible in higher-degree polynomials, it should be evident that one general rule for interpreting the results of the root-squaring process for any nth-degree polynomial is a practical impossibility. It is possible to formulate rules for particular combinations of roots—2 real and equal roots, 3 real and equal roots, equal pairs of complex roots, and so on—in the manner by which the coefficient relationships were developed for various types of roots in the preceding sections. This involved the assumption of a particular combination of root types, the substitution of the assumption into Eq. 3-37, and the consideration of the dominant terms resulting from the root-squaring process. The use of such rules should be predicated upon a thorough understanding of the process from which they are determined, since, once the procedure is understood, any combination of root types may be analyzed.

Programming Graeffe's Method.   It should now be evident that a *general* computer program for solving any nth-degree polynomial would involve very complex logic, since the program would have to be capable of *interpreting* the many combinations of coefficient relationships which might be encountered in the root-squaring process, before a solution could be obtained. Programming is further complicated by the possibility of encountering derived coefficient values having magnitudes which exceed the limits of the compiler being used. If the roots of the polynomial are fairly large, the coefficient values of the derived polynomials will obviously also be large (see Eq. 3-33). If several roots are very close in magnitude, the derived coefficient values also become very large, since more applications of the root-squaring process than usual must be made to establish dominant terms in the coefficient-root relationships. (If r_i and r_{i+1} are close in magnitude, m must be very large to make $r_i \gg r_{i+1}$.)

The problem of excessively large derived coefficient values can be alleviated by *scaling* the polynomial which is to be solved. However, the program logic required in writing a general program for obtaining complete solutions presents a challenge. Fortunately, a practical consideration of the solution of polynomials in certain engineering applications can often reduce this difficulty, to some extent. The polynomials which stem from various types of physical systems often have certain kinds of root systems which are characteristic of the system. For example, the polynomials defining the modes of free undamped vibration, in systems with various degrees of freedom, characteristically have real and distinct roots, since the roots of the polynomial yield the natural circular frequencies of vibration of the system. Thus, it can be seen that, if one were working in a particular area such as the one just described, a general computer program for determining the roots of polynomials known to have *only* real and distinct roots would be considerably less difficult to formulate.

Another practical approach may be made by combining human logic with a rather general program. The program is written so that the interpretation of the results of the root-squaring process can be supplemented by human logic. The computer process is interrupted at key points, and the programmer performs some degree of interpretation which is provided as input to the program at that point, after which the computer process is resumed.

In still another method, the computer performs the tedious task of determining the coefficients in the root-squaring process, after which the programmer interprets the tabulated results and performs the relatively easy job of determining the root values. An application of the last approach will be illustrated after we have discussed the scaling of a polynomial.

Scaling of Polynomials. As mentioned earlier, if the roots of a polynomial are large or if several of the roots are close together, very large coefficient values may be encountered in the root-squaring process. The scaling of such a polynomial will reduce the magnitude of the derived coefficient values so that they can be handled by many of the widely used compilers.

Consider the third-degree polynomial

$$x^3 + a_1 x^2 + a_2 x + a_3 = 0 \qquad (3\text{-}55)$$

having the roots x_1, x_2, and x_3 and the Enke roots r_1, r_2, and r_3.[3] The polynomial is scaled by scaling its roots, so, letting α be the *scale factor*,

---

[3]The coefficient a_0 of x^3 is unity in Eq. 3-55. If $a_0 \neq 0$ for the given polynomial, the first step in the scaling process is to reduce a_0 to unity by dividing each coefficient of the polynomial by a_0.

we write

$$x_1 = \alpha \bar{x}_1 \qquad\qquad r_1 = \alpha \bar{r}_1$$
$$x_2 = \alpha \bar{x}_2 \quad \text{and} \quad r_2 = \alpha \bar{r}_2 \qquad (3\text{-}56)$$
$$x_3 = \alpha \bar{x}_3 \qquad\qquad r_3 = \alpha \bar{r}_3$$

where the quantities with bars over them are the roots and the Enke roots, respectively, of the *scaled polynomial*. The relationships between the coefficients and the Enke roots of the scaled polynomial are

$$\bar{a}_1 = \bar{r}_1 + \bar{r}_2 + \bar{r}_3$$
$$\bar{a}_2 = \bar{r}_1\bar{r}_2 + \bar{r}_1\bar{r}_3 + \bar{r}_2\bar{r}_3 \qquad (3\text{-}57)$$
$$\bar{a}_3 = \bar{r}_1\bar{r}_2\bar{r}_3$$

Substituting the relationships of Eq. 3-56 into Eq. 3-57 yields

$$\alpha \bar{a}_1 = r_1 + r_2 + r_3$$
$$\alpha^2 \bar{a}_2 = r_1 r_2 + r_1 r_3 + r_2 r_3 \qquad (3\text{-}58)$$
$$\alpha^3 \bar{a}_3 = r_1 r_2 r_3$$

Comparing Eqs. 3-58 and 3-31, we see that the coefficients of the scaled polynomial $\bar{a}_i$ are related to the coefficients of the given polynomial by

$$\bar{a}_1 = a_1/\alpha, \qquad \bar{a}_2 = a_2/\alpha^2, \qquad \bar{a}_3 = a_3/\alpha^3 \qquad (3\text{-}59)$$

To determine a magnitude for the scale factor α, consider the relationships of Eq. 3-57. The final derived coefficient values, obtained by applying the root-squaring process to the scaled polynomial, may be kept to a minimum by letting the absolute value of the product of the scaled roots equal unity.[4] That is,

$$|\bar{r}_1\bar{r}_2\bar{r}_3| = 1$$

so that the absolute value of the scaled coefficient $|\bar{a}_3| = 1$. Since α is always positive, it can be seen, from the last relationship of Eq. 3-59, that the magnitude of the scale factor is determined from

$$\alpha = |a_3|^{1/3}$$

Having found the value of α from the above relationship, the other scaled-coefficient values may be determined from Eq. 3-59. This process yields a scaled polynomial

$$\bar{x}^3 + \frac{a_1}{\alpha} \bar{x}^2 + \frac{a_2}{\alpha^2} \bar{x} + 1 = 0 \qquad (3\text{-}60)$$

In general, for scaling an nth-degree polynomial,

$$\alpha = |a_n|^{1/n} \qquad (3\text{-}61)$$

and the scaled coefficients are

$$\bar{a}_i = a_i/\alpha^i \qquad (i = 1, 2, \ldots, n) \qquad (3\text{-}62)$$

---

[4] If $|\bar{r}_1\bar{r}_2\bar{r}_3| < 1$ were selected, $(\bar{r}_1\bar{r}_2\bar{r}_3)^m$ could become *small* enough to exceed the limit of the compiler.

After solving the scaled polynomial for the scaled Enke roots, by Graeffe's method, the Enke roots of the original polynomial are determined from Eq. 3-56. The roots of the given polynomial are then found by substituting the plus and minus values of the Enke roots into the original polynomial, as explained before.

Example 3-9

A general computer program for performing the root-squaring process for any nth-degree polynomial is to be written so that the original polynomials are scaled, as described above, before the root-squaring process is applied. (It might be well, at this point, for the reader to review Eqs. 3-27, 3-61, and 3-62, since these are the pertinent equations for scaling a polynomial and for applying the root-squaring process.)

The flow chart for the program is shown in Fig. 3-20. The FORTRAN variable names used and the quantities that they represent as as follows:

FORTRAN

Name	Quantity
N	Integer name for degree of polynomial
DEG	Real name for degree of polynomial
ITMAX	Number of iterations which the computer is to perform (number of applications of root-squaring process)
A(I)	Polynomial coefficients, scaled-polynomial coefficients, and derived coefficients before determining new derived coefficients
SCF	Scale factor used in scaling original polynomial
IT	Index of a DO loop controlling the number of iterations
M	Power of roots of original polynomial resulting from root-squaring process
S	Quantity having value of ± 1.0 used to control sign of product terms
K	Subscript of variable A
J	Subscript of variable A
SUM	Sum of products of coefficients
B(I)	Derived coefficients

Utilizing the flow chart of Fig. 3-20 as a guide, the following FORTRAN program is obtained, showing the specific steps necessary to get the derived coefficients of the scaled polynomial by the root-squaring process.

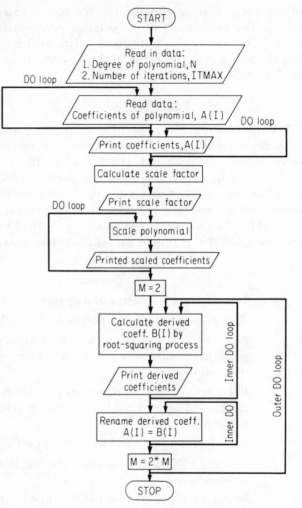

FIG. 3-20. Flow chart for root-squaring process.

```
   DIMENSION  A(10),B(10)
 1 FORMAT(2I3)
 2 FORMAT(E14.0)
 3 FORMAT(26HCOEFFICIENTS OF POLYNOMIAL/)
 4 FORMAT(//13HSCALE FACTOR=,E14.8)
 5 FORMAT(//20HDERIVED COEFFICIENTS)
 6 FORMAT(//30H   SCALED COEFFICIENTS   M=   1/)
 7 FORMAT(//11H   ITER. NO.,I3,5H   M=,I4/)
 8 FORMAT(4X,E14.8)
   READ 1,N,ITMAX
   DO9I=1,N
```

```
 9 READ  2,A(I)
   PRINT 3
   DO10I=1,N
10 PRINT 8,A(I)
   DEG=N
   SCF=ABS(A(N))**(1./DEG)
   PRINT 4,SCF
   PRINT 5
   PRINT 6
   DO 11I=1,N
   A(I) = A(I)/SCF**I
11 PRINT 8,A(I)
   M=2
   DO20IT=1,ITMAX
   PRINT 7,IT,M
   DO18I=1,N
   S=1.
   K=I
   J=I
   SUM=0.
12 K=K-1
   J=J+1
   IF(K)15,15,13
13 IF(J-N)14,14,17
14 S=S*(-1.)
   SUM=SUM+2.*S*A(K)*A(J)
   GO TO 12
15 IF(J-N)16,16,17
16 B(I)=A(I)**2+SUM-2.*S*A(J)
   GO TO 18
17 B(I)=A(I)**2+SUM
18 PRINT 8,B(I)
   DO19I=1,N
19 A(I)=B(I)
20 M=2*M
   STOP
   END
```

This program is capable of handling polynomials of any reasonable degree. The degree of the particular polynomial under consideration is specified in the program by an input data value assigned to N. The dimension statement also reflects the degree of the polynomial being considered, since the higher the degree of the polynomial, the more memory space must be reserved for storing coefficient values. (The dimension statement in the program shown has reserved memory space for handling up to and including a 10th-degree polynomial.)

The value assigned to ITMAX specifies the number of times the root-squaring process is to be applied. (Note its use as the *test value* of a DO statement.) For most polynomials, 6 iterations ($m = 64$) are usually sufficient to establish the regular, half-squared, or fluctuating sign relationships of the derived coefficients. However, since the computing time of each iteration is small, additional iterations could be made to obviate any chance of terminating the root-squaring process too soon. In this event, some provision should be made for checking for overflow, if the compiler being used does not contain such a check.

Note that the program specifies that the printout of the coefficient values is to be in column form rather than in rows, as shown in preceding discussions. This is done to avoid exceeding the limit of characters allowable in a given row for the printout device, in case a polynomial of high degree is handled.

EXAMPLE 3-10

The program of the preceding example will be used to provide a root-squaring table for the sixth-degree polynomial

$$x^6 - 1389x^4 + 5(10)^5 x^2 - 37.1(10)^6 = 0 \qquad (3\text{-}63)$$

The computer printout of the table is displayed in the 2 columns shown:

COEFFICIENTS OF POLYNOMIAL

.00000000E − 99
−.13890000E + 04
.00000000E − 99
.50000000E + 06
.00000000E − 99
−.37100000E + 08

SCALE FACTOR = .18262583E + 02

DERIVED COEFFICIENTS

SCALED COEFFICIENTS M = 1

.00000000E − 99
−.41646436E + 01
.00000000E − 99
.44949125E + 01
.00000000E − 99
−.10000017E + 01

ITER. NO. 1 M = 2

.83292872E + 01
.26334081E + 02

.39439420E + 02
.28533539E + 02
.89898402E + 01
.10000034E + 01

ITER. NO. 2 M = 4

.16708863E + 02
.93546408E + 02
.20041670E + 03
.15772302E + 03
.23749954E + 02
.10000068E + 01

ITER. NO. 3 M = 8

.92093290E + 02
.23689061E + 04
.11449679E + 05
.15543871E + 05
.24861213E + 03
.10000136E + 01

ITER. NO. 4 M= 16

.37433618E+04
.35339266E+07
.57496988E+08
.23592360E+09
.30719827E+05
.10000272E+01

ITER. NO. 5 M= 32

.69449040E+07
.12058644E+14
.16384305E+16
.55656413E+17
.47184774E+09
.10000544E+01

ITER. NO. 6 M= 64

.24114403E+14
.14538814E+27
.13421728E+31
.30976363E+34
.11132141E+18
.10001088E+01

ITER. NO. 7 M= 128

.29072815E+27
.21137711E+53
.90070870E+60
.95953506E+67
.61965100E+34
.10002176E+01

STOP 0000

Inspection of the printout reveals that no coefficients have fluctuating signs, so all the roots of the polynomial are real. Further examination of the coefficient values in the last 2 iterations reveals the following relationships between corresponding coefficients:

$$\bar{b}_1' \simeq \frac{(\bar{b}_1)^2}{2}$$

$$\bar{b}_2' \simeq (\bar{b}_2)^2$$

$$\bar{b}_3' \simeq \frac{(\bar{b}_3)^2}{2}$$

$$\bar{b}_4' \simeq (\bar{b}_4)^2 \qquad (3\text{-}64)$$

$$\bar{b}_5' \simeq \frac{(\bar{b}_5)^2}{2}$$

$$\bar{b}_6' = (\bar{b}_6)^2$$

Equation 3-64 indicates the 3 pairs of equal roots

$$\bar{r}_1 = \bar{r}_2 \qquad \bar{r}_3 = \bar{r}_4 \qquad \bar{r}_5 = \bar{r}_6$$

Utilizing these relationships in Eq. 3-37, we find that

$$\left.
\begin{aligned}
\bar{b}_1 &= 2\bar{r}_1^m + 2\bar{r}_3^m + 2\bar{r}_5^m \\
\bar{b}_2 &= \bar{r}_1^{2m} + 2(\bar{r}_1\bar{r}_3)^m + 2(\bar{r}_1\bar{r}_6)^m + 2(\bar{r}_2\bar{r}_3)^m + \cdots + r_5^{2m} \\
\bar{b}_3 &= 2\bar{r}_1^{2m}\bar{r}_3^m + 2\bar{r}_1^{2m}\bar{r}_5^m + \cdots + \bar{r}_4^m\bar{r}_5^{2m} \\
\bar{b}_4 &= \bar{r}_1^{2m}\bar{r}_3^{2m} + 2\bar{r}_1^{2m}\bar{r}_3^m\bar{r}_5^m + 2\bar{r}_2^m\bar{r}_3^{2m}\bar{r}_5^m + r_3^{2m}r_5^{2m} \\
\bar{b}_5 &= 2\bar{r}_1^{2m}\bar{r}_3^{2m}\bar{r}_5^m + \bar{r}_2^m\bar{r}_3^{2m}\bar{r}_5^{2m} \\
\bar{b}_6 &= \bar{r}_1^{2m}\bar{r}_3^{2m}\bar{r}_5^{2m}
\end{aligned}
\right\} \qquad (3\text{-}65)$$

Considering the dominant terms $(r_1^m = r_2^m \gg r_3^m = r_4^m \gg r_5^m = r_6^m)$, we obtain

$$\bar{b}_1 \cong 2\bar{r}_1^m$$
$$\bar{b}_2 \cong \bar{r}_1^{2m}$$
$$\bar{b}_3 \cong 2\bar{r}_1^{2m}\bar{r}_3^m$$
$$\bar{b}_4 \cong \bar{r}_1^{2m}\bar{r}_3^m\bar{r}_4^m \qquad\qquad (3\text{-}66)$$
$$\bar{b}_5 \cong 2\bar{r}_1^{2m}\bar{r}_3^{2m}\bar{r}_5^m$$
$$\bar{b}_6 = \bar{r}_1^{2m}\bar{r}_3^{2m}r_5^{2m}$$

Using the coefficient values of the last iteration in the table, we solve Eq. 3-66 for the Enke roots of the scaled polynomial and obtain

$$\bar{r}_1 = \pm 1.6$$
$$\bar{r}_3 = \pm 1.141$$
$$\bar{r}_5 = \pm 0.548$$

Noting (in the printout) that $\alpha = 18.2625$, Eq. 3-56 is next utilized to determine the value of the Enke roots of the original polynomial. Thus,

$$r_1 = 18.2625(\pm 1.6) = \pm 29.2$$
$$r_3 = 18.2625(\pm 1.141) = \pm 20.8$$
$$r_5 = 18.2625(\pm 0.548) = \pm 10$$

Substituting the plus and minus values obtained into the original polynomial, we find that the polynomial is satisfied for both signs of each coefficient, so the roots of the polynomial are

$$x_1 = +29.2$$
$$x_2 = -29.2$$
$$x_3 = +20.8$$
$$x_4 = -20.8$$
$$x_5 = +10$$
$$x_6 = -10$$

Problems

3-1. Using the trial-and-error method, write a program for determining the first 3 positive nonzero roots of the transcendental equation

$$\cos x \cosh x = 1$$

3-2. Using the Newton-Raphson method, write a program for determining the first 3 positive nonzero roots of the transcendental equation

$$\cos x \cosh x = 1$$

3-3. Using the trial-and-error method, write a program for determining the first 3 positive roots of the transcendental equation

$$\cos x \cosh x = -1$$

3-4. Using the Newton-Raphson method, write a program for determining the first 4 positive roots of the transcendental equation

$$\cos x \cosh x = -1$$

3-5. The frequency equation of the vibrating beam shown in the accompanying figure is

$$\cos kl \cosh kl = -1$$

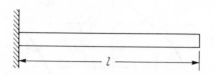

PROB. 3-5

where

$$k^2 = \frac{p}{a}$$

$$a^2 = \frac{EIg}{A\gamma}$$

p = natural circular frequency of beam, radians/sec
l = 120 in. (length of beam)
I = 170.6 in.^{4} (area moment of inertia of beam)
E = 3(10)^6 lb/in.^{2} (elastic modulus of beam material)
γ = 0.066 lb/in.^{3} (density of beam material)
A = 32 in.^{2} (cross-sectional area of beam)
g = acceleration of gravity, in./sec^2

Write a program for determining the natural circular frequency of the beam, for each of the first 3 modes of vibration, by a) the Newton-Raphson method and b) the trial-and-error method.

3-6. By Newton's second-order method, write a program for determining the nonzero root of the transcendental equation

$$2x^2 + 1 - e^x = 0$$

3-7. Using Newton's second-order method, write a program for determining the positive root of the transcendental equation

$$x^2 + 1 - 2e^{-x} = 0$$

3-8. Example 3-4 illustrated the application of the Newton-Raphson method in solving Freudenstein's equation. This method was used in the example to determine the angle ϕ which the output crank of a 4-bar mechanism made with the line of fixed points for each corresponding angle θ which the input crank made with the same line.

Write a computer program, patterned after the one shown in Example 3-4 but using Newton's second-order method for solving Freudenstein's equation.

3-9. The frequency equations for elastic beams with various boundary conditions may be found in most texts in the field of vibrations. The frequency equa-

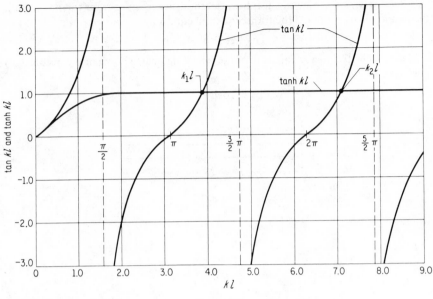

tion for a cantilever beam of length l, fixed at $x = 0$ and pinned at $x = l$, is

$$\tan kl = \tanh kl$$

By determining the real positive roots of this equation, the natural circular frequencies p of the various beam modes may be determined from the relation

$$p = k^2 \sqrt{\frac{EI}{\gamma}}$$

where

    E = modulus of elasticity of beam
    I = moment of inertia of cross section of beam
    γ = mass of beam per unit length

Write a **FORTRAN** program for determining the first 3 real positive roots of the given frequency equation and the associated natural circular frequencies. Approximate values of the first 2 real positive roots are shown in the accompanying figure.

3-10. Determine the first nonzero positive root of the transcendental equation

$$\tan kl = kl.$$

Plot the functions as was done in the figure of Prob. 3-9.

3-11. An interesting problem in space dynamics involves the interception and rendezvous of 2 vehicles orbiting the earth. One of the simplest cases is concerned with the rendezvousing of 2 vehicles which are initially orbiting in the same circular orbit.

Referring to the figure accompanying this problem, it can be seen that

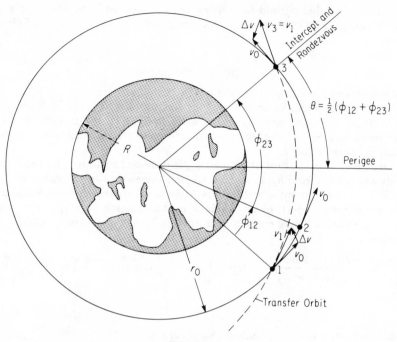

$$\theta = \tfrac{1}{2}(\phi_{12} + \phi_{23})$$

PROB. 3-11

vehicles 1 and 2 are moving in a circular orbit of radius r_o, each with a velocity v_o. Vehicle 2 is leading vehicle 1 by the angle ϕ_{12}, as shown. If vehicle 1 is to intercept vehicle 2 at some position 3, vehicle 1 must be transferred into a new orbit (usually hyperbolic), as indicated by the dashed line in the figure. Vehicle 1 is placed in the transfer orbit by an impulsive thrust which causes the velocity increment Δv. The velocity v_1 of vehicle 1 on the transfer orbit is the vector sum of v_o and Δv, as shown. At position 3, vehicle 1 is given another impulsive thrust, causing a resulting Δv such that vehicle 1 again assumes a velocity v_o in the same direction as the velocity of vehicle 2, and the two vehicles move off together.

To determine Δv at either position 1 or position 3, for given values of r_o, ϕ_{12}, and ϕ_{23}, the eccentricity e of the transfer orbit must be known. This eccentricity is determined from the fact that the time t_{23} for vehicle 2 to move to position 3 must equal the time t_{13} for vehicle 1 to move to position 3. Using the equations of motion of a body in a central force field, and the geometry of conic sections, the transcendental equation resulting from making $t_{13} = t_{23}$ is

$$\frac{\pi \phi_{23}}{360} = \sqrt{\left(\frac{1 + e \cos \theta}{e^2 - 1}\right)^3}\left[\frac{e \sqrt{e^2 - 1}}{1 + e \cos \theta} \sin \theta - \ln\left(\frac{\sqrt{e + 1} + \sqrt{e - 1} \tan \dfrac{\theta}{2}}{\sqrt{e + 1} - \sqrt{e - 1} \tan \dfrac{\theta}{2}}\right)\right]$$

$$(e > 1)$$

where $\theta = (\phi_{12} + \phi_{23})/2$, and a hyperbolic transfer orbit has been used.

Select a suitable method for solving the transcendental equation for e, and write a general **FORTRAN** program for obtaining values of e for the following data:

$$\phi_{12} = 30°$$

$$\phi_{23} = 20°, 30°, 40°, \text{ and } 50°$$

The eccentricity e will be greater than 1 for hyperbolic orbits.

3-12. (The background material for this problem is given in Prob. 3-11.) When $20° \le \phi_{23} \le 50°$ and $\phi_{12} = 30°$, as in Prob. 3-11, the transfer orbits are hyperbolic, and the transcendental equation for such transfer orbits is satisfied by values of e greater than 1.

However, if ϕ_{12} is kept at $30°$ and ϕ_{23} is increased to above $50°$, the transfer orbits will change from hyperbolic to elliptic, somewhere in the range of $55° < \phi_{23} < 75°$. At this point it will be impossible to satisfy the transcendental equation, given in Prob. 3-11, by any value of e. An equation for elliptic orbits must then be used to obtain the required eccentricity of the elliptic transfer orbits. This equation is

$$\frac{\pi \phi_{23}}{360} = \left(\frac{1 + e \cos \theta}{1 - e^2} \right)^{3/2} \left[2 \tan^{-1} \left(\sqrt{\frac{1 - e}{1 + e}} \tan \frac{\theta}{2} \right) - \frac{e \sqrt{1 - e^2} \sin \theta}{1 + e \cos \theta} \right]$$

$$(e < 1)$$

and, as indicated, is satisfied only for values of $e \le 1$.

Thus, to write a general **FORTRAN** program for determining the eccentricity of the transfer orbits for the data

$$\phi_{12} = 30°$$

$$20° \le \phi_{23} \le 120° \qquad \text{(use } 10° \text{ increments)}$$

it will be necessary to utilize both the equation given in Prob. 3-11 and the equation given above.

Write a general **FORTRAN** program for determining the eccentricity of the transfer orbits for the range of data given. (HINT: Since $e < 1$ for elliptic orbits and is thus bounded by 0 and 1, while e may approach infinity for hyperbolic orbits, begin with $\phi_{23} = 120°$ and then decrease by $10°$ increments. Use a trial-and-error method.)

In Probs. 3-13 through 3-16, both negative and positive real roots may be present. Write a computer program for determining, by the methods specified, the value of all the roots. All root values of these polynomials are less than 10 in absolute magnitude.

3-13. Determine the roots of the polynomial

$$x^4 - 10x^3 + 35x^2 - 50x + 24 = 0$$

a) by the trial-and-error method and b) by Newton's second-order method.

3-14. Determine the roots of the polynomial

$$x^5 - 9x^4 + 25x^3 - 5x^2 - 26x + 24 = 0$$

a) by the trial-and-error method and b) by the Newton-Raphson method. c) Compare the computing times for the two methods.

3-15. Determine the roots of the polynomial

$$x^5 - 15x^4 + 85x^3 - 225x^2 + 274x - 120 = 0$$

a) by the trial-and-error method and b) by the linear-interpolation method.

3-16. Determine the roots of the polynomial

$$x^4 - 5x^2 + 4 = 0$$

a) by the trial-and-error method and b) by Newton's second-order method. c) Compare the computing times for the two methods.

3-17. The roots of the polynomial

$$x^5 - 3x^4 - 23x^3 + 55x^2 + 74x - 120 = 0$$

consist of both positive and negative real roots. Write a computer program for obtaining a quick approximation of the graph of the function, and then write a program for determining the roots of the polynomial, using the information from the graph obtained to make the root-determining program as efficient as possible with respect to machine time. Use the trial-and-error method.

In Probs. 3-18 through 3-25, utilize the computer program, Example 3-9, to determine the Graeffe table for the given polynomial. After computing the table, determine, by use of a slide rule, the roots of the polynomial.

3-18. $x^4 - 5x^3 + 13x^2 - 19x + 10 = 0$

3-19. $x^5 - 2x^4 - 2x^3 + 20x^2 - 47x + 30 = 0$

3-20. $x^6 + x^5 - 8x^4 + 14x^3 + 13x^2 - 111x + 90 = 0$

3-21. $x^4 - 6x^3 + 29x^2 - 52x + 80 = 0$

3-22. $x^4 - 2x^3 + 3x^2 + 4x + 4 = 0$

3-23. $x^8 + x^7 - 9x^6 + 13x^5 + 21x^4 - 125x^3$

$$+ 77x^2 + 111x - 90 = 0$$

3-24. $x^6 - 8x^5 + 25x^4 - 32x^3 - x^2 + 40x - 25 = 0$

3-25. $x^8 - 7x^7 + 11x^6 + 41x^5 - 183x^4$

$$+ 231x^3 + 21x^2 - 265x + 150 = 0$$

chapter 4

Solution of Simultaneous Linear Algebraic Equations

4-1. Introduction

Engineers frequently encounter problems involving the solution of sets of simultaneous linear algebraic equations. Such problems arise in the areas of elasticity, electrical-circuit analysis, heat transfer, vibrations, and so on. We shall see later that the numerical integration of some types of ordinary and partial differential equations may be reduced to the solution of such a set of equations.

From a study of algebra, we are familiar with two common methods of solving simultaneous equations: the elimination of unknowns by combining equations, and the use of determinants (Cramer's rule). When three simultaneous equations are to be solved, Cramer's rule appears to have an advantage over the elimination method. However, the method of determinants with expansion by minors is completely impractical when large numbers of equations must be solved simultaneously. Forsythe[1] points out that the solution of n simultaneous equations by Cramer's rule, evaluating determinants in the usual manner of expansion by minors, requires $(n - 1)(n + 1)!$ multiplications. Thus, the solution of 10 simultaneous equations by determinants would require 359,251,200 multiplications. With the multiplications performed on the computer at the rate of 2600 per second, approximately 38 hr would be required to obtain a solution. For $n = 26$, $3(10)^{18}$ *years* would be required to obtain a solution. Yet in some engineering problems it may be necessary to solve hundreds, or even thousands, of simultaneous equations. Obviously, a solution involving the use of determinants with expansion by minors is not practical.

---

[1]Beckenbach, Edwin F., ed. *Modern Mathematics for the Engineer*, University of California Engineering Extension Series. New York: McGraw-Hill Book Company, 1956, p. 436.

In this chapter we shall consider the solution of both *homogeneous* and *nonhomogeneous* sets of linear algebraic equations, since both types appear in engineering problems. The sets of equations with which we shall be concerned will involve n equations in n unknowns having the general form

$$
\left.
\begin{aligned}
a_{11}x_1 + a_{12}x_2 + \cdots + a_{1n}x_n &= C_1 \quad \text{(a)} \\
a_{21}x_1 + a_{22}x_2 + \cdots + a_{2n}x_n &= C_2 \quad \text{(b)} \\
\vdots \qquad \vdots \qquad\qquad \vdots \qquad \vdots \\
a_{n1}x_1 + a_{n2}x_2 + \cdots + a_{nn}x_n &= C_n
\end{aligned}
\right\} \quad (4\text{-}1)
$$

If the C's are not all zero, the set of equations is *nonhomogeneous*, and we will find that all the equations must be independent to obtain *unique* solutions. If the C's are all zero, the set of equations is *homogeneous*, and we will find that *nontrivial* solutions exist only if all the equations are *not* independent.

The *coefficient matrix* of the set of equations in Eq. 4-1 is

$$
\mathbf{A} =
\begin{bmatrix}
a_{11} & a_{12} \cdots a_{1n} \\
a_{21} & \cdots\cdots a_{2n} \\
\vdots & \vdots \\
a_{n1} & \cdots\cdots a_{nn}
\end{bmatrix}
\quad (4\text{-}2)
$$

A comparison of Eqs. 4-1 and 4-2 shows that a coefficient matrix is a matrix whose elements are the coefficients of the unknowns in the set of equations. If the constants of Eq. 4-1 are added to the coefficient matrix as a column of elements in the position shown in Eq. 4-3, the *augmented matrix* of Eq. 4-1 is formed as

$$
\mathbf{B} =
\begin{bmatrix}
a_{11} & a_{12} \cdots a_{1n} & C_1 \\
a_{21} & a_{22} \cdots a_{2n} & C_2 \\
\vdots & & \vdots \\
a_{n1} & \cdots\cdots a_{nn} & C_n
\end{bmatrix}
\quad (4\text{-}3)
$$

In many instances in computer programming, it may be found convenient to express the column of C's (the constants) as simply an additional column of a_{ij}'s. In such an instance the matrix of Eq. 4-3 might be expressed as

$$
\mathbf{B} =
\begin{bmatrix}
a_{11} & a_{12} \cdots a_{1n} & a_{1,n+1} \\
a_{21} & a_{22} \cdots a_{2n} & a_{2,n+1} \\
\vdots & & \vdots \\
a_{n1} & \cdots\cdots a_{nn} & a_{n,n+1}
\end{bmatrix}
\quad (4\text{-}4)
$$

This form will be used in the discussions in the sections to follow.

We shall first consider the solution of nonhomogeneous equations, and four methods commonly used on the computer will be discussed. Since a nonhomogeneous set of equations, such as Eq. 4-1, describing a physical system, generally consists of linearly independent equations, it will be assumed that such is the case for the sets of equations considered, so that unique solutions exist. A unique solution exists for such a set of simultaneous equations if the coefficient matrix of the set (see Eq. 4-2) is *nonsingular*; that is, if it has linearly independent rows (and columns) or, stated in another way, if the *determinant* of the coefficient matrix is *nonzero*. We shall now consider the first of the four methods.

4-2. Gauss' Elimination Method

The first method usually presented in algebra for the solution of simultaneous linear algebraic equations is one in which the unknowns are eliminated by combining equations. Such a method is known as an *elimination* method. It is called *Gaussian elimination* if a particular systematic scheme, attributed to Gauss, is used in the elimination process.

Using Gauss' method, a set of n equations in n unknowns is reduced to an *equivalent* triangular set (an equivalent set is a set having identical solution values), which is then easily solved by "back substitution," a simple procedure which will be illustrated in the following explanation.

Gauss' scheme begins by reducing a set of simultaneous equations, such as those given by Eq. 4-1, to an equivalent triangular set such as

$$
\left.
\begin{aligned}
a_{11}x_1 + a_{12}x_2 + a_{13}x_3 + a_{14}x_4 + \cdots \cdots + &\ a_{1n}x_n = C_1 \\
a_{22}'x_2 + a_{23}'x_3 + a_{24}'x_4 + \quad \cdots + &\ a_{2n}'x_n = C_2' \\
a_{33}''x_3 + a_{34}''x_4 + \quad \cdots + &\ a_{3n}''x_n = C_3'' \\
\cdots\cdots\cdots\cdots\cdots\cdots\cdots\cdots\cdots\cdots&\cdots\cdots \\
a^{n-2}_{n-1,n-1}x_{n-1} + a^{n-2}_{n-1,n}x_n = &\ C^{n-2}_{n-1} \\
a^{n-1}_{nn}x_n = &\ C^{n-1}_n
\end{aligned}
\right\}
\quad (4\text{-}5)
$$

where the prime superscripts indicate the new coefficients which are formed in the reduction process. The actual reduction is accomplished in the following manner:

1. Equation 4-1a is divided by the coefficient of x_1 in that equation to obtain

$$
x_1 + \frac{a_{12}}{a_{11}}x_2 + \frac{a_{13}}{a_{11}}x_3 + \cdots + \frac{a_{1n}}{a_{11}}x_n = \frac{C_1}{a_{11}}
\quad (4\text{-}6)
$$

Equation 4-6 is next multiplied by the coefficient of x_1 in Eq. 4-1b, and the resulting equation is subtracted from Eq. 4-1b, thus eliminating x_1 from Eq. 4-1b. Equation 4-6 is then multiplied by the coefficient of x_1 in Eq. 4-1c, and the resulting equation is subtracted from Eq. 4-1c to eliminate

x_1 from Eq. 4-1c. In a similar manner, x_1 is eliminated from all equations of the set except the first, so that the set assumes the form

$$a_{11}x_1 + a_{12}x_2 + a_{13}x_3 + \cdots + a_{1n}x_n = C_1 \quad \text{(a)}$$
$$a'_{22}x_2 + a'_{23}x_3 + \cdots + a'_{2n}x_n = C'_2 \quad \text{(b)}$$
$$a'_{32}x_2 + a'_{33}x_3 + \cdots + a'_{3n}x_n = C'_3 \quad \text{(c)} \qquad (4\text{-}7)$$
$$\vdots \qquad \vdots \qquad \qquad \vdots \qquad \vdots$$
$$a'_{n2}x_2 + a'_{n3}x_3 + \cdots + a'_{nn}x_n = C'_n$$

The equation used to eliminate the unknowns in the equations which follow it is called the *pivot equation* (Eq. 4-1a in the preceding steps). In the pivot equation the coefficient of the unknown which is to be eliminated from subsequent equations is known as the *pivot coefficient* (a_{11} in the preceding steps).

2. Following the above steps, Eq. 4-7b becomes the pivot equation, and the steps of part 1 are repeated to eliminate x_2 from all the equations following this pivot equation. This reduction yields

$$a_{11}x_1 + a_{12}x_2 + a_{13}x_3 + \cdots + a_{1n}x_n = C_1 \quad \text{(a)}$$
$$a'_{22}x_2 + a'_{23}x_3 + \cdots + a'_{2n}x_n = C'_2 \quad \text{(b)}$$
$$a''_{33}x_3 + \cdots + a''_{3n}x_n = C''_3 \quad \text{(c)}$$
$$a''_{43}x_3 + \cdots + a''_{4n}x_n = C''_4 \quad \text{(d)} \qquad (4\text{-}8)$$
$$\vdots \qquad \qquad \vdots \qquad \vdots$$
$$a''_{n3}x_3 + \cdots + a''_{nn}x_n = C''_n$$

3. Equation 4-8c is next used as the pivot equation, and the procedure described is used to eliminate x_3 from all equations following Eq. 4-8c. This procedure, using successive pivot equations, is continued until the original set of equations has been reduced to a triangular set, such as that given by Eq. 4-5.

4. After the triangular set of equations has been obtained, the last equation in this equivalent set yields the value of x_n directly (see Eq. 4-5). This value is then substituted into the next-to-the-last equation of the triangular set to obtain a value of x_{n-1}, which is, in turn, used along with the value of x_n in the second-to-the-last equation to obtain a value of x_{n-2}, and so on. This is the *back-substitution* procedure referred to earlier.

To illustrate the method with a numerical example, let us apply these procedures to solving the following set of equations:

$$x_1 + 4x_2 + x_3 = 7$$
$$x_1 + 6x_2 - x_3 = 13 \qquad (4\text{-}9)$$
$$2x_1 - x_2 + 2x_3 = 5$$

Using the first equation as the pivot equation (the pivot coefficient is unity), we obtain

$$x_1 + 4x_2 + x_3 = 7$$
$$2x_2 - 2x_3 = 6 \qquad (4\text{-}10)$$
$$-9x_2 + (0)x_3 = -9$$

Next, using the second equation of Eq. 4-10 as the pivot equation, and repeating the procedure, the following triangular set of equations is obtained:

$$x_1 + 4x_2 + x_3 = 7$$
$$2x_2 - 2x_3 = 6 \qquad (4\text{-}11)$$
$$-9x_3 = 18$$

Finally, through back substitution, beginning with the last of Eqs. 4-11, the following values are obtained:

$$x_3 = -2$$
$$x_2 = 1$$
$$x_1 = 5$$

In the above example the solution yielded values which were exact, since only whole numbers were encountered in the elimination process. In most instances, however, fractions will be encountered in the reduction process. The computer handles fractions in decimal form to a certain limited number of decimal places, and, in handling fractions which transform to nonterminating decimals, an error is introduced in the computer solution. This is called *roundoff error*.

When only a small number of equations is to be solved, the roundoff error is small and usually does not substantially affect the accuracy of the results,[2] but if many equations are to be solved simultaneously, the *cumulative* effect of roundoff error can introduce relatively large solution errors. For this reason, the number of simultaneous equations which can be satisfactorily solved by Gauss' elimination method, using 8 to 10 significant digits in the arithmetic operations, is generally limited to 15 to 20.

Let us now turn our attention to the implementation of Gauss' elimination method on the computer. Since the computer can handle only numerical data, the use of matrices is required in programming. Referring again to the set of equations given in Eq. 4-9, we can write the aug-

---

[2]Ill-conditioned equations are equations in which a small error in one or more of the coefficients greatly affects the accuracy of the solution. In such equations roundoff errors can obviously affect the accuracy of the solution.

mented matrix of this set as

$$
A = \begin{bmatrix} 1 & 4 & 1 & 7 \\ 1 & 6 & -1 & 13 \\ 2 & -1 & 2 & 5 \end{bmatrix} \qquad (4\text{-}12)
$$

The computer solution is involved with the reduction of this augmented matrix to the augmented matrix of the equivalent triangular set
of equations in Eq. 4-11. The necessary successive matrix reductions are
accomplished by the same procedures given in steps 1 through 3, above,
although in working with matrices we are now concerned with the *pivot
row* and *pivot element* rather than with the pivot equation and pivot coefficient, as before.

The first matrix reduction should result in the augmented matrix of
Eq. 4-10, which is

$$
A' = \begin{bmatrix} 1 & 4 & 1 & 7 \\ 0 & 2 & -2 & 6 \\ 0 & -9 & 0 & -9 \end{bmatrix} \qquad (4\text{-}13)
$$

Reviewing the procedure outlined in step 1, it can be seen that the
elements of the reduced matrix A' can be written directly from the original
matrix A, using the following formula:

$$
a'_{ij} = a_{ij} - \frac{a_{ik}}{a_{kk}} (a_{kj}) \qquad \left\{ \begin{array}{c} k \le j \le m \\ k + 1 \le i \le n \end{array} \right\} \qquad (4\text{-}14)
$$

where

a = an element of original matrix A
a' = an element of reduced matrix A'
i = row number of matrices
j = column number of matrices
k = number identifying pivot row ($k = 1, 2, \ldots, n - 1$)
n = number of rows in matrices
m = number of columns in matrices

At this point the reader should utilize Eq. 4-14 with $k = 1$ to confirm
several of the elements of the matrix A' given by Eq. 4-13. Then confirm
several of the elements of the next reduced matrix

$$
A'' = \begin{bmatrix} 1 & 4 & 1 & 7 \\ 0 & 2 & -2 & 6 \\ 0 & 0 & -9 & 18 \end{bmatrix} \qquad (4\text{-}15)
$$

which is determined from the matrix $\mathbf{A}'$ utilizing Eq. 4-14 with $k = 2$. Note that the matrix of Eq. 4-15 is the augmented matrix of Eq. 4-11.

After obtaining the augmented matrix of the equivalent triangular set of equations, the x_i values are obtained by back substitution. (The procedure will be generalized in a following paragraph.)

Having studied the general procedure for reducing matrices, let us now concern ourselves with an efficient way of programming Gauss' elimination method for the computer. We can rewrite Eq. 4-14 as

$$a_{ij}^k = a_{ij}^{k-1} - \frac{a_{kj}^{k-1}}{a_{kk}^{k-1}}(a_{ik}^{k-1}) \qquad \left\{ \begin{array}{l} k + 1 \leq j \leq m \\ k + 1 \leq i \leq n \end{array} \right\} \qquad (4\text{-}16)$$

where the i's, j's, k's, and so on, are as previously defined. The superscripts shown merely correspond to the primes used in identifying successive reduced matrices, in preceding discussions, and are not needed in a computer program. Note that, in Eq. 4-16, the lower limit of j is $k + 1$ instead of k, as in Eq. 4-14. This limit is used because there is no need to calculate the initial zero values which occur in each row owing to the reduction process, since we know the sequence of these zero values. Furthermore, these zero values are not pertinent to the back-substitution process, so they need not appear as values in the computer.

The back-substitution procedure may be generalized in the form of the following set of equations:

$$x_n = \frac{a_{nm}}{a_{nn}}$$

$$x_i = \frac{a_{im} - \sum_{j=i+1}^{n} a_{ij}x_j}{a_{ii}} \qquad i = n - 1, n - 2, \ldots, 1 \qquad (4\text{-}17)$$

The reader should pause here to use Eq. 4-17, with the augmented matrix given by Eq. 4-15, to confirm the values of x_1, x_2, and x_3 given following Eq. 4-11.

Before writing a computer program to solve a set of simultaneous equations by Gauss' elimination method, let us consider two important points: First, it has been tacitly assumed, thus far, that every pivot element encountered in the reduction process has been a nonzero element. If this is not the case, the procedure, as discussed, must be modified. If the pivot row has a zero pivot element, the row may be interchanged with any row *following* it which, upon becoming the pivot row, will not have a zero pivot element. For example, suppose that the pivot element of the matrix of Eq. 4-13, a_{22}, were zero instead of 2, as shown. This row could be interchanged with the last row, which would provide a new pivot row with a pivot element having a value of -9, and the procedure could then be continued.

If a pivot element should theoretically have a value of zero but actually retains a very small nonzero value, due to roundoff error, we will find that it will still be desirable to utilize row interchanges. This leads us to the second important point, namely, the effect of the magnitude of the pivot elements on the accuracy of the solution. It can be demonstrated that if the magnitude of the pivot element is appreciably smaller than the magnitude, in general, of the other elements in the matrix, the use of the small pivot element will cause a decrease in solution accuracy.[3] Therefore, for overall accuracy, each reduction should be made by using as a pivot row the row having the largest pivot element. For example, suppose that we were ready to reduce the augmented matrix of the set of equations in Eq. 4-7. The value of a'_{22} would be checked against the values of $a'_{32} \ldots a'_{n2}$, and a row interchange would be made if one of these latter values were larger than a'_{22}, so that the row containing the largest of these elements would become the pivot row for that reduction. Such a provision should always be incorporated in a computer program that is to solve fairly large numbers of simultaneous equations.

The results shown below indicate the improvement in solution accuracy obtained in a particular case by using the largest pivot element available. The exact solutions are the whole numbers 1 through 10.

	Without Largest Pivot Element	With Largest Pivot Element
$x_1 =$	1.0000000	0.9999996
$x_2 =$	1.9999955	1.9999992
$x_3 =$	2.9999983	3.0000001
$x_4 =$	4.0000302	4.0000109
$x_5 =$	5.0000021	4.9999999
$x_6 =$	5.9999964	6.0000039
$x_7 =$	6.9999956	7.0000094
$x_8 =$	8.0000311	8.0000036
$x_9 =$	8.9999557	8.9999822
$x_{10} =$	9.9999531	9.9999913

EXAMPLE 4-1

Let us write a general FORTRAN program for solving up to 15 simultaneous linear algebraic equations (limited to 15 only by the DIMENSION statement).

---

[3]The magnitudes referred to in this paragraph are the absolute values of the elements.

The **FORTRAN** names used in the program, and the quantities they represent, are as follows:

FORTRAN *Name*	*Quantity*
N	Number of simultaneous equations (number of rows in the augmented matrix)
M	Number of columns in the augmented matrix
L	$N - 1$
A(I,J)	Elements of the augmented matrices
I	Matrix row number
J	Matrix column number
JJ	Takes on values of the row numbers which are possible pivot rows, eventually taking on the value identifying the row having the largest pivot element
BIG	Takes on values of the elements in the column containing possible pivot elements, eventually taking on the value of the pivot element used
TEMP	Temporary name used for the elements of the row selected to become the pivot row, before the interchange is made
K	Index of a **DO** loop taking on values from 1 to $n - 1$; it identifies the column containing possible pivot elements
KP1	$K + 1$
AB	Absolute value of a_{ik}
QUOT	Quotient a_{ik}/a_{kk}
X(I)	Unknowns of the set of equations being solved
SUM	$\sum\limits_{j=i+1}^{n} a_{ij}x_j$
NN	Index of a **DO** loop taking on values from 1 to $n - 1$
IP1	$I + 1$

The flow chart for the program is shown in Fig. 4-1. The **FORTRAN IV** program is as follows:

```
C       SOLUTION OF SIMULTANEOUS EQUATIONS BY
                              GAUSSIAN ELIMINATION
        DIMENSION A(15,16),X(15)
    1 FORMAT(18H1X(1) THROUGH X(N)/)
```

```
  2 FORMAT(1H ,E14.8)
  3 FORMAT (I3)
  4 FORMAT (E14.0)
    READ(5,3)N
    M = N+1
    L = N-1
    DO5J = 1,M
    DO5I = 1,N
  5 READ(5,4)A(I,J)
    DO12K = 1,L
    JJ = K
    BIG = ABS(A(K,K))
    KP1 = K+1
    DO7I = KP1,N
    AB = ABS(A(I,K))
    IF(BIG-AB)6,7,7
  6 BIG = AB
    JJ = I
  7 CONTINUE
    IF(JJ-K)8,10,8
  8 DO9J = K,M
    TEMP = A(JJ,J)
    A(JJ,J) = A(K,J)
  9 A(K,J) = TEMP
 10 DO 11 I = KP1,N
    QUOT = A(I,K)/A(K,K)
    DO 11 J = KP1,M
 11 A(I,J) = A(I,J)-QUOT*A(K,J)
    DO 12 I = KP1,N
 12 A(I,K) = 0.
    X(N) = A(N,M)/A(N,N)
    DO 14 NN = 1,L
    SUM = 0.
    I = N-NN
    IP1 = I+1
    DO 13 J = IP1,N
 13 SUM = SUM + A(I,J)*X(J)
 14 X(I) = (A(I,M)-SUM)/A(I,I)
    WRITE(6,1)
    DO 15 I = 1,N
 15 WRITE(6,2)X(I)
    STOP
    END
```

Search for largest possible pivot element

Decision on necessity of row interchange

Row interchange

Calculation of elements of new matrix

First step in back substitution

Remainder of back-substitution process

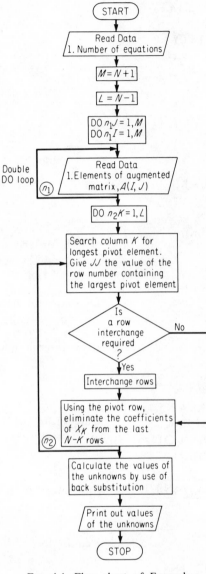

FIG. 4-1. Flow chart of Example
4-1.

In the above program, various groups of statements have been identified with respect to their functions in the computing process. Note the correlation of this breakdown with the flow chart of Fig. 4-1. The reader may find it helpful to employ such a procedure in analyzing the various programs which follow.

An application of this general program will be made in the next example, which is concerned with the design of a mechanism.

EXAMPLE 4-2

To illustrate a computer application of Gauss' elimination method in design, let us consider the design of a mechanism which is a component of an automatic packaging machine. In this device it is required that a point on the mechanism link be constrained to move over a path having the approximate shape shown in Fig. 4-2. The 5 points E_1 through E_5 are selected on this curve, with the requirement that the driven point E must pass through each of these 5 points. The bearing for the drive shaft is at O.

A length OA is arbitrarily selected for the driving crank, and the crank circle is drawn as shown. With a reasonable length arbitrarily selected for EA, arcs of this radius are swung, with the points E_1 through E_5 as centers. These arcs intersect the crank circle at points A_1 through A_5. The 5 lines formed by connecting the centers of the arcs and their respective intersections with the crank circle (E_1A_1 through E_5A_5) determine the

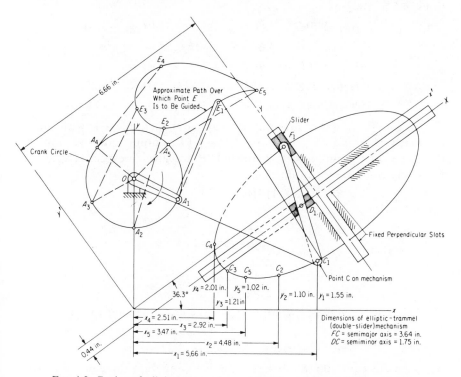

FIG. 4-2. Design of a linkage to guide a point E through 5 specified positions.

5 positions which the moving plane containing the line EA would have. The corresponding 5 positions of any point arbitrarily chosen in this plane will, in general, lie on a conic section (they could lie on a degenerate conic section such as 2 straight lines), since 5 points determine a conic section just as 3 points determine a circle.

The point labeled C in Fig. 4-2 is thus arbitrarily chosen in the plane, and its 5 positions C_1 through C_5 are found, with the coordinates of each point determined in the xy-coordinate system.

From analytical geometry we recall that the general equation of a conic section is

$$Ax^2 + Bxy + Cy^2 + Dx + Ey + F = 0 \qquad (4\text{-}18)$$

The coefficient A may be considered to have a magnitude of unity, since the entire equation may be divided by the coefficient of x^2 to establish this value. Appropriate values of the remaining coefficients B, C, D, E, and F will establish the equation of a conic curve passing through points C_1 through C_5. These coefficient values are determined by solving the 5 equations formed by substituting the coordinates of each point into Eq. 4-18. Performing these substitutions, we obtain the following 5 equations in 5 unknowns.

$$8.77B + 2.40C + 5.66D + 1.55E + 1.0F = -32.04$$
$$4.93B + 1.21C + 4.48D + 1.10E + 1.0F = -20.07$$
$$3.53B + 1.46C + 2.92D + 1.21E + 1.0F = -8.53 \qquad (4\text{-}19)$$
$$5.05B + 4.04C + 2.51D + 2.01E + 1.0F = -6.30$$
$$3.54B + 1.04C + 3.47D + 1.02E + 1.0F = -12.04$$

Using the computer program developed in Example 4-1, with the coefficient values and the constants of Eq. 4-19 as input data, we find that the values of the unknowns B through F are given, respectively, by the following computer printout:

X(1) THROUGH X(N)

$-.14649491E+01$

$.14581413E+01$

$-.60048293E+01$

$-.22090783E+01$

$.14719469E+02$

STOP 00000

Using these values, the equation of the conic passing through points $C_1 \ldots C_5$ is

$$x^2 - 1.46xy + 1.46y^2 - 6.00x - 2.21y + 14.72 = 0 \qquad (4\text{-}20)$$

Since, in this equation, $B^2 - 4AC < 0$, we know that the equation is that of an ellipse. This is desirable, since a point can easily be constrained to move on an elliptical path by the use of a double-slider mechanism called an *elliptic trammel.*

Unfortunately, Eq. 4-20 is not in a form suitable for designing the trammel mechanism. To design the elliptic trammel and properly orient it, the length of the semimajor and semiminor axes of the ellipse must be known, as well as the orientation and location of these particular axes with the xy-coordinate system used in obtaining Eq. 4-20. This information is required, since the link FC of the trammel must be equal in length to the semimajor axis of the ellipse, the length DC must be equal to the length of the semiminor axis, and the center lines of the slots in which the sliders move must lie along the axes of the ellipse.

The xy term appearing in Eq. 4-20 is first eliminated by rotating the xy axes to the $x'y'$ position shown in Fig. 4-2. The required angle of rotation is determined from the relationship

$$\cot 2\theta = \frac{A - C}{B} \qquad (4\text{-}21)$$

From this relationship we find that $\theta = 36.3°$. Then, using the well-known transformation equations

$$x = x' \cos \theta - y' \sin \theta$$
$$y = x' \sin \theta + y' \cos \theta \qquad (4\text{-}22)$$

the equation of the ellipse in the $x'y'$-coordinate system is obtained as

$$(x')^2 + 4.33(y')^2 + 13.3(x') + 3.85(y') + 31.9 = 0 \qquad (4\text{-}23)$$

By completing the square in x' and y', Eq. 4-23 may be written as

$$\frac{(x' - 6.66)^2}{(3.64)^2} + \frac{(y' + 0.445)^2}{(1.75)^2} = 1 \qquad (4\text{-}24)$$

The equation of the ellipse in the form of Eq. 4-24 reveals that the axes of the ellipse (the XY axes shown in Fig. 4-2) are displaced 6.66 in. in the positive x' direction and 0.445 in. in the negative y' direction from the origin of the $x'y'$ axes. It also shows that the semimajor and semiminor axes are, respectively, 3.64 and 1.75 in. in length.

With these data the elliptic-trammel mechanism can be properly designed and oriented to perform its desired function. With point A constrained to move on a circle, and point C constrained to move on the lower portion of the ellipse just determined, point E will pass through the specified points $E_1 \ldots E_5$.

The point C shown in Fig. 4-2 was actually not the first one selected in the procedure just described. In a problem of this type, several arbitrary selections of a point C may be necessary before a suitable design is obtained, for, with any arbitrary choice of a point C, the curve through the points $C_1 \ldots C_5$ could turn out to be a hyperbola, a parabola, or an ellipse of unsuitable size, rather than the ellipse obtained which could be conveniently implemented by the elliptic-trammel mechanism used.

With the possibility that many trial values of C may be required before a suitable design is obtained, it can be seen that the computer is a very handy tool for such design work. The example just given is concerned with a relatively simple mechanism. In the design of more complicated systems with many more parameters to consider, the computer becomes invaluable.

4-3. Gauss-Jordan Elimination Method

This method, which is a variation of the Gaussian elimination method, is suitable for solving as many as 15 to 20 simultaneous equations, with 8 to 10 significant digits used in the arithmetic operations of the computer. This procedure varies from the Gaussian method in that, when an unknown is eliminated, it is eliminated from *all* the other equations, that is, from those preceding the pivot equation as well as those following it. For example, in the preceding section describing Gauss' method, Eq. 4-7b was used as the pivot equation in eliminating x_2 from all the equations below it in obtaining Eq. 4-8. In the Gauss-Jordan method, the pivot equation would be used to eliminate x_2 from Eq. 4-7a as well. In the subsequent step, in which Eq. 4-8c was used as the pivot equation, x_3 would be eliminated from Eqs. 4-8a and 4-8b as well as from the equations below the pivot equation. This eliminates the necessity of using the back-substitution process employed in Gauss' method.

To illustrate the Gauss-Jordan elimination method, let us solve the following set of equations:

$$2x_1 - 2x_2 + 5x_3 = 13 \qquad \text{(a)}$$
$$2x_1 + 3x_2 + 4x_3 = 20 \qquad \text{(b)} \qquad \text{(4-25)}$$
$$3x_1 - x_2 + 3x_3 = 10 \qquad \text{(c)}$$

We begin by dividing the first equation of the set, Eq. 4-25a, by the coefficient of the *first* unknown in that equation, which gives us Eq. 4-26a below. We then multiply Eq. 4-26a, respectively, by the coefficient of the *first* unknown in each of the remaining equations (Eqs. 4-25 b and c) to get

$$x_1 - x_2 + \frac{5}{2}x_3 = \frac{13}{2} \qquad \text{(a)}$$
$$2x_1 - 2x_2 + 5x_3 = 13 \qquad \text{(b)} \qquad \text{(4-26)}$$
$$3x_1 - 3x_2 + \frac{15}{2}x_3 = \frac{39}{2} \qquad \text{(c)}$$

Now we subtract Eq. 4-26b from Eq. 4-25b and Eq. 4-26c from Eq. 4-25c, and we let Eq. 4-26a become Eq. 4-27c, obtaining

$$5x_2 - x_3 = 7 \qquad\qquad \text{(a)}$$

$$2x_2 - \frac{9}{2}x_3 = -\frac{19}{2} \qquad\qquad \text{(b)} \qquad \text{(4-27)}$$

$$x_1 - x_2 + \frac{5}{2}x_3 = \frac{13}{2} \qquad\qquad \text{(c)}$$

Next, we divide Eq. 4-27a by the coefficient of the *first* unknown in that equation (the coefficient of x_2) to obtain Eq. 4-28a. We then multiply Eq. 4-28a, respectively, by the coefficient of the x_2 term in each of Eqs. 4-27b and c. This yields

$$x_2 - \frac{1}{5}x_3 = \frac{7}{5} \qquad\qquad \text{(a)}$$

$$2x_2 - \frac{2}{5}x_3 = \frac{14}{5} \qquad\qquad \text{(b)} \qquad \text{(4-28)}$$

$$-x_2 + \frac{1}{5}x_3 = -\frac{7}{5} \qquad\qquad \text{(c)}$$

We next subtract Eq. 4-28b from Eq. 4-27b and Eq. 4-28c from Eq. 4-27c, and we let Eq. 4-28a become Eq. 4-29c, obtaining

$$-\frac{41}{10}x_3 = -\frac{123}{10} \qquad\qquad \text{(a)}$$

$$x_1 + \frac{23}{10}x_3 = \frac{79}{10} \qquad\qquad \text{(b)} \qquad \text{(4-29)}$$

$$x_2 - \frac{1}{5}x_3 = \frac{7}{5} \qquad\qquad \text{(c)}$$

Repeating the procedure yields

$$x_3 = 3 \qquad\qquad \text{(a)}$$

$$\frac{23}{10}x_3 = \frac{69}{10} \qquad\qquad \text{(b)} \qquad \text{(4-30)}$$

$$-\frac{1}{5}x_3 = -\frac{3}{5} \qquad\qquad \text{(c)}$$

and finally

$$x_1 = 1 \qquad\qquad \text{(a)}$$

$$x_2 = 2 \qquad\qquad \text{(b)} \qquad \text{(4-31)}$$

$$x_3 = 3 \qquad\qquad \text{(c)}$$

which constitutes the desired solution of the simultaneous equations.

Having solved Eq. 4-25 by the procedure shown, let us see how we can obtain the same result by working with just the coefficients and constants of these equations. Associated with Eq. 4-25 is a matrix $\mathbf{A}$, which is the *augmented* matrix of the set of equations. This matrix is

$$\mathbf{A} = \begin{bmatrix} 2 & -2 & 5 & 13 \\ 2 & 3 & 4 & 20 \\ 3 & -1 & 3 & 10 \end{bmatrix}$$

We next associate an augmented matrix $\mathbf{B}$ with Eq. 4-27, in which the first column of coefficients (0, 0, and 1) is omitted, and we write

$$\mathbf{B} = \begin{bmatrix} 5 & -1 & 7 \\ 2 & -9/2 & -19/2 \\ -1 & 5/2 & 13/2 \end{bmatrix}$$

Having established matrix $\mathbf{B}$ from Eq. 4-27, we note, from the way in which Eq. 4-27 was obtained from Eq. 4-25 in the first procedure, that we can write the elements of $\mathbf{B}$ directly from the elements of $\mathbf{A}$ by using the following formulas:

$$b_{i-1,j-1} = a_{ij} - \frac{a_{1j}a_{i1}}{a_{11}} \quad \begin{cases} 1 < i \le n \\ 1 < j \le m \\ a_{11} \ne 0 \end{cases} \tag{4-32}$$

$$b_{n,j-1} = \frac{a_{1j}}{a_{11}} \quad \begin{cases} 1 < j \le m \\ a_{11} \ne 0 \end{cases} \tag{4-33}$$

Equation 4-32 is used to find all elements of the new matrix $\mathbf{B}$ except those making up the last row of that matrix. For determining the elements of the last row of the new matrix, Eq. 4-33 is used. In these equations,

i = row number of old matrix $\mathbf{A}$

j = column number of old matrix $\mathbf{A}$

n = maximum row number

m = maximum column number

a = an element of old matrix $\mathbf{A}$

b = an element of new matrix $\mathbf{B}$

Now, if we write the augmented matrix of Eq. 4-29, this time omitting the first 2 columns (elements 0, 1, 0 and 0, 0, 1), we get

$$\mathbf{C} = \begin{bmatrix} -41/10 & -123/10 \\ 23/10 & 79/10 \\ -1/5 & 7/5 \end{bmatrix}$$

Again, we note that the elements of $\mathbf{C}$ can be obtained directly from the elements of $\mathbf{B}$ by utilizing Eqs. 4-32 and 4-33, where $\mathbf{C}$ is now the *new* matrix and $\mathbf{B}$ is the *old* matrix.

The augmented matrix of Eq. 4-31, with the first 3 columns (1, 0, 0; 0,1,0; and 0,0,1) omitted, is simply the matrix whose elements are the solution of the set of simultaneous equations with which we started,

$$\mathbf{D} = \begin{bmatrix} 1 \\ 2 \\ 3 \end{bmatrix}$$

Just as with the previous matrices, matrix **D** can be obtained from matrix **C** by application of Eqs. 4-32 and 4-33. The elements shown in **D** are associated, respectively, with x_1, x_2, and x_3 by the above procedure.

Thus, it can be seen that the roots of a set of n simultaneous equations can be obtained by successive applications of Eqs. 4-32 and 4-33 to get n new matrices, the last of which will be a *column* matrix whose elements are the roots of the set of simultaneous equations.

It is possible that the pivot element a_{11} of 1 or more of the matrices obtained during the elimination process could have a zero value, in which case divisions by a_{11} in Eqs. 4-32 and 4-33 would be invalid. If this occurs, the first row can be interchanged with one of the first $m - 1$ rows of the matrix which has a first element not equal to zero, where m is the number of columns in the current matrix. The use of a row beyond row $m - 1$ as a pivot row in the elimination process would reintroduce one of the previously eliminated unknowns into the equations. The elimination process then continues as before, until a solution is reached. In obtaining a computer solution utilizing Eqs. 4-32 and 4-33, the program must provide the computer logic necessary to check element a_{11} in each of the matrices obtained during the reduction, and to perform the row interchange if necessary. Interchanging the rows will not alter the order of the unknowns in the final column matrix.

In instances in which a_{11} is not zero but is very small in comparison with the general magnitude of the other elements of the matrix, its use could cause a decrease in solution accuracy, as discussed in Gauss' elimination method. For improved accuracy the applicable row having the largest potential pivot element (the row among the first $m - 1$ rows having the largest pivot element) should be placed in the first or pivot position if it is not already there. This would be accomplished by checking the value of a_{11} against the values of a_{21}, a_{31}, ... , $a_{m-1,1}$ and making the appropriate row interchange if one of these latter values were larger than a_{11}. This provision should always be incorporated in a computer program used for solving fairly large numbers of simultaneous equations.

It should be noted that, if it were desired to solve a second set of simultaneous equations which differed from a first set only in the constant terms which appeared, both sets could be solved at the same time by representing each set of constants as a separate column in augmenting the coefficient matrix. Actually, 2 or more sets of simultaneous equations, differing only in their constant terms, can be solved in a single elimination procedure by placing the constants of each set in a separate column to the right of the coefficient columns in the augmented matrix, and applying Eqs. 4-32 and 4-33 until a reduced matrix is obtained which has the same number of columns as the number of *sets* of simultaneous equations being solved. Such a solution will be illustrated in Sec. 4-5.

In Example 4-3, the computer program shown does not contain the provision discussed for interchanging rows for increased accuracy. In this program a row interchange is made only if a_{11} is zero. It is left as a problem for the reader (see Prob. 4-8 at end of chapter) to modify the given program for improved accuracy.

Example 4-3

As an example of a case involving the solution of simultaneous algebraic equations, let us consider a portion of an overall cam-design problem concerned with determining a cam profile for a flat-faced follower-cam system. We wish to make a *displacement diagram* from which the cam profile will be determined. The displacement diagram relates the follower-motion to the cam rotation and is a function of the design conditions imposed on the system. A typical displacement diagram is shown in Fig. 4-3.

Several standard displacement curves are available, for determining cam profiles, which yield simple harmonic motion, constant acceleration and deceleration, and so on. They provide cams which perform acceptably at moderate operating speeds, but which are not entirely adequate at higher operating speeds. In finding the displacement curve for a cam which is to operate at high speeds, we must be concerned with the

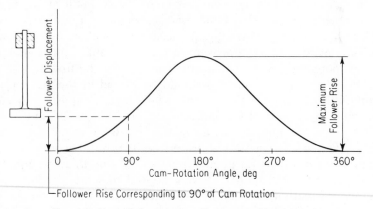

Fig. 4-3. Typical displacement diagram used in cam design.

acceleration and rate of change acceleration (often called second acceleration, jerk, or pulse) of the follower system as well as with the velocity and displacement. It should be noted here that the velocities, accelerations, and second accelerations referred to are not successive time derivatives in this instance; instead, they refer to successive derivatives of the follower displacement with respect to the cam-rotation angle, and are so commonly referred to in cam design.

Restrictions or conditions may be imposed on the velocity, acceleration, and second-acceleration curves by utilizing *polynomial equations* to relate the follower motion to the rotation of the cam. These equations have the general form

$$y = C_0 + C_1\theta + C_2\theta^2 + C_3\theta^3 + C_4\theta^4 \ldots C_n\theta^n \qquad (4\text{-}34)$$

where

$$y = \text{displacement of follower, in.}$$

$$\theta = \text{cam rotation angle, deg}$$

$$C_i = \text{constants}$$

In using polynomial equations, it is convenient to measure the cam angle, positively and negatively, from a zero position corresponding to the maximum rise of the follower, as illustrated in Fig. 4-4, rather than in the more conventional manner shown in Fig. 4-3.

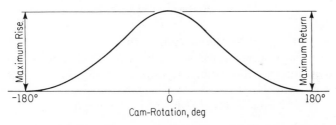

FIG. 4-4. Coordinate system for polynomial displacement equations.

In this example we shall be concerned with determining the displacement diagram for the return portion of a follower motion occurring between 2 successive dwells. The general form of the curve is shown in Fig. 4-5, plotted by using the dimensionless coordinates y and θ, which are related to the coordinates of a *particular* follower-cam system by the ratios shown in the figure, where

y_a = displacement of a particular follower, in.

y_d = total return between successive dwells of the particular follower, in.

θ_a = cam-rotation angle of a particular cam, deg

θ_d = total return cam-rotation angle between successive dwells, deg

By using the dimensionless coordinates y and θ, we can determine a displacement curve which will yield solutions for systems having various combinations of y_d and θ_d values.

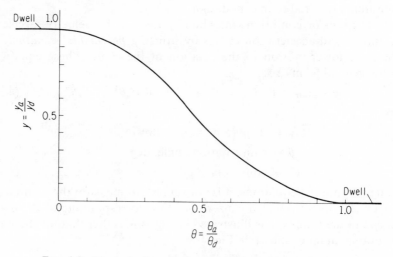

FIG. 4-5. Dimensionless displacement diagram for dwell-return-dwell portion of polynomial cam motion.

It is desired to control the motion of the follower so that it will have zero velocity, zero acceleration, and zero rate of change of acceleration at the ends (zero and maximum-rise points) of the motion, and a maximum velocity such that $y' = dy/d\theta = -2.0$ at $\theta = 0.5$. Stated in mathematical form, the conditions which are to be imposed on the follower motion are

When $\theta = 0$: $y = 1, y' = 0, y'' = 0, y''' = 0$ (a)

When $\theta = 1$: $y = 0, y' = 0, y'' = 0, y''' = 0$ (b)   (4-35)

When $\theta = 0.5$: $y' = -2.0, y'' = 0$ (c)

With the 10 conditions shown, it will be necessary to use 10 constants in the polynomial describing the follower motion. Hence

$$y = C_0 + C_1\theta + C_2\theta^2 + C_3\theta^3 + \cdots + C_9\theta^9 \qquad (4\text{-}36)$$

Three successive differentiations of Eq. 4-36 with respect to θ yield the following:

$$y' = C_1 + 2C_2\theta + 3C_3\theta^2 + 4C_4\theta^3 + 5C_5\theta^4$$
$$+ 6C_6\theta^5 + 7C_7\theta^6 + 8C_8\theta^7 + 9C_9\theta^8 \qquad (4\text{-}37)$$

$$y'' = 2C_2 + 6C_3\theta + 12C_4\theta^2 + 20C_5\theta^3 + 30C_6\theta^4$$
$$+ 42C_7\theta^5 + 56C_8\theta^6 + 72C_9\theta^7 \qquad (4\text{-}38)$$
$$y''' = 6C_3 + 24C_4\theta + 60C_5\theta^2 + 120C_6\theta^3$$
$$+ 210C_7\theta^4 + 336C_8\theta^5 + 504C_9\theta^6 \qquad (4\text{-}39)$$

Substituting the boundary conditions of Eq. 4-35a into Eqs. 4-36 through 4-39 reveals that

$$C_0 = 1$$
$$C_1 = C_2 = C_3 = 0$$

Substituting the conditions of Eq. 4-35b into Eqs. 4-36 through 4-39, and the conditions of Eq. 4-35c into Eqs. 4-37 and 4-38, and utilizing the known values of C_0 through C_3, yields the following 6 equations containing 6 unknowns:

$$-1 = C_4 + C_5 + C_6 + C_7 + C_8 + C_9$$
$$0 = 4C_4 + 5C_5 + 6C_6 + 7C_7 + 8C_8 + 9C_9$$
$$0 = 12C_4 + 20C_5 + 30C_6 + 42C_7 + 56C_8 + 72C_9$$
$$0 = 24C_4 + 60C_5 + 120C_6 + 210C_7 + 336C_8 + 504C_9 \qquad (4\text{-}40)$$
$$-2 = 0.5C_4 + 0.3125C_5 + 0.1875C_6 + 0.109375C_7$$
$$+ 0.0625C_8 + 0.03515625C_9$$
$$0 = 3C_4 + 2.5C_5 + 1.875C_6 + 1.3125C_7$$
$$+ 0.875C_8 + 0.5625C_9$$

Since the displacement curve which we wish to determine has the form

$$y = 1 + C_4\theta^4 + C_5\theta^5 + \cdots + C_9\theta^9$$

it is evident that we must determine the roots of the set of simultaneous equations displayed as Eq. 4-40. The determination of these roots will yield not only the displacement curve but also the velocity, acceleration, and second-acceleration curves when the constant values are substituted in Eqs. 4-37 through 4-39, respectively.

Let us now consider a **FORTRAN** program for solving Eq. 4-40, utilizing the Gauss-Jordan elimination method. Although the set contains only 6 simultaneous equations, let us write a program capable of handling up to 15 simultaneous equations, where the appropriate coefficients and constants prerequisite to the solution of a desired set of equations are introduced into the program by means of data cards. Since the program will utilize Eqs. 4-32 and 4-33, and is to be written as a general program, it must contain instructions to the computer to check the initial element in each matrix appearing in the reduction process for a zero value, to avoid division by zero when such an element exists. If the initial element has a zero value, the program must instruct the computer to interchange rows within the matrix to provide a pivot row containing

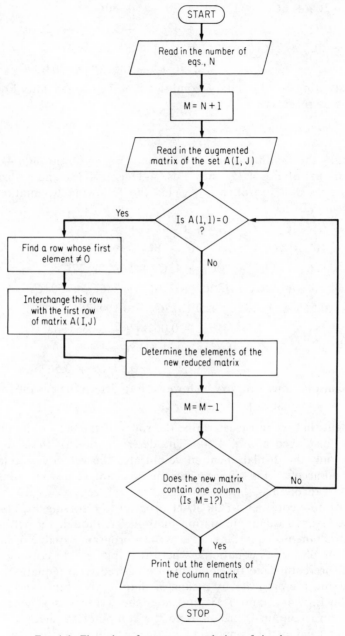

Fig. 4-6. Flow chart for computer solution of simultaneous equations by elimination method.

a nonzero initial element. The flow chart for the problem is shown in Fig. 4-6.

The variable names used in the FORTRAN program represent the following quantities:

FORTRAN *Name*	*Quantity*
A(I,J)	Elements of augmented and reduced matrices
B(I,J)	Temporary name for elements of reduced matrices
TEMP	Temporary name for matrix elements used in interchanging rows of the matrix when A(1,1) = 0
N	Number of equations in set being solved (number of rows in augmented and reduced matrices)
M	Number of columns in augmented and reduced matrices
K	Number of rows in matrix in memory which are possible pivot rows, M − 1

The reader should note, in the FORTRAN IV program which follows, that:

1. Statement 5 checks the first element A(1,1) of the augmented and reduced matrices for a zero value.

2. The DO loop, initiated after statement 6, searches down the first column of the matrix for a nonzero element.

3. The inner DO loop, initiated by statement 7 (it is in the DO loop beginning after statement 6), provides an interchange of rows after a row with a nonzero A(I, 1) has been located by the outer DO loop.

4. In the event that all elements A(I,1) in the first $m - 1$ rows of the matrix (m is the number of columns in the current matrix) are found to be zero, no unique solution exists, and the computer is instructed to WRITE statement 10 and then STOP.

5. As mentioned earlier, the program does not include a provision for interchanging rows to obtain the largest applicable pivot element for improved accuracy.

The FORTRAN IV program is as follows:

```
  DIMENSION  A(15,16),B(15,15)
  WRITE(6,1)
1 FORMAT(50H1SOLUTION OF SIMULTANEOUS EQUATIONS BY
                                      ELIMINATION)
  READ(5,2)N
2 FORMAT(I3)
  M=N+1
3 FORMAT(E14.8)
  DO  4J=1,M
  DO  4I=1,N
```

```
  4 READ(5,3)A(I,J)
  5 IF(A(1,1))11,6,11
  6 K=M−1
    DO 9I=2,K
    IF(A(I,1))7,9,7
  7 DO 8J=1,M
    TEMP=A(I,J)
    A(I,J)=A(1,J)
  8 A(1,J)=TEMP
    GO TO 11
  9 CONTINUE
    WRITE(6,10)
 10 FORMAT(I9H0NO UNIQUE SOLUTION)
    GO TO 18
 11 DO 12J=2,M
    DO 12I=2,N
 12 B(I−1,J−1)=A(I,J)−A(1,J)*A(I,1)/A(1,1)
    DO 13J=2,M
 13 B(N,J−1)=A(1,J)/A(1,1)
    M=M−1
    DO 14J=1,M
    DO 14I=1,N
 14 A(I,J)=B(I,J)
    IF(M−1)5,16,5
 15 FORMAT(1H ,E14.8)
 16 DO 17I=1,N
 17 WRITE(6,15)A(I,1)
 18 STOP
    END
```

The computer solution obtained with this program is

SOLUTION OF SIMULTANEOUS EQUATIONS BY ELIMINATION

```
−.59000000E+02
 .22800000E+03
−.40600000E+03
 .40400000E+03
−.21600000E+03
 .48000000E+02
```

STOP 00000

The numerical values shown are $C_4, C_5, \ldots, C_9$, respectively. From these results we obtain the equation of the required displacement curve, in dimensionless form, as

$$y = 1 - 59\theta^4 + 228\theta^5 - 406\theta^6 + 404\theta^7 - 216\theta^8 + 48\theta^9 \qquad (4\text{-}41)$$

Using the constant values determined, Eqs. 4-36 through 4-39 will yield the dynamic-characteristic curves shown in Fig. 4-7. It is left as an exercise for the reader to find the relationships existing, respectively, between the y', y'', and y''' values shown, and the velocity, acceleration, and second-acceleration values of a particular system as defined by a particular dwell-to-dwell follower displacement y_d and the corresponding cam-rotation angle θ_d.

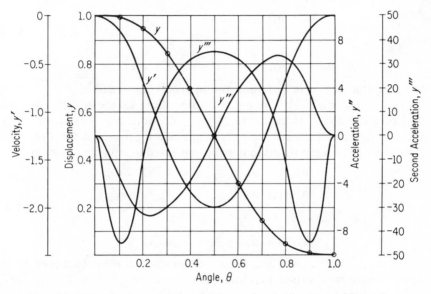

FIG. 4-7. Dynamic characteristics of follower for dwell-return-dwell portion of polynomial cam motion.

4-4. The Use of Error Equations

Error equations are used to increase the accuracy with which the roots of simultaneous equations may be determined. For example, when the elimination method, just discussed, is used to find the roots of simultaneous equations, there may be a considerable loss of accuracy in the results, owing to *roundoff error* which accumulates during the large number of arithmetic operations performed in obtaining a solution. (Roundoff error is defined as the error which results from replacing a number having more than n digits by a number having n digits.)

Suppose that the computer were used to solve, for example, 15 to 20 simultaneous equations by the elimination method, and that 8 significant digits were retained in the result of each calculation. The final results might have only 2- or 3-digit accuracy, owing to the cumulative errors introduced by rounding off numbers in the hundreds of arithmetic operations performed. Such an error is aggravated when the 8 digits retained in a calculation result from arbitrarily lopping off all digits beyond the eighth rather than using some averaging process.

Error equations can be used to reduce the error introduced by rounding off. Their use is explained in the following discussion.

Consider a set of equations of the form

$$
\begin{aligned}
a_{11}x_1 + a_{12}x_2 + a_{13}x_3 + \cdots + a_{1n}x_n &= C_1 \\
a_{21}x_1 + a_{22}x_2 + a_{23}x_3 + \cdots + a_{2n}x_n &= C_2 \\
&\ \ \vdots \\
a_{n1}x_1 + a_{n2}x_2 + a_{n3}x_3 + \cdots + a_{nn}x_n &= C_n
\end{aligned}
\tag{4-42}
$$

Suppose that we have obtained the approximate roots $x_1', x_2', \ldots, x_n'$ by the elimination method. Upon substituting these values into Eq. 4-42, we find that the constant values $C_1', C_2', \ldots, C_n'$ obtained vary from the respective original values $C_1, C_2, \ldots, C_n$, since the roots substituted were not exact. Such a substitution may be expressed in equation form as

$$
\begin{aligned}
a_{11}x_1' + a_{12}x_2' + \cdots + a_{1n}x_n' &= C_1' \\
a_{21}x_1' + a_{22}x_2' + \cdots + a_{2n}x_n' &= C_2' \\
&\ \ \vdots \\
a_{n1}x_1' + a_{n2}x_2' + \cdots + a_{nn}x_n' &= C_n'
\end{aligned}
\tag{4-43}
$$

If $\Delta x_1, \Delta x_2, \ldots, \Delta x_n$ are the corrections which must be added to the approximate root values to obtain the *exact* root values $\bar{x}_1, \bar{x}_2, \ldots, \bar{x}_n$, it follows that

$$
\begin{aligned}
\bar{x}_1 &= x_1' + \Delta x_1 \\
\bar{x}_2 &= x_2' + \Delta x_2 \\
&\ \ \vdots \\
\bar{x}_n &= x_n' + \Delta x_n
\end{aligned}
\tag{4-44}
$$

If we substitute these expressions for the exact roots into Eq. 4-42, we obtain

$$
\begin{aligned}
a_{11}(x_1' + \Delta x_1) + a_{12}(x_2' + \Delta x_2) + \cdots + a_{1n}(x_n' + \Delta x_n) &= C_1 \\
a_{21}(x_1' + \Delta x_1) + a_{22}(x_2' + \Delta x_2) + \cdots + a_{2n}(x_n' + \Delta x_n) &= C_2 \\
&\ \ \vdots \\
a_{n1}(x_1' + \Delta x_1) + a_{n2}(x_2' + \Delta x_2) + \cdots + a_{nn}(x_n' + \Delta x_n) &= C_n
\end{aligned}
\tag{4-45}
$$

If Eq. 4-43 is then subtracted from Eq. 4-45, we obtain the following set of simultaneous equations, involving the root corrections:

$$
a_{11}\Delta x_1 + a_{12}\Delta x_2 + \cdots + a_{1n}\Delta x_n = (C_1 - C_1') = e_1
$$

$$a_{21}\Delta x_1 + a_{22}\Delta x_2 + \cdots + a_{2n}\Delta x_n = (C_2 - C_2') = e_2$$

$$\vdots \qquad \vdots \qquad \qquad \vdots \qquad \qquad \vdots \qquad \qquad \vdots \qquad (4\text{-}46)$$

$$a_{n1}\Delta x_1 + a_{n2}\Delta x_2 + \cdots + a_{nn}\Delta x_n = (C_n - C_n') = e_n$$

Inspection of Eq. 4-46 reveals that the required root corrections are, themselves, the roots of a set of equations which differs from the original set (Eq. 4-42) only in the respective constant values. The constants e_i of Eq. 4-46 express the error resulting from inaccurate root values, and the equations are called *error equations*.

In a computer solution of a set of simultaneous equations by the elimination method, in which error equations are to be employed, the augmented matrix of the original set of equations should be left stored in memory during its use in obtaining the approximate roots. The corrections to the roots may then be obtained by simply replacing the values in the right-hand column of this matrix by the e_i values calculated, and repeating the reduction of the matrix to a column matrix by the method of elimination. The corrections obtained are then added, respectively, to the approximate root values found in the original elimination process, to obtain more accurate root values.

If still greater accuracy is desired, corrections may be made in the values obtained as the root corrections from solving Eq. 4-46. If we designate the corrections to the corrections by $\Delta^2 x_i$, then the exact roots $\bar{x}_i$ are given by

$$\bar{x}_i = x_i' + \Delta x_i + \Delta^2 x_i \qquad (4\text{-}47)$$

This process of using error equations to correct the roots of other error equations can be carried as far as necessary to obtain roots of the desired accuracy. The use of error equations is illustrated in Example 4-4.

EXAMPLE 4-4

The following set of simultaneous equations defines the motion of a dwell-return-dwell cam, such as the one of Example 4-3.

$$
\begin{aligned}
C_4 + \quad C_5 + \quad C_6 + \quad\quad C_7 &= -1 \\
4C_4 + \quad 5C_5 + \quad 6C_6 + \quad\quad 7C_7 &= 0 \\
6C_4 + 10C_5 + 15C_6 + \quad 21C_7 &= 0 \\
12C_4 + 30C_5 + 60C_6 + 105C_7 &= 0
\end{aligned}
\qquad (4\text{-}48)
$$

The roots of this set of equations have been determined by the Gauss-Jordan elimination method (p. 198) and have the following values:

$$C_4 = -35$$
$$C_5 = 84$$
$$C_6 = -70$$
$$C_7 = 20$$

Since all the coefficients of Eq. 4-48 are whole numbers, and since the arithmetic operations used in solving the roots did not involve any numbers with sufficient significant digits to exceed the computer capacity, no roundoff error occurred in obtaining the roots, which are whole numbers themselves and are thus the exact roots of Eq. 4-48.

However, for the purpose of illustrating the use of error equations, let us suppose that the roots to Eq. 4-48, obtained by some less exact method, are found to be

$$C_4' = -35.1$$
$$C_5' = 83.9$$
$$C_6' = -70.3$$
$$C_7' = 20.2$$

If we substitute these roots into Eq. 4-48 to determine how accurate they are, we find that

$$\begin{aligned}
C_4 + C_5 + C_6 + C_7 &= -1.3 \\
4C_4 + 5C_5 + 6C_6 + 7C_7 &= -1.3 \\
6C_4 + 10C_5 + 15C_6 + 21C_7 &= -1.9 \\
12C_4 + 30C_5 + 60C_6 + 105C_7 &= -1.2
\end{aligned} \tag{4-49}$$

A comparison of the constant values of Eq. 4-49 with the respective constant values of Eq. 4-48 reveals that considerable error exists in the roots. Therefore, we introduce the use of error equations to determine more accurate values. Referring to Eqs. 4-46 and 4-49, we obtain the following set of error equations:

$$\begin{aligned}
\Delta C_4 + \Delta C_5 + \Delta C_6 + \Delta C_7 &= -1.0 - (-1.3) = 0.3 \\
4\Delta C_4 + 5\Delta C_5 + 6\Delta C_6 + 7\Delta C_7 &= 0.0 - (-1.3) = 1.3 \\
6\Delta C_4 + 10\Delta C_5 + 15\Delta C_6 + 21\Delta C_7 &= 0.0 - (-1.9) = 1.9 \\
12\Delta C_4 + 30\Delta C_5 + 60\Delta C_6 + 105\Delta C_7 &= 0.0 - (-1.2) = 1.2
\end{aligned} \tag{4-50}$$

Using the matrix-reduction method (the matrix form of the Gauss-Jordan elimination method), we find that the augmented and reduced matrices are

$$\mathbf{A} = \begin{bmatrix} 1 & 1 & 1 & 1 & 0.3 \\ 4 & 5 & 6 & 7 & 1.3 \\ 6 & 10 & 15 & 21 & 1.9 \\ 12 & 30 & 60 & 105 & 1.2 \end{bmatrix}$$

$$\mathbf{B} = \begin{bmatrix} 1 & 2 & 3 & 0.10 \\ 4 & 9 & 15 & 0.10 \\ 18 & 48 & 93 & -2.40 \\ 1 & 1 & 1 & 0.30 \end{bmatrix}$$

$$\mathbf{C} = \begin{bmatrix} 1 & 3 & -0.30 \\ 12 & 39 & -4.20 \\ -1 & -2 & 0.20 \\ 2 & 3 & 0.10 \end{bmatrix}$$

$$\mathbf{D} = \begin{bmatrix} 3 & -0.6 \\ 1 & -0.1 \\ -3 & 0.7 \\ 3 & -0.3 \end{bmatrix}$$

$$\mathbf{E} = \begin{Bmatrix} 0.1 \\ 0.1 \\ 0.3 \\ -0.2 \end{Bmatrix} \dagger$$

Using the corrections shown in the column matrix, the corrected values of the roots are

$$
\begin{aligned}
C_4 &= C_4' + \Delta C_4 = -35.1 + 0.1 = -35.0 \\
C_5 &= C_5' + \Delta C_5 = 83.9 + 0.1 = 84.0 \\
C_6 &= C_6' + \Delta C_6 = -70.3 + 0.3 = -70.0 \\
C_7 &= C_7' + \Delta C_7 = 20.2 + (-0.2) = 20.0
\end{aligned}
\qquad (4\text{-}51)
$$

Since no roundoff error was introduced in solving the error equations, the corrections are exact corrections and, when added to the approximate values of the roots assumed, yield the exact roots determined in the actual solution.

As was evident at the beginning of this discussion, this example does not involve equations whose solution requires the use of error equations. Such an example was used, for the sake of simplicity, to illustrate the actual matrix reductions which resulted in the root corrections. It should be obvious to the reader, at this point, why error equations would be necessary in solving a set of, say, 30 simultaneous equations, involving coefficients as follows, on a computer having the capacity of handling perhaps only 8 significant digits with the particular language used:

$$0.86746C_1 + 0.97121C_2 + 1.67543C_3 + \cdots + 0.23456C_{30} = 1.76408$$
$$0.34657C_1 + 0.78645C_2 + \cdots = 2.67823$$
$$\vdots \qquad \vdots \qquad \qquad \vdots \qquad (4\text{-}52)$$
$$0.54236C_1 + \cdots = 1.53266$$

The procedure discussed in this example would be used to obtain roots of the desired accuracy for Eq. 4-52, except that the whole procedure

†This form will be used henceforth in this text to represent a *column matrix*.

would be programmed to let the computer perform all the tedious reduction operations, which are complicated by the numerical values of the coefficients.

4-5. Matrix-Inversion Method

When it is necessary to solve a large number of different *sets* of simultaneous equations which differ only by the constant values appearing in the respective equations, the matrix-inversion method may be used to advantage in reducing the number of operations required.

Before proceeding to the discussion of this method, let us very briefly review some of the rules governing the multiplication of matrices. The product of 2 matrices $\mathbf{A} = [a_{ij}]$ and $\mathbf{B} = [b_{ij}]$ may be written as

$$[a_{ij}][b_{ij}] = [c_{ij}]$$

or, more simply, as

$$\mathbf{A}\,\mathbf{B} = \mathbf{C}$$

where it is understood that

$$c_{ij} = \sum_{k=1}^{k=p} a_{ik}\, b_{kj} \tag{4-53}$$

In the latter expression, k identifies the kth element in the ith *row* of $\mathbf{A}$ and the kth element in the jth *column* of $\mathbf{B}$, and p is the number of columns in $\mathbf{A}$. The limit p could also be defined as the number of rows in $\mathbf{B}$, since the product of 2 matrices is defined only if the number of columns in $\mathbf{A}$ is equal to the number of rows in $\mathbf{B}$. It should also be remembered that matrix multiplication is, in general, not commutative ($\mathbf{A}\,\mathbf{B} \neq \mathbf{B}\,\mathbf{A}$). The following examples may best suffice to illustrate the multiplication of matrices.

In the following equation, matrix $\mathbf{C}$ is the product of the matrices $\mathbf{A}$ and $\mathbf{B}$.

$$\begin{bmatrix} a_{11} & a_{12} & a_{13} \\ a_{21} & a_{22} & a_{23} \\ a_{31} & a_{32} & a_{33} \end{bmatrix} \begin{bmatrix} b_{11} & b_{12} & b_{13} \\ b_{21} & b_{22} & b_{23} \\ b_{31} & b_{32} & b_{33} \end{bmatrix} = \begin{bmatrix} c_{11} & c_{12} & c_{13} \\ c_{21} & c_{22} & c_{23} \\ c_{31} & c_{32} & c_{33} \end{bmatrix}$$

Utilizing Eq. 4-53, we find that

$$c_{11} = (a_{11} b_{11}) + (a_{12} b_{21}) + (a_{13} b_{31})$$
$$c_{21} = (a_{21} b_{11}) + (a_{22} b_{21}) + (a_{23} b_{31})$$
$$\vdots \qquad \vdots \qquad \vdots \qquad \vdots$$
$$c_{33} = (a_{31} b_{13}) + (a_{32} b_{23}) + (a_{33} b_{33})$$

A more specific example is given by the multiplication of the matrix **A** by the column matrix **B**, as follows:

$$\begin{bmatrix} 1 & 2 & 5 \\ 4 & 6 & 3 \\ 0 & 1 & 7 \end{bmatrix} \begin{Bmatrix} 1 \\ 2 \\ 3 \end{Bmatrix} = \begin{Bmatrix} (1)(1) + (2)(2) + (5)(3) \\ (4)(1) + (6)(2) + (3)(3) \\ (0)(1) + (1)(2) + (7)(3) \end{Bmatrix} = \begin{Bmatrix} 20 \\ 25 \\ 23 \end{Bmatrix}$$

From these examples it can be seen that the matrix multiplication consists of a *row-on-column* multiplication sequence.

Let us consider again the set of simultaneous equations given by Eq. 4-42, to resume our discussion of the matrix-inversion method of solving simultaneous equations. From the preceding exposition of matrix multiplication, it can be seen that Eq. 4-42 may be expressed by the single matrix equation

$$\begin{bmatrix} a_{11} & a_{12} & \cdots & a_{1n} \\ a_{21} & a_{22} & \cdots & a_{2n} \\ \vdots & \vdots & & \vdots \\ & & & a_{nn} \end{bmatrix} \begin{Bmatrix} x_1 \\ x_2 \\ \vdots \\ x_n \end{Bmatrix} = \begin{Bmatrix} c_1 \\ c_2 \\ \vdots \\ c_n \end{Bmatrix} \qquad (4\text{-}54)$$

If we let **A** represent the coefficient matrix, $\{X\}$ the column matrix of the unknowns, and $\{C\}$ the column matrix of the constants, we can express Eq. 4-54 as

$$\mathbf{A}\{X\} = \{C\} \qquad \text{or} \qquad \mathbf{AX} = \mathbf{C} \qquad (4\text{-}55)$$

If the given set of equations (Eq. 4-42) has a unique solution, the coefficient matrix **A** is nonsingular, and, as such, there exists for **A** an inverse matrix $\mathbf{A}^{-1}$ such that

$$\mathbf{A}^{-1}\mathbf{A} = \mathbf{I}$$

where **I** is the *identity* or *unit* matrix. The identity matrix, which is an *n*-by-*n* matrix with its main diagonal consisting of *ones* and zeros everywhere else (see Eq. 4-58), is to matrix algebra what the identity number (1) is to ordinary algebra; that is, $\mathbf{IA} = \mathbf{A}$ or $\mathbf{AI} = \mathbf{A}$.

Premultiplying both sides of Eq. 4-55 by $\mathbf{A}^{-1}$ gives

$$(\mathbf{A}^{-1}\mathbf{A})\{X\} = \mathbf{A}^{-1}\{C\}$$
$$\mathbf{I}\{X\} = \mathbf{A}^{-1}\{C\} \qquad (4\text{-}56)$$
$$\{X\} = \mathbf{A}^{-1}\{C\}$$

Inspection of Eq. 4-56 reveals that if $\mathbf{A}^{-1}$ is known, the elements of $\{X\}$ can easily be determined for any number of different $\{C\}$ matrices by merely premultiplying the particular constant matrix by the inverse matrix.

The inverse of **A** can be determined from the equation

$$\mathbf{AA}^{-1} = \mathbf{I} \qquad (4\text{-}57)$$

If we let a_{ij} be the general element of $\mathbf{A}$ and b_{ij} be the general element of $\mathbf{A}^{-1}$, Eq. 4-57 may be expressed as

$$\begin{bmatrix} a_{11} & a_{12} & \cdots & a_{1n} \\ a_{21} & a_{22} & \cdots & a_{2n} \\ \vdots & \vdots & & \vdots \\ a_{n1} & a_{n2} & \cdots & a_{nn} \end{bmatrix} \begin{bmatrix} b_{11} & b_{12} & \cdots & b_{1n} \\ b_{21} & b_{22} & \cdots & b_{2n} \\ \vdots & \vdots & & \vdots \\ b_{n1} & b_{n2} & \cdots & b_{nn} \end{bmatrix} = \begin{bmatrix} 1 & 0 & \cdots & 0 \\ 0 & 1 & & 0 \\ \vdots & & & \vdots \\ 0 & 0 & \cdots & 1 \end{bmatrix} \quad (4\text{-}58)$$

where the identity matrix on the right side of the equation has the same n-by-n order as the $\mathbf{A}$ and $\mathbf{A}^{-1}$ matrices.

From the rules of matrix multiplication, Eq. 4-58 is equivalent to the following n *sets* of simultaneous equations:

$$\left.\begin{array}{l} a_{11}b_{11} + a_{12}b_{21} + \cdots + a_{1n}b_{n1} = 1 \\ a_{21}b_{11} + a_{22}b_{21} + \cdots + a_{2n}b_{n1} = 0 \\ \vdots \qquad\qquad \vdots \qquad\qquad \vdots \qquad \vdots \\ a_{n1}b_{11} + a_{n2}b_{21} + \cdots + a_{nn}b_{n1} = 0 \end{array}\right\} \quad (1)$$

$$\left.\begin{array}{l} a_{11}b_{12} + a_{12}b_{22} + \cdots + a_{1n}b_{n2} = 0 \\ a_{21}b_{12} + a_{22}b_{22} + \cdots + a_{2n}b_{n2} = 1 \\ \vdots \qquad\qquad \vdots \qquad\qquad \vdots \qquad \vdots \\ a_{n1}b_{12} + a_{n2}b_{22} + \cdots + a_{nn}b_{n2} = 0 \end{array}\right\} \quad (2) \qquad (4\text{-}59)$$

$$\left.\begin{array}{l} a_{11}b_{1n} + a_{12}b_{2n} + \cdots + a_{1n}b_{nn} = 0 \\ a_{21}b_{1n} + a_{22}b_{2n} + \cdots + a_{2n}b_{nn} = 0 \\ \vdots \qquad\qquad \vdots \qquad\qquad \vdots \qquad \vdots \\ a_{n1}b_{1n} + a_{n2}b_{2n} + \cdots + a_{nn}b_{nn} = 1 \end{array}\right\} \quad (n)$$

Inspection of Eq. 4-59 reveals that all the n sets of equations have identical known coefficients a_{ij}, and that each set contains 1 column of elements of the inverse matrix $\mathbf{A}^{-1}$ as unknowns and the corresponding column of the identity matrix $\mathbf{I}$ (see Eq. 4-58) as constants. Thus, we have n sets of simultaneous equations which differ only by the constants associated with each set.

It was stated on p. 202 that the Gauss-Jordan elimination method could be utilized to solve simultaneously n sets of simultaneous equations, differing only in their constants, by including the column of constants associated with each set of equations on the right side of the coefficient matrix in the augmented matrix. Utilizing the Gauss-Jordan elimination method, we first form the augmented matrix

$$\begin{bmatrix} a_{11} & a_{12} & \cdots & a_{1n} & 1 & 0 & \cdots & 0 \\ a_{21} & a_{22} & \cdots & a_{2n} & 0 & 1 & \cdots & 0 \\ \vdots & \vdots & & \vdots & \vdots & \vdots & & \vdots \\ a_{n1} & a_{n2} & \cdots & a_{nn} & 0 & 0 & \cdots & 1 \end{bmatrix}$$

The elements of the inverse matrix (the b_{ij}'s) may then be obtained by successive applications of Eqs. 4-32 and 4-33, continuing the reduction process until n columns remain. These n columns will be the inverse matrix A^{-1}.

In accomplishing the matrix reductions on the computer, it is usually not desirable to place the identity matrix in memory because of the amount of data and memory capacity required. Since the elements in this matrix consist only of ones and zeros, appropriate statements may be used in the program to select the proper one of these two values when its use is required in a step of the matrix reduction (for example, see Prob. 4-12).

EXAMPLE 4-5

Let us solve Eq. 4-48 of Example 4-4 using the matrix-inversion method. The coefficient matrix is

$$A = \begin{bmatrix} 1 & 1 & 1 & 1 \\ 4 & 5 & 6 & 7 \\ 6 & 10 & 15 & 21 \\ 12 & 30 & 60 & 105 \end{bmatrix}$$

We begin the matrix reduction with the augmented matrix

$$\begin{bmatrix} 1 & 1 & 1 & 1 & 1 & 0 & 0 & 0 \\ 4 & 5 & 6 & 7 & 0 & 1 & 0 & 0 \\ 6 & 10 & 15 & 21 & 0 & 0 & 1 & 0 \\ 12 & 30 & 60 & 105 & 0 & 0 & 0 & 1 \end{bmatrix}$$

Successive reductions, applying Eqs. 4-32 and 4-33, yield the inverted matrix

$$A^{-1} = \begin{bmatrix} 35 & -15 & 5 & -\frac{1}{3} \\ -84 & 39 & -14 & 1 \\ 70 & -34 & 13 & -1 \\ -20 & 10 & -4 & \frac{1}{3} \end{bmatrix}$$

The correctness of the inverse matrix can easily be checked by multiplying it by the matrix **A**. If it is correct, the resulting product will be the identity matrix.

If $\{K\}$ represents the column matrix of the constants of Eq. 4-48, and $\{C\}$ represents the column matrix of the unknowns C_4, C_5, C_6, and C_7, then, from Eq. 4-56,

$$\{C\} = \mathbf{A}^{-1}\{K\}$$

or

$$\{C\} = \begin{bmatrix} 35 & -15 & 5 & -\frac{1}{3} \\ -84 & 39 & -14 & 1 \\ 70 & -34 & 13 & -1 \\ -20 & 10 & -4 & \frac{1}{3} \end{bmatrix} \begin{Bmatrix} -1 \\ 0 \\ 0 \\ 0 \end{Bmatrix} = \begin{Bmatrix} -35 \\ 84 \\ -70 \\ 20 \end{Bmatrix}$$

These are the same values which were obtained much more simply by the elimination method illustrated in Example 4-4. Comparing the two methods, it is evident that the matrix-inversion method is not practical for solving a single set (or even 2 or 3 sets) of simultaneous equations, because of the amount of calculation involved in determining the inverse matrix. If, however, 20 sets of 10 simultaneous equations, differing only in their constants, were to be solved, an augmented matrix containing 20 columns of constants (which would be used in the elimination method) would be cumbersome to reduce, and the matrix-inversion method could be used to advantage.

4-6. Gauss-Seidel Method

The elimination method of solving simultaneous equations yields sufficiently accurate solutions for as many as 15 to 20 equations, the exact number depending on the actual equations, the number of digits retained in the results of the arithmetic operations, and the roundoff procedure. By using error equations, the number of equations which can be handled can be raised considerably above 15 to 20, but this method also is impractical when perhaps hundreds or thousands of equations must be solved simultaneously. The matrix-inversion procedure has similar limitations when very large numbers of simultaneous equations are involved.

There are, however, several techniques which can be used to solve large numbers of simultaneous equations. One of the most useful is the Gauss-Seidel method. None of the several approaches is completely satisfactory, and the Gauss-Seidel method has the disadvantages of not always converging to a solution and of sometimes converging very slowly when it does converge. However, this method will always converge to a solution when the magnitude of a coefficient of a different unknown, in each equation of the set, is sufficiently dominant with respect to the magnitudes of the other coefficients in that equation. It is difficult to define the exact minimum margin by which such a coefficient must dominate the other coefficients to ensure convergence, and it is even more difficult to predict the rate of convergence for some combination of coefficient values when convergence exists. However, when the absolute value of the dominant coefficient for a different unknown in each equation is larger than the sum of the absolute values of the other coefficients in that equation, convergence is assured. Such a set of linear simultaneous equations is known as a *diagonal* system. A diagonal system is *sufficient* to ensure convergence but is not *necessary*. Fortunately, the linear simultaneous equations which derive from many engineering problems are of the type in which dominant coefficients are present.

As a simple example of a set of simultaneous equations which are solvable by the Gauss-Seidel method, let us consider

$$10x_1 + \quad x_2 + \quad 2x_3 = 44$$
$$2x_1 + 10x_2 + \quad x_3 = 51 \qquad\qquad (4\text{-}60)$$
$$x_1 + \quad 2x_2 + 10x_3 = 61$$

It can be seen that the coefficient of x_1 is dominant in the first equation of the set, and that the coefficients of x_2 and x_3 are dominant in the second and third equations, respectively. Since the dominant coefficient in each equation is larger than the sum of the other coefficients in that equation, Eq. 4-60 represents a diagonal system, and convergence is assured.

The sequence of steps constituting the Gauss-Seidel method is as follows:

1. Assign an initial value for each unknown appearing in the set. If it is possible to make a reasonable assumption of these values, do so. If not, any arbitrarily selected values may be assigned. The initial values used will not affect the convergence, as such, but will affect the number of iterations required for convergence.

2. Starting with the first equation, solve that equation for a new value of the unknown which has the largest coefficient in that equation, using the assumed values for the other unknowns.

3. Go to the second equation and solve it for the unknown having the largest coefficient in that equation, using the value calculated for the unknown in step 2 and the assumed values for the remaining unknowns.

4. Proceed with the remaining equations, always solving for the unknown having the largest coefficient in the particular equation, and always using the *last calculated* values for the other unknowns in the equation. (During the first iteration, assumed values must be used for the unknowns until a calculated value has been obtained.) When the final equation has been solved, yielding a value for the last unknown, 1 iteration is said to have been completed.

5. Continue iterating until the value of each unknown determined in

a particular iteration differs from its respective value obtained in the preceding iteration by an amount less than some arbitrarily selected epsilon. The procedure is then complete.

Referring to step 5, the smaller the magnitude of the epsilon selected, the greater will be the accuracy of the solution. However, the magnitude of epsilon does not specify the error which may exist in the values obtained for the unknowns, as this is a function of the rate of convergence. The faster the rate of convergence, the greater will be the accuracy obtained in the values of the unknowns for a given epsilon.

As a simple illustration of the steps just discussed, let us solve Eq. 4-60, using a value of $\epsilon = 0.02$. Assuming initial values of zero for all 3 unknowns, the steps appear as follows:

(1)
$$\begin{bmatrix} 10x_1 + 0 + 0 = 44 \\ x_1 = 4.40 \end{bmatrix}$$

(2)
$$\begin{bmatrix} 2(4.40) + 10x_2 + 0 = 51 \\ x_2 = 4.22 \end{bmatrix}$$

(3)
$$\begin{bmatrix} 4.40 + 2(4.22) + 10x_3 = 61 \\ x_3 = 4.81 \end{bmatrix}$$

The first iteration has now been completed. A second iteration yields

(1)
$$\begin{bmatrix} 10x_1 + 4.22 + 2(4.81) = 44 \\ x_1 = 3.01 \end{bmatrix}$$

(2)
$$\begin{bmatrix} 2(3.01) + 10x_2 + 4.81 = 51 \\ x_2 = 4.01 \end{bmatrix}$$

(3)
$$\begin{bmatrix} 3.01 + 2(4.01) + 10x_3 = 61 \\ x_3 = 4.99 \end{bmatrix}$$

Comparing the last values with the respective values obtained in the previous iteration, it can be seen that Δx_1, Δx_2, and Δx_3 are all greater than the ϵ chosen. Therefore, a third iteration is indicated. This iteration yields

$$x_1 = 3.00$$
$$x_2 = 4.00$$
$$x_3 = 5.00$$

Comparing these values with the respective values obtained in the previous iteration, it can be seen that Δx_1, Δx_2, and Δx_3 are all less than ϵ, indicating that only 3 iterations are required. In this example, a fourth iteration would be found to give no change in the values of the unknowns, indicating that an exact solution has been reached.

In obtaining the above solution, only 3 digits were retained in the result of each calculation. This was done by arbitrarily lopping off all the excess digits which appeared. In a computer solution the computer might retain approximately 8 to 12 digits in the result of each calculation, depending on the language and on the computer being used. Although this example is a simple one, it serves very well to illustrate the Gauss-Seidel method, since the solution of a much larger set of simultaneous equations would proceed in exactly the same manner, differing only in that many more calculations would be required.

The Gauss-Seidel method is used frequently in the solution of Laplace's and Poisson's partial differential equations, and an example of an engineering problem in which this method is employed will be discussed in Sec. 8-2.

4-7. Homogeneous Algebraic Equations—Eigenvalue Problems

In the preceding sections several methods were presented for solving n nonhomogeneous simultaneous linear algebraic equations in n unknowns. It was assumed that the equations were such that their solutions yielded unique values for the unknowns, since that is generally the case for nonhomogeneous equations describing the characteristics of physical systems. It was noted that the determinants of the coefficient matrices of the sets of equations had to be nonzero (all the equations of the set had to be linearly independent) before unique solutions could be obtained.

Let us now consider the solution of *homogeneous* simultaneous linear algebraic equations which have the general form

$$
\begin{aligned}
a_{11}x_1 + a_{12}x_2 + a_{13}x_3 + \cdots + a_{1n}x_n &= 0 \\
a_{21}x_1 + a_{22}x_2 + \cdots\cdots\cdots + a_{2n}x_n &= 0 \\
\vdots \qquad\qquad\qquad\qquad \vdots \quad\ \ \vdots & \\
a_{n1}x_1 + \cdots\cdots\cdots\cdots\cdots + a_{nn}x_n &= 0
\end{aligned}
\tag{4-61}
$$

or, in matrix notation,

$$
\begin{bmatrix}
a_{11} & a_{12} & \cdots & a_{1n} \\
a_{21} & a_{22} & \cdots & a_{2n} \\
\vdots & & & \vdots \\
a_{n1} & a_{n2} & \cdots & a_{nn}
\end{bmatrix}
\begin{Bmatrix}
x_1 \\
x_2 \\
\vdots \\
x_n
\end{Bmatrix}
= \mathbf{0}
\tag{4-62}
$$

In linear algebra it is proved that any system of m linear algebraic equations in n unknowns has a solution if, and only if, the coefficient matrix and the augmented matrix of the set have the same *rank*.[5] Therefore, a set of homogeneous equations such as Eq. 4-62 always has a solution (that is, they are consistent), since the augmented matrix and the coefficient matrix of the set are always necessarily of the same rank.

---

[5]The rank of a matrix is the order of the largest nonzero determinant which can be obtained considering all minors of the matrix. Or, stated in another way, it is the number of linearly independent rows (or columns) of the matrix.

If the rank r of the coefficient matrix of the set of equations is equal to the order n, the set has a *unique* solution which is the *zero* or *trivial* solution ($x_1 = x_2 = \cdots = x_n = 0$). For such a set of equations the determinant of the coefficient matrix is *nonzero*. (All the equations of the set are linearly independent.)

Nontrivial solutions exist for a set of homogeneous equations if, and only if, the rank r of the coefficient matrix of the set is *less* than the order n. For such a set of equations, the determinant of the coefficient matrix is *zero*, and the set will consist of r linearly independent equations and $n - r$ dependent equations which are linear combinations of the independent equations. In obtaining nontrivial solutions of a set of homogeneous equations, unique values are not obtained for the unknowns. Rather, *relationships* are established between the unknowns (the x's of Eq. 4-61). Any combination of x_i values which satisfies these relationships constitutes a solution. Such solutions will be discussed further later in this section.

To understand the application of homogeneous equations in the analysis of engineering problems, let us consider the solution of *eigenvalue problems* (*characteristic-value* problems) which occur in the areas of vibration analysis, electric-circuit analysis, theory of elasticity, and so on. In developing the mathematical models of systems in these areas, the equations generally have the form

$$
\begin{aligned}
(a_{11} - \lambda)x_1 + \quad & a_{12}x_2 + \quad a_{13}x_3 + \cdots + a_{1n}x_n = 0 \\
a_{21}x_1 + (a_{22} - \lambda)x_2 + \quad & a_{23}x_3 + \cdots + a_{2n}x_n = 0 \\
a_{31}x_1 + \quad & a_{32}x_2 + (a_{33} - \lambda)x_3 + \cdots + a_{3n}x_n = 0 \qquad (4\text{-}63) \\
\vdots \quad & \qquad\qquad \vdots \qquad \vdots \\
a_{n1}x_1 + \quad & \cdots\cdots\cdots\cdots\cdots\cdots\cdots + (a_{nn} - \lambda)x_n = 0
\end{aligned}
$$

where the coefficients a_{ij} are real, the x's are system variables, and λ is a particular parameter of the system having unknown values. For example, in a vibrating system having several degrees of freedom, such as the one shown in Fig. 4-8, the coefficient values would derive from the m_i and k_i values (masses and spring constants, respectively), and x_i would be the displacements of the respective masses, and the values of λ would be the squares of the natural frequencies of the system.

In matrix notation Eq. 4-63 is expressed as

$$
\begin{bmatrix}
(a_{11} - \lambda) & a_{12} & a_{13}\cdots\cdots a_{1n} \\
a_{21} & (a_{22} - \lambda) & a_{23}\cdots\cdots a_{2n} \\
a_{31} & a_{32} & (a_{33} - \lambda)\cdots a_{3n} \\
\vdots & \vdots & \vdots \quad \vdots \\
a_{n1} & \cdots\cdots & \cdots\cdots (a_{nn} - \lambda)
\end{bmatrix}
\begin{Bmatrix}
x_1 \\ x_2 \\ x_3 \\ \vdots \\ x_n
\end{Bmatrix} = \mathbf{0} \qquad (4\text{-}64)
$$

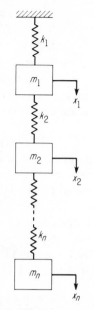

Fig. 4-8. Vibrating system with
multiple degrees of freedom.

or more compactly as

$$(\mathbf{A} - \lambda\mathbf{I})\mathbf{X} = 0 \qquad (4\text{-}65)$$

where the use of the *identity* matrix $\mathbf{I}$ allows us to use $(\mathbf{A} - \lambda\mathbf{I})$ as a coefficient matrix. The column matrix $\mathbf{X}$ is frequently referred to as an *eigen-
vector*, with $x_1, x_2, x_3, \ldots, x_n$ considered as the *components* of the eigenvector. The values obtained for λ are known as *eigenvalues* or *characteristic values* of the matrix $\mathbf{A}$.

Thinking of Eq. 4-63 or Eq. 4-64 as being the mathematical model of
a physical system, it is obvious that the trivial solution has no physical
significance and that we are interested in nontrivial solutions. As stated
earlier, nontrivial solutions exist if the determinant of the coefficient
matrix is equal to zero. With λ appearing as an unknown in the coefficient
matrix, we may arbitrarily set the determinant of the coefficient matrix
equal to zero,

$$|D| = \begin{vmatrix} (a_{11} - \lambda) & a_{12} & a_{13} & a_{1n} \\ a_{21} & (a_{22} - \lambda) & a_{23} & a_{2n} \\ a_{31} & a_{32} & (a_{33} - \lambda) & a_{3n} \\ \vdots & \vdots & \vdots & \vdots \\ a_{n1} & \cdots\cdots\cdots\cdots\cdots\cdots\cdots\cdots & (a_{nn} - \lambda) \end{vmatrix} = 0$$

and find values of λ which will make the determinant equal to zero.

The expansion of such a determinant results in an nth-degree polynomial

$$\lambda^n + b_1\lambda^{n-1} + b_2\lambda^{n-2} + \cdots + b_n = 0 \qquad (4\text{-}66)$$

which is solved to obtain the λ_i values that will make $|D| = 0$. (There will be n values of λ appearing as the n roots of the polynomial.) This polynomial is referred to as the *characteristic equation* of the matrix $\mathbf{A}$, and the roots of the polynomial are known as *eigenvalues* or *characteristic values*.

After determining the eigenvalues, these values may be substituted, 1 value at a time, back into the given set of equations to obtain a corresponding *set of relationships* between the unknowns x_i for each substitution. The relationships obtained will depend upon the rank r of the coefficient matrix $(\mathbf{A} - \lambda\mathbf{I})$. If $r = n - 1$, the relationships will be such that the assumption of a value for 1 unknown will yield a corresponding value for each of the remaining unknowns; if $r = n - 2$, the relationships will be such that values will have to be assumed for 2 unknowns in order to obtain a corresponding value for each of the remaining unknowns; and so forth.

In many engineering applications the rank of the coefficient matrix is 1 less than the order (we will see later that this corresponds to only 1 linearly *dependent* equation in the set), and the relationships between the unknowns may be obtained as the ratios $x_1/x_2 = \alpha_1$, $x_1/x_3 = \alpha_2, \ldots$, $x_1/x_n = \alpha_{n-1}$. The unknowns x_i are known as *eigenvector components*. They will be discussed in more detail in Sec. 4-9.

When n is small ($n = 2$ or 3), the expansion of the determinant by minors to obtain the polynomial in λ is not difficult, nor is the subsequent determination of the roots of the polynomial. However, when n becomes larger, the determination of the coefficients of the polynomial becomes more difficult, and a procedure more practical than an expansion by minors must be employed. (Such a procedure will be discussed in the next section.) These higher-degree polynomials may be solved by one of the methods discussed in Chapter 3.

EXAMPLE 4-6

To make the preceding discussion a little more specific, let us consider a simple set of just 2 equations,

$$\begin{aligned} (a_{11} - \lambda)x_1 + \quad\quad a_{12}x_2 &= 0 \\ a_{21}x_1 + (a_{22} - \lambda)x_2 &= 0 \end{aligned} \qquad (4\text{-}67)$$

which may be written in matrix notation as

$$\begin{bmatrix} (a_{11} - \lambda) & a_{12} \\ a_{21} & (a_{22} - \lambda) \end{bmatrix} \begin{Bmatrix} x_1 \\ x_2 \end{Bmatrix} = \mathbf{0} \qquad (4\text{-}68)$$

Using Cramer's rule to solve for x_1 and x_2, we obtain

$$x_1 = \frac{0}{\begin{vmatrix} (a_{11} - \lambda) & a_{12} \\ a_{21} & (a_{22} - \lambda) \end{vmatrix}} \quad \text{and} \quad x_2 = \frac{0}{\begin{vmatrix} (a_{11} - \lambda) & a_{12} \\ a_{21} & (a_{22} - \lambda) \end{vmatrix}} \quad (4\text{-}69)$$

Looking at Eq. 4-69 it is obvious that if the determinant of the coefficient matrix appearing in the denominator of each equation is nonzero, only a trivial solution will be obtained. However, if $|D| = 0$,

$$x_1 = 0/0 \quad \text{and} \quad x_2 = 0/0 \quad (4\text{-}70)$$

which shows that nontrivial solutions *may* exist. We know, from the previous discussion, that when $|D| = 0$ nontrivial solutions *do* exist.

Expanding the determinant by minors yields the characteristic equation

$$\lambda^2 - (a_{11} + a_{22})\lambda + (a_{11}a_{22} - a_{21}a_{12}) = 0 \quad (4\text{-}71)$$

which is a second-degree polynomial in this simple example. The roots λ_1 and λ_2 (the eigenvalues) of Eq. 4-71 are the 2 values of λ which will make the determinant of the coefficient matrix of Eq. 4-68 equal to zero, thus yielding a nontrivial solution.

After obtaining λ_1 and λ_2, their substitution into either Eq. 4-67 or Eq. 4-68 yields 2 relationships between the unknowns x_1 and x_2. For example, using λ_1 in Eq. 4-67, we obtain

$$x_1 = \frac{-a_{12}x_2}{(a_{11} - \lambda_1)} = \frac{-(a_{22} - \lambda_1)x_2}{a_{21}} \quad (4\text{-}72)$$

Similarly, using λ_2 in Eq. 4-67 yields another relationship

$$x_1 = \frac{-a_{12}x_2}{(a_{11} - \lambda_2)} = \frac{-(a_{22} - \lambda_2)x_2}{a_{21}} \quad (4\text{-}73)$$

It is apparent, from an inspection of Eqs. 4-72 and 4-73, that unique values of x_1 and x_2 cannot be determined. However, any *combination* of values of x_1 and x_2 constitutes a solution of Eq. 4-67, as long as the combination satisfies Eq. 4-72 when λ_1 is used, or Eq. 4-73 when λ_2 is used.

EXAMPLE 4-7

To illustrate the solution of a physically significant characteristic-value problem, let us determine the principal stresses at a point in a body in a state of plane stress.

Figure 4-9a shows an infinitesimal element of material subjected to the normal stresses σ_x and σ_y and the shear stress τ_{xy}. Since all stresses in the z direction are zero, the element is in a state of plane stress. In deriving the equilibrium equations, we consider a wedge-shaped portion of the element, formed by cutting the element with an inclined plane at

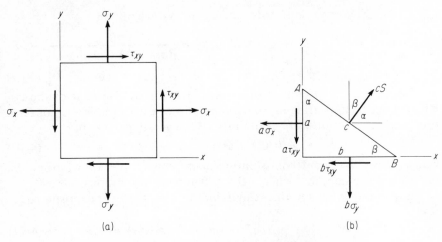

FIG. 4-9. Element of material in a state of plane stress.

some angle α to the yz plane. This plane AB is arbitrarily designated as a principal plane upon which one of the principal normal stresses acts. We know, from mechanics-of-materials theory, that the shear stress is zero on a principal plane. Therefore, the only stress shown acting on plane AB is the principal normal stress, which will be designated by S. Considering the element to have a depth of unity, with sides of lengths a, b, and c, as shown, the corresponding areas of the sides upon which the stresses act are of magnitudes a, b, and c. The forces shown in Fig. 4-9b which maintain the wedge-shaped element in equilibrium are obtained by multiplying the stresses acting on these areas by the respective areas of the element.

Since the element is in equilibrium,

$$\Sigma F_x = 0 = cS \cos \alpha - a\sigma_x - b\tau_{xy}$$

from which

$$\frac{a}{c} \sigma_x - S \cos \alpha + \frac{b}{c} \tau_{xy} = 0 \qquad (4\text{-}74)$$

Also,

$$\Sigma F_y = 0 = cS \cos \beta - a\tau_{xy} - b\sigma_y$$

from which

$$\frac{a}{c} \tau_{xy} - S \cos \beta + \frac{b}{c} \sigma_y = 0 \qquad (4\text{-}75)$$

Denoting the direction cosines l and m of the normal to the principal plane as

$$l = \cos \alpha = \frac{a}{c}$$

$$m = \cos \beta = \frac{b}{c}$$

Eqs. 4-74 and 4-75 may be written as

$$(\sigma_x - S)l + \tau_{xy}m = 0$$
$$\tau_{xy}l + (\sigma_y - S)m = 0 \tag{4-76}$$

or, in matrix notation, as

$$\begin{bmatrix} (\sigma_x - S) & \tau_{xy} \\ \tau_{xy} & (\sigma_y - S) \end{bmatrix} \begin{Bmatrix} l \\ m \end{Bmatrix} = 0 \tag{4-77}$$

Comparing Eq. 4-77 with Eq. 4-64, we see that the normal and shear stresses correspond to the coefficients a_{ij}, the direction cosines correspond to the unknowns x_i, and the principal stresses S are λ's or the eigenvalues necessary to satisfy the equilibrium equations of Eq. 4-76.

Remembering that the determinant of the coefficient matrix of Eq. 4-77 must equal zero to obtain a nontrivial solution,

$$|D| = \begin{vmatrix} (\sigma_x - S) & \tau_{xy} \\ \tau_{xy} & (\sigma_y - S) \end{vmatrix} = 0 \tag{4-78}$$

Expanding the determinant yields

$$S^2 - (\sigma_x + \sigma_y)S + \sigma_x\sigma_y - \tau_{xy}^2 = 0 \tag{4-79}$$

Using the binomial theorem, the roots or eigenvalues of Eq. 4-79 are found to be

$$S_{1,2} = \frac{\sigma_x + \sigma_y}{2} \pm \sqrt{\left(\frac{\sigma_x - \sigma_y}{2}\right)^2 + \tau_{xy}^2} \tag{4-80}$$

Equation 4-80 is the familiar equation, found in mechanics of materials, relating the principal stresses to the stresses acting on any 2 orthogonal planes.

Suppose that the orthogonal stresses at the point are given by

$$\sigma_x = 1000 \text{ psi}$$
$$\sigma_y = 500 \text{ psi}$$
$$\tau_{xy} = 500 \text{ psi}$$

From Eq. 4-80 we can compute the principal stresses as

$$S_1 = 1310 \text{ psi}$$
$$S_2 = 190 \text{ psi}$$

Then the relationships between the direction cosines l and m may be determined by substituting the principal-stress values into Eq. 4-77. Using the value of S_2

$$\begin{bmatrix} (1000 - 190) & 500 \\ 500 & (500 - 190) \end{bmatrix} \begin{Bmatrix} l \\ m \end{Bmatrix} = \mathbf{0} \tag{4-81}$$

which yields the relationship

$$\frac{m}{l} = \frac{\cos \beta}{\cos \alpha} = -\frac{810}{500} \tag{4-82}$$

The direction-cosine relationships for the principal stress S_1 are determined similarly, where

$$\begin{bmatrix} (1000 - 1310) & 500 \\ 500 & (500 - 1310) \end{bmatrix} \begin{Bmatrix} l \\ m \end{Bmatrix} = 0 \qquad (4\text{-}83)$$

which yields

$$\frac{m}{l} = \frac{\cos \beta}{\cos \alpha} = \frac{310}{500} \qquad (4\text{-}84)$$

In this particular example unique values may be determined for l and m, since an additional relationship exists in that the angles α and β are complementary angles. Thus, since $\sin \alpha = \cos \beta$,

$$(\text{for } S_2) \qquad \tan \alpha = -\frac{810}{500}$$

$$\alpha = -58.3°$$

$$(\text{for } S_1) \qquad \tan \alpha = \frac{310}{500}$$

$$\alpha = 31.7°$$

These angles locate the principal planes (the planes upon which the respective principal stresses act) with α measured positive counterclockwise from the y axis and negative clockwise (see Fig. 4-9b).

It should be emphasized that the unique values obtained for l and m resulted from the availability of the *additional* relationship between the angles α and β. In general, in characteristic-value problems, such additional relationships will not be available, and only ratios of the components of the eigenvector will be obtainable, as discussed before.

EXAMPLE 4-8

As another example of a characteristic-value problem, let us analyze the free undamped vibrational characteristics of the three-degrees-of-freedom system shown schematically in Fig. 4-10. The system consists of the 3 masses m_1, m_2, and m_3, connected by the 3 springs shown, with spring constants k_1, k_2, and k_3. The displacements of the masses are defined by the generalized coordinates x_1, x_2, and x_3, respectively, each displacement being measured from the static-equilibrium position of the respective mass.

Utilizing either Lagrange's equation or Newton's second law, the differential equations of motion of the system are found to be

$$m_1 \ddot{x}_1 + (k_1 + k_2)x_1 - k_2 x_2 = 0$$
$$m_2 \ddot{x}_2 - k_2 x_1 + (k_2 + k_3)x_2 - k_3 x_3 = 0 \qquad (4\text{-}85)$$
$$m_3 \ddot{x}_3 - k_3 x_2 + k_3 x_3 = 0$$

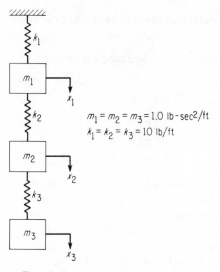

FIG. 4-10.   Three-degrees-of-freedom system.

$$m_1 = m_2 = m_3 = 1.0 \text{ lb-sec}^2/\text{ft}$$
$$k_1 = k_2 = k_3 = 10 \text{ lb/ft}$$

It is well known, from vibration theory, that the solution of Eq. 4-85 may be taken in the form

$$x_1 = X_1 \sin pt$$
$$x_2 = X_2 \sin pt \qquad (4\text{-}86)$$
$$x_3 = X_3 \sin pt$$

where X_1, X_2, and X_3 are the *amplitudes* of motion of the respective masses, and p denotes the natural circular frequencies corresponding to the principal modes of vibration of the system.

Substituting Eq. 4-86 and appropriate derivatives of these expressions into Eq. 4-85, and using the spring-constant and mass values shown in Fig. 4-10, we obtain the following set of homogeneous algebraic equations:

$$(20 - p^2)X_1 \qquad\quad -10X_2 \qquad\qquad\qquad = 0$$
$$-10X_1 + (20 - p^2)X_2 \qquad\quad -10X_3 = 0 \qquad (4\text{-}87)$$
$$-10X_2 + (10 - p^2)X_3 = 0$$

To obtain a nontrivial solution of Eq. 4-87, we know that the determinant of the coefficients of X_i must be equal to zero, so that

$$|D| = \begin{vmatrix} (20 - p^2) & -10 & 0 \\ -10 & (20 - p^2) & -10 \\ 0 & -10 & (10 - p^2) \end{vmatrix} = 0 \qquad (4\text{-}88)$$

Expansion of this determinant results in the characteristic polynomial

$$p^6 - 50p^4 + 600p^2 - 1000 = 0 \qquad (4\text{-}89)$$

which may be written as a cubic equation in p^2 as

$$(p^2)^3 - 50(p^2)^2 + 600(p^2) - 1000 = 0 \qquad (4\text{-}90)$$

The roots of Eq. 4-90 are found to be

$$p_1^2 = 1.98 \text{ sec}^{-2}$$
$$p_2^2 = 15.5 \text{ sec}^{-2}$$
$$p_3^2 = 32.5 \text{ sec}^{-2}$$

These eigenvalues are the squares of the natural circular frequencies of the first, second, and third modes of vibration of the system, respectively.

Since Eq. 4-87 constitutes a homogeneous set of simultaneous equations, a unique set of values cannot be obtained for X_1, X_2, and X_3. However, various ratios of the amplitudes may be determined which will yield the configuration of the system for the various modes when the amplitude of any 1 of the masses is defined. For example, substituting $p^2 = 1.98$ into Eq. 4-87 yields the following configuration for the *first* mode:

$$\left.\begin{array}{l} X_2 = 1.80X_1 \\ X_3 = 2.25X_1 \end{array}\right\} \quad \text{first mode} \qquad (4\text{-}91)$$

Similarly, the second- and third-mode configurations, using $p_2^2 = 15.5$ and $p_3^2 = 32.5$, respectively, are

$$\left.\begin{array}{l} X_2 = 0.45X_1 \\ X_3 = -0.80X_1 \end{array}\right\} \quad \text{second mode} \qquad (4\text{-}92)$$

$$\left.\begin{array}{l} X_2 = -1.25X_1 \\ X_3 = 0.555X_1 \end{array}\right\} \quad \text{third mode} \qquad (4\text{-}93)$$

From the last 3 equations it can be seen that if the amplitude of any one of the three masses is known or assumed for a particular mode of vibration, the configuration of the system may be determined for that mode. Since Eqs. 4-91 through 4-93 consist of ratios of amplitudes X_i, the substitution of Eq. 4-86 into these equations reveals that the ratios shown are also the ratios of the *displacements*. For example, when m_1 has a displacement of 1 in. and the system is vibrating in the second mode, the corresponding displacements of m_2 and m_3 will be 0.45 in. and -0.80 in., respectively, and the motion of m_3 will be 180° out of phase with that of m_1. It might be added here that the configuration of a system, as given by the above ratios, also defines the *initial* displacements which would have to be given to the masses to have the system vibrate in the mode associated with that configuration, with no other harmonics present, when the system is released from rest.

4-8. Computer Determination of Characteristic Polynomials

In the examples presented in the preceding section, the determination of the eigenvalues involved two major steps: 1) obtaining the characteristic polynomial, by expanding the determinant of the coefficient matrix $(A - \lambda I)$, and 2) solving for the roots of the polynomial. Both steps employed familiar elementary methods, since we were concerned with matrices of low order.

When the order of the matrices becomes larger, computer methods must be adopted to accomplish efficiently each of these steps. Since, as mentioned previously, the roots of the polynomial can be found by one of the methods already covered in Chapter 3, we shall be concerned here with a computer method for determining the characteristic equation.[6]

Many methods have been proposed for generating the coefficients p_k of the characteristic equation

$$\lambda^n + p_1 \lambda^{n-1} + p_2 \lambda^{n-2} + p_3 \lambda^{n-3} + \cdots + p_n = 0 \quad (k = 1, 2, \ldots, n) \quad (4\text{-}94)$$

when the order n of the set of algebraic equations is large. Of these methods, we shall discuss the *Faddeev-Leverrier method*, an efficient technique which is equally suitable for generating the polynomial coefficients whether the coefficient matrix of the equations is symmetrical or unsymmetrical. This method has an additional feature in that the *inverse* of the matrix for which the eigenvalues are desired is, essentially, obtained in the process of generating the coefficients of the characteristic polynomial. This is advantageous in instances where one may wish to check the accuracy of the eigenvalues obtained by the polynomial method, by using an iterative method, since an inversion of the matrix may be desired in an iterative procedure (see Sec. 4-9). Proof of the validity of the Faddeev-Leverrier method is beyond the intended scope of this text, but it may be found elsewhere.[7] (This reference also includes numerous other methods and their derivations.)

Before outlining the method we have chosen, let us define the *trace* of a matrix, since it is an integral part of the method. Given the matrix

$$\begin{bmatrix} a_{11} & a_{12} & a_{13} & \cdots & a_{1n} \\ a_{21} & a_{22} & a_{23} & \cdots & a_{2n} \\ a_{31} & a_{32} & a_{33} & \cdots & a_{3n} \\ \vdots & \vdots & & & \vdots \\ a_{n1} & a_{n2} & & \cdots & a_{nn} \end{bmatrix} \quad (4\text{-}95)$$

[6] In Example 7-3 (Chapter 7) a characteristic-value problem arising from the finite-difference form of a differential equation is solved, in which Graeffe's method is used to find the roots of the characteristic polynomial.

[7] See Faddeev, D. K., and Faddeeva, U. N. *Computational Methods of Linear Algebra* (tr. by Robert C. Williams). San Francisco: W. H. Freeman & Co., 1963. For other methods see Lapidus, Leon. *Digital Computation for Chemical Engineers*. New York: McGraw-Hill Book Company, 1962.

the trace of the matrix, written as "tr $\mathbf{A}$," is

$$\text{tr } \mathbf{A} = a_{11} + a_{22} + a_{33} + \cdots + a_{nn} \qquad (4\text{-}96)$$

The Faddeev-Leverrier method generates the polynomial coefficients p_k ($k = 1, 2, 3, \ldots, n$) from the matrix $\mathbf{A}$ of the given set of equations written as

$$(\mathbf{A} - \lambda \mathbf{I})\mathbf{X} = 0 \qquad (4\text{-}97)$$

by forming a *sequence* of matrices $\mathbf{B}_1, \mathbf{B}_2, \ldots, \mathbf{B}_n$ from which the p_k values are determined. These p_k values are then substituted in the following basic form of the characteristic polynomial:

$$(-1)^n(\lambda^n - p_1 \lambda^{n-1} - p_2 \lambda^{n-2} - p_3 \lambda^{n-3} - \cdots - p_n) = 0 \qquad (4\text{-}98)$$

where the $(-1)^n$ is used merely to give the terms of the polynomial the same signs that they would have if the polynomial were generated by expanding a determinant. The p_k values are determined as follows:

$$
\left.
\begin{aligned}
\mathbf{B}_1 &= \mathbf{A} & \text{and} \quad p_1 &= \text{tr } \mathbf{B}_1 \\[2mm]
\mathbf{B}_2 &= \mathbf{A}(\mathbf{B}_1 - p_1 \mathbf{I}) & \text{and} \quad p_2 &= \frac{1}{2} \text{tr } \mathbf{B}_2 \\[2mm]
\mathbf{B}_3 &= \mathbf{A}(\mathbf{B}_2 - p_2 \mathbf{I}) & \text{and} \quad p_3 &= \frac{1}{3} \text{tr } \mathbf{B}_3 \\
&\ \ \vdots & \vdots \\
\mathbf{B}_k &= \mathbf{A}(\mathbf{B}_{k-1} - p_{k-1} \mathbf{I}) & \text{and} \quad p_k &= \frac{1}{k} \text{tr } \mathbf{B}_k \\
&\ \ \vdots & \vdots \\
\mathbf{B}_n &= \mathbf{A}(\mathbf{B}_{n-1} - p_{n-1} \mathbf{I}) & \text{and} \quad p_n &= \frac{1}{n} \text{tr } \mathbf{B}_n
\end{aligned}
\right\} \qquad (4\text{-}99)
$$

Referring to the generation of the inverse of the matrix for which the eigenvalues are desired, mentioned earlier, Faddeev has shown that the inverse of $\mathbf{A}$ can be determined from

$$\mathbf{A}^{-1} = \frac{1}{p_n}(\mathbf{B}_{n-1} - p_{n-1} \mathbf{I}) \qquad (4\text{-}100)$$

EXAMPLE 4-9

Let us suppose that the homogeneous set of algebraic equations

$$
\begin{aligned}
(3 - \lambda)x_1 + \qquad 2x_2 + \qquad\quad 4x_3 &= 0 \\
2x_1 + (0 - \lambda)x_2 + \qquad\quad 2x_3 &= 0 \qquad (4\text{-}101) \\
4x_1 + \qquad\quad 2x_2 + (3 - \lambda)x_3 &= 0
\end{aligned}
$$

has been obtained as the mathematical model of some physical system which we are analyzing. In matrix notation, Eq. 4-101 appears as

$$
\begin{bmatrix}
(3 - \lambda) & 2 & 4 \\
2 & (0 - \lambda) & 2 \\
4 & 2 & (3 - \lambda)
\end{bmatrix}
\begin{Bmatrix}
x_1 \\
x_2 \\
x_3
\end{Bmatrix}
= 0 \qquad (4\text{-}102)
$$

Our problem will be to find the characteristic polynomial, using the Faddeev-Leverrier method, and then to solve the resulting polynomial for its roots which are the eigenvalues of the matrix

$$\mathbf{A} = \begin{bmatrix} 3 & 2 & 4 \\ 2 & 0 & 2 \\ 4 & 2 & 3 \end{bmatrix}$$

of the equation

$$(\mathbf{A} - \lambda\mathbf{I})\mathbf{X} = 0 \tag{4-103}$$

Using the procedure indicated in Eq. 4-99,

$$\mathbf{B}_1 = \mathbf{A} = \begin{bmatrix} 3 & 2 & 4 \\ 2 & 0 & 2 \\ 4 & 2 & 3 \end{bmatrix}$$

and

$$p_1 = \text{tr } \mathbf{B}_1 = 3 + 0 + 3 = 6$$

$$\mathbf{B}_2 = \mathbf{A}(\mathbf{B}_1 - p_1\mathbf{I}) = \begin{bmatrix} 3 & 2 & 4 \\ 2 & 0 & 2 \\ 4 & 2 & 3 \end{bmatrix} \left(\begin{bmatrix} 3 & 2 & 4 \\ 2 & 0 & 2 \\ 4 & 2 & 3 \end{bmatrix} - \begin{bmatrix} 6 & 0 & 0 \\ 0 & 6 & 0 \\ 0 & 0 & 6 \end{bmatrix} \right)$$

$$= \begin{bmatrix} 3 & 2 & 4 \\ 2 & 0 & 2 \\ 4 & 2 & 3 \end{bmatrix} \begin{bmatrix} -3 & 2 & 4 \\ 2 & -6 & 2 \\ 4 & 2 & -3 \end{bmatrix}$$

$$= \begin{bmatrix} 11 & 2 & 4 \\ 2 & 8 & 2 \\ 4 & 2 & 11 \end{bmatrix}$$

and

$$p_2 = \tfrac{1}{2} \text{tr } \mathbf{B}_2 = \tfrac{1}{2}(11 + 8 + 11) = 15$$

$$\mathbf{B}_3 = \mathbf{A}(\mathbf{B}_2 - p_2\mathbf{I}) = \begin{bmatrix} 3 & 2 & 4 \\ 2 & 0 & 2 \\ 4 & 2 & 3 \end{bmatrix} \left(\begin{bmatrix} 11 & 2 & 4 \\ 2 & 8 & 2 \\ 4 & 2 & 11 \end{bmatrix} - \begin{bmatrix} 15 & 0 & 0 \\ 0 & 15 & 0 \\ 0 & 0 & 15 \end{bmatrix} \right)$$

$$\begin{bmatrix} 3 & 2 & 4 \\ 2 & 0 & 2 \\ 4 & 2 & 3 \end{bmatrix} \begin{bmatrix} -4 & 2 & 4 \\ 2 & -7 & 2 \\ 4 & 2 & -4 \end{bmatrix} = \begin{bmatrix} 8 & 0 & 0 \\ 0 & 8 & 0 \\ 0 & 0 & 8 \end{bmatrix}$$

and

$$p_3 = \tfrac{1}{3} \text{tr } \mathbf{B}_3 = \tfrac{1}{3}(8 + 8 + 8) = 8$$

Substituting the values to p_1, p_2, and p_3 into Eq. 4-98, we obtain

$$(-1)^3(\lambda^3 - 6\lambda^2 - 15\lambda - 8) = 0 \tag{4-104}$$

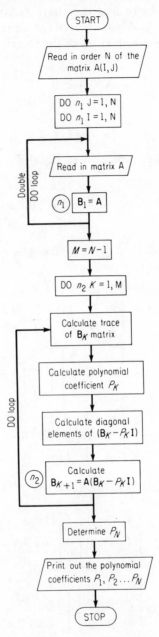

FIG. 4-11. Flow chart for generating coefficients of a characteristic polynomial.

The roots of Eq. 4-104 are simply obtained, since the polynomial may be factored as

$$(\lambda - 8)(\lambda + 1)(\lambda + 1) = 0 \qquad (4\text{-}105)$$

from which the eigenvalues are

$$\lambda_1 = 8$$
$$\lambda_2 = -1 \qquad (4\text{-}106)$$
$$\lambda_3 = -1$$

Reviewing the determination of the coefficient p_3 in the procedure just finished, we observe that

$$\mathbf{B}_3 = p_3 \mathbf{I} \qquad (4\text{-}107)$$

Faddeev has proved that for an nth-order matrix

$$\mathbf{B}_n = p_n \mathbf{I} \qquad (4\text{-}108)$$

from which we see than we can always obtain p_n simply as

$$p_n = b_{11} = b_{22} = b_{33} = \cdots = b_{nn} \qquad (4\text{-}109)$$

where the b_{ii} are *identical* elements composing the trace of $\mathbf{B}_n$.

At this point the interested reader might expand the determinant of the coefficient matrix of Eq. 4-102

$$|D| = \begin{vmatrix} (3 - \lambda) & 2 & 4 \\ 2 & (0 - \lambda) & 2 \\ 4 & 2 & (3 - \lambda) \end{vmatrix} = 0$$

by minors and check the polynomial obtained in Eq. 4-104.

The generation of the coefficients of the characteristic polynomial, by the Faddeev-Leverrier method, on the computer is outlined in the flow chart of Fig. 4-11. The variable names and the quantities they represent in the **FORTRAN** source program are as follows:

FORTRAN *Name*	Quantity
N	Order of the **A** matrix for which the characteristic polynomial is to be determined
A(I, J)	Elements of the **A** matrix
B(I, J)	Elements of the $\mathbf{B}_k$ matrices formed by the Faddeev-Leverrier method; also used for elements of $(\mathbf{B}_k - p_k \mathbf{I})$
I	Row numbers of **A** and $\mathbf{B}_k$ matrices
J	Column numbers of **A** and $\mathbf{B}_k$ matrices
M	$N - 1$
TRACE	Traces of $\mathbf{B}_k$ matrices
P(K)	Coefficients of characteristic polynomial

K	Subscript of P(K) used as index of a DO loop
AK	Floating-point name for the subscript K of P(K)
COLB(I)	Elements of the columns of the $(\mathbf{B}_{k-1} - p_{k-1}\mathbf{I})$ matrices

The IBM 1620 source program, written to implement the flow chart of Fig. 4-11, is as follows:

```
   DIMENSION  A(15,15),B(15,15),P(15),COLB(15)
 1 FORMAT (I3)
 2 FORMAT (E14.0)
 3 FORMAT (E14.8)
 4 FORMAT (42HTHE CHARACTERISTIC POLYNOMIAL COEFFICIENTS)
 5 FORMAT (22HP(1) THROUGH P(N) ARE,/)
   ACCEPT TAPE 1,N
   DO 6J = 1,N
   DO 6I = 1,N
   ACCEPT TAPE 2,A(I,J)
 6 B(I,J) = A(I,J)
   M = N − 1
   DO 10K = 1,M
   TRACE = 0.
   DO 7I = 1,N
 7 TRACE = TRACE + B(I,I)
   AK = K
   P(K) = TRACE/AK
   DO 8I = 1,N
 8 B(I,I) = B(I,I) − P(K)
   DO 10J = 1,N
   DO 9I = 1,N
 9 COLB(I) = B(I,J)
   DO 10I = 1,N
   B(I,J) = 0.
   DO 10L = 1,N
10 B(I,J) = B(I,J) + A(I,L)*COLB(L)
   P(N) = B(1,1)
   PRINT 4
   PRINT 5
   DO 11K = 1,N
11 PRINT 3,P(K)
   STOP
   END
```

4-9. Computer Determination of Eigenvectors

In the preceding sections we discussed in some detail the steps involved in the solution of characteristic-value problems up to and including the determination of the eigenvalues which were obtained as the roots of the characteristic equation. However, little has been said about the determination of eigenvectors. Now we shall be concerned with a general approach to the determination of the eigenvectors associated with real eigenvalues.[8] We have seen that after determining the eigenvalues of a matrix **A**, the eigenvalues may be substituted, one at a time, back into the original set of homogeneous equations to obtain a new set of n homogeneous equations in n unknowns (eigenvector components) for each eigenvalue.

Since the eigenvalues are values which make the determinant of the coefficient matrix $(\mathbf{A} - \lambda\mathbf{I})$ zero, the rank r of the coefficient matrix must necessarily be less than the order n of the matrix (not all of the equations obtained are independent). Therefore, although we have n equations in n unknowns, the problem is actually that of solving r equations in n unknowns, since the number of linearly independent equations in the set is equal to the rank of the coefficient matrix.

In the majority of engineering problems, the rank of the coefficient matrix is 1 less than the order. (This is always the case when all the eigenvalues are discrete.) In such problems, then, the set of homogeneous equations to be solved contains $n - 1$ independent equations for determining the n eigenvector components. Therefore, by assuming a value for 1 eigenvector component, values may be obtained for the remaining components. There will be 1 eigenvector associated with each eigenvalue.

In solving such a set of equations on the computer, the Gaussian or Gauss-Jordan elimination method can be used to reduce the set of n equations to an equivalent set of $n - 1$ independent equations. (This will be illustrated later, using the Gauss-Jordan method.)

Infrequently, in engineering problems, the eigenvalues obtained from the characteristic equation may not all be discrete. For example, in solving for the principal stresses at a point in a body, suppose that 2 principal stresses were equal. Since the eigenvalues are the principal stresses in such a problem (see Example 4-7), the 2 eigenvalues obtained in the solution would be equal (have a multiplicity of 2). In general, when an eigenvalue obtained has a multiplicity of k, the rank of the coefficient matrix for that eigenvalue may be from 1 to k less than the order of the matrix, and there will be that same number of linearly independent eigenvectors associated with the eigenvalue having the multiplicity.

---

[8]In some problems the determination of eigenvalues constitutes the desired solution; in others, the solution includes the determination of the associated eigenvectors.

If the rank of the coefficient matrix is 2 less than the order, it is necessary to assume values for 2 eigenvector components to determine values for the remaining components. (There will be only $n - 2$ linearly independent equations in the set of n equations.) Two linearly independent eigenvectors can be obtained, and any linear combination of these 2 eigenvectors constitutes a possible solution vector. Thus, the solution space is described as being 2-dimensional. If the rank of the coefficient matrix is 3 less than the order, 3 eigenvector-component values must be assumed, 3 linearly independent eigenvectors are obtained, and the solution space is 3-dimensional, and so forth.

Although the rank of the coefficient matrix is 1 less than the order in most engineering problems, a computer program for determining eigenvectors should be versatile enough to handle the occasional case in which the eigenvalues have some multiplicity, as discussed above. Before developing such a computer program, let us study several simple examples of the determination of eigenvectors. (It might be well, at this point, for the reader to review briefly the Gauss-Jordan elimination method, Sec. 4-3.)

To begin with, let us determine the eigenvalues and associated eigenvectors for the set of homogeneous equations

$$
\begin{array}{llll}
(4 - \lambda)x_1 + & 2x_2 - & 2x_3 = 0 & \text{(a)} \\
-5x_1 + (3 - \lambda)x_2 + & 2x_3 = 0 & & \text{(b)} \\
-2x_1 + & 4x_2 + (1 - \lambda)x_3 = 0 & & \text{(c)}
\end{array}
\right\} \quad \text{(4-110)}
$$

The characteristic equation of this set may be written as

$$
\begin{vmatrix}
(4 - \lambda) & 2 & -2 \\
-5 & (3 - \lambda) & 2 \\
-2 & 4 & (1 - \lambda)
\end{vmatrix} = 0
$$

or, in factored form, as

$$
(\lambda - 1)(\lambda - 5)(\lambda - 2) = 0 \quad \text{(4-111)}
$$

where the eigenvalues are $\lambda = 1$, $\lambda = 2$, and $\lambda = 5$.

Knowing the eigenvalues, we are next interested in obtaining the eigenvector associated with each discrete eigenvalue shown. To determine the eigenvector associated with $\lambda = 1$, we substitute this value into Eq. 4-110 to obtain the homogeneous set of equations

$$
\begin{array}{ll}
3x_1 + 2x_2 - 2x_3 = 0 & \text{(a)} \\
-5x_1 + 2x_2 + 2x_3 = 0 & \text{(b)} \\
-2x_1 + 4x_2 + (0)x_3 = 0 & \text{(c)}
\end{array}
\right\} \quad \text{(4-112)}
$$

We next apply the Gauss-Jordan elimination process to reduce Eq. 4-112 to an *equivalent* set consisting only of *independent* equations. The number of independent equations obtained by this process will be equal to the rank of the coefficient matrix of Eq. 4-112. In the Gaussian elimination method, we performed an interchange of equations to get the largest coefficient in the pivot column into the pivot position. This resulted in improved accuracy and prevented the appearance of a zero pivot element. We could have obtained even greater accuracy, in cases in which the largest coefficient of the set of equations appeared in a column other than the pivot column, by interchanging the sequence of the unknowns in the equations (a column interchange) to get this coefficient into the pivot column. If necessary, an equation interchange would then place it in the pivot position. However, such column interchanges were not used in implementing either the Gaussian or the Gauss-Jordan method, in previous discussions, since this would have unnecessarily complicated the "bookkeeping" in the computer program.

However, in using the Gauss-Jordan method to reduce a set of equations which are not all independent to an equivalent set which are all independent, we will find that, in many instances, we *must* interchange the sequence of the unknowns in the equations to avoid a zero pivot element. Therefore, to obtain maximum accuracy and to avoid the possibility of a zero pivot element, we will always place the largest applicable coefficient (the applicable coefficient having the largest *absolute value*) in the pivot position. This may require an interchange of equations, an interchange in the sequence of the unknowns, or both.

In Eq. 4-112 no change is required in the sequence of the unknowns, but parts a and b should be interchanged to make -5 the pivot element for eliminating x_1. Making this interchange, we obtain

$$\left. \begin{array}{rl} -5x_1 + 2x_2 + 2x_3 = 0 & \quad \text{(a)} \\ 3x_1 + 2x_2 - 2x_3 = 0 & \quad \text{(b)} \\ -2x_1 + 4x_2 + (0)x_3 = 0 & \quad \text{(c)} \end{array} \right\} \quad \text{(4-113)}$$

Applying the Gauss-Jordan process in which we first divide Eq. 4-113a by -5, use the resulting equation to eliminate x_1 from parts b and c, and finally move Eq. 4-113a from the top to the bottom position, we obtain

$$\left. \begin{array}{rl} (0)x_1 + \dfrac{16}{5}x_2 - \dfrac{4}{5}x_3 = 0 & \quad \text{(a)} \\[2mm] (0)x_1 + \dfrac{16}{5}x_2 - \dfrac{4}{5}x_3 = 0 & \quad \text{(b)} \\[2mm] x_1 - \dfrac{2}{5}x_2 - \dfrac{2}{5}x_3 = 0 & \quad \text{(c)} \end{array} \right\} \quad \text{(4-114)}$$

In considering the elimination of x_2 or x_3 in the next step, we look for the coefficient, in Eq. 4-114a or b, having the largest absolute value for use as a pivot element. Since the coefficient of x_2 in Eq. 4-114a is the largest coefficient and is already in the pivot position, no equation interchange or change in the sequence of the unknowns is necessary, and we are ready to eliminate x_2. Note that the coefficients in Eq. 4-114c were not considered in the search for a pivot element. These coefficients cannot be considered, regardless of their magnitude, since the use of this equation to eliminate x_2 or x_3 would reintroduce the previously eliminated x_1 into the equations. In general, only the coefficients in the first $n - q$ equations are candidates for the pivot element, where q is the number of eliminations *already completed*.

Again applying the Gauss-Jordan elimination procedure, we obtain

$$
\left.
\begin{array}{ll}
(0)x_1 + (0)x_2 + (0)x_3 = 0 & \text{(a)} \\
x_1 + (0)x_2 - \tfrac{1}{2}x_3 = 0 & \text{(b)} \\
(0)x_1 + x_2 - \tfrac{1}{4}x_3 = 0 & \text{(c)}
\end{array}
\right\} \quad (4\text{-}115)
$$

This final equivalent set of equations consists only of the independent equations b and c, and contains the 3 unknown eigenvector components x_1, x_2, and x_3. By assuming a value for any one of these 3 unknowns, values can be determined for the other two.

With 2 independent equations in the equivalent set, we know that the rank of the coefficient matrix of Eq. 4-110 is 2. The eigenvectors for the other 2 eigenvalues are determined by the identical process just described.

Now let us turn our attention to implementing this method on the computer. With the coefficient matrix of Eq. 4-112 in memory, the computer would perform the required row interchange and would then utilize the general equations

$$
\left.
\begin{array}{ll}
b_{i-1,j-1} = a_{ij} - \dfrac{a_{1j}a_{i1}}{a_{11}} & \left\{ \begin{array}{l} 1 < i \le n \\ 1 < j \le m \\ a_{11} \ne 0 \end{array} \right\} \\[2em]
b_{n,j-1} = \dfrac{a_{1j}}{a_{11}} & \left\{ \begin{array}{l} 1 < j \le m \\ a_{11} \ne 0 \end{array} \right\}
\end{array}
\right\} \quad (4\text{-}116)
$$

where

$$
\begin{aligned}
i &= \text{row number of old matrix } \mathbf{A} \\
j &= \text{column number of old matrix } \mathbf{A} \\
n &= \text{maximum row number} \\
m &= \text{maximum column number} \\
a &= \text{an element of old matrix } \mathbf{A} \\
b &= \text{an element of new matrix } \mathbf{B}
\end{aligned}
$$

to obtain the new matrix

$$\mathbf{B} = \begin{bmatrix} \dfrac{16}{5} & -\dfrac{4}{5} \\[2mm] \dfrac{16}{5} & -\dfrac{4}{5} \\[2mm] -\dfrac{2}{5} & -\dfrac{2}{5} \end{bmatrix} \qquad (4\text{-}117)$$

This matrix is the coefficient matrix of Eq. 4-114 with the column consisting only of *zeros* and a *one* omitted.

Before moving to the next elimination process, the computer would search the first 2 rows of the matrix of Eq. 4-117 for the coefficient having the largest absolute value, and would make any necessary interchanges before performing the next elimination. In general, with all columns containing only zeros and ones dropped from the matrices formed in each elimination, the computer would search only the first k rows of the matrix being considered, where k is the number of columns in that matrix. The use of any rows beyond k in eliminating the next unknown would reintroduce a previously eliminated unknown into the equations, as explained above.

Repeating the Gauss-Jordan procedure, the computer would obtain the column matrix

$$\mathbf{B'} = \left\{ \begin{array}{c} 0 \\[2mm] -\dfrac{1}{2} \\[2mm] -\dfrac{1}{4} \end{array} \right\} \qquad (4\text{-}118)$$

which corresponds to Eq. 4-115 with the 2 columns containing only zeros and ones omitted. No further application of Eq. 4-116 is possible, and the number of columns in the final matrix, which is in computer memory, is equal to the difference between the rank and order of the coefficient matrix $(\mathbf{A} - \lambda\mathbf{I})$ of Eq. 4-110.

Thus, it is apparent from Eq. 4-115 (a set of equations equivalent to the original set) that there are only 2 independent equations in the set. Therefore, the rank of the coefficient matrix is 2, while the order is 3. Since there are 3 unknowns in the 2 independent equations of the set of Eq. 4-115, the computer must be given an arbitrary value for 1 unknown so that it may solve the resulting 2 *nonhomogeneous* equations for the 2 remaining unknowns.

In determining the eigenvector on the computer, note the convenience of arbitrarily choosing a value of -1 for x_3. By choosing this value for

x_3, a consideration of Eq. 4-115 reveals that the components x_1 and x_2 will have the respective values shown for the nonzero coefficients of x_3 in that equation which appears as elements of the matrix of Eq. 4-118, which is in computer memory. The computer need only place these matrix values and the assumed value for x_3 in the usual sequence

$$\left\{ \begin{array}{c} x_1 \\ x_2 \\ x_3 \end{array} \right\}$$

to obtain the desired eigenvector. In this manner the eigenvector is easily found from the final matrix in computer memory by instructing the computer, in this case, to replace the zero with -1 and to move it to the bottom position so that

$$\mathbf{X} = \left\{ \begin{array}{c} -\dfrac{1}{2} \\ -\dfrac{1}{4} \\ -1 \end{array} \right\}$$

or, more generally,

$$\mathbf{X} = \mathbf{C} \left\{ \begin{array}{c} -\dfrac{1}{2} \\ -\dfrac{1}{4} \\ -1 \end{array} \right\} \tag{4-119}$$

where C is any arbitrary constant.

In the example just completed, the coefficients of x_3 appeared in the final column matrix of Eq. 4-118, and a procedure was described for utilizing these values in determining the eigenvector in its correct x_1, x_2, $x_3, \dots$, sequence. With the various column interchanges which could be required in arriving at this final matrix for equations with other coefficients, the final matrix could contain coefficients of any one of the x's. In each case, -1 would be substituted for the zero coefficient in the column matrix and would then be moved to the bottom position. After this basic step, different manipulations would be required, in each case, to arrange the eigenvector components in their proper sequence in representing the eigenvector. Therefore, a general computer program must include some provision for keeping track of the column interchanges performed during the elimination processes, and for utilizing this information later to place the eigenvector components in their proper sequence. (The relationship between the column interchanges and the resulting sequence of the eigenvector components in computer memory will be explained later in this section.)

As a further illustration of the method we shall use on the computer to determine eigenvectors, let us consider an example in which there will be 2 linearly independent eigenvectors associated with an eigenvalue. Let us find the eigenvalues of the matrix

$$\mathbf{A} = \begin{bmatrix} 3 & 2 & 4 \\ 2 & 0 & 2 \\ 4 & 2 & 3 \end{bmatrix} \tag{4-120}$$

The characteristic equation is

$$\begin{vmatrix} 3-\lambda & 2 & 4 \\ 2 & 0-\lambda & 2 \\ 4 & 2 & 3-\lambda \end{vmatrix} = 0 \tag{4-121}$$

or

$$(\lambda + 1)(\lambda + 1)(\lambda - 8) = 0$$

eigenvector(s) associated with $\lambda = -1$, we substitute this value in the equation $(\mathbf{A} - \lambda\mathbf{I})\mathbf{X} = \mathbf{O}$ and obtain

$$\begin{bmatrix} 4 & 2 & 4 \\ 2 & 1 & 2 \\ 4 & 2 & 4 \end{bmatrix} \begin{Bmatrix} x_1 \\ x_2 \\ x_3 \end{Bmatrix} = \mathbf{0} \tag{4-122}$$

We then apply the Gauss-Jordan elimination procedure. One application yields

$$\begin{bmatrix} 0 & 0 & 0 \\ 0 & 0 & 0 \\ 1 & \frac{1}{2} & 1 \end{bmatrix} \begin{Bmatrix} x_1 \\ x_2 \\ x_3 \end{Bmatrix} = \mathbf{0} \tag{4-123}$$

Using the computer, we would begin by storing the matrix

$$\mathbf{A} = \begin{bmatrix} 4 & 2 & 4 \\ 2 & 1 & 2 \\ 4 & 2 & 4 \end{bmatrix} \tag{4-124}$$

in memory. Then, with a single application of Eq. 4-116, the computer would obtain

$$\mathbf{B} = \begin{bmatrix} 0 & 0 \\ 0 & 0 \\ \frac{1}{2} & 1 \end{bmatrix} \tag{4-125}$$

The only applicable pivot elements for further elimination are

$$0 \quad 0$$
$$0 \quad 0$$

so no further application of Eq. 4-116 is possible. There are 2 columns remaining in the matrix of Eq. 4-125, and it is apparent, from inspection of Eq. 4-123, that the rank of the coefficient matrix is 1, which is 2 less than the order. Thus, in general, the *rank* of the *coefficient matrix* is equal to the order of the coefficient matrix minus the number of columns remaining in the final **B** matrix obtained from the applications of Eq. 4-116. Therefore, there will be 2 linearly independent eigenvectors associated with $\lambda = -1$. We must choose arbitrary values for 2 of the unknowns in determining each of these linearly independent eigenvectors. It is convenient to choose the values -1 and 0 for x_2 and x_3, respectively, in obtaining 1 eigenvector, and 0 and -1 for the same unknowns in obtaining the second eigenvector. This leads to the 2 linearly independent eigenvectors

$$\begin{Bmatrix} \frac{1}{2} \\ -1 \\ 0 \end{Bmatrix} \quad \text{and} \quad \begin{Bmatrix} 1 \\ 0 \\ -1 \end{Bmatrix}$$

It should be noted that these eigenvectors may be conveniently obtained from the matrix of Eq. 4-125, which is in computer memory, by replacing the first zero in the first column with -1 and the second zero in the second column with -1, followed by bringing the first and second rows, in turn, to the bottom position.

Any solution vector in the 2-dimensional solution space can be formed by the combination of the linearly independent eigenvectors such as

$$C_1 \begin{Bmatrix} \frac{1}{2} \\ -1 \\ 0 \end{Bmatrix} + C_2 \begin{Bmatrix} 1 \\ 0 \\ -1 \end{Bmatrix}$$

where C_1 and C_2 are arbitrary constants.

To illustrate why it may be necessary to make column interchanges to prevent having a zero pivot element, let us find the eigenvalues of the matrix

$$\mathbf{A} = \begin{bmatrix} -2 & -8 & -12 \\ 1 & 4 & 4 \\ 0 & 0 & 1 \end{bmatrix} \tag{4-126}$$

without performing any column interchanges. The characteristic equation is

$$(\lambda - 2)(\lambda)(\lambda - 1) = 0 \tag{4-127}$$

To find the eigenvector associated with $\lambda = 2$, we write

$$\begin{bmatrix} -4 & -8 & -12 \\ 1 & 2 & 4 \\ 0 & 0 & -1 \end{bmatrix} \begin{Bmatrix} x_1 \\ x_2 \\ x_3 \end{Bmatrix} = 0 \qquad (4\text{-}128)$$

One application of the Gauss-Jordan procedure gives

$$\begin{bmatrix} 0 & 0 & 1 \\ 0 & 0 & -1 \\ 1 & 2 & 3 \end{bmatrix} \begin{Bmatrix} x_1 \\ x_2 \\ x_3 \end{Bmatrix} = 0 \qquad (4\text{-}129)$$

Thus, the possible pivot elements, without considering column interchange, are

$$0$$
$$0$$

and no further elimination is possible because of division by zero. Therefore, a column interchange (a change in the sequence of the unknowns) would have to be made to continue the elimination process.

Proceeding again with the same problem but putting the largest applicable coefficient in the pivot position by means of a column interchange, Eq. 4-128 becomes

$$\begin{bmatrix} -12 & -8 & -4 \\ 4 & 2 & 1 \\ -1 & 0 & 0 \end{bmatrix} \begin{Bmatrix} x_3 \\ x_2 \\ x_1 \end{Bmatrix} = 0 \qquad (4\text{-}130)$$

Note that an interchange of the first and third columns of the coefficient matrix requires an interchange of the position of the elements x_3 and x_1 of the X matrix if the equations are to remain the same.

Applying the Gauss-Jordan elimination procedure to Eq. 4-130, we obtain

$$\begin{bmatrix} 0 & -\dfrac{2}{3} & -\dfrac{1}{3} \\ 0 & \dfrac{2}{3} & \dfrac{1}{3} \\ 1 & \dfrac{2}{3} & \dfrac{1}{3} \end{bmatrix} \begin{Bmatrix} x_3 \\ x_2 \\ x_1 \end{Bmatrix} = 0 \qquad (4\text{-}131)$$

One additional application yields

$$\begin{bmatrix} 0 & 0 & 0 \\ 1 & 0 & 0 \\ 0 & 1 & \dfrac{1}{2} \end{bmatrix} \begin{Bmatrix} x_3 \\ x_2 \\ x_1 \end{Bmatrix} = 0 \qquad (4\text{-}132)$$

In using the computer, the single-column matrix

would be in memory. Referring to Eq. 4-132, we see that if we arbitrarily assume a value of -1 for the unknown in the third position in the column matrix of Eq. 4-132 (x_1), the values $x_2 = \frac{1}{2}$ and $x_3 = 0$ are obtained. If the computer replaces the first element of the column matrix by -1 and then moves it to the bottom position in the column, the following matrix is formed:

These are the eigenvector components and they are now in the order shown in the column matrix of Eq. 4-132. The computer would next utilize the information stored referring to the column interchanges made during the elimination processes to arrange the eigenvector components in the usual x_1, x_2, x_3 sequence to obtain the general eigenvector

$$\mathbf{X} = C \left\{ \begin{array}{c} -1 \\ \frac{1}{2} \\ 0 \end{array} \right\} \tag{4-133}$$

It should be noted, at this point, that each time it is necessary to interchange the columns of a coefficient matrix in the elimination processes, it is also necessary to interchange the eigenvector components associated with these columns to maintain the correct matrix equation. The sequence of the eigenvector components appearing in the final matrix (after always replacing the zero in the top position with -1 and shifting it to the bottom position) will thus depend upon the column interchanges made during the successive elimination processes. The computer program must keep track, in memory, of these column interchanges, so that this information can be used to rearrange the eigenvector components in the usual x_1, x_2, ..., x_n sequence in determining the eigenvector in the final step (Eq. 4-133, for example).

With the preceding discussion and examples as background, we are

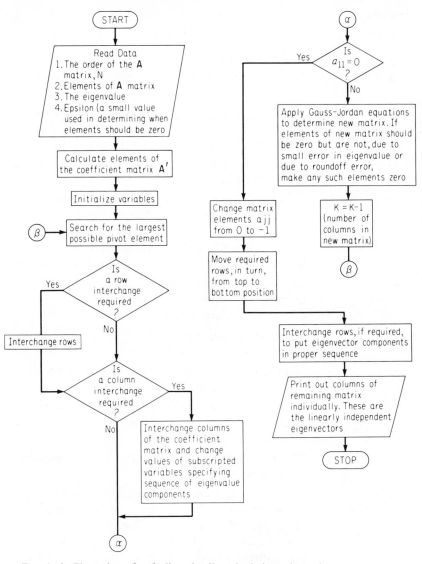

FIG. 4-12. Flow chart for finding the linearly independent eigenvectors associated with a particular eigenvalue of a matrix A.

now in a position to formulate a computer program which will determine the eigenvector (or linearly independent eigenvectors, as the case may be) associated with any eigenvalue. The complete computer procedure is outlined in the flow chart of Fig. 4-12. The **FORTRAN** names and associated quantities used in the source program are as follows:

FORTRAN *Name*	*Quantity*
N	Order of **A** matrix
EIGEN	Eigenvalue for which the eigenvector or -vectors are to be determined
EPSI	A small quantity used in determining when a matrix element should be zero but is not, due to roundoff error or a small error in eigenvalue
A(I,J)	Elements of **A** matrix; also used for elements of coefficient matrix $\mathbf{A} - \lambda\mathbf{I}$
IX(I)	A variable used to keep track of the sequence of eigenvector components in the equation $(\mathbf{A} - \lambda\mathbf{I})\mathbf{X} = \mathbf{0}$. For example, if IX(3) has the value 3, then X(3) is in the third position. If IX(3) has the value 1, then X(3) is in the first position
K	The number of columns of the reduced matrix in memory (equivalent to original **A** matrix), *not counting columns of zeros and ones*
M	The column number of the pivot *column, counting columns of ones and zeros*
JJ	The column number in which the largest possible pivot element is found
L	The column number of the column containing the largest possible pivot element, *counting columns of zeros and ones*
II	The row number in which the largest possible pivot element is found
TEMP	A name used, at different times in the program, to designate *temporarily* elements of the matrix row to be moved to pivot position, elements of the matrix column to be moved into pivot position, and values of IX(I) when new values must be assigned to these variables accompanying an interchange of columns
B(I,J)	Elements of new equivalent matrix determined by Gauss-Jordan method—columns of zeros and ones omitted
Y	The quantity $\mid b_{i-1,j-1}\mid - \epsilon\mid a_{ij}\mid$; when this quantity is negative, $b_{i-1,j-1}$ should be equal to zero

MM   Index of a DO loop, varying from 1 to K, control-
                      ling the number of elements moved from top
                      position of the matrix in computer memory to
                      bottom position in forming eigenvectors from the
                      matrix elements

NUM   Used as both an index of a DO loop and a sub-
                      script in arranging components of eigenvectors in
                      proper order

One of the steps involved in the computer program should be clarified
before studying the source program. In applying the Gauss-Jordan elimination procedure in the program for finding the linearly independent
eigenvectors, the computation

$$b_{i-1,j-1} = a_{ij} - \frac{(a_{1j})(a_{i1})}{a_{11}}$$

as we have seen, should result in a zero value in one or more instances.
Such zero elements can be noted in the second and third columns of Eq.
4-123. However, owing to roundoff error or a small inaccuracy in the
eigenvalue, the computation in these instances will usually result in some
small value instead of zero. It is, however, important in this program
that the value be *exactly* zero. Therefore, it must be set equal to zero in
all cases where it should be zero but is not. That is, whenever the difference computed in the above equation is much smaller than the numbers
being subtracted, we set $b_{i-1,j-1} = 0$. This is done by comparing the difference $(b_{i-1,j-1})$ with the product of a small quantity ϵ and either of the
quantities involved in the subtraction, and, if the difference is found to be
less in *absolute* value than this product, the difference is set equal to zero.

Choosing a suitable value for epsilon may present a problem. If we
have an eigenvalue that is obtained with slide-rule accuracy, we may need
an epsilon as large as 0.01 or more to make the elements that should be
zero actually zero. If we make epsilon too large, however, we may make
some matrix elements zero which should not be zero, and a result will not
be obtained. If the eigenvalue is exact, an epsilon value of 0.0001 or less
may be suitable. Obviously, if we make epsilon either too small or too
large we cannot obtain a result from the program. Instead, it prints out

RANK NOT LESS THAN ORDER. USE MORE ACCURATE EIGENVALUE OR ADJUST EPSI

Several trial values of epsilon may have to be used to place it within permissible limits. If the eigenvalue is too inaccurate, there is *no* suitable
range of epsilon, and a more accurate eigenvalue *must* be used.

The **FORTRAN** source program for finding the linearly independent eigenvectors associated with an eigenvalue is as follows:

```
C       PROGRAM FOR FINDING THE LINEARLY INDEPENDENT
C       EIGENVECTORS ASSOCIATED WITH AN EIGENVALUE
C
        DIMENSION A(11,10),B(10,9),X(10,3),IX(10)
      1 FORMAT (I3)
      2 FORMAT (E14.0)
      3 FORMAT (42HTHE LINEARLY INDEPENDENT EIGENVECTORS
                                                    ARE,/)
      4 FORMAT (E14.8)
      5 FORMAT (1H)
     32 FORMAT(44HRANK NOT LESS THAN ORDER. USE MORE
                                            ACCURATE)
     33 FORMAT(25HEIGENVALUE OR ADJUST EPSI)
C       READ IN THE DATA
        READ 1,N
        DO 6 J=1,N
        DO 6 I=1,N
      6 READ 2,A(I,J)
        READ 2,EIGEN,EPSI
C       CALCULATE THE DIAGONAL ELEMENTS OF THE
                                    COEFFICIENT MATRIX
        DO 7 J=1,N
      7 A(J,J)=A(J,J)-EIGEN
C       INITIALIZE THE SUBSCRIPTED VARIABLES SPECIFYING THE
                                                    ORDER
C       OF THE EIGENVECTOR COMPONENTS IN THE EQUATION
                                        (A-LAMBDA*I)X=0
        DO 8 I=1,N
      8 IX(I)=I
C       INITIALIZE VARIABLES
        K=N
      9 M=N-K+1
C       SEARCH FOR THE LARGEST POSSIBLE PIVOT ELEMENT
        JJ=1
        II=1
        BIG=ABS(A(1,1))
        DO 11 J=1,K
        DO 11 I=1,K
        DIFF=BIG-ABS(A(I,J))
        IF(DIFF)10,11,11
```

```
    10 JJ = J
       II = I
       BIG = ABS(A(I,J))
    11 CONTINUE
C      CHECK TO SEE IF ROW AND/OR COLUMN
                            INTERCHANGES ARE REQUIRED
C      AND MAKE INTERCHANGES IF REQUIRED
       IF(II − 1)14,14,12
    12 DO 13 J = 1,K
       TEMP = A(II,J)
       A(II,J) = A(1,J)
    13 A(1,J) = TEMP
    14 IF (JJ − 1)17,17,15
    15 TEMP = IX(M)
       L = JJ + N − K
       IX(M) = IX(L)
       IX(L) = TEMP
       DO 16 I = 1,N
       TEMP = A(I,JJ)
       A(I,JJ) = A(I,1)
    16 A(I,1) = TEMP
    17 CONTINUE
C      CHECK TO SEE IF ELIMINATION PROCESS IS COMPLETE
       IF(A(1,1))18,23,18
C      APPLY GAUSS-JORDAN ELIMINATION PROCEDURE
    18 DO 20 J = 2,K
       DO 20 I = 2,N
       B(I − 1,J − 1) = A(I,J) − A(1,J)*A(I,1)/A(1,1)
       Y = ABS(B(I − 1,J − 1)) − EPSI*ABS(A(I,J))
       IF(Y)19,20,20
    19 B(I − 1,J − 1) = 0.
    20 CONTINUE
       DO 21 J = 2,K
    21 B(N,J − 1) = A(1,J)/A(1,1)
       K = K − 1
       IF(K)31,31,30
    30 DO 22 J = 1,K
       DO 22 I = 1,N
    22 A(I,J) = B(I,J)
       GO TO 9
C      OBTAIN LINEARLY INDEPENDENT EIGENVECTORS FROM
                            MATRIX IN MEMORY
    23 DO 24 J = 1,K
```

```
 24 A(J,J) = -1.
    DO 25 MM = 1,K
    DO 25 J = 1,K
    A(N+1,J) = A(1,J)
    DO 25 I = 1,N
 25 A(I,J) = A(I+1,J)
    DO 27 J = 1,K
    DO 27 I = 1,N
    DO 27 NUM = 1,N
    IF(IX(NUM)-I)27,26,27
 26 X(I,J) = A(NUM,J)
 27 CONTINUE
C   PRINT OUT LINEARLY INDEPENDENT EIGENVECTORS
    PRINT 3
    DO 29 J = 1,K
    DO 28 I = 1,N
 28 PRINT 4,X(I,J)
 29 PRINT 5
    GO TO 34
 31 PRINT 32
    PRINT 33
 34 STOP
    END
```

4-10. Iteration Method of Determining Eigenvalues

In addition to the polynomial method discussed in the preceding section, there are various iterative methods to determine eigenvalues. Of these, the one most commonly used in engineering problems is the *power method*.

An iterative method is used most frequently when only the *smallest* and/or *largest* eigenvalue(s) of a matrix are desired, since the determination of all the eigenvalues of a matrix by this method is quite complex, particularly if the matrix is of large order. (When all the eigenvalues are desired, the polynomial method may be used.) An advantage of the iterative method is that the eigenvectors are obtained simultaneously with the associated eigenvalues rather than requiring separate operations, as in the polynomial method.

To illustrate the power method, let us first use it to determine the largest eigenvalue of a matrix. We shall assume that both the elements of the matrix and its eigenvalues are real, although the use of iterative methods is not thus restricted.

Suppose that, in the analysis of a physical system, we have obtained, as a mathematical model of the system, the following set of simultaneous homogeneous linear algebraic equations:

$$
\left.
\begin{aligned}
(a_{11} - \lambda)x_1 + \quad a_{12}x_2 + a_{13}x_3 + \cdots + \quad a_{1n}x_n &= 0 \\
a_{21}x_1 + (a_{22} - \lambda)x_2 + a_{23}x_3 + \cdots + \quad a_{2n}x_n &= 0 \\
\vdots \qquad\qquad \vdots \qquad\qquad \vdots \\
a_{n1}x_1 + \quad a_{n2}x_2 + a_{n3}x_3 + \cdots + (a_{nn} - \lambda)x_n &= 0
\end{aligned}
\right\} \quad (4\text{-}134)
$$

which may be expressed more compactly, in matrix notation, as

$$(\mathbf{A} - \lambda \mathbf{I})\mathbf{X} = \mathbf{0} \quad (4\text{-}135)$$

To find the largest eigenvalue λ_1, we rewrite Eq. 4-135 in the form

$$\mathbf{AX} = \lambda \mathbf{X} \quad (4\text{-}136)$$

and carry out the following steps:

1. Arbitrarily assume values for the components of the eigenvector $\mathbf{X} = (x_1, x_2, \ldots, x_n)$. This assumed vector will subsequently be referred to as $\mathbf{X}_0$. Choosing all components of $\mathbf{X}_0$ equal to unity is generally satisfactory. Upon substituting the components of $\mathbf{X}_0$ into the left side of Eq. 4-136 as the elements of the matrix $\mathbf{X}$ and carrying out the matrix multiplication, a first approximation to the right side of Eq. 4-136 is obtained, where

$$
\lambda \mathbf{X} = \left\{
\begin{array}{c}
\lambda x_1 \\
\lambda x_2 \\
\lambda x_3 \\
\vdots \\
\lambda x_n
\end{array}
\right\} \quad (4\text{-}137)
$$

2. Normalize the vector $\lambda \mathbf{X}$ obtained in step 1. This is done by dividing the vector by the magnitude of its first component, by its largest component, or by normalizing the vector $\mathbf{X}$ to a unit length. In this case, let us normalize by dividing the vector by the magnitude of the first component, reducing that component to unity.

3. Use the components of the normalized vector as improved values of x_i to be substituted into the left side of Eq. 4-136. Carrying out the matrix multiplication, a still better approximation of the right-hand side of Eq. 4-136 is obtained.

4. Repeat steps 2 and 3 until Eq. 4-136 is essentially satisfied; that is, until the eigenvector components in step 2 vary from the previously obtained values by less than some small preassigned ϵ value, in 2 successive iterations. The normalizing factor will be the *largest eigenvalue* λ_1, and the elements of $\mathbf{X}$ will be the components of the eigenvector associated with it.

In carrying out the iteration procedure we are, in effect, forming a sequence of vectors $\mathbf{AX}_0, \mathbf{A}^2\mathbf{X}_0, \mathbf{A}^3\mathbf{X}_0, \ldots, \mathbf{A}^k\mathbf{X}_0$, where $\mathbf{X}_0$ is the arbitrary vector initially assumed. (The name "power method" comes from the fact that the sequence is made up of powers of the matrix $\mathbf{A}$.)

To illustrate the steps just outlined, let us consider the equations

$$
\begin{aligned}
(2 - \lambda)x_1 + 4x_2 &= 0 \\
3x_1 + (13 - \lambda)x_2 &= 0
\end{aligned}
\tag{4-138}
$$

and determine the value of λ_1, the *largest eigenvalue*. Putting Eq. 4-138 in the form of Eq. 4-136, we have

$$
\begin{bmatrix} 2 & 4 \\ 3 & 13 \end{bmatrix} \begin{Bmatrix} x_1 \\ x_2 \end{Bmatrix} = \lambda \begin{Bmatrix} x_1 \\ x_2 \end{Bmatrix}
$$

Carrying out steps 1 and 2, we obtain

$$
\begin{bmatrix} 2 & 4 \\ 3 & 13 \end{bmatrix} \begin{Bmatrix} 1 \\ 1 \end{Bmatrix} = \begin{Bmatrix} 6 \\ 16 \end{Bmatrix} = 6 \begin{Bmatrix} 1 \\ 16/6 \end{Bmatrix}
$$

Applying step 3 gives

$$
\begin{bmatrix} 2 & 4 \\ 3 & 13 \end{bmatrix} \begin{Bmatrix} 1 \\ 16/6 \end{Bmatrix} = \begin{Bmatrix} 38/3 \\ 113/3 \end{Bmatrix} = \frac{38}{3} \begin{Bmatrix} 1 \\ 113/38 \end{Bmatrix}
$$

The next iteration yields

$$
\begin{bmatrix} 2 & 4 \\ 3 & 13 \end{bmatrix} \begin{Bmatrix} 1 \\ 113/38 \end{Bmatrix} = \begin{Bmatrix} 264/19 \\ 1538/38 \end{Bmatrix} = 13.9 \begin{Bmatrix} 1 \\ 2.998 \end{Bmatrix}
$$

Comparing the normalizing factors of the *second* and *third* iterations (38/3 and 13.9), it is apparent that the third iteration results in only a minor change of the normalizing factor obtained in the second iteration. Thus, a good approximation to λ_1 is $\lambda_1 = 13.9$. The eigenvector associated with λ_1 is $\mathbf{X} = (1, 2.998)$. A fourth iteration would, of course, yield a still-better approximation to λ_1 and the corresponding components of the eigenvector. Application of the polynomial method readily reveals that the exact values are $\lambda_1 = 14$ and $\mathbf{X} = (1, 3)$.

In many physical problems the *smallest* eigenvalue turns out to be the one of primary importance. To arrange the matrix equation in a form in which the iteration converges to the smallest eigenvalue, we first premultiply Eq. 4-136 by the inverse matrix $\mathbf{A}^{-1}$, obtaining

$$
\mathbf{A}^{-1}\mathbf{A}\mathbf{X} = \mathbf{A}^{-1}\lambda\mathbf{X} = \lambda\mathbf{A}^{-1}\mathbf{X}
$$

or

$$
\mathbf{X} = \lambda\mathbf{A}^{-1}\mathbf{X}
\tag{4-139}
$$

Dividing Eq. 4-139 by λ gives

$$
\mathbf{A}^{-1}\mathbf{X} = \frac{1}{\lambda} \mathbf{X}
\tag{4-140}
$$

Equation 4-140 is in a form which will result in convergence to the *smallest value* of λ.

Let us now find the smallest eigenvalue of the same matrix

$$A = \begin{Bmatrix} 2 & 4 \\ 3 & 13 \end{Bmatrix}$$

for which we previously found the largest eigenvalue. Using the procedure discussed in Sec. 4-5, the inverse matrix A^{-1} is readily found to be

$$A^{-1} = \begin{Bmatrix} \dfrac{13}{14} & -\dfrac{2}{7} \\[2mm] -\dfrac{3}{14} & \dfrac{1}{7} \end{Bmatrix}$$

Proceeding as outlined in steps 1 through 4, we obtain

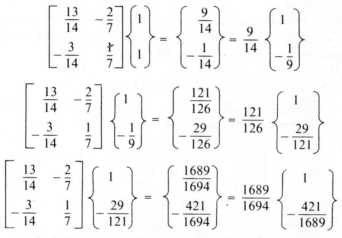

$$\begin{bmatrix} \dfrac{13}{14} & -\dfrac{2}{7} \\[2mm] -\dfrac{3}{14} & \dfrac{1}{7} \end{bmatrix} \begin{Bmatrix} 1 \\ 1 \end{Bmatrix} = \begin{Bmatrix} \dfrac{9}{14} \\[2mm] -\dfrac{1}{14} \end{Bmatrix} = \dfrac{9}{14} \begin{Bmatrix} 1 \\ -\dfrac{1}{9} \end{Bmatrix}$$

$$\begin{bmatrix} \dfrac{13}{14} & -\dfrac{2}{7} \\[2mm] -\dfrac{3}{14} & \dfrac{1}{7} \end{bmatrix} \begin{Bmatrix} 1 \\ -\dfrac{1}{9} \end{Bmatrix} = \begin{Bmatrix} \dfrac{121}{126} \\[2mm] -\dfrac{29}{126} \end{Bmatrix} = \dfrac{121}{126} \begin{Bmatrix} 1 \\ -\dfrac{29}{121} \end{Bmatrix}$$

$$\begin{bmatrix} \dfrac{13}{14} & -\dfrac{2}{7} \\[2mm] -\dfrac{3}{14} & \dfrac{1}{7} \end{bmatrix} \begin{Bmatrix} 1 \\ -\dfrac{29}{121} \end{Bmatrix} = \begin{Bmatrix} \dfrac{1689}{1694} \\[2mm] -\dfrac{421}{1694} \end{Bmatrix} = \dfrac{1689}{1694} \begin{Bmatrix} 1 \\ -\dfrac{421}{1689} \end{Bmatrix}$$

Therefore, we find that the *smallest eigenvalue* $\lambda_2 \simeq 1.025$, and the associated vector $X \simeq (1, -0.2493)$. The polynomial solution shows that the exact solution is $\lambda_2 = 1$ and $X = (1, -0.25)$.

It should be apparent, from the discussion thus far, that the iteration method is ideally suited for computer calculation. In the solution of engineering problems there is rarely any difficulty in its use. If the largest and next-to-the-largest or the smallest and next-to-the-smallest eigenvalues have nearly the same value, convergence to the largest or smallest value, respectively, may be slow. If the largest eigenvalue has a multiplicity of 2 ($\lambda_1 = \lambda_2$), convergence is to the largest eigenvalue, but the components of the eigenvector converge to any of the eigenvectors (which usually form a 2-dimensional space) associated with λ_1. The eigenvector obtained depends on the vector assumed initially.

In the event that the vector initially assumed is *orthogonal* to the eigenvector associated with the largest eigenvalue of the *transposed* matrix (their dot product is equal to zero), convergence will be to the *second-largest* eigenvalue instead of to the *largest*. To illustrate this point, consider the matrix

$$\mathbf{A} = \begin{bmatrix} 1 & 0 & -1 \\ 1 & 2 & 1 \\ 2 & 2 & 3 \end{bmatrix}$$

in which the second-largest and the largest eigenvalues are $\lambda_2 = 2$ and $\lambda_1 = 3$, respectively. The transpose of matrix $\mathbf{A}$, formed by interchanging rows and columns, is

$$\mathbf{A}' = \begin{bmatrix} 1 & 1 & 2 \\ 0 & 2 & 2 \\ -1 & 1 & 3 \end{bmatrix}$$

The largest eigenvalue of the transposed matrix is $\lambda = 3$ with the associated eigenvector $(1, 1, 1/2)$. An arbitrary vector orthogonal to this eigenvector is $(4, -3, -2)$. That is, the dot product of the 2 orthogonal vectors is

$$1(4) + 1(-3) + \tfrac{1}{2}(-2) = 0$$

If we use the vector $(4, -3, -2)$ as the initially assumed vector in determining the largest eigenvalue of the matrix $\mathbf{A}$, we write, for the first iteration

$$\begin{bmatrix} 1 & 0 & -1 \\ 1 & 2 & 1 \\ 2 & 2 & 3 \end{bmatrix} \begin{Bmatrix} 4 \\ -3 \\ -2 \end{Bmatrix} = 6 \begin{Bmatrix} 1 \\ -2/3 \\ -2/3 \end{Bmatrix}$$

After 3 more iterations we finally obtain

$$\begin{bmatrix} 1 & 0 & -1 \\ 1 & 2 & 1 \\ 2 & 2 & 3 \end{bmatrix} \begin{Bmatrix} 1 \\ -5/9 \\ -8/9 \end{Bmatrix} = \frac{17}{9} \begin{Bmatrix} 1 \\ -9/17 \\ -16/17 \end{Bmatrix}$$

which is converging to $\lambda_2 = 2$ with the associated eigenvector $(1, -\tfrac{1}{2}, -1)$ rather than to $\lambda_1 = 3$ with the associated eigenvector $(1, -1, -2)$.

Other special cases, which would be encountered only rarely in engineering analysis, are discussed by Faddeev and Faddeeva.[9]

EXAMPLE 4-10

It is desired to write a *general* FORTRAN program for obtaining, by the iteration method, the *smallest eigenvalue* of a matrix and the components of the associated eigenvector. The program will be written to handle up to and including a tenth-order matrix. It will be left as an

---

[9] Faddeev and Faddeeva, *op. cit.*

exercise for the reader (see Prob. 4-30) to modify the program to determine the *largest* eigenvalue and associated eigenvector.

To illustrate the use of the general **FORTRAN** program, the appropriate data for the 4-story building (Fig. 4-13) will be used as input data. The smallest eigenvalue and associated eigenvector will correspond to the square of the circular frequency and to the amplitude configuration, respectively, for the *fundamental mode* of vibration of the building. As we shall soon see, the equations for the 4-story building result in a fourth-order matrix. Since the **FORTRAN** program will accomodate a tenth-

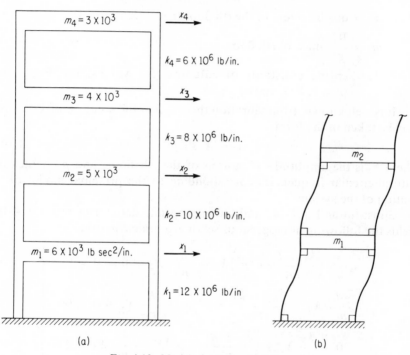

$m_4 = 3 \times 10^3$

x_4

$k_4 = 6 \times 10^6$ lb/in.

$m_3 = 4 \times 10^3$

x_3

$k_3 = 8 \times 10^6$ lb/in.

$m_2 = 5 \times 10^3$

x_2

$k_2 = 10 \times 10^6$ lb/in.

$m_1 = 6 \times 10^3$ lb sec^2/in.

x_1

$k_1 = 12 \times 10^6$ lb/in

m_2

m_1

(a)   (b)

FIG. 4-13. Model of a 4-story building.

order matrix, we could, with the program written, determine the fundamental frequency and corresponding configuration of a building with up to 10 stories.

The 4-story building is shown schematically in Fig. 4-13a. It is assumed that the weight distribution of the building may be represented in the form of concentrated loads at each floor level, as shown. It is further assumed that the girders of the structure are infinitely rigid, in comparison with the supporting columns, so that a general configuration between floors will be obtained, as shown in Fig. 4-13b. The spring constants in the figure are *equivalent* constants representing the aggregate stiffness of the number of columns supporting a given floor, and they were obtained by considering the columns as springs in parallel.

Utilizing either Lagrange's equation or Newton's second law, the differential equations of motion of the system are found to be

$$m_1\ddot{x}_1 + (k_1 + k_2)x_1 - k_2x_2 = 0$$
$$m_2\ddot{x}_2 - k_2x_1 + (k_2 + k_3)x_2 - k_3x_3 = 0$$
$$m_3\ddot{x}_3 - k_3x_2 + (k_3 + k_4)x_3 - k_4x_4 = 0 \qquad (4\text{-}141)$$
$$m_4\ddot{x}_4 - k_4x_3 + k_4x_4 = 0$$

where x_i = displacement of the ith floor (i = 1, 2, 3, and 4)

$$m_i = \frac{W_i}{g}, \text{ mass of } i\text{th floor}$$

k_i = spring constants of columns (for values, see Fig. 4-13) (i = 1, 2, 3, and 4)

It is well known, from vibration theory, that the solution of Eq. 4-141 may be taken in the form

$$x_i = X_i \sin pt \qquad (4\text{-}142)$$

where X_i is the amplitude of motion of the ith floor, and p denotes the natural circular frequencies corresponding to the principal modes of vibration of the system.

Substituting Eq. 4-142 and the appropriate derivatives into Eq. 4-141 yields the following homogeneous set of algebraic equations

$$\left.\begin{array}{l} \left(\dfrac{k_1 + k_2}{m_1} - p^2\right)X_1 - \dfrac{k_2}{m_1}X_2 + 0 + 0 = 0 \\[2mm] \dfrac{-k_2}{m_2}X_1 + \left(\dfrac{k_2 + k_3}{m_2} - p^2\right)X_2 - \dfrac{k_3}{m_2}X_3 + 0 = 0 \\[2mm] 0 - \dfrac{k_3}{m_3}X_2 + \left(\dfrac{k_3 + k_4}{m_3} - p^2\right)X_3 - \dfrac{k_4}{m_3}X_4 = 0 \\[2mm] 0 + 0 + \dfrac{-k_4}{m_4}X_3 + \left(\dfrac{k_4}{m_4} - p^2\right)X_4 = 0 \end{array}\right\} \qquad (4\text{-}143)$$

Comparing Eq. 4-143 with Eq. 4-134, we see that p^2 corresponds to λ and that the quantities $(k_1 + k_2)/m_1$, $-k_2/m_1$, and so on, correspond to the elements a_{ij}. Thus, Eq. 4-143 may be written, in matrix notation, in the form of Eq. 4-135, so that

$$(\mathbf{A} - \lambda\mathbf{I})\mathbf{X} = \mathbf{0} \qquad (4\text{-}144)$$

where the elements of the matrix $\mathbf{A}$ are formed by the appropriate spring constants and masses. Since we are to determine the *smallest* eigenvalue, we transform Eq. 4-144 to the form

$$\mathbf{A}^{-1}\mathbf{X} = \frac{1}{\lambda}\,\mathbf{X} \tag{4-145}$$

for the iteration process (see Eq. 4-140).

For the 4-story building of our example, the elements (see Eq. 4-143 and Fig. 4-13) of the matrix $\mathbf{A}$ are as follows:

$$a_{11} = \frac{k_1 + k_2}{m_1} = \frac{(12 + 10)10^6}{6 \times 10^3} = 3.66667 \times 10^3$$

$$a_{12} = \frac{-k_2}{m_1} = \frac{-10^7}{6 \times 10^3} = -1.66667 \times 10^3$$

$$a_{13} = a_{14} = 0$$

$$a_{21} = \frac{-k_2}{m_2} = \frac{-10^7}{5 \times 10^3} = -2 \times 10^3$$

$$a_{22} = \frac{k_2 + k_3}{m_2} = \frac{(10 + 8)10^6}{5 \times 10^3} = 3.6 \times 10^3$$

$$a_{23} = \frac{-k_3}{m_2} = \frac{-8 \times 10^6}{5 \times 10^3} = -1.6 \times 10^3$$

$$a_{24} = 0$$

$$a_{31} = 0$$

$$a_{32} = \frac{-k_3}{m_3} = \frac{-8 \times 10^6}{4 \times 10^3} = -2 \times 10^3$$

$$a_{33} = \frac{k_3 + k_4}{m_3} = \frac{(8 + 6)10^6}{4 \times 10^3} = 3.5 \times 10^3$$

$$a_{34} = \frac{-k_4}{m_3} = \frac{-6 \times 10^6}{4 \times 10^3} = -1.5 \times 10^3$$

$$a_{41} = a_{42} = 0$$

$$a_{43} = \frac{-k_4}{m_4} = \frac{-6 \times 10^6}{3 \times 10^3} = -2 \times 10^3$$

$$a_{44} = \frac{k_4}{m_4} = 2 \times 10^3$$

These values of the elements a_{ij} of the matrix $\mathbf{A}$ will be used as input data in the FORTRAN program.

The FORTRAN program for obtaining, by the iteration method, the *smallest* eigenvalue of a matrix $\mathbf{A}$ and the corresponding eigenvector is

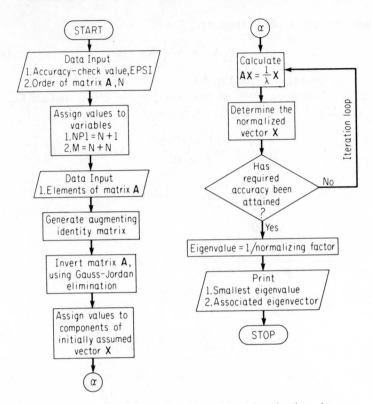

FIG. 4-14. Flow chart for determining, by the iteration method, the smallest eigenvalue of a matrix A.

outlined in the flow chart of Fig. 4-14. The FORTRAN names used in the source program and the quantities they represent are as follows:

FORTRAN Name	Quantity	Data Values Used in 4-Story-Building Problem
A(I,J)	Elements of matrix **A** and augmenting identity matrix	(see calculated values)
B(I,J)	Elements of new matrices formed by the Gauss-Jordan method	
EPSI	Accuracy-check value	0.00001
N	Order of matrix **A** for which eigenvalue is to be determined	4

NP1	$N + 1$
M	Initially, the number of columns in matrix **A** augmented by an N-by-N identity matrix; the quantity M is reduced 1 for each new matrix formed in the inversion process until it reaches the number of columns in the inverted matrix
K	Maximum row number to be searched for finding a nonzero pivot element
TEMP	Temporary name for matrix elements used in interchanging rows of the matrix when $A(1, 1) = 0$
X(I) or X(J)	Initially assumed vector (column matrix) **X** and subsequent vectors **X** obtained by iteration
EIGEN	Smallest eigenvalue λ
C(I)	Elements of new vector (column matrix) $1./\lambda*X$
D(I)	Normalized elements of new vector (column matrix) $1./\lambda*X$
DIFF	Difference between respective components of vector **X** in successive iterations

The following source program, which implements the flow chart of Fig. 4-14, consists of two major parts (see comment statements in source program). Part 1 inverts the matrix **A,** and part 2 executes the iteration procedure.

```
C       THIS PROGRAM DETERMINES THE SMALLEST REAL
C       EIGENVALUE OF A MATRIX A
C       AND THE ASSOCIATED EIGENVECTOR BY THE ITERATION
C       METHOD
C
C       PART 1-INVERSION OF MATRIX A USING GAUSS-
C       JORDAN ELIMINATION
C
        DIMENSION A(10,20),B(10,19),X(10),C(10),D(10)
      1 FORMAT(23HSMALLEST EIGENVALUE IS ,E14.8/)
      2 FORMAT(41HTHE ASSOCIATED EIGENVECTOR
                                  COMPONENTS ARE/)
      3 FORMAT(I3)
```

```
 4 FORMAT(E14.8)
   READ 4,EPSI
   READ 3,N
   NP1=N+1
   M=N+N
C    READ IN THE MATRIX A OF ORDER N
   DO 5 J=1,N
   DO 5 I=1,N
 5 READ 4,A(I,J)
C    GENERATE AUGMENTING IDENTITY MATRIX
   DO 8 J=NP1,M
   DO 8 I=1,N
   IF(J-N-I)7,6,7
 6 A(I,J)=1.
   GO TO 8
 7 A(I,J)=0.
 8 CONTINUE
C    CHECK PIVOT ELEMENT FOR ZERO VALUE AND
                    INTERCHANGE ROWS IF REQUIRED
 9 IF(A(1,1))15,10,15
10 K=M-N
   DO 13 I=2,K
   IF(A(I,1))11,13,11
11 DO 12 J=1,M
   TEMP=A(I,J)
   A(I,J)=A(1,J)
12 A(1,J)=TEMP
   GO TO 15
13 CONTINUE
   PRINT 14
14 FORMAT (18HMATRIX IS SINGULAR)
   GO TO 29
C    DETERMINE THE ELEMENTS OF THE NEW MATRIX
15 DO 16 J=2,M
   DO 16 I=2,N
16 B(I-1,J-1)=A(I,J)-A(1,J)*A(I,1)/A(1,1)
   DO 17 J=2,M
17 B(N,J-1)=A(1,J)/A(1,1)
   M=M-1
   DO 18 J=1,M
   DO 18 I=1,N
18 A(I,J)=B(I,J)
   IF(M-N)9,19,9
19 CONTINUE
```

```
C
C         PART 2 -- THE ITERATION PROCEDURE
C
C         ASSIGN VALUES TO COMPONENTS OF INITIALLY
                                       ASSUMED VECTOR X
          DO 20 I=1,N
     20 X(I)=1.
C         CALCULATE COMPONENTS OF THE VECTOR (1./LAMBDA*X)
     21 DO 22 I=1,N
          C(I)=0.
          DO 22 J=1,N
     22 C(I)=C(I)+A(I,J)*X(J)
C         NORMALIZE THE VECTOR (1./LAMBDA*X)
          DO 23 I=1,N
     23 D(I)=C(I)/C(1)
C         CHECK TO SEE IF REQUIRED ACCURACY HAS BEEN
                                              ATTAINED
          DO 24 I=1,N
          DIFF=X(I)-D(I)
          IF(ABS(DIFF)-EPSI)24,25,25
     24 CONTINUE
          GO TO 27
     25 DO 26 I=1,N
     26 X(I)=D(I)
          GO TO 21
     27 EIGEN=1./C(1)
          PRINT 1,EIGEN
          PRINT 2
          DO 28 I=1,N
     28 PRINT 4,D(I)
     29 STOP
          END
```

The computer printout for the smallest eigenvalue and associated eigenvector for the 4-story building is as follows:

SMALLEST EIGENVALUE IS .31762813E 03

THE ASSOCIATED EIGENVECTOR COMPONENTS ARE

```
 .10000000E 01
 .20094232E 01
 .28722964E 01
 .34145793E 01
STOP 0000
```

The computer printout shows that

$$\lambda = p^2 = 317.6$$

Hence, the natural circular frequency of the first or fundamental mode of vibration is

$$p = \sqrt{317.6} = 17.82 \text{ radians/sec}$$

and the frequency, in cycles per second, is

$$f = \frac{p}{2\pi} = \frac{17.82}{6.28} = 2.84 \text{ cycles per second}$$

From the components of the eigenvector, we obtain the configuration for the first mode of vibration, shown in Fig. 4-15.

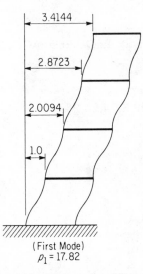

(First Mode)
$p_1 = 17.82$

Fig. 4-15. First-mode configuration of the 4-story building.

4-11. Summary of Eigenvalue Problems

Sections 4-7 through 4-10 were concerned with the solution of eigenvalue or characteristic-value problems. In these sections we discussed two separate methods, the *polynomial* method and the *iteration* method.

The polynomial method involved several distinct operations in obtaining a complete solution of a set of homogeneous linear algebraic equations. These included: 1) the determination of the coefficients of the characteristic polynomial by the Faddeev-Leverrier method (discussed in Sec. 4-8, with a **FORTRAN** program shown for utilizing the method on the computer; 2) the determination of the roots (eigenvalues) of the characteristic polynomial by the use of Graeffe's method (discussed in Sec. 3-7, with a **FORTRAN** program for implementing the method on the computer); and 3) the determination of the eigenvectors associated with the eigenvalues (discussed in Sec. 4-9, with a general **FORTRAN** program for nth-order matrices of various ranks). This method can be used when it is desired to obtain all the eigenvalues of the set of equations.

The iteration method was found to be desirable when only the smallest and/or largest eigenvalues are of interest, since the method is compact and yields, simultaneously, the eigenvalues and associated eigenvectors. A **FORTRAN** program for obtaining the *smallest* eigenvalue of a set of equations is shown in Sec. 4-10. This program is easily modified to obtain the largest eigenvalue of the set (see Prob. 4-30).

Problems

4-1.   A parabola having an equation of the form $y = Ax^2 + Bx + C$ goes through the points $(1, 8)$, $(2, 13)$, and $(3, 20)$. *Manually* determine the equation of this parabola.

4-2.   Determine the equation of the third-degree polynomial of the form $y = Ax^3 + Bx^2 + Cx + D$ which passes through the points $(1, 10)$, $(2, 26)$, $(-1, 2)$, and $(0, 4)$.

4-3.   Determine the coefficients of the polynomial $y = Ax^3 + Bx^2 + Cx + D$ which passes through the points $(1, 10)$, $(2, 26)$, $(-1, 2)$ and has a slope of 10 at the point $(1, 10)$.

4-4.   Determine the coefficients of the polynomial $y = Ax^4 + Bx^3 + Cx^2 + Dx + E$ which passes through the points $(1, 8)$, $(2, 44)$, $(-1, 2)$, $(-3, 44)$, and $(-2, 8)$.

4-5.   Determine the coefficients of the polynomial $y = Ax^5 + Bx^4 + Cx^3 + Dx^2 + Ex + F$ which passes through the points $(1, -7)$, $(2, 2)$, $(-1, -7)$, $(-2, -34)$, $(3, 121)$, and $(0, -8)$.

4-6.   Determine the coefficients of the polynomial $y = Ax^5 + Bx^4 + Cx^3 + Dx^2 + Ex + F$ which passes through the points $(-2, -34)$, $(1, -7)$, $(2, 2)$, $(-1, -7)$, and has a slope of 0 at the points $(1, -7)$, and $(-1, -7)$.

4-7.   The general equation of a conic section can be written as $x^2 + Bxy + Cy^2 + Dx + Ey + F = 0$. Determine the equation of the conic passing through the points $(0, 1/2)$, $(1/2, 4/9)$, $(-2, 57/2)$, $(1, 3/22)$, and $(-1/2, 0)$.

4-8.   Referring to the **FORTRAN** program written for Example 4-3, modify this program to bring the largest *applicable* element in the *pivot column* into the pivot position by the use of row interchange. Use the program given in Example 4-1 as a guide.

4-9.   Referring to the **FORTRAN** program written for Example 4-3, modify the program to bring the largest *applicable* element in the *matrix* into the pivot position by the use of row and/or column interchange. Use the program given in Sec. 4-9 as a guide.

4-10.   A computer program for solving up to 15 simultaneous linear algebraic equations by the Gauss-Jordan elimination method is shown in Example 4-3.

Using this program as a guide, write a computer program for solving up to 25 simultaneous linear algebraic equations in which the *error equations* are applied once to improve the accuracy of the results.

4-11. The **FORTRAN** program of Example 4-3 was written for solving up to 15 simultaneous linear algebraic equations by the Gauss-Jordan elimination method. Modify this program so that it can be used to invert matrices of order up to 15. Write the program so that the complete augmented matrix is read into memory, remembering that the *augmented matrix* is composed of the matrix which is to be inverted and the identity matrix.

4-12. Write a **FORTRAN** program for inverting a matrix of order up to 15 by the method discussed in Sec. 4-5 and used in Example 4-5. In writing this program, do not place the identity matrix, which augments the matrix to be inverted, in memory. There are several ways to program the problem in this manner. The *partial* flow chart shown in the accompanying figure suggests one such method. Note that in using this method the **DIMENSION** statement must provide memory

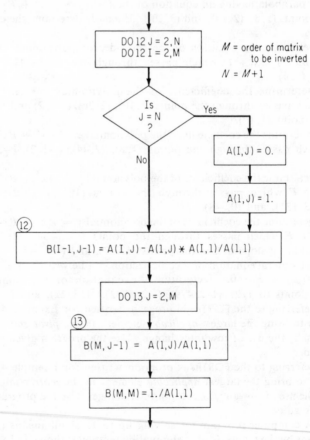

PROB. 4-12

space for the matrix which is to be inverted, plus 1 additional column. If the method suggested by this flow chart is used, row interchange should not be used.

In Probs. 4-13 through 4-18, determine the coefficients of the characteristic polynomial of the matrix **A** by manual use of the Faddeev-Leverrier method.

4-13.
$$\begin{bmatrix} (3 - \lambda) & -3 & 1 \\ 4 & (3 - \lambda) & -2 \\ 4 & 4 & (-2 - \lambda) \end{bmatrix} \begin{Bmatrix} x_1 \\ x_2 \\ x_3 \end{Bmatrix} = \{0\}$$

4-14.
$$\begin{bmatrix} (1 - \lambda) & 2 & 3 \\ -10 & (0 - \lambda) & 2 \\ -2 & 4 & (8 - \lambda) \end{bmatrix} \begin{Bmatrix} x_1 \\ x_2 \\ x_3 \end{Bmatrix} = \{0\}$$

4-15.
$$\begin{bmatrix} (0 - \lambda) & 2 & 3 \\ -10 & (-1 - \lambda) & 2 \\ -2 & 4 & (7 - \lambda) \end{bmatrix} \begin{Bmatrix} x_1 \\ x_2 \\ x_3 \end{Bmatrix} = \{0\}$$

4-16.
$$\begin{bmatrix} (5 - \lambda) & 2 & -1 \\ 2 & (5 - \lambda) & 1 \\ 1 & 4 & (5 - \lambda) \end{bmatrix} \begin{Bmatrix} x_1 \\ x_2 \\ x_3 \end{Bmatrix} = \{0\}$$

4-17.
$$2x_1 + 2x_2 + 3x_3 = \lambda x_1$$
$$-10x_1 + x_2 + 2x_3 = \lambda x_2$$
$$-2x_1 + 4x_2 + 9x_3 = \lambda x_3$$

4-18.
$$3x_1 - x_2 - x_3 = \lambda x_1$$
$$4x_1 - x_2 - 2x_3 = \lambda x_2$$
$$3x_1 - 2x_2 = \lambda x_3$$

In Probs. 4-19 through 4-21, the eigenvalues are given below the equations. Using the method discussed in Sec. 4-9, *manually* determine the eigenvector associated with each eigenvalue given.

4-19.
$$\begin{bmatrix} (1 - \lambda) & 2 & 3 \\ -10 & (0 - \lambda) & 2 \\ -2 & 4 & (8 - \lambda) \end{bmatrix} \begin{Bmatrix} x_1 \\ x_2 \\ x_3 \end{Bmatrix} = \{0\}$$
$$(\lambda_1 = 2, \quad \lambda_2 = 3, \quad \lambda_3 = 4)$$

4-20.
$$\begin{bmatrix} (0 - \lambda) & 2 & 3 \\ -10 & (-1 - \lambda) & 2 \\ -2 & 4 & (7 - \lambda) \end{bmatrix} \begin{Bmatrix} x_1 \\ x_2 \\ x_3 \end{Bmatrix} = \{0\}$$
$$(\lambda_1 = 1, \quad \lambda_2 = 2, \quad \lambda_3 = 3)$$

4-21.
$$\begin{bmatrix} (2 - \lambda) & 2 & 3 \\ -10 & (1 - \lambda) & 2 \\ -2 & 4 & (9 - \lambda) \end{bmatrix} \begin{Bmatrix} x_1 \\ x_2 \\ x_3 \end{Bmatrix} = \{0\}$$

$$(\lambda_1 = 3, \quad \lambda_2 = 4, \quad \lambda_3 = 5)$$

4-22. If the voltage drop across an induction coil is $L\, di/dt$ and the voltage drop across a capacitor is $1/C \int i\, dt$, derive the differential equations, for the circuit shown, in terms of the charges q_1, q_2, and q_3 flowing in the respective loops. The currents and charges are related by $i_1 = dq_1/dt$, $i_2 = dq_2/dt$, and $i_3 = dq_3/dt$. a) Using solutions of the form $q_i = Q_i \sin pt$, and letting $E = 0$, transform the set of simultaneous differential equations, obtained above, into a set of homogeneous linear algebraic equations. b) Write the set of equations, obtained in part a, in matrix form and determine, by the iteration method, the largest eigenvalue (p^2) and associated eigenvector, with $L_1 = L_2 = L_3 = 0.001$ henry and $C_1 = C_2 = C_3 = 0.001$ farad. It is suggested that the iterations be made by using a slide rule, in order to familiarize the reader with the process.

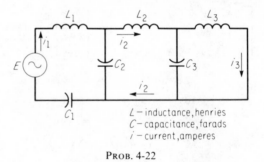

L — inductance, henries
C — capacitance, farads
i — current, amperes

PROB. 4-22

4-23. Referring to Prob. 4-22 and using the data given there, determine, by the iteration method, the smallest eigenvalue (p^2) and associated eigenvector.

4-24. Referring to Prob. 4-22 and using the data given there, determine, by the polynomial method, the eigenvalues and corresponding eigenvectors for the electric circuit. It is suggested that the reader refer to the summary, in Sec. 4-11, as a guide to the general procedure for solving this problem.

4-25. A cylinder, shown in the accompanying figure, rolls without slipping and has a mass m_1 and a moment of inertia $\bar{I}$. Determine a) the differential equations of motion, in terms of the coordinates θ and x, and b) the characteristic equation, by assuming solution of the form $\theta = \Theta \sin pt$ and $x = X \sin pt$.

4-26. Referring to Prob. 4-25, let $m_1 = m_2 = 2$ lb-sec²/ft, $\bar{I} = 1.0$ lb-ft-sec², $r = 1.0$ ft, and $k = 200$ lb/ft, and determine, by the polynomial method, the eigenvalues and associated eigenvectors.

4-27. Referring to Prob. 4-25 and using the data of Prob. 4-26, determine, by the iteration method, the smallest eigenvalue and associated eigenvector.

4-28. Two disks are attached to the ends of a shaft having a torsional spring constant of k lb-in./radian. The differential equations of motion of the system

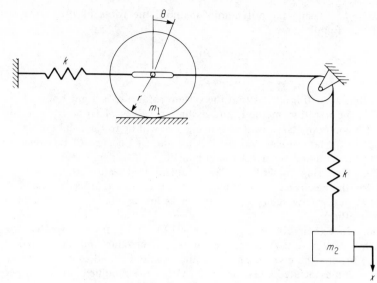

PROB. 4-25

are found to be

$$\bar{I}_1 \ddot{\theta}_1 + k\theta_1 - k\theta_2 = 0$$
$$\bar{I}_2 \ddot{\theta}_2 + k\theta_2 - k\theta_1 = 0$$

Assuming solutions of the form $\theta_i = \Theta_i \sin pt$ and noting that $\bar{I}_2 = 2\bar{I}_1$, we obtain the set of homogeneous equations

$$\left(\frac{k}{\bar{I}_1} - \lambda\right)\Theta_1 - \frac{k}{\bar{I}_1}\Theta_2 = 0$$

$$-\frac{k}{2\bar{I}_1}\Theta_1 + \left(\frac{k}{2\bar{I}_1} - \lambda\right)\Theta_2 = 0$$

PROB. 4-28

where $\lambda_i = p_i^2$. Using the polynomial method, the roots of the characteristic equation are found to be

$$\lambda_1 = p_1^2 = \frac{3}{2}\frac{k}{\bar{I}_1}$$

$$\lambda_2 = p_2^2 = 0$$

The fact that $\lambda_2 = 0$ indicates that the system rotates as a rigid body ($\theta_1 = \theta_2$).

Using the iteration method, and assuming values of $\theta_1 = \theta_2 = 1$ for the eigenvector components, show that convergence will be to the smallest eigenvalue instead of to the largest eigenvalue. Discuss the significance of this result, with respect to the assumed eigenvector components.

4-29. Referring to Prob. 4-28, assume initial values of $\theta_1 = -1$ and $\theta_2 = 1$ for the eigenvector components in the iteration procedure, and determine the largest eigenvalue (p^2 when the disks are oscillating 180° out of phase with each other).

4-30. In Example 4-10 a general **FORTRAN** program was written for obtaining, by the iteration method, the smallest eigenvalue and associated eigenvector. a) Modify the given program so that it may be used to obtain the largest eigenvalue and associated eigenvector. b) Using the modified program specified in part a of this problem, determine the largest circular frequency and associated configuration of the 4-story building discussed in Example 4-10. (The desired frequency and configuration correspond to the fourth mode of vibration of the building.)

4-31. Four disks are attached to a shaft which is supported by bearings, as shown in the accompanying figure. a) Using Lagrange's equation

$$\frac{d}{dt}\left(\frac{\partial T}{\partial \dot{\theta}_i}\right) - \frac{\partial T}{\partial \theta_i} + \frac{\partial V}{\partial \theta_i} = 0$$

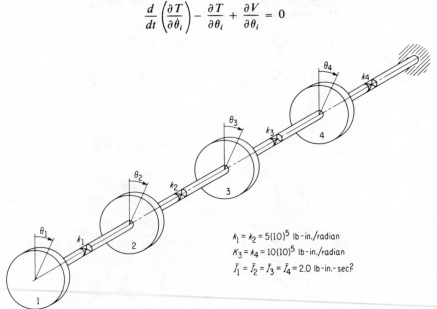

$k_1 = k_2 = 5(10)^5$ lb-in./radian
$k_3 = k_4 = 10(10)^5$ lb-in./radian
$\bar{I}_1 = \bar{I}_2 = \bar{I}_3 = \bar{I}_4 = 2.0$ lb-in.-sec^2

PROB. 4-31

derive the differential equations of motion of the system, where T is the kinetic energy of the system, and V is the strain energy stored in the shaft. b) Assuming solutions of the form $\theta_i = \Theta_i \sin pt$ for the differential equations derived in part a, transform them to a set of homogeneous algebraic equations. c) Using the values of k_i and $\bar{I}_i$, shown in the accompanying figure, as input data to the computer, determine, by the polynomial method, the eigenvalues and associated eigenvectors for the four principal modes of vibration. (Refer to Sec. 4-11.)

chapter 5

Numerical Integration and Differentiation

5-1. Introduction

Engineers are frequently confronted with the problem of differentiating or integrating functions which are defined in tabular or graphical form rather than as explicit functions. The interpretation of experimentally obtained data is a good example of this. A similar situation involves the integration of functions which have explicit forms that are difficult or impossible to integrate in terms of elementary functions. Graphical techniques, employing the construction of tangents to curves and the estimation of areas under curves, are commonly used in solving such problems, when great accuracy is not a prerequisite for the results.

However, there are occasions when a higher degree of accuracy is desired, and, for these, various numerical methods are available. It is with these techniques that this chapter will be concerned. Although both integration and differentiation formulas will be discussed, it should be pointed out that numerical differentiation is inherently much less accurate than numerical integration, and its application is generally avoided whenever possible. Nevertheless, it has been used successfully in certain applications, so an example will be included later.

Numerical integration, or numerical *quadrature*, as it is often called, consists essentially of finding a close approximation to the area under a curve of a function $f(x)$ which has been determined either from experimental data or from a mathematical expression. Here, we shall include only the simpler methods given by the *trapezoid rule* and *Simpson's* (parabolic) *rule*. The trapezoid and parabolic formulas are special cases of what are known as Newton-Cotes quadrature formulas. The use of higher-order Newton-Cotes formulas for greater accuracy is seldom necessary or justified in engineering applications, particularly if the curve of the function is based upon experimental data. We shall include, in the same discussion with the problem of evaluating definite integrals, the problem of evaluating indefinite integrals of the type

$$g(x) = \int_0^x f(x)\,dx$$

since $g(x)$ values for various x values of such an indefinite integral may be determined numerically by evaluating a corresponding number of definite integrals defined by the values assigned to the upper limit.

5-2. Integration by the Trapezoid Rule

Consider the function $f(x)$, whose graph between $x = a$ and $x = b$ is shown in Fig. 5-1. A close approximation to the area under the curve is

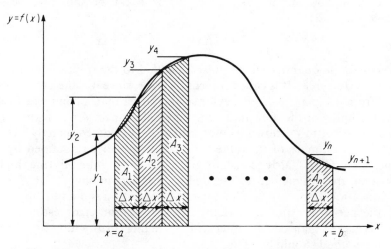

FIG. 5-1. Approximation, by the trapezoid rule, of the area under a curve.

obtained by dividing it into n strips Δx in width and approximating the area of each strip by that of a trapezoid, as shown in the figure. Calling the ordinates $y_i (i = 1, 2, \ldots, n + 1)$, the areas of the trapezoids are

$$A_1 = \Delta x \left(\frac{y_1 + y_2}{2} \right)$$

$$A_2 = \Delta x \left(\frac{y_2 + y_3}{2} \right)$$

$$\vdots \qquad \vdots$$

$$A_n = \Delta x \left(\frac{y_n + y_{n+1}}{2} \right)$$

$$(5\text{-}1)$$

The total area lying between $x = a$ and $x = b$ is given by

$$A = \int_a^b f(x)\,dx \cong A_1 + A_2 + A_3 + \cdots + A_n$$

Substituting Eq. 5-1 into this expression yields

$$A = \int_a^b f(x)\,dx \cong \frac{\Delta x}{2}\,(y_1 + 2y_2 + 2y_3 + \cdots + 2y_n + y_{n+1}) \qquad (5\text{-}2)$$

Equation 5-2 is referred to as the *trapezoid rule*.

If the function $f(x)$ can be expressed as a continuous mathematical function having continuous derivatives $f'(x)$ and $f''(x)$, the error resulting from approximating the true area in a strip under the curve of $f(x)$ between x_i and x_{i+1} by the area of a trapezoid can be shown to be (see Sec. 6-9, Eq. 6-121)

$$E_T = -\frac{1}{12}\,f''(\xi)(\Delta x)^3 \qquad x_i < \xi < x_{i+1}$$

This error is the quantity which must be added to the trapezoidal area to obtain the true area. It is called *truncation error*, since it is the error which results from using a truncated Taylor series, rather than a complete Taylor series, to represent the area in an incremental strip in series form. The truncation-error term shown cannot usually be evaluated directly. However, a good estimate of its value for each strip can be obtained by assuming that f'' is fairly constant over the strip interval (the higher derivatives are assumed to be negligible) and evaluating f'' at $\xi = x_i$. The truncation-error estimate for the total integration is obtained by summing the per-strip estimates. If the total truncation-error estimate obtained is larger than can be tolerated, a smaller strip width or a more accurate method should be used.

Another error which is introduced in obtaining the approximate area of each strip is *roundoff error*. This arises from performing the required arithmetic operations with numerical values having a limited number of significant digits. Roundoff error can be minimized by the use of double-precision arithmetic or of compilers capable of handling a large number of significant digits.

From the preceding facts it can be seen that the total error over the desired interval of integration is the sum of the truncation and roundoff errors. If the total error were due only to truncation error, it could be made as small as desired by merely reducing the strip width sufficiently. For example, halving the strip width would double the number of per-strip truncation errors summed, but the expression given for the per-strip error reveals that each would be approximately one eighth of its previous size.

However, decreasing the strip width also affects the total error by increasing the total roundoff error due to the larger number of calculations in evaluating Eq. 5-2. Thus, in decreasing the strip width to decrease the total error, there is an optimum point at which further decreases in strip width will cause the total error to increase rather than decrease as the roundoff error becomes dominant. The optimum strip width for a particular function is easily determined experimentally on the computer (assuming that the true area under the graph of the function can be evaluated) but is difficult to define analytically.

EXAMPLE 5-1

Let us consider a U.S. Army M-14 rifle having a 24-in. barrel and a 0.300-in. bore with 0.004-in.-deep rifling grooves. The lead bullet used weighs 150.5 grains (0.0215 lb). The gas-pressure curve varies with the temperature of the barrel, but, for purposes of illustration, we will use the gas-pressure data for a particular firing condition, as shown in Fig. 5-2. The frictional resistance exerted on the bullet is to be considered small as compared with the propulsive force of the gas on the bullet, and the cross-sectional area of the rifling grooves is considered negligible. Our problem will be to determine 1) the *muzzle* velocity of the bullet, using the trapezoid rule for the required integration (we will use the 49 pressure readings given in Fig. 5-2 and the given weight of the bullet, but will write the computer program so that any number of ordinates up to 100, or any weight of bullet, could be used if desired); and 2) the complete velocity-displacement and time-displacement curves for the bullet during the course of its travel in the barrel, again using the trapezoid rule for integration.

The solution of part 1 is begun by considering that the work done on the bullet while it is in the barrel is given by

$$\text{Work} = \int_0^{x_{final}} F(x)\, dx \tag{5-3}$$

where $F(x)$ is the force of the gas acting on the bullet as a function of the displacement x. The work is thus represented by the area under the pressure-displacement curve of Fig. 5-2, multiplied by the cross-sectional area of the bore (0.07069 in.²). The work done on the bullet by the gas must equal the change in the kinetic energy (K.E.) of the bullet, since we are neglecting any energy loss due to frictional resistance. Therefore,

$$\int_0^{x_{final}} F(x)\, dx = \Delta\text{K.E.} = \frac{1}{2} m\dot{x}_{final}^2 - \frac{1}{2} m\dot{x}_{initial}^2 \tag{5-4}$$

Since the initial kinetic energy is zero, we may write, from Eq. 5-4,

$$\dot{x}_{final} = \sqrt{\frac{2}{m} \int_0^{x_{final}} F(x)\, dx} = \sqrt{\frac{2(0.07069)}{W/386} \int_0^{x_{final}} P(x)\, dx} \tag{5-5}$$

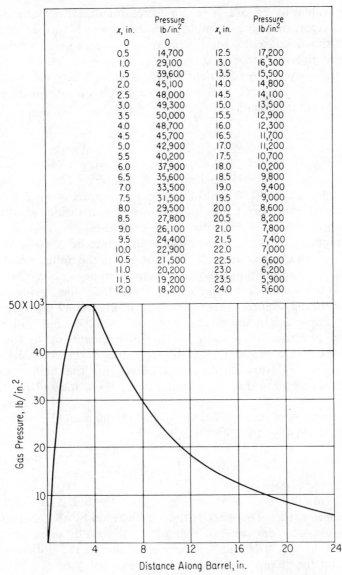

x, in.	Pressure lb/in.^{2}	x, in.	Pressure lb/in.^{2}
0	0		
0.5	14,700	12.5	17,200
1.0	29,100	13.0	16,300
1.5	39,600	13.5	15,500
2.0	45,100	14.0	14,800
2.5	48,000	14.5	14,100
3.0	49,300	15.0	13,500
3.5	50,000	15.5	12,900
4.0	48,700	16.0	12,300
4.5	45,700	16.5	11,700
5.0	42,900	17.0	11,200
5.5	40,200	17.5	10,700
6.0	37,900	18.0	10,200
6.5	35,600	18.5	9,800
7.0	33,500	19.0	9,400
7.5	31,500	19.5	9,000
8.0	29,500	20.0	8,600
8.5	27,800	20.5	8,200
9.0	26,100	21.0	7,800
9.5	24,400	21.5	7,400
10.0	22,900	22.0	7,000
10.5	21,500	22.5	6,600
11.0	20,200	23.0	6,200
11.5	19,200	23.5	5,900
12.0	18,200	24.0	5,600

FIG. 5-2. Gas-pressure–bullet-displacement data for the M-14 rifle for a particular firing condition.

where $P(x)$ is the gas pressure in terms of the displacement, as given in Fig. 5-2, and

$$\int_0^{x_{\text{final}}} P(x) \, dx$$

is the area under the pressure-displacement curve, which we shall obtain by using Eq. 5-2.

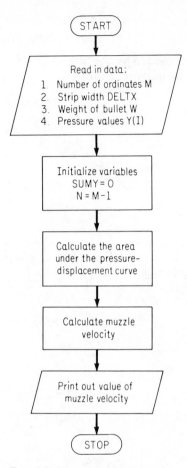

FIG. 5-3. Flow chart for determining muzzle velocity of a rifle bullet,
Example 5-1.

A flow chart for the computer solution is shown in Fig. 5-3.   The
FORTRAN names selected to represent the variable quantities are

FORTRAN *Name*	*Quantity*
N	Number of strips
M	Number of ordinates
DELTX	Width of each strip
W	Weight of bullet
Y(I)	Values of pressure readings
SUMY	Sum of ordinates
AREA	Area under pressure curve

XDSQ	Square of muzzle velocity
XD	Muzzle velocity

From the outline provided by the flow chart of Fig. 5-3, the FORTRAN IV source program is formulated as follows:

```
  DIMENSION (Y100)
1 FORMAT (I3,F3.1,F5.4)
  READ(5,1)M,DELTX,W
2 FORMAT (F5.0)
  DO 3 I = 1,M
3 READ(5,2)Y(I)
  SUMY = 0.
  N = M−1
  DO 4 I=2,N
4 SUMY = SUMY + Y(I)
  AREA = DELTX/2. * (Y(1)+2.*SUMY + Y(M))
  XDSQ = 2.*.07069*386./W*AREA
  XD = SQRT(XDSQ)
  WRITE(6,5)XD
5 FORMAT (18H1MUZZLE VELOCITY =,F7.0,18H INCHES PER
                                              SECOND)
  STOP
  END
```

The muzzle velocity is shown in the following computer printout:

MUZZLE VELOCITY = 36516. INCHES PER SECOND

STOP 00000

The muzzle velocity of 36,516 in./sec, or 3043 ft/sec, obtained in this solution is somewhat higher than the actual average muzzle velocity of 2780 ft/sec for the M-14 rifle. This was to be expected, in view of the fact that friction was neglected in the solution.

The solution of part 2 is begun by again considering Eq. 5-5. In part 1 the integral expression in this equation was evaluated as a definite integral with an upper limit corresponding to the length of the barrel. In this part of the solution, we shall treat this same integral expression as an indefinite integral by assigning it a variable upper limit, so that it has the form

$$\dot{x} = f(x) = \sqrt{\frac{2(0.07069)}{W/386} \int_0^x P(x)\, dx} \qquad (5\text{-}6)$$

The velocity-displacement curve of the bullet can be obtained from Eq. 5-6 by computing $\dot{x}$ for a number of consecutive values of the upper limit corresponding to various displacements along the barrel. This may be accomplished as follows: Letting $x = x_{i+1}$ in Eq. 5-6, we can write the velocity at station $i + 1$ as

$$\dot{x}_{i+1} = \sqrt{\frac{2(0.07069)}{W/386} \left[\int_0^{x_i} P(x)\, dx + \int_{x_i}^{x_{i+1}} P(x)\, dx \right]} \qquad (5\text{-}7)$$

Since

$$\dot{x}_i^2 = \frac{2(0.07069)}{W/386} \int_0^{x_i} P(x)\, dx$$

we can write Eq. 5-7 as

$$\dot{x}_{i+1} = \sqrt{\dot{x}_i^2 + \frac{2(0.07069)}{W/386} \int_{x_i}^{x_{i+1}} P(x)\, dx)} \qquad (5\text{-}8)$$

Equation 5-8 has the form of a recurrence equation and will give the velocity at one x value in terms of the velocity at the previous x value. Actually, Eq. 5-8 could have been derived more simply by equating the work done by the gas on the bullet over 1 increment of x to the change in kinetic energy of the bullet in that increment. However, the derivation used emphasizes the fact that we are actually evaluating an indefinite integral which is a function of its upper limit.

The desired time-displacement relationship may be obtained as follows. By definition,

$$\dot{x} = \frac{dx}{dt}$$

from which

$$dt = \frac{dx}{\dot{x}}$$

Integrating the right side of the preceding equation over an interval of 1 increment of x, and integrating the left side over the corresponding time increment, we have

$$\int_{t_i}^{t_{i+1}} dt = \int_{x_i}^{x_{i+1}} \frac{1}{\dot{x}}\, dx \qquad (5\text{-}9)$$

which may be written in the form of a recurrence formula as

$$t_{i+1} = t_i + \int_{x_i}^{x_{i+1}} \frac{1}{\dot{x}}\, dx \qquad (5\text{-}10)$$

The integration indicated in Eq. 5-10 for each recurrence will be approximated by the area of the trapezoid formed from the appropriate strip of area under the $(1/\dot{x})$ versus x curve. Evaluating the area for the first strip, however, presents a problem, for at $x = 0$ the value of $(1/\dot{x})$ is infinitely large, since the initial velocity is zero at that point. We can circumvent this difficulty by an interpretation of the physical problem. Noting the pressure-displacement curve of Fig. 5-2, we see that there is very little change in the slope of that curve near $x = 0$. Since the acceleration of the bullet is proportional to the pressure being exerted upon it by the gas, we may make the reasonable assumption that there is correspondingly little change in the rate of change of acceleration near the origin, so that $\dddot{x} \cong$ constant. With these observations in mind, an expression for the time corresponding to the first increment of x may be obtained by starting with

$$\dddot{x} = C \qquad (5\text{-}11)$$

Integrating this expression gives

$$\ddot{x} = Ct + C_1$$

At $t = 0$, $\ddot{x} = 0$, so that $C_1 = 0$, and the equation for acceleration becomes

$$\ddot{x} = Ct$$

Integrating again gives

$$\dot{x} = \frac{Ct^2}{2} + C_2$$

At $t = 0$, $\dot{x} = 0$, so that $C_2 = 0$, and the equation for the velocity is

$$\dot{x} = \frac{Ct^2}{2} \qquad (5\text{-}12)$$

Integrating once more to obtain an expression for the displacement yields

$$x = \frac{1}{6} Ct^3 + C_3$$

At $t = 0$, $x = 0$, so that $C_3 = 0$, and the displacement equation reduces to

$$x = \frac{1}{6} Ct^3 \qquad (5\text{-}13)$$

Substituting Eq. 5-12 into Eq. 5-13 gives

$$x = \frac{1}{3} \dot{x}t \qquad (5\text{-}14)$$

Denoting x_1 as the value of x at the end of the first increment, and the corresponding time as t_1, we may write, from Eq. 5-14,

$$t_1 = \frac{3x_1}{\dot{x}_1} \qquad (5\text{-}15)$$

The velocity $\dot{x}_1$ at the end of the first increment of x is obtained from Eq. 5-8, and the corresponding time t_1 is obtained from Eq. 5-15. For subsequent calculations we continue to use Eq. 5-8 to find the desired velocities, but we revert to the use of Eq. 5-10 to get the time values.

A flow chart for the computer solution is given in Fig. 5-4. The FORTRAN names used in the computer program, along with the quantities they represent, follow.

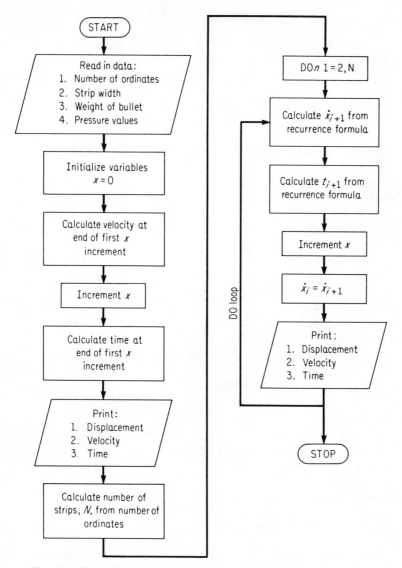

FIG. 5-4. Flow chart for obtaining velocity-displacement and time-displacement relationships for rifle bullet in barrel, Example 5-1.

FORTRAN *Name*	*Quantity*	*Data Values Used*
M	Number of ordinates	49
N	Number of strips of area	
DELTX	Increment of x	0.5 in.

W	Weight of bullet	0.0215 lb
Y(I)	Values of pressure readings, lb/in.^{2}	
XD	Bullet velocity at x, in./sec	
XD1	Bullet velocity at $(x + \Delta x)$, in./sec	
T	Time, sec	
X	Displacement, in.	

The **FORTRAN IV** program is as follows:

```
  DIMENSION Y(100)
1 FORMAT (I3,F3.1,F5.4)
  READ(5,1)M,DELTX,W
2 FORMAT (F5.0)
  DO 3 I=1,M
3 READ(5,2)Y(I)
  X = 0.
  XD = SQRT(2.*.07069*386./W*(Y(1)+Y(2))/2.*DELTX)
  X = X + DELTX
  T = 3.*X/XD
  WRITE(6,4)
4 FORMAT (1H1,23H DISPL   VELOCITY   TIME//)
  WRITE(6,5)X,XD,T
5 FORMAT (1H ,F6.1,F9.0,F10.6)
  N = M-1
  DO 6 I=2,N
  XD1 = SQRT(XD*XD+2.*.07069*386./W*(Y(I)+Y(I+1))/2.*DELTX)
  T = T + (1./XD1+1./XD)/2.*DELTX
  X = X + DELTX
  XD = XD1
6 WRITE(6,5)X,XD,T
  STOP
  END
```

The computer printout of the results is in tabular form, as follows:

DISPL	VELOCITY	TIME
.5	3054.	.000491
1.0	6092.	.000614
1.5	8984.	.000682
2.0	11595.	.000732
2.5	13911.	.000771
3.0	15977.	.000805

DISPL	VELOCITY	TIME
3.5	17840.	.000835
4.0	19517.	.000861
4.5	20996.	.000886
5.0	22294.	.000909
5.5	23447.	.000931
6.0	24481.	.000952
6.5	25416.	.000972
7.0	26264.	.000991
7.5	27038.	.001010
8.0	27745.	.001028
8.5	28392.	.001046
9.0	28988.	.001064
9.5	29536.	.001081
10.0	30040.	.001098
10.5	30505.	.001114
11.0	30936.	.001130
11.5	31337.	.001146
12.0	31714.	.001162
12.5	32066.	.001178
13.0	32396.	.001193
13.5	32706.	.001209
14.0	32998.	.001224
14.5	33275.	.001239
15.0	33537.	.001254
15.5	33786.	.001269
16.0	34022.	.001284
16.5	34245.	.001298
17.0	34456.	.001313
17.5	34657.	.001327
18.0	34848.	.001342
18.5	35030.	.001356
19.0	35203.	.001370
19.5	35369.	.001384
20.0	35526.	.001399
20.5	35676.	.001413
21.0	35818.	.001427
21.5	35952.	.001441
22.0	36079.	.001454
22.5	36199.	.001468
23.0	36311.	.001482
23.5	36416.	.001496
24.0	36516.	.001509

The computer printout may be displayed in graphical form, as in Fig. 5-5.

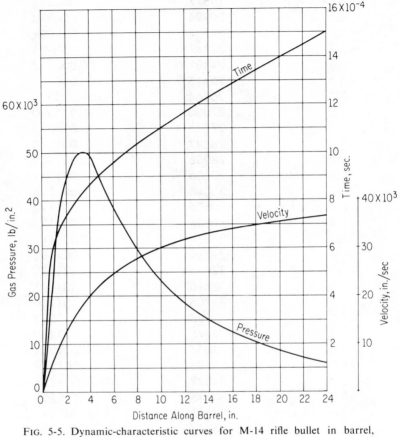

FIG. 5-5. Dynamic-characteristic curves for M-14 rifle bullet in barrel, Example 5-1.

5-3. Integration by Simpson's Rule

The trapezoid rule approximates the area under a curve by summing the areas of uniform-width trapezoids formed by connecting successive points on the curve by straight lines. Simpson's rule gives a more accurate approximation, since it consists of connecting successive groups of 3 points on the curve, by second-degree parabolas, and summing the areas under the parabolas to obtain the approximate area under the curve. For example, the area contained in the 2 strips under the curve of $f(x)$, in Fig. 5-6, is approximated by the crosshatched area under a parabola passing through the 3 points (x_i, y_i), (x_{i+1}, y_{i+1}), and (x_{i+2}, y_{i+2}).

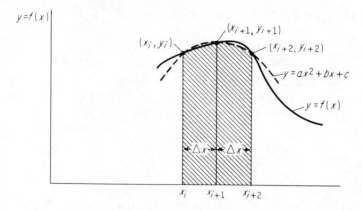

FIG. 5-6. Approximation of area under a curve by use of a
second-degree parabola.

For convenience in deriving an expression for this area, let us assume
that the 2 strips comprising the area under the parabola lie on opposite
sides of the origin, as shown in Fig. 5-7. Such an arrangement will not
compromise the generality of the derivation. The general form of the
equation of the second-degree parabola connecting the 3 points is

$$y = ax^2 + bx + c \qquad (5\text{-}16)$$

The integration of Eq. 5-16 from $-\Delta x$ to Δx gives the area contained in the 2 strips shown under the parabola. Hence

$$A_{2\,\text{strips}} = \int_{-\Delta x}^{\Delta x} (ax^2 + bx + c)\,dx = \left[\frac{ax^3}{3} + \frac{bx^2}{2} + cx\right]_{-\Delta x}^{\Delta x} \qquad (5\text{-}17)$$

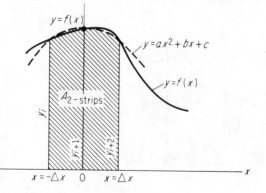

FIG. 5-7. Area in 2 strips under a curve
centered on y axis.

Substituting the limits into Eq. 5-17 yields

$$A_{2\,\text{strips}} = \frac{2}{3} a(\Delta x)^3 + 2c(\Delta x) \tag{5-18}$$

The constants a and c can be determined from the fact that points $(-\Delta x, y_i)$, $(0, y_{i+1})$, and $(\Delta x, y_{i+2})$ must all satisfy Eq. 5-16. The substitution of these 3 sets of coordinates into Eq. 5-16 yields

$$y_i = a(-\Delta x)^2 + b(-\Delta x) + c$$
$$y_{i+1} = c \tag{5-19}$$
$$y_{i+2} = a(\Delta x)^2 + b(\Delta x) + c$$

Solving these equations simultaneously for the constants a, b, and c, we find that

$$a = \frac{y_i - 2y_{i+1} + y_{i+2}}{2(\Delta x)^2}$$
$$b = \frac{y_{i+2} - y_i}{2(\Delta x)} \tag{5-20}$$
$$c = y_{i+1}$$

The substitution of the first and third parts of Eq. 5-20 into Eq. 5-18 yields

$$A_{2\,\text{strips}} = \frac{\Delta x}{3} (y_i + 4y_{i+1} + y_{i+2}) \tag{5-21}$$

which gives the area in terms of the 3 ordinates y_i, y_{i+1}, and y_{i+2} and the width Δx of a single strip. This constitutes Simpson's rule for obtaining the approximate area contained in 2 equal-width strips under a curve.

If the area under a curve between 2 values of x is divided into n uniform strips (n even), as shown in Fig. 5-8, the application of Eq. 5-21

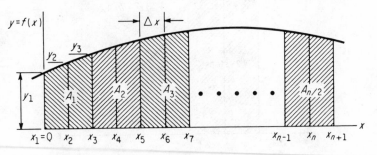

FIG. 5-8. Area under curve divided into an even number of strips for approximation by Simpson's rule.

shows that

$$A_1 = \frac{\Delta x}{3}(y_1 + 4y_2 + y_3)$$

$$A_2 = \frac{\Delta x}{3}(y_3 + 4y_4 + y_5)$$

$$A_3 = \frac{\Delta x}{3}(y_5 + 4y_6 + y_7) \qquad (5\text{-}22)$$

$$\vdots \qquad \vdots \qquad \vdots \qquad \vdots \qquad \vdots$$

$$A_{n/2} = \frac{\Delta x}{3}(y_{n-1} + 4y_n + y_{n+1})$$

Summing these areas, we can write

$$\int_{x_1=0}^{x_{n+1}} f(x)\,dx = \sum_{i=1}^{i=n/2} A_i = \frac{\Delta x}{3}(y_1 + 4y_2 + 2y_3 + 4y_4$$

$$+\ 2y_5 + \cdots + 2y_{n-1} + 4y_n + y_{n+1})$$

or

$$\int_{x_1=0}^{x_{n+1}} f(x)\,dx = \frac{\Delta x}{3}\left(y_1 + 4\sum_{i=2,4,6}^{i=n} y_i + 2\sum_{i=3,5,7}^{i=n-1} y_i + y_{n+1}\right) \qquad (5\text{-}23)$$

where n is even.

Equation 5-23 is called Simpson's one-third rule for obtaining the approximate area under a curve. It may be used when the area is divided into an *even* number of strips of width Δx.

If the function $f(x)$ can be expressed as a continuous mathematical function having continuous derivatives $f'(x)$ through $f^{IV}(x)$, the error resulting from approximating the true area in 2 strips under the curve of $f(x)$ between x_{i-1} and x_{i+1} by the area under a second-degree parabola can be shown to be (see Sec. 6-9, Eq. 6-154)

$$E_T = -\frac{1}{90}f^{IV}(\xi)(\Delta x)^5 \qquad x_{i-1} < \xi < x_{i+1}$$

This *truncation* error is the quantity which must be added to the approximate area in 2 strips, obtained by Simpson's one-third rule, to get the true area under the curve in this interval. The truncation-error term shown cannot usually be evaluated directly. However, a good estimate of its value for each 2-strip interval can be obtained by assuming that f^{IV} is fairly constant over the interval (the higher derivatives are assumed to be negligible) and evaluating f^{IV} at $\xi = x_i$. The truncation-error estimate for the total integration is obtained by summing the 2-strip estimates. If the total truncation-error estimate is larger than can be tolerated, smaller 2-strip intervals should be used. Considering roundoff error, which is also present, there is an optimum strip width for obtaining a minimum total error in the integration. (See the error analysis of the trapezoid method, preceding.)

In utilizing Simpson's rule for integrating a function, it might be desirable to use an odd number of strips to approximate the true area under the curve. If an odd number of strips is used, Simpson's three-eighths rule for obtaining the area contained in 3 strips under a curve can be used, in conjunction with Eq. 5-23, to find the total area. For example, if 97 strips were used, Simpson's three-eighths rule could be used to approximate the area under the curve occupied by the first 3 strips. The remaining 94 strips would then be summed, using Simpson's one-third rule. The derivation of the three-eighths rule is similar to that for the one-third rule, except that it determines the area under a *third*-degree parabola connecting 4 points on the given curve. The general form of the third-degree parabola is

$$y = ax^3 + bx^2 + cx + d \tag{5-24}$$

In the derivation, the constants are determined by requiring that the parabola pass through the 4 points indicated on the curve shown in Fig. 5-9. The range of integration is from $-3(\Delta x)/2$ to $3(\Delta x)/2$, resulting in

$$A_{3\,strips} = \int_{-3(\Delta x)/2}^{3(\Delta x)/2} (ax^3 + bx^2 + cx + d)\,dx$$

$$= \frac{3(\Delta x)}{8}\,(y_i + 3y_{i+1} + 3y_{i+2} + y_{i+3}) \tag{5-25}$$

which is Simpson's three-eighths rule.

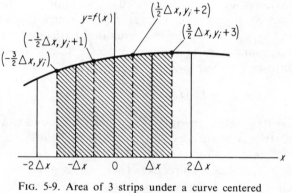

FIG. 5-9. Area of 3 strips under a curve centered on y axis.

EXAMPLE 5-2

Let us solve part 1 of Example 5-1, using Simpson's one-third rule. The equation which must be solved to find the velocity of the bullet is repeated here for convenience:

$$\dot{x}_{final} = \sqrt{\frac{2(0.07069)}{W/386} \int_0^{x_{final}} P(x)\,dx} \tag{5-26}$$

The area under the pressure curve

$$\int_0^{x_{final}} P(x)\,dx$$

will be determined by dividing the curve of Fig. 5-2 into 48 equal strips and summing the area contained in the 24 *pairs* of strips by the use of Eq. 5-23. The source program will be written, however, so that any even number of strips up to 100 may be used, if desired. The same flow chart as used in part 1 of Example 5-1 (Fig. 5-3) will be utilized here to write the FORTRAN IV source program. The FORTRAN names and the quantities they represent are the same as in part 1 of Example 5-1, with the following additions:

FORTRAN *Name*	*Quantity*
SUMEV	Sum of the even ordinates, $\displaystyle\sum_{i=2,4,6}^{i=n} y_i$
SUMOD	Sum of the odd ordinates, $\displaystyle\sum_{i=3,5,7}^{i=n-1} y_i$
K	Number of strips less 1, $(n-1)$

The FORTRAN IV program is as follows:

```
   DIMENSION Y(100)
 1 FORMAT (I3,F3.1,F5.4)
   READ(5,1)M,DELTX,W
 2 FORMAT (F5.0)
   DO 3 I=1,M
 3 READ(5,2)Y(I)
   SUMEV = 0.
   SUMOD = 0.
   N = M-1
   K = N-1
   DO 4 I = 2,N,2
 4 SUMEV = SUMEV + Y(I)
   DO 5 I = 3,K,2
 5 SUMOD = SUMOD + Y(I)
   AREA = DELTX/3.*(Y(1) + 4.*SUMEV + 2.*SUMOD + Y(M))
   XDSQ = 2.*.07069*386./W*AREA
   XD = SQRT(XDSQ)
   WRITE(6,6)XD
```

6 FORMAT (19H1MUZZLE VELOCITY = ,F7.0,18H INCHES PER
SECOND)
  STOP
  END

The execution of the preceding program yielded this computer print-out

  MUZZLE VELOCITY = 36538. INCHES PER SECOND

which reveals that the result obtained by using Simpson's one-third rule differs but little from the result (36,516 in./sec) we got by using the trapezoid rule in Example 5-1. Thus, only a relatively small gain in accuracy resulted from employing Simpson's rule, in this particular problem.

To determine the complete velocity-displacement curve by using Simpson's rule, Eq. 5-8, which was used for this purpose in Example 5-1, would have to be modified to

$$\dot{x}_{i+2} = \sqrt{\dot{x}_i^2 + \frac{2(0.07069)}{W/386} \int_{x_i}^{x_{i+2}} P(x) \, dx} \qquad (5\text{-}27)$$

where the integral expression

$$\int_{x_i}^{x_{i+2}} P(x) \, dx$$

is the area contained in *2* strips under the pressure curve. It should be noted that the use of Eq. 5-27 consists of "stepping forward" 2 increments each time a new velocity is computed. As a result, the only velocity values calculated are those corresponding to *every other* datum point on the pressure curve.

Comparing the trapezoid rule and Simpson's one-third rule, we see that the trapezoid rule requires $n + 1$ data points for obtaining the area in n subintervals of width Δx, whereas Simpson's one-third rule requires $n + 1$ data points for obtaining the area in $n/2$ subintervals of width $2(\Delta x)$.

5-4. Numerical Differentiation

We shall now direct our attention to ways of numerically differentiating functions which are defined only by tabulated data or by experimentally determined curves. One approach is to approximate the function, in the neighborhood of the point at which the derivative is desired, by a second-, third-, or higher-degree parabola, and then use the derivative of the parabola at that point as the approximate derivative of the function. Another method, the one discussed here, makes use of Taylor-series expansions.

The Taylor series for a function $y = f(x)$ at $(x_i + \Delta x)$ expanded about x_i is

$$y(x_i + \Delta x) = y_i + y_i'(\Delta x) + \frac{y_i''(\Delta x)^2}{2!} + \frac{y_i'''(\Delta x)^3}{3!} + \cdots \qquad (5\text{-}28)$$

where y_i is the ordinate corresponding to x_i and $(x_i + \Delta x)$ is in the region of convergence. The function at $(x_i - \Delta x)$ is similarly given by

$$y(x_i - \Delta x) = y_i - y_i'(\Delta x) + \frac{y_i''(\Delta x)^2}{2!} - \frac{y_i'''(\Delta x)^3}{3!} + \cdots \qquad (5\text{-}29)$$

Using only the first 3 terms of each expansion, we can obtain an expression for y_i' by subtracting Eq. 5-29 from Eq. 5-28, yielding

$$y_i' = \frac{y(x_i + \Delta x) - y(x_i - \Delta x)}{2(\Delta x)} \qquad (5\text{-}30)$$

Looking at Fig. 5-10, we see that if we designate equally spaced points

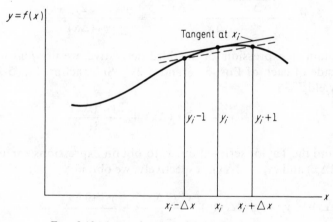

FIG. 5-10. Approximation of the derivative at x_i.

to the right of x_i as x_{i+1}, x_{i+2}, and so on, and those to the left of x_i as x_{i-1}, x_{i-2}, and identify the corresponding ordinates as y_{i+1}, y_{i+2}, y_{i-1} and y_{i-2}, respectively, Eq. 5-30 can be written in the form

$$y_i' = \frac{y_{i+1} - y_{i-1}}{2(\Delta x)} \qquad (5\text{-}31)$$

Equation 5-31 is called the first *central-difference* approximation of y' at x_i. Graphically, the approximation represents the slope of the dashed line in Fig. 5-10. The actual derivative is represented by the solid line drawn tangent to the curve at x_i.

If we add Eqs. 5-28 and 5-29 and use the notation previously described, we may write the following expression for the second derivative:

$$y_i'' = \frac{y_{i+1} - 2y_i + y_{i-1}}{(\Delta x)^2} \tag{5-32}$$

Equation 5-32 is the first central-difference approximation[1] of the second derivative of the function at x_i. This expression may be interpreted graphically as the slope of the line tangent to the curve at $x_{i+\frac{1}{2}}$ minus the slope of the line tangent to the curve at $x_{i-\frac{1}{2}}$ divided by Δx, where the slopes of the tangent lines are approximated by the expressions,

$$y_{i+1/2}' = \frac{y_{i+1} - y_i}{\Delta x}$$

$$y_{i-1/2}' = \frac{y_i - y_{i-1}}{\Delta x}$$

That is,

$$y_i'' = \frac{\dfrac{y_{i+1} - y_i}{\Delta x} - \dfrac{y_i - y_{i-1}}{\Delta x}}{\Delta x} = \frac{y_{i+1} - 2y_i + y_{i-1}}{(\Delta x)^2}$$

To obtain an expression for the third derivative, we use *four* terms on the right side of each of Eqs. 5-28 and 5-29. Subtracting Eq. 5-29 from Eq. 5-28 yields

$$y_{i+1} - y_{i-1} = 2y_i'(\Delta x) + \frac{2y_i'''(\Delta x)^3}{3!} \tag{5-33}$$

If we expand the Taylor series about x_i to obtain expressions for $y = f(x)$ at $(x_i + 2\Delta x)$ and $(x_i - 2\Delta x)$, respectively, we obtain

$$y(x_i + 2\Delta x) = y_i + y_i'(2\Delta x) + \frac{y_i''(2\Delta x)^2}{2!} + \frac{y_i'''(2\Delta x)^3}{3!} + \cdots \tag{5-34}$$

$$y(x_i - 2\Delta x) = y_i - y_i'(2\Delta x) + \frac{y_i''(2\Delta x)^2}{2!} - \frac{y_i'''(2\Delta x)^3}{3!} + \cdots \tag{5-35}$$

Subtracting Eq. 5-35 from Eq. 5-34, and using just the 4 terms of each expansion shown, gives

$$y_{i+2} - y_{i-2} = 4y_i'(\Delta x) + \frac{8}{3} y_i'''(\Delta x)^3 \tag{5-36}$$

---

[1] Some authors refer to Eq. 5-32 as the *second central-difference quotient*, since the numerator is, by definition, the second central difference of $y(x)$ at x_i. However, use of this nomenclature leads to difficulty in describing the more accurate finite-difference expressions.

The simultaneous solution of Eqs. 5-33 and 5-36 for the third derivative yields

$$y_i''' = \frac{y_{i+2} - 2y_{i+1} + 2y_{i-1} - y_{i-2}}{2(\Delta x)^3} \tag{5-37}$$

Equation 5-37 gives the first central-difference expression for the third derivative of y at x_i.

Successively higher derivatives can be obtained by this method, but, since they require the solution of increasingly larger numbers of simultaneous equations, the process becomes quite tedious. The same technique may also be used to find more accurate expressions for the derivatives by using additional terms in the Taylor-series expansion. However, the derivations of these more accurate expressions, particularly for derivatives higher than the second, become very laborious because of the numbers of simultaneous equations which must be solved. Derivations of the more accurate expressions are not given here, but such expressions for several derivatives are included in the summary which follows this discussion. Derivations for the higher derivatives are accomplished with much greater facility and far less labor by using *difference*, *averaging*, and *derivative* operators. Such a method is outside the scope of this text, but it can be found in various books concerned with numerical analysis.[2]

It has been shown that the central-difference expressions for the various derivatives involve values of the function on both sides of the x value at which the derivative of the function is desired. By utilizing the appropriate Taylor-series expansions, one can easily obtain expressions for the derivatives which are entirely in terms of values of the function at x_i and points to the right of x_i. These are known as *forward-finite-difference* expressions. In a similar manner, derivative expressions which are entirely in terms of values of the function at x_i and points to the *left* of x_i can be found. These are known as *backward-finite-difference* expressions. In numerical differentiation, forward-difference expressions are used when data to the left of a point at which a derivative is desired are not available, and backward-difference expressions are used when data to the right of the desired point are not available. Central-difference expressions, however, are more accurate than either forward- or backward-difference expressions.

The following is a summary of the differentiation formulas which may be obtained from Taylor-series expansions.

[2] Hildebrand, F. B. *Introduction to Numerical Analysis*. New York: McGraw-Hill Book Company, 1956. Salvadori, M. G., and Baron, M. L. *Numerical Methods in Engineering*. Englewood Cliffs, N. J.: Prentice-Hall, Inc., 1961.

First Central-Difference Expressions

$$y_i' = \frac{y_{i+1} - y_{i-1}}{2(\Delta x)}$$

$$y_i'' = \frac{y_{i+1} - 2y_i + y_{i-1}}{(\Delta x)^2}$$

$$y_i''' = \frac{y_{i+2} - 2y_{i+1} + 2y_{i-1} - y_{i-2}}{2(\Delta x)^3}$$

$$y_i'''' = \frac{y_{i+2} - 4y_{i+1} + 6y_i - 4y_{i-1} + y_{i-2}}{(\Delta x)^4}$$

(5-38)

Second Central-Difference Expressions

$$y_i' = \frac{-y_{i+2} + 8y_{i+1} - 8y_{i-1} + y_{i-2}}{12(\Delta x)}$$

$$y_i'' = \frac{-y_{i+2} + 16y_{i+1} - 30y_i + 16y_{i-1} - y_{i-2}}{12(\Delta x)^2}$$

$$y_i''' = \frac{-y_{i+3} + 8y_{i+2} - 13y_{i+1} + 13y_{i-1} - 8y_{i-2} + y_{i-3}}{8(\Delta x)^3}$$

$$y_i'''' = \frac{-y_{i+3} + 12y_{i+2} - 39y_{i+1} + 56y_i - 39y_{i-1} + 12y_{i-2} - y_{i-3}}{6(\Delta x)^4}$$

(5-39)

First Forward-Difference Expressions

$$y_i' = \frac{y_{i+1} - y_i}{(\Delta x)}$$

$$y_i'' = \frac{y_{i+2} - 2y_{i+1} + y_i}{(\Delta x)^2}$$

$$y_i''' = \frac{y_{i+3} - 3y_{i+2} + 3y_{i+1} - y_i}{(\Delta x)^3}$$

$$y_i'''' = \frac{y_{i+4} - 4y_{i+3} + 6y_{i+2} - 4y_{i+1} + y_i}{(\Delta x)^4}$$

(5-40)

Second Forward-Difference Expressions

$$y_i' = \frac{-y_{i+2} + 4y_{i+1} - 3y_i}{2(\Delta x)}$$

$$y_i'' = \frac{-y_{i+3} + 4y_{i+2} - 5y_{i+1} + 2y_i}{(\Delta x)^2}$$

$$y_i''' = \frac{-3y_{i+4} + 14y_{i+3} - 24y_{i+2} + 18y_{i+1} - 5y_i}{2(\Delta x)^3}$$

$$y_i'''' = \frac{-2y_{i+5} + 11y_{i+4} - 24y_{i+3} + 26y_{i+2} - 14y_{i+1} + 3y_i}{(\Delta x)^4}$$

(5-41)

First Backward-Difference Expressions

$$y_i' = \frac{y_i - y_{i-1}}{(\Delta x)}$$

$$y_i'' = \frac{y_i - 2y_{i-1} + y_{i-2}}{(\Delta x)^2}$$

$$y_i''' = \frac{y_i - 3y_{i-1} + 3y_{i-2} - y_{i-3}}{(\Delta x)^3} \qquad (5\text{-}42)$$

$$y_i'''' = \frac{y_i - 4y_{i-1} + 6y_{i-2} - 4y_{i-3} + y_{i-4}}{(\Delta x)^4}$$

Second Backward-Difference Expressions

$$y_i' = \frac{3y_i - 4y_{i-1} + y_{i-2}}{2(\Delta x)}$$

$$y_i'' = \frac{2y_i - 5y_{i-1} + 4y_{i-2} - y_{i-3}}{(\Delta x)^2}$$

$$y_i''' = \frac{5y_i - 18y_{i-1} + 24y_{i-2} - 14y_{i-3} + 3y_{i-4}}{2(\Delta x)^3} \qquad (5\text{-}43)$$

$$y_i'''' = \frac{3y_i - 14y_{i-1} + 26y_{i-2} - 24y_{i-3} + 11y_{i-4} - 2y_{i-5}}{(\Delta x)^4}$$

EXAMPLE 5-3

In Example 3-4 the Newton-Raphson method was used to determine the output lever angles of a crank-and-lever 4-bar linkage system for each 5° of rotation of the input crank. Now we shall determine the angular velocity and the angular acceleration of the output lever of the same type of mechanism for each 5° of rotation of the input crank, with the latter rotating at a uniform angular velocity of 100 radians/sec.

We can determine the output lever positions ϕ, corresponding to each 5° of crank rotation θ, by utilizing Freudenstein's equation and the Newton-Raphson method, as was done in Example 3-4. Such a set of values, in effect, gives us a series of points on the ϕ versus θ curve, and the ϕ values are stored in memory to provide data for the differentiation processes which follow. The slope of the ϕ-θ curve may be related to the angular velocity of the output lever $d\phi/dt$ if we realize that, with the crank rotating at a constant ω, its angular position is given by

$$\theta = \omega t$$

so that

$$\frac{d\phi}{d\theta} = \frac{1}{\omega} \frac{d\phi}{dt}$$

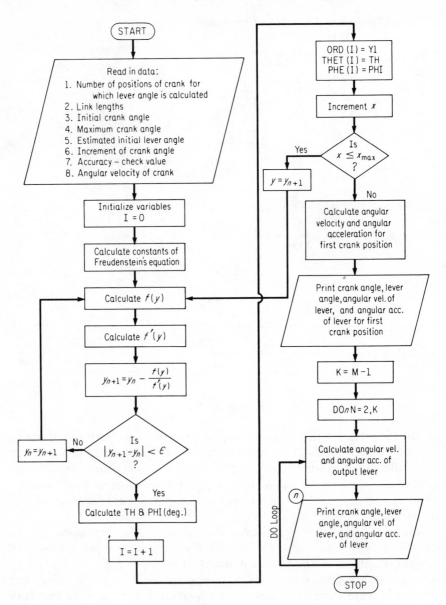

FIG. 5-11. Flow chart for Example 5-3.

The angular acceleration of the output lever $d^2\phi/dt^2$ may be related to this curve by realizing that since

$$\frac{d\phi}{d\theta} = \frac{1}{\omega}\frac{d\phi}{dt}$$

it follows that

$$\frac{d^2\phi}{d\theta^2} = \frac{1}{\omega}\left(\frac{d^2\phi}{d\theta\,dt}\right)$$

But, since $d\theta = \omega\,dt$,

$$\frac{d^2\phi}{d\theta^2} = \frac{1}{\omega^2}\left(\frac{d^2\phi}{dt^2}\right)$$

Thus, in performing the numerical differentiation indicated by Eqs. 5-31 and 5-32, using the ϕ values stored in memory (where θ is the independent variable), we multiply these expressions by ω and ω^2, respectively, to obtain the desired angular-velocity and acceleration values. A flow chart is shown in Fig. 5-11.

In the program which follows, the input crank angles and corresponding lever angles will be stored in memory in terms of degrees and will be printed out along with the angular-velocity and acceleration values. Subscripted variables are used for preserving these values in memory. The variable names used in the FORTRAN program are as follows:

FORTRAN *Name*	*Quantity*	*Given Value*
A	Length of crank a, in.	1
B	Length of crank b, in.	2
C	Length of crank c, in.	2
D	Length of crank d, in.	2
EPSI	Accuracy-check value ϵ, radians	0.00001
M	Number of positions of crank for which lever angle is determined	73
DELTH	Increment of crank angle $\Delta\theta$, deg	5
DELX	Increment of crank angle $\Delta\theta$, radians	
PHEST	Estimated value of ϕ corresponding to θ_{min}, deg	41
TH	Crank angle θ, deg	$\theta_0 = 0$
THMX	Maximum value of crank angle θ, deg	360
X	Crank angle θ, radians	
XMAX	Maximum value of crank angle θ, radians	
R1	d/c	
R2	d/a	
R3	$(d^2 + a^2 - b^2 + c^2)/2ca$	

FOFY	$f(y) = R_1 \cos x - R_2 \cos y$ $+ R_3 - \cos(x - y)$	
DFOFY	$f'(y) = R_2 \sin y - \sin(x - y)$	
PHI	Output lever angle ϕ, deg	
Y	Output lever angle ϕ, radians	
Y1	Improved value of output angle ϕ, for a given crank angle θ, radians	
OMEGA	Angular velocity of crank ω, radians/sec	100
I	Subscript	
N	Subscript	
K	Number of crank positions less 1	
PHE(I)	Output-lever-angle values stored in memory, deg	
ORD(I)	Output-lever-angle values stored in memory, radians	
THET(I)	Crank-angle values stored in memory, deg	
ANG V	Angular velocity of output lever, radians/sec	
ANG A	Angular acceleration of output lever, radians/sec^2	

The **FORTRAN** program is as follows:

```
  DIMENSION ORD(73),THET(73),PHE(73)
  PRINT 1
1 FORMAT (35HCRANK AND ROCKER KINEMATIC ANALYSIS//)
  READ 2, M
2 FORMAT (I4)
  READ 3,A,B,C,D,TH,THMX,PHEST,DELTH,EPSI,OMEGA
3 FORMAT (4F3.1,4F3.0,F6.5,F4.0)
  PRINT 4,A,B,C,D
4 FORMAT(3HA =,F8.4,7X,3HB =,F8.4,7X,3HC =,F8.4,7X,
                                        3HD =,F8.4/)
  PRINT 5,OMEGA
5 FORMAT(22HANGULAR VEL OF CRANK =,F9.4,12H RAD
                                        PER SEC//)
  PRINT 6
6 FORMAT(2X,5HTHETA,11X,3HPHI,11X,5HANG V,11X,5HANG A//)
  DELX = DELTH * .0174533
```

```
    XMAX  =  THMX  *  .0174533
    I  =  0
    R1  =  D/C
    R2  =  D/A
    R3  =  (D*D+A*A−B*B+C*C)/(2.*C*A)
    X  =  TH  *  .0174533
    Y  =  PHEST  *  .0174533
  7 FOFY  =  R1*COS(X)−R2*COS(Y)+R3−COS(X−Y)
    DFOFY  =  R2*SIN(Y)−SIN(X−Y)
    Y1  =  Y−FOFY/DFOFY
    IF(ABS(Y1−Y)−EPSI)9,9,8
  8 Y = Y1
    GO TO 7
  9 TH  =  X/.0174533
    PHI  =  Y1/.0174533
    I  =  I+1
    ORD(I)  =  Y1
    THET(I)  =  TH
    PHE(I)  =  PHI
    X  =  X+DELX
    IF(X−XMAX)10,10,11
 10 Y=Y1
    GO TO 7
 11 ANG V  =  (ORD(2)−ORD(M−1))/(2.*DELX)*OMEGA
    ANG A  =  (ORD(2)−2.*ORD(1)+ORD(M−1))/(DELX*DELX)*
                                      OMEGA*OMEGA
    PRINT 12,THET(1),PHE(1),ANG V, ANG A
 12 FORMAT(F10.5,4X,F10.5,5X,F10.4,6X,F10.0)
    K  =  M−1
    DO 13N=2,K
    ANG V=(ORD(N+1)−ORD(N−1))/(2.*DELX)*OMEGA
    ANG A=(ORD(N+1)−2.*ORD(N)+ORD(N−1))/(DELX*DELX)*
                                      OMEGA*OMEGA
 13 PRINT 12, THET(N),PHE(N),ANG V,ANG A
    STOP
    END
```

The computer printout of the results of the calculation is as follows:

CRANK AND ROCKER KINEMATIC ANALYSIS

A = 1.0000   B = 2.0000   C = 2.0000   D = 2.0000

ANGULAR VEL OF CRANK = 100.0000 RAD PER SEC

THETA	PHI	ANG V	ANG A
.00000	41.40960	33.3234	2519.
5.00000	43.13073	35.4879	2441.
10.00000	44.95839	37.5753	2342.
15.00000	46.88826	39.5662	2220.
20.00000	48.91502	41.4411	2076.
25.00000	51.03237	43.1817	1912.
30.00000	53.23319	44.7714	1730.
35.00000	55.50952	46.1945	1531.
40.00000	57.85265	47.4372	1316.
45.00000	60.25324	48.4865	1088.
50.00000	62.70130	49.3303	845.
55.00000	65.18627	49.9566	589.
60.00000	67.69696	50.3525	318.
65.00000	70.22153	50.5042	29.
70.00000	72.74739	50.3954	−279.
75.00000	75.26107	50.0068	−611.
80.00000	77.74807	49.3149	−973.
85.00000	80.19257	48.2911	−1372.
90.00000	82.57719	46.8997	−1816.
95.00000	84.88255	45.0972	−2314.
100.00000	87.08691	42.8297	−2881.
105.00000	89.16552	40.0317	−3530.
110.00000	91.09008	36.6236	−4279.
115.00000	92.82789	32.5098	−5148.
120.00000	94.34107	27.5772	−6156.
125.00000	95.58561	21.6955	−7323.
130.00000	96.51062	14.7201	−8662.
135.00000	97.05763	6.5015	−10172.
140.00000	97.16077	−3.0958	−11822.
145.00000	96.74805	−14.1574	−13528.
150.00000	95.74503	−26.6609	−15127.
155.00000	94.08195	−40.3939	−16346.
160.00000	91.70564	−54.8581	−16803.
165.00000	88.59613	−69.2008	−16067.
170.00000	84.78555	−82.2366	−13808.
175.00000	80.37247	−92.6317	−10015.
180.00000	75.52237	−99.2457	−5142.
185.00000	70.44790	−101.4979	−19.
190.00000	65.37257	−99.5560	4470.
195.00000	60.49229	−94.2292	7737.
200.00000	55.94964	−86.6485	9635.
205.00000	51.82744	−77.9260	10354.

THETA	PHI	ANG V	ANG A
210.00000	48.15704	−68.9413	10236.
215.00000	44.93330	−60.2778	9618.
220.00000	42.12925	−52.2579	8761.
225.00000	39.70751	−45.0158	7835.
230.00000	37.62767	−38.5681	6941.
235.00000	35.85069	−32.8662	6126.
240.00000	34.34104	−27.8312	5412.
245.00000	33.06757	−23.3747	4800.
250.00000	32.00357	−19.4098	4285.
255.00000	31.12658	−15.8565	3857.
260.00000	30.41791	−12.6435	3506.
265.00000	29.86223	−9.7083	3220.
270.00000	29.44708	−6.9973	2992.
275.00000	29.16250	−4.4640	2813.
280.00000	29.00067	−2.0687	2676.
285.00000	28.95562	.2228	2575.
290.00000	29.02296	2.4400	2505.
295.00000	29.19963	4.6080	2462.
300.00000	29.48376	6.7480	2441.
305.00000	29.87444	8.8779	2439.
310.00000	30.37156	11.0119	2451.
315.00000	30.97564	13.1613	2474.
320.00000	31.68769	15.3337	2504.
325.00000	32.50902	17.5335	2537.
330.00000	33.44104	19.7614	2568.
335.00000	34.48516	22.0146	2595.
340.00000	35.64251	24.2867	2611.
345.00000	36.91383	26.5680	2616.
350.00000	38.29931	28.8454	2603.
355.00000	39.79838	31.1034	2571.

STOP 0000

To illustrate the accuracy of the results obtained by the numerical-differentiation method, a computer program was written for the same problem to determine corresponding angular-velocity and acceleration values of the output lever, using a purely analytical method. The printout of this solution is shown at the conclusion of this paragraph. Comparing values of this solution with corresponding values of the numerically obtained solution reveals that, although the latter values are sufficiently accurate for almost all practical purposes, the number of significant digits retained in these values is unwarranted, particularly for the angular-velocity values shown. Very few values of the approximate solution match their corresponding values in the exact solution closely enough to warrant the number of digits used. If greater accuracy should be desired from the numerical method, the expressions for y_i' and y_i'' of Eq. 5-39 could be used instead of Eqs. 5-31 and 5-32.

ANALYTICAL SOLUTION

THETA	ANG V	ANG A
.00	33.3333	2519.
5.00	35.5006	2443.
10.00	37.5914	2344.
15.00	39.5855	2222.
20.00	41.4635	2078.
25.00	43.2070	1914.
30.00	44.7991	1731.
35.00	46.2246	1532.
40.00	47.4694	1317.
45.00	48.5208	1089.
50.00	49.3666	846.
55.00	49.9949	590.
60.00	50.3932	319.
65.00	50.5475	31.
70.00	50.4419	−276.
75.00	50.0572	−609.
80.00	49.3701	−970.
85.00	48.3521	−1368.
90.00	46.9679	−1811.
95.00	45.1742	−2309.
100.00	42.9176	−2874.
105.00	40.1328	−3522.
110.00	36.7406	−4269.
115.00	32.6457	−5136.
120.00	27.7349	−6143.
125.00	21.8776	−7308.
130.00	14.9277	−8648.
135.00	6.7327	−10160.
140.00	−2.8484	−11816.
145.00	−13.9109	−13536.
150.00	−26.4464	−15157.
155.00	−40.2594	−16408.
160.00	−54.8661	−16904.
165.00	−69.4124	−16197.
170.00	−82.6828	−13941.
175.00	−93.2820	−10110.
180.00	−100.0000	−5163.

THETA	ANG V	ANG A
185.00	−102.2201	37.
190.00	−100.1309	4577.
195.00	−94.6032	7856.
200.00	−86.8297	9735.
205.00	−77.9591	10424.
210.00	−68.8790	10277.
215.00	−60.1643	9637.
220.00	−52.1244	8766.
225.00	−44.8814	7832.
230.00	−38.4430	6934.
235.00	−32.7548	6118.
240.00	−27.7349	5403.
245.00	−23.2930	4792.
250.00	−19.3415	4278.
255.00	−15.8001	3851.
260.00	−12.5974	3500.
265.00	−9.6712	3215.
270.00	−6.9679	2988.
275.00	−4.4412	2809.
280.00	−2.0516	2673.
285.00	.2350	2573.
290.00	2.4481	2503.
295.00	4.6126	2460.
300.00	6.7496	2440.
305.00	8.8771	2438.
310.00	11.0093	2450.
315.00	13.1573	2473.
320.00	15.3290	2504.
325.00	17.5287	2537.
330.00	19.7570	2569.
335.00	22.0113	2595.
340.00	24.2851	2613.
345.00	26.5686	2617.
350.00	28.8486	2605.
355.00	31.1095	2573.
360.00	33.3334	2519.

STOP 0000

Problems

5-1. The arc length BP of an ellipse is given by

$$BP = a \int_0^\phi \sqrt{1 - \left(\frac{a^2 - b^2}{a^2} \right) \sin^2 \phi} \, d\phi$$

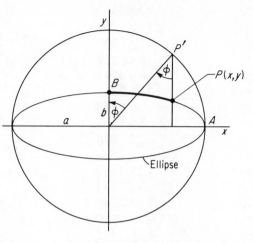

where a and b are, respectively, the semimajor and semiminor axes of the ellipse, and ϕ is the angle shown in the accompanying figure. It has been proved that the preceding integral cannot be evaluated in finite form in terms of elementary functions of ϕ.

Write a general **FORTRAN** program for determining, by the trapezoid rule, the arc length of an ellipse corresponding to any desired angle ϕ. Then use the program, with appropriate data input, to determine the circumference of an ellipse whose equation is given by $4x^2 + 9y^2 = 36$.

5-2. The equation of the lemniscate shown in the accompanying figure is

$$\rho^2 = a^2 \cos 2\theta$$

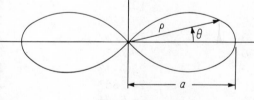

Prob. 5-2

An element of arc length ds is equal to $\sqrt{(d\rho)^2 + (\rho d\theta)^2}$ from which

$$ds = \frac{a d\theta}{\sqrt{\cos 2\theta}}$$

and

$$s = \int_0^\theta \frac{a d\theta}{\sqrt{\cos 2\theta}}$$

Write a **FORTRAN** program for determining the total arc length of the lemniscate by use of the trapezoid rule.

5-3.   A particle P of mass m is attracted toward a fixed point C by a force that varies inversely as the distance between them. It is desired to determine the time required for the particle to reach point C when starting from rest at a distance r from C.

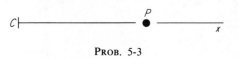

Prob. 5-3

Applying Newton's second law to the particle, we obtain the following equation of motion:

$$\frac{d^2x}{dt^2} = -\frac{k}{mx}$$

The initial conditions are

$$t = 0 \left|\begin{array}{l} \dfrac{dx}{dt} = 0 \\[2mm] x = r \end{array}\right.$$

Letting $v = dx/dt$, it can be seen that

$$\frac{dv}{dt} = \frac{d^2x}{dt^2} = \left(\frac{dv}{dx}\right)\left(\frac{dx}{dt}\right) = v\frac{dv}{dx}$$

Substituting the latter expression into the equation of motion yields

$$v\,dv = -\frac{k}{mx}\,dx$$

Integrating this equation, we obtain

$$\frac{v^2}{2} = -\frac{k}{m}\ln x + C$$

Application of the given initial conditions shows that

$$C = \frac{k}{m}\ln r$$

Substituting this expression for the constant of integration and the relation $v^2 = (dx/dt)^2$ into the equation resulting from the integration, we find that

$$t = -\frac{1}{\sqrt{\dfrac{2k}{m}}}\int_r^0 \frac{dx}{\sqrt{\ln\dfrac{r}{x}}}$$

Write a **FORTRAN** program for evaluating the integral by the trapezoid rule.

5-4.   The system of the accompanying illustration is released from rest in the position shown. Each of the cylinders A and B weighs 32.2 lb, and C weighs 16.1 lb. The cord attached to C winds around cylinder B as cylinder B rotates about its pivot axis O. A light rod of negligible weight is attached to cylinders A and B. a) Noting that the centroidal mass moment of inertia for each cylinder

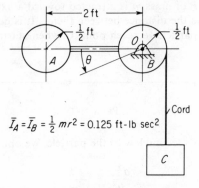

$$\bar{I}_A = \bar{I}_B = \tfrac{1}{2}\,mr^2 = 0.125 \text{ ft-lb sec}^2$$

PROB. 5-4

is $\bar{I}_A = \bar{I}_B = 0.125$ ft-lb sec^2, show that the equation of motion of the system is

$$\frac{d\dot{\theta}}{dt} = \frac{64.4 \cos \theta - 8.05}{4.375}$$

where θ is the angular displacement of the light rod and cylinders. b) From the equation of motion, formulate the integral which may be used to calculate the time t for the system to rotate through the angle θ. c) Using the integral of part b, write a **FORTRAN** program for obtaining the t vs θ values for one half of a cycle of motion. Use either the trapezoid rule or Simpson's rule.

5-5. An Alnico magnet A exerts a force on a steel block of weight W that is inversely proportional to the square of the distance between the mass centers of

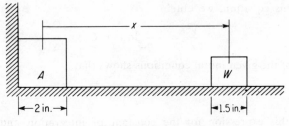

PROB. 5-5

the magnet and the block. If the coefficient of friction between the block and the fixed surface is f, the equation of motion of the block is found to be

$$\frac{d\dot{x}}{dt} = -\frac{kg}{Wx^2} + fg$$

where k is a constant, and g is the acceleration of gravity. a) Considering that the block is released from rest with an initial displacement of x_0, show that the expression for the velocity is

$$\dot{x} = \sqrt{\frac{2kg}{W}\left(\frac{1}{x} - \frac{1}{x_0}\right) + fg(x - x_0)}$$

b) Formulate the integral for calculating the time t for different values of x.
c) Write a **FORTRAN** program for obtaining the t vs x values. Use either the trapezoid rule or Simpson's rule. For a computer solution, take $f = 0.2$, $k = 1000$ lb-in.^{2}, $g = 386$ in./sec^2, $W = 10$ lb, and $x_0 = 12$ in.

5-6. Referring to Prob. 5-5, write a **FORTRAN** program for obtaining the t vs x values for coefficient-of-friction values of 0.1, 0.2, 0.3, 0.4, and 0.5. Use Simpson's rule.

5-7. A particle of mass m is released from rest at the edge of a hemispherical bowl such as the one shown in the accompanying figure. The particle then slides down the inside surface of the bowl which is assumed frictionless. It is desired to find the time required for the particle to reach the bottom of the bowl.

Applying Newton's second law in the tangential direction, write the differential equation of motion of the mass with θ as the dependent variable. Using the method of Prob. 5-3 as a reference, determine the integral which may be evaluated to find the required time for the mass to slide to the bottom of the bowl.

Write a **FORTRAN** program for evaluating the integral determined. Use the trapezoid rule.

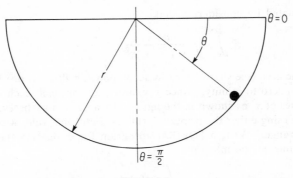

PROB. 5-7

5-8. Write a **FORTRAN** program for determining the arc length of an ellipse, corresponding to any angle ϕ, by the use of Simpson's rule. Refer to Prob. 5-1 and its accompanying figure for the necessary problem information.

5-9. Write a **FORTRAN** program for determining the total arc length of a lemniscate by the use of Simpson's rule. Refer to Prob. 5-2 and its accompanying figure for the necessary problem information.

5-10. Write a **FORTRAN** program for evaluating the integral of Prob. 5-3 by Simpson's rule.

5-11. The functions $f(x) = 1/(1 + x^2)$ and $g(x) = 1/(1 + e^{-x} + x^2)$ are shown graphically in the accompanying illustration. The evaluation

$$\int_0^\infty \frac{dx}{1 + x^2} = \frac{\pi}{2}$$

may be obtained by the direct integration of $f(x)$. Thus, the integral

$$\int_0^\infty g(x)\, dx$$

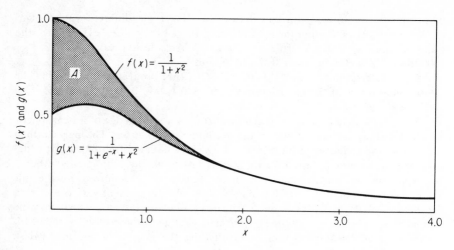

PROB. 5-11

may be evaluated by considering that

$$\int_0^\infty \frac{dx}{1 + e^{-x} + x^2} = \frac{\pi}{2} - A$$

where A is the area (see shaded area in accompanying illustration) between $f(x)$ and $g(x)$ from zero to infinity. Since $f(x)$ and $g(x)$ approach each other rapidly for finite values of x, as shown in the figure, the area A may be evaluated quite accurately by using either the trapezoid rule or Simpson's rule, with integration over a finite range. Write a **FORTRAN** program for evaluating the area A and obtain the value of the integral

$$\int_0^\infty g(x)\, dx$$

by utilizing the relationship

$$\int_0^\infty g(x)\, dx = \frac{\pi}{2} - A$$

5-12. A satellite, having unequal principal moments of inertia, is subjected to a gravity-stabilizing torque which tends to align the axis of the minimum moment of inertia with the radius vector connecting the mass centers of the earth and the satellite. For the satellite shown in the accompanying figure, the minimum moment of inertia is about the x axis, and the gravity torque tends to align this axis with the radius vector r_0. However, since the inertia of the satellite causes it to overshoot the equilibrium position, thus introducing a torque in the opposite direction, the satellite oscillates very slowly as it moves on its orbital path.

The gravity torque can be visualized, in a qualitative sense, by considering the differential gravity forces dF_1 and dF_2, which are shown acting on the differential masses dm_1 and dm_2, respectively. If these differential masses are equidistant

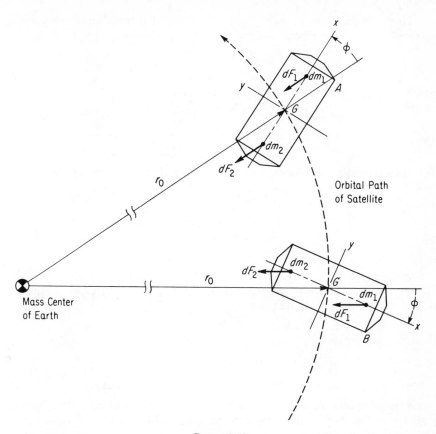

PROB. 5-12

from the mass center G of the satellite, then $dF_2 > dF_1$, since dm_2 is closer to the mass center of the earth than is dm_1. Thus, in position A the differential gravity torque due to dF_1 and dF_2 is clockwise. Similarly, in position B the differential gravity torque is counterclockwise. By integrating over the mass of the satellite, the differential equation of motion, describing the oscillation of a satellite moving in a circular orbit, is found to be

$$\frac{d\dot{\phi}}{dt} + \frac{3}{2}\frac{R^2 g}{r_0^3}\left(\frac{I_y - I_x}{I_z}\right)\sin 2\phi = 0$$

where

$$R = \text{radius of earth, } 20.9(10)^6 \text{ ft}$$
$$g = \text{acceleration of gravity at earth's surface, } 32.2 \text{ ft/sec}^2$$
$$R^2 g = 1.407(10)^6 \text{ ft}^3/\text{sec}^2$$
$$r_0 = \text{radius of circular orbital path}$$
$$I_x, I_y, \text{ and } I_z = \text{principal moments of inertia } (I_x \text{ is minimum})$$
$$\phi = \text{angular displacement measured from line connecting mass centers of earth and satellite}$$

To obtain the period of oscillation τ, the differential equation of motion in ϕ is transformed to the elliptic integral

$$\tau = \frac{4}{C\sqrt{2}} \int_0^{\pi/2} \frac{d\beta}{\sqrt{1 - \sin^2 \phi_0 \sin^2 \beta}}$$

where

$$C = \sqrt{\frac{3}{2} \frac{R^2 g}{r_0^3} \left(\frac{I_y - I_x}{I_z}\right)}$$

and

ϕ_0 = amplitude of oscillation

The elliptic integral is obtained from the differential equation of motion by utilizing the relations

$$\frac{d\phi}{dt} = \dot{\phi}$$

$$\cos 2\phi = 1 - \sin^2 \phi$$

$$\sin \phi = \sin \phi_0 \sin \beta$$

Write a **FORTRAN** program for obtaining the period of oscillation by integrating the elliptic integral, given by either the trapezoid rule or by Simpson's rule, with the following data:

$$r_0 = 1.1R$$

$$I_y = I_z$$

$$I_x = 0.5 I_y$$

$$\phi_0 = 10°, 20°, 30°, 40°, 50°, 60°, 70°, 80°, \text{ and } 85°$$

Using the computer results, plot the period τ as a function of ϕ_0. Compute the period τ for the above conditions, utilizing a table of values for elliptic integrals, and compare with the computer results.

5-13. In the slider-crank mechanism shown in part a of the accompanying figure, the slider B is driven by a Scotch-yoke mechanism shown in part b which gives it simple harmonic motion. Its displacement x is given by

$$x = R(1 - \cos \omega t)$$

where

ωt = crank angle of Scotch-yoke mechanism (see figure)
R = crank lengths of slider-crank and Scotch-yoke mechanisms

From geometry, x may be related to the crank angle θ by the formula

$$x = R + L - R \cos \theta - L \cos \phi$$
$$= R(1 - \cos \theta) + L(1 - \cos \phi)$$
$$= R(1 - \cos \theta) + L\left(1 - \sqrt{1 - \sin^2 \phi}\right)$$
$$= R(1 - \cos \theta) + L\left[1 - \sqrt{1 - (R/L)^2 \sin^2 \theta}\right]$$

where θ, ϕ, and L are as shown in the figure.

Using the following data, determine the values of θ corresponding to values of ωt from 0° to 350° (use 10° increments), using the Newton-Raphson method.

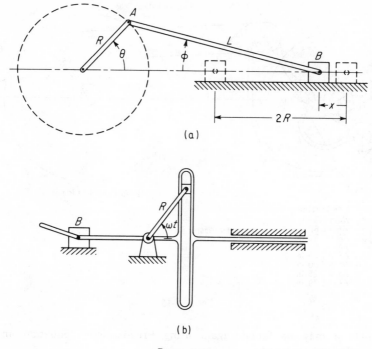

(a)

(b)

PROB. 5-13

Then determine the values of $d\theta/(d\omega t)$ and $d^2\theta/d(\omega t)^2$ by numerical differentiation.

$$R = 4 \text{ in.}$$

$$L = 6 \text{ in.}$$

5-14. The computer program shown in Example 5-3 was used for determining the angular velocity and acceleration of the output lever of a crank-and-lever mechanism using the first two numerical differentiation formulas of Eq. 5-38. Modify this program to utilize the first two differentiation formulas of Eq. 5-39, so that more accurate results may be obtained. Compare the solution obtained with the analytical solution given in Example 5-3.

5-15. An automatic washer transmission uses the linkage shown in the accompanying figure to convert rotary motion from the drive motor to a large oscillating output of the agitator shaft G. The 79-tooth helical gear is driven by the 12-tooth helical pinion which rotates at a constant speed of 435 rpm. Links 2, 4, and 6 rotate or oscillate about fixed axes. Links 2, 3, and 4 (DA, AB, and BC) along with the fixed base constitute a four-bar linkage. Links 4, 5, and 6 (CE, EF, and FG) along with the fixed base constitute a second four-bar linkage in series with the first. Angle ϕ may be found for any angle θ using Freudenstein's equation and the Newton-Raphson root-finding technique as in Examples 3-4 and 5-3. Angle α is equal to angle ϕ plus a constant. With angle α known, the correspond-

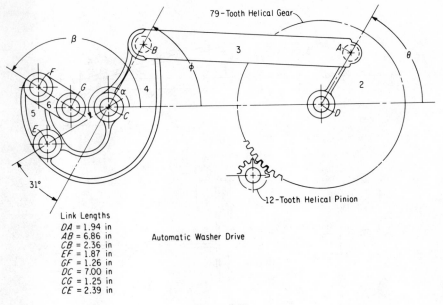

79-Tooth Helical Gear

12-Tooth Helical Pinion

Link Lengths
DA = 1.94 in
AB = 6.86 in
CB = 2.36 in
EF = 1.87 in
GF = 1.26 in
DC = 7.00 in
CG = 1.25 in
CE = 2.39 in

Automatic Washer Drive

PROB. 5-15

ing angle β may be found, again using Freudenstein's equation and the Newton-Raphson method.

Write a **FORTRAN** program which determines and stores values of angle β for every degree of angle θ. Using these stored values of β and numerical differentiation, determine the angular velocity and angular acceleration of link 6 for every 5 degrees of angle θ. Use Example 5-3 as a guide. For the numerical differentiation, use a $\Delta\theta$ value of 1 degree (or the corresponding value in radians). Print out values of θ and β in degrees and the angular velocity and angular acceleration of link 6 for every 5 degrees of angle θ.

Numerical Integration of Ordinary Differential Equations: Initial-Value Problems

6-1. Introduction

Initial-value problems are problems in which the values of the dependent variable and the necessary derivatives are known at the point at which integration begins. Such a large number of integration methods are available to handle problems of this type that an engineer may have difficulty in deciding which to use. In this chapter the most widely used methods are presented in some detail, and a summary is included to aid the reader in selecting one of these methods for a particular application.

The methods discussed will vary in complexity, since, in general, the greater the accuracy of a method, the greater is its complexity. Included are Euler's, Euler's modified, Runge-Kutta, Milne's, and Hamming's methods. The error analysis of each of these methods is explained in detail.

This chapter will be concerned primarily with the solution of first-order differential equations and of sets of simultaneous first-order differential equations, since, as will be seen later, an nth-order differential equation may be solved by transforming it to a set of n simultaneous first-order differential equations. Several examples will be given in which the methods developed for solving first-order differential equations are extended to solve equations of higher order.

6-2. Direct Numerical-Integration Method

Let us consider the cantilever beam shown in Fig. 6-1. The intensity of loading is some function of the displacement x along the beam, x being measured positively from the left end of the beam. The bending moment

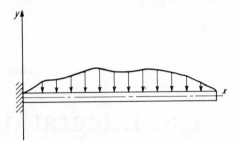

FIG. 6-1. Cantilever beam with intensity of loading indicated by length
of arrows.

M along the beam will also be some function of x, and the M/EI diagram
will have the general form shown in Fig. 6-2.

The differential equation of the elastic curve of a beam with a uniform cross section is

$$\frac{d^2y}{dx^2} = \frac{M(x)}{EI} \tag{6-1}$$

where E and I are the modulus of elasticity and the moment of inertia of

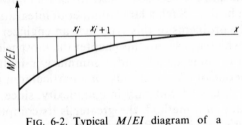

FIG. 6-2. Typical M/EI diagram of a
cantilever beam.

the cross section, respectively. The initial conditions for the cantilever
beam are

$$x = 0 \left| \begin{array}{l} y = 0 \\ y' = 0 \end{array} \right.$$

The numerical solution of Eq. 6-1 presents no particular difficulty. Its
solution involves the determination of the deflection y for a series of
equally spaced x values and is accomplished by 2 successive integrations.
The curve of y' (the slope of the elastic curve) versus x may easily be
obtained, since the value of y' is known at $x = 0$, and the change in y'
from x_i to x_{i+1} is represented by the area under the M/EI curve between
the given x values. The general form of the y' versus x curve is shown in
Fig. 6-3. The y versus x curve, which is known as the elastic curve of the

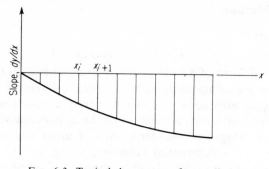

FIG. 6-3. Typical slope curve of a cantilever
beam.

beam, is obtained in a similar manner, since the value of y is known at
$x = 0$, and the change in y over an x interval is given by the corresponding area under the y' versus x curve. Either the trapezoid rule or Simpson's rule can be used for determining the areas mentioned. The general
form of the elastic curve of a cantilever beam is shown in Fig. 6-4.

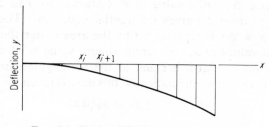

FIG. 6-4. Typical deflection curve of a cantilever beam.

It now should be apparent that the numerical solution of a differential
equation, in which the curve of the highest-order derivative is known, may
be obtained by direct numerical integration, provided the necessary initial
conditions are known. Denoting $y^n = d^n y/dx^n$, we may generalize that
all nth-order differential equations of the form

$$y^n = f(x) \qquad (6-2)$$

with the initial conditions

$$x = x_0 \left| \begin{array}{rcl} y &=& y_0 \\ y' &=& y'_0 \\ \cdot & & \cdot \\ \cdot & & \cdot \\ \cdot & & \cdot \\ y^{n-1} &=& y_0^{n-1} \end{array} \right.$$

can be solved in the manner discussed.

6-3. Euler's Method

The expression

$$y^n = f(x, y, y', y'', \ldots, y^{n-1})$$ (6-3)

is a more general form of an nth-order differential equation than the one described in the preceding paragraphs. In such a differential equation the highest-order (the nth) derivative is not merely a function of the independent variable but is also a function of the dependent variable, whose values we are seeking, and the derivatives of order less than n. *Direct* integration of such a differential equation, using the trapezoid rule or Simpson's rule, is not possible. To illustrate a simple method of obtaining an approximate solution of a differential equation of this type, let us consider the first-order equation

$$y' = f(x, y)$$ (6-4)

with the initial condition of $y = 0$ when $x = 0$. We wish to obtain the y versus x curve, which suggests using the area under the y' versus x curve. However, the latter curve is unknown, since y' is a function of y. To illustrate, let us assume that these curves have the general form of those shown in Fig. 6-5. Since the initial value of y is known, we can determine the initial value of y' from the given differential equation. The change in y from $x = 0$ to $x = \Delta x$ is represented by the area under the y' curve between the given values of x. An approximate value of this area can be obtained by assuming that it is equal to the rectangular area A_1, shown in Fig. 6-5a. Expressed mathematically, this area is given by

$$A_1 = y_1 - y_0 = y_0'(\Delta x)$$

from which

$$y_1 = y_0 + y_0'(\Delta x)$$ (6-5)

Having determined a close approximation of the value of y_1 by the use of Eq. 6-5 (by using small Δx values), we can get a good approximation of y_1' from the given differential equation, since

$$y_1' = f(x_1, y_1)$$

Then, since $y_2 - y_1$ is approximately equal to the area under the y' curve from x_1 to x_2, as shown by the rectangular area A_2 in Fig. 6-5,

$$y_2 = y_1 + y_1'(\Delta x)$$ (6-6)

Proceeding as before, y_2' may next be determined from the differential equation, by using the value of y_2 obtained from Eq. 6-6 and a value of $x_2 = 2(\Delta x)$. The subsequent y_i and y_i' values are found in a similar manner. Equations 6-5 and 6-6 may be expressed, in general form, as

$$y_{i+1} = y_i + y_i'(\Delta x)$$ (6-7)

Equation 6-7 is known as Euler's forward-integration equation. Euler's method is called a "self-starting" method, since it requires a value of the dependent variable at only 1 point to start the procedure.

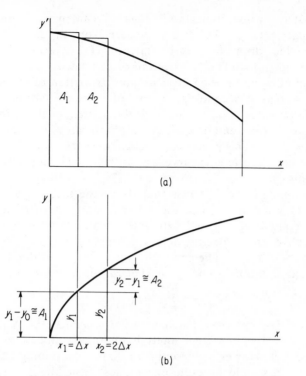

FIG. 6-5. Assumed curves of y' and y versus x
satisfying $y' = f(x, y)$.

A graphical representation of a portion of the function $y(x)$, as obtained by Euler's method, is shown in Fig. 6-6. Let us assume the initial condition of $y = 0$ at $x = 0$. With a known initial value of y, the initial slope of the curve can be determined from the differential equation. The

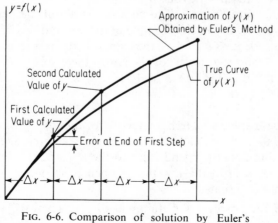

FIG. 6-6. Comparison of solution by Euler's
method to true solution.

first calculated y value, indicated in Fig. 6-6, can then be obtained from Euler's equation (Eq. 6-7). It can be seen from the figure that Euler's method, in effect, approximates the function $y(x)$ over the first-step interval by a straight line. The substitution of this calculated value of y into the differential equation then gives an approximation of the slope of the curve at $x = \Delta x$. A second application of Euler's equation yields a second calculated value of y, as shown in the figure, which is, in turn, substituted into the differential equation to obtain an approximation of the slope at $x = 2\,\Delta x$. This process is repeated over the desired range of integration, so that the true $y(x)$ curve is approximated by a series of straight-line segments.

Inspection of Eq. 6-7 reveals that it has the form of a Taylor-series expansion of y about x_i, with the expansion truncated after the first 2 terms. By comparing Eq. 6-7 with the complete Taylor series, it is apparent that we are neglecting terms containing $(\Delta x)^2$ and subsequent higher powers of (Δx). The error introduced in 1 step due to the use of the truncated equation is known as the *truncation error* and may be expressed as

$$E_T = c(\Delta x)^2 \qquad (6\text{-}8)$$

Such a local per-step error is said to be *of order* $(\Delta x)^2$. A detailed discussion of the truncation-error analysis of Euler's and other methods is given in Sec. 6-9. However, the importance of maintaining (Δx) small, in Euler's method, should be quite evident just from the preceding discussion.

EXAMPLE 6-1

The rattrap shown in Fig. 6-7 consists of a movable jaw, trip arm, torsion spring, and trip pan. Upon release of the trip arm owing to a slight disturbance of the trip pan, the torque of the torsion spring closes the rotating jaw and kills the rodent.

The manufacturer has received complaints about the performance of the trap with respect to the closure time of the jaw and the impact force of the jaw on the rodent. To analyze the trap, it is desired to obtain data for drawing θ-t, ω-t, and ω-θ curves for the jaw of the trap.

The data for the trap are $A = 1.125$ in., $B = 0.5$ in., $R = 3.75$ in., and $I_O = 0.0006$ lb-ft-sec^2 (mass moment of inertia of the jaw about the pivot axis).

The torque-displacement characteristic of the linear torsion spring is shown in Fig. 6-8. When closed, the jaw exerts a force against the base which has a component perpendicular to the jaw of 2 lb, and a force of 9 lb is required to hold the jaw in the open position. From the given information, we find that

$\theta_k = 2.97$ radians or $170.4°$ (angular displacement of jaw upon contact with rat)

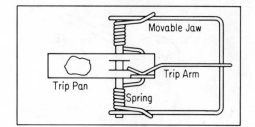

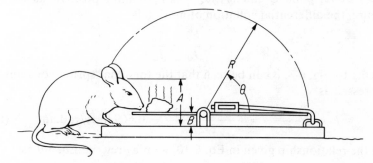

FIG. 6-7. Rattrap shown in open position.

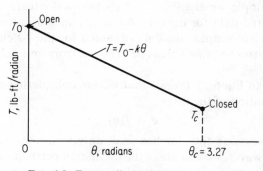

FIG. 6-8. Torque-displacement characteristic
of torsion spring.

θ_c = 3.27 radians or 187.7° (angular displacement of jaw in the closed position)

$$T_0 = \frac{9(3.75)}{12} = 2.81 \text{ lb-ft (torque of spring in open position; } \theta = 0)$$

$$T_c = \frac{2(3.75)}{12} = 0.625 \text{ lb-ft (torque of spring in closed position)}$$

Upon release, the jaw is subjected to the torque T of the spring, as shown in Fig. 6-9. From elementary dynamics we know that the external

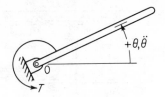

FIG. 6-9. Movable jaw after release.

torque T about point O equals $I_o\ddot{\theta}$. Taking θ and $\ddot{\theta}$ positive, as shown in the figure, the differential equation of motion is

$$\ddot{\theta} + \frac{k\theta}{I_o} = \frac{T_0}{I_o} \tag{6-9}$$

Referring to Fig. 6-8, it can be seen that the torsional spring constant may be expressed as

$$k = \frac{T_0 - T_c}{\theta_c} = \frac{2.81 - 0.625}{3.27} = 0.669 \text{ lb-ft/radian} \tag{6-10}$$

Using the relationship given in Eq. 6-10, we may rewrite Eq. 6-9 as

$$\ddot{\theta} + \frac{k\theta}{I_o} = \frac{T_c + k\theta_c}{I_o} \tag{6-11}$$

In this example we shall use Euler's forward-integration method to obtain the desired data for drawing θ-t, ω-t, and ω-θ curves for the trap jaw. We shall also compare the data obtained for the θ-t curve by Euler's method with corresponding values determined from an analytical solution of Eq. 6-9.

Inspection of Eq. 6-11 reveals that we are considering a second-order differential equation of the form

$$\ddot{\theta} = f(\theta) \tag{6-12}$$

whereas the discussion thus far has dealt only with first-order differential equations. However, we can make the discussion pertinent to the solution of second-order equations, since the latter may be reduced to a set of 2 first-order equations which can be solved simultaneously. Realizing that

$$\dot{\theta} = \omega$$

and

$$\ddot{\theta} = \dot{\omega}$$

Eq. 6-11 can be reduced to the 2 first-order differential equations

$$\dot{\theta} = \omega \qquad \text{(a)}$$

$$\dot{\omega} + \frac{k\theta}{I_o} = \frac{T_c + k\theta_c}{I_o} \qquad \text{(b)} \tag{6-13}$$

which can be solved simultaneously to obtain the desired data of the problem.

Using Euler's forward-integration equation (Eq. 6-7) with Eq. 6-13b, we can write

$$\omega_{i+1} = \omega_i + \dot{\omega}_i(\Delta t) \qquad (6\text{-}14)$$

in which the term $\dot{\omega}_i(\Delta t)$ approximates the area in 1 strip under the $\dot{\omega}\text{-}t$ curve. This approximate area is shown as the crosshatched area A_1 in Fig. 6-10a. We next apply Euler's equation to Eq. 6-13a and obtain

$$\theta_{i+1} = \theta_i + \omega_i(\Delta t) \qquad (6\text{-}15)$$

Let us now write Eqs. 6-13b, 6-14, and 6-15 as a set, so that we may examine their interdependence, writing Eq. 6-13b in the subscripted form in which it will be used in the numerical process.

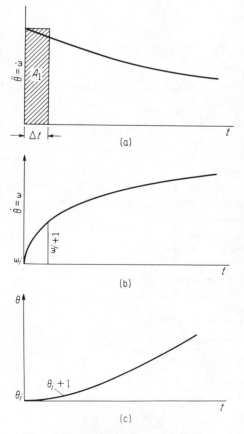

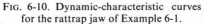

Fig. 6-10. Dynamic-characteristic curves
for the rattrap jaw of Example 6-1.

$$\dot{\omega}_i = \left(\frac{T_c + k\theta_c}{I_0}\right) - \frac{k\theta_i}{I_0}$$

$$\omega_{i+1} = \omega_i + \dot{\omega}_i(\Delta t) \tag{6-16}$$

$$\theta_{i+1} = \theta_i + \omega_i(\Delta t)$$

Selecting a value for Δt and remembering that the initial conditions are $\theta = \omega = 0$ when $t = 0$, we see that $\dot{\omega}_0$, ω_1, and θ_1 can be evaluated

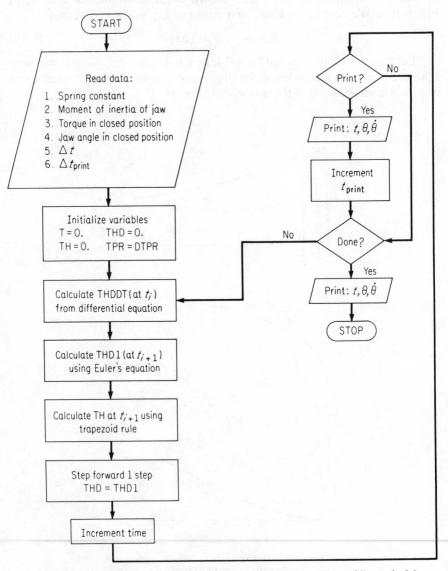

FIG. 6-11. Flow chart for numerical solution of rattrap problem of Example 6-1.

from Eq. 6-16. However, we find, in doing this, that we obtain $\theta_1 = 0$, which we know is in error. If Δt is very small, the error introduced in continuing the process, using this erroneous value of θ_1, will be very small. However, we can reduce this error and improve the accuracy of the solution if we realize that, since both ω_i and ω_{i+1} are known, we can use the trapezoid rule to obtain θ_{i+1}, as follows:

$$\theta_{i+1} = \theta_i + \left(\frac{\omega_i + \omega_{i+1}}{2}\right)\Delta t \tag{6-17}$$

It can be seen that the following value will be obtained for θ_1

$$\theta_1 = \frac{\omega_1(\Delta t)}{2}$$

which is a closer approximation of the value of θ at the end of the first Δt interval.

Hence, we shall program the problem for a solution on the computer, using the following set of equations:

$$\dot{\omega}_i = \left(\frac{T_c + k\theta_c}{I_o}\right) - \frac{k\theta_i}{I_o}$$

$$\omega_{i+1} = \omega_i + \dot{\omega}_i(\Delta t) \tag{6-18}$$

$$\theta_{i+1} = \theta_i + \left(\frac{\omega_i + \omega_{i+1}}{2}\right)\Delta t$$

where we are using Euler's forward-integration equation to solve Eq. 6-13b and the trapezoid rule to solve Eq. 6-13a.

The flow chart for the computer solution is shown in Fig. 6-11. The variable names selected for the program are as follows:

FORTRAN *Name*	*Quantity*	*Numerical Value Used in Solution*
SK	Spring constant k, lb-ft/radian	0.669
EYE	Moment of inertia I_o, lb-ft-sec^2	0.0006
TORCL	Torque in closed position T_c, lb-ft	0.625
THCL	Jaw angle θ in closed position θ_c, radians	3.270
DELT	Time increment Δt, sec	0.0001
DTPR	Print increment, Δt_{print}, sec	0.0010
T	Time t, sec	
TH	Jaw angle θ_i	
THD	Jaw angular velocity $\dot{\theta}_i$	

THDDT	Jaw angular acceleration $\ddot{\theta}_i$
THD1	Jaw angular velocity 1 station ahead of THD, $\dot{\theta}_{i+1}$
TPR	Time value at each printout

The FORTRAN IV program for the problem is as follows:

```
  WRITE(6,1)
1 FORMAT (1H1,23H   TIME      THETA      ANG V//)
  READ(5,2)SK,EYE,TORCL,THCL,DELT,DTPR
2 FORMAT  (F4.3,F5.4,F4.3,F5.3,2F5.4)
  T = 0.
  TH = 0.
  THD = 0.
  TPR = DTPR
3 THDDT = (TORCL + SK*THCL)/EYE−SK*TH/EYE
  THD1 = THD + THDDT*DELT
  TH = TH + (THD + THD1)/2.*DELT
  THD = THD1
  T = T + DELT
  IF (T−TPR)6,4,4
4 WRITE(6,5)T,TH,THD
  TPR = TPR + DTPR
5 FORMAT (1H ,F7.4,F8.4,F8.2)
6 IF (TH−THCL) 3,7,7
7 WRITE(6,5)T,TH,THD
  STOP
  END
```

The results obtained from the binary-coded decimal-computer solution are given by the following printout:[1]

TIME	THETA	ANG V
.0010	.0023	4.68
.0020	.0093	9.36
.0030	.0210	14.04
.0040	.0374	18.69
.0050	.0584	23.33
.0060	.0841	27.94
.0070	.1143	32.52
.0080	.1491	37.06
.0090	.1884	41.56

[1]See Example 6-4 for a discussion of changes which should be made in a program such as this one when the program is to be used with a pure binary computer.

TIME	THETA	ANG V
.0100	.2322	46.02
.0110	.2804	50.42
.0120	.3330	54.77
.0130	.3900	59.06
.0140	.4511	63.28
.0150	.5165	67.43
.0160	.5860	71.51
.0170	.6595	75.51
.0180	.7370	79.42
.0190	.8183	83.25
.0200	.9035	86.98
.0210	.9923	90.61
.0220	1.0847	94.15
.0230	1.1805	97.58
.0240	1.2798	100.90
.0250	1.3823	104.11
.0260	1.4880	107.20
.0270	1.5967	110.18
.0280	1.7083	113.03
.0290	1.8227	115.76
.0300	1.9398	118.35
.0310	2.0594	120.82
.0320	2.1814	123.15
.0330	2.3056	125.34
.0340	2.4320	127.39
.0350	2.5604	129.31
.0360	2.6906	131.07
.0370	2.8225	132.70
.0380	2.9560	134.17
.0390	3.0908	135.49
.0400	3.2269	136.67
.0404	3.2816	137.09

STOP 00000

To check the accuracy of the numerical method used, the angular displacements were solved on the computer, using the equation

$$\theta = T_c + k\,\theta_c \left(1 - \cos \sqrt{\frac{k}{I_o}}\, t\right)$$

which is the analytical solution of Eq. 6-11. To save space, the complete printout for the latter solution is not shown, but some of the results are reproduced below, to afford a comparison with the numerical solution.

Time	Theta (Numerical)	Theta (Analytical)
0.0010	0.0023	0.0023
0.0050	0.0584	0.0584
0.0100	0.2322	0.2322
0.0200	0.9035	0.9032
0.0250	1.3823	1.3817
0.0300	1.9398	1.9388
0.0400	3.2269	3.2247
0.0404	3.2816	3.2794

It is apparent that the numerically obtained values compare quite closely with those determined analytically.

6-4. Euler's Modified Methods

The Self-starting Modification. This is a self-starting method of the predictor-corrector type, having greater accuracy than Euler's method. It is known by many engineers as Quinn's method[2] and is also sometimes referred to as Euler's improved method.

We again consider a first-order differential equation of the form

$$y' = f(x, y) \qquad (6\text{-}19)$$

where the value of y is known when $x = 0$. Let us assume that the curves of y' and y versus x are those shown in Fig. 6-12. If we substitute the known initial value of y into Eq. 6-19, we obtain the value of y' at $x = 0$. Next, a *predicted* value of y at $x = \Delta x$ is found by using Euler's equation

$$P(y_1) = y_0 + y_0'(\Delta x) \qquad (6\text{-}20)$$

where $P(y_1)$ is the predicted value of y_1. In using Eq. 6-20 to obtain the predicted value of y_1, the term $y_0'(\Delta x)$ is the rectangular area A_1 shown in Fig. 6-12a. This area is obviously larger than the true area under the given curve, so the predicted value of y_1 obtained is too large by some small amount. However, if the predicted value of y_1 is substituted into the given differential equation (Eq. 6-19), an approximate value of y_1' may be obtained. Since this value of y_1' is based on the predicted value of y_1, $P(y_1)$, we shall use the notation $P(y_1')$ to represent it. Then, using the shaded *trapezoidal* area shown in Fig. 6-12a as the approximation of the true area under the y' curve, a corrected value of y_1, which we shall denote by $C(y_1)$, can be determined as

$$C(y_1) = y_0 + \left(\frac{y_0' + P(y_1')}{2}\right)\Delta x \qquad (6\text{-}21)$$

---

[2]After B. E. Quinn, Professor of Machine Design at Purdue University, who developed the method independently and has taught it in his design classes for many years.

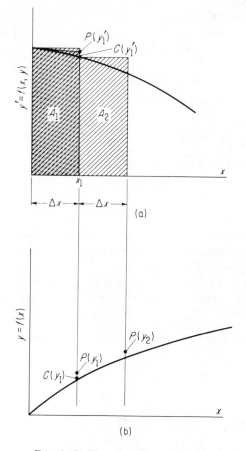

FIG. 6-12. The y' and y versus x
curves satisfying $y' = f(x, y)$.

Equation 6-21 is thus known as the *corrector* equation.   The corrected
value of y_1 is next substituted into Eq. 6-19 to obtain a corrected value of
y_1'. The latter value is denoted by $C(y_1')$, as indicated in Fig. 6-12a.   The
iteration process continues, by using $C(y_1')$ in place of $P(y_1')$ in Eq. 6-21,
to obtain a still better value of y_1, and then using this improved value in
Eq. 6-19 to get a further improved value of y_1'.   The process is repeated
until successive values of y_1 differ by less than some prescribed epsilon
value selected to specify the accuracy desired.

   With the desired value of y_1 obtained, we are ready to move ahead
1 step to determine the value of y_2.   This begins by using the predictor
equation

$$P(y_2) = y_1 + y_1'(\Delta x) \qquad (6\text{-}22)$$

where $P(y_2)$ is the first predicted value of y_2, and y_1 and y_1' are the most accurate values obtained for these quantities in the preceding iteration. The iterative process described for determining an accurate value of y_1 is then repeated, and so on.

The general form of Eqs. 6-20 and 6-21, for application at any step, is

(Predictor) $\qquad P(y_{i+1}) = y_i + y_i'(\Delta x) \qquad\qquad$ (a)

$\qquad\qquad\qquad\qquad\qquad\qquad\qquad\qquad\qquad\qquad$ (6-23)

(Corrector) $\qquad C(y_{i+1}) = y_i + \left[\dfrac{y_i' + P(y_{i+1}')}{2} \right] \Delta x \qquad$ (b)

It can be shown that the error per step resulting from the use of Eq. 6-23 is of order $(\Delta x)^3$. (See Eq. 6-121.)

EXAMPLE 6-2

When a paratrooper jumps from an aircraft which is in straight and level flight, he has an initial velocity equal to that of the aircraft, and he is a freely falling body during the time interval before opening his parachute. The velocity of the paratrooper during this free-fall interval may be described by a set of rectangular components, as shown in Fig. 6-13.

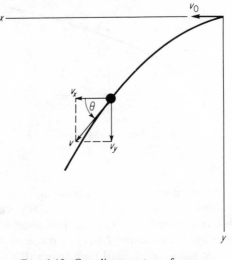

FIG. 6-13. Coordinate system of para-
trooper problem.

The decelerating force to which the paratrooper is subjected when the parachute opens is essentially proportional to the square of his free-fall velocity at the time the chute opens. With slow-flying aircraft, this decelerating force is not excessive. The paratrooper jumps, and a relatively short static line, attached to both the rip cord of the chute and the aircraft, opens the chute after a short free fall which is just sufficient to clear the aircraft. However, aircraft dropping paratroopers while flying at slow speeds present ideal targets for enemy ground fire. Therefore, it is desirable to drop the paratroopers from faster-flying aircraft. Since the impact force on the paratrooper increases approximately as the *square* of the velocity at the time the chute opens, it is desirable to open the chute at the instant when the free-fall velocity is at a minimum.

It is a well-known fact that a body falling freely in a resisting medium, if allowed to fall far enough, will eventually reach a limiting or *terminal* velocity. This limiting velocity is reached when the resistive force, or drag due to the fluid medium, just balances the weight of the falling body. It has been claimed that, for any horizontal launching speed, the velocity of the paratrooper falling freely will pass through a *minimum* value *less* than either the *launching* or the terminal velocity.

In general, the drag force D on a body, owing to air resistance, is proportional to the projected area of the body normal to the direction of motion, the air density, and approximately the square of the velocity. Usually, the drag force D is expressed in the form

$$D = \frac{C\gamma A v^2}{2} \tag{6-24}$$

where

γ = mass density of the fluid medium, lb sec^2/ft^4
A = projected area of the body normal to the direction of motion, ft^2
C = drag coefficient, dimensionless
v = velocity, ft/sec

If we assume that the projected area A of the paratrooper is essentially constant, that the drag coefficient C is constant over the range of velocities encountered, and that the mass density γ of the air is a constant, then the quantity $C\gamma A$ may be considered as a constant, so that

$$\frac{C\gamma A}{2} = \text{constant} = K$$

and, from Eq. 6-24,

$$D = Kv^2 \tag{6-25}$$

Referring to Fig. 6-13 and considering Newton's second law, the equations of motion in rectangular coordinates are readily found to be

(x direction)
$$\frac{W}{g}\frac{dv_x}{dt} = -Kv^2 \cos\theta \tag{6-26}$$

and

(y direction)
$$\frac{W}{g}\frac{dv_y}{dt} = W - Kv^2 \sin\theta \tag{6-27}$$

where

v_x = horizontal component of velocity, ft/sec
v_y = vertical component of velocity, ft/sec
$v = \sqrt{v_x^2 + v_y^2}$ = resultant velocity, ft/sec
W = weight of paratrooper and equipment, lb
g = acceleration of gravity = 32.2 ft/sec²
K = coefficient of aerodynamic resistance, lb-sec²/ft²

Noting that $\cos\theta = v_x/v$ and that $\sin\theta = v_y/v$, Eqs. 6-26 and 6-27 may be written in the form

$$\frac{W}{g}\frac{dv_x}{dt} = -Kvv_x \tag{6-28}$$

$$\frac{W}{g}\frac{dv_y}{dt} = W - Kvv_y \tag{6-29}$$

Substituting

$$v = \sqrt{v_x^2 + v_y^2}$$

in Eqs. 6-28 and 6-29, expressing the time-dependent variables in Newtonian notation, and rearranging algebraically, we obtain the equations of motion in a form convenient for solution by numerical integration. They are

(x direction) $$\ddot{x} = -\frac{Kg}{W}\sqrt{\dot{x}^2 + \dot{y}^2}\,\dot{x} \tag{6-30}$$

and

(y direction) $$\ddot{y} = g - \frac{Kg}{W}\sqrt{\dot{x}^2 + \dot{y}^2}\,\dot{y} \tag{6-31}$$

where

$\dot{x}$ = horizontal component of velocity, ft/sec
$\dot{y}$ = vertical component of velocity, ft/sec
K = coefficient of aerodynamic resistance, lb-sec²/ft²
g = acceleration of gravity, ft/sec²
W = weight of paratrooper and equipment, lb

The coefficient of aerodynamic resistance K can be determined from the fact that the average terminal velocity reached by paratroopers falling with unopened parachutes has been found to be approximately 160 ft/sec at sea level. Applying the equation of equilibrium in the vertical direction to a body falling at terminal velocity gives

$$W = K(V_t)^2$$

or

$$K = \frac{W}{V_t^2} \tag{6-32}$$

where V_t is the terminal velocity, in feet per second, and W is the weight of the body. Substituting this expression for K into Eqs. 6-30 and 6-31, we obtain

$$\ddot{x} = -\frac{g}{V_t^2}\sqrt{\dot{x}^2 + \dot{y}^2}\,\dot{x} \tag{6-33}$$

and

$$\ddot{y} = g - \frac{g}{V_t^2}\sqrt{\dot{x}^2 + \dot{y}^2}\,\dot{y} \tag{6-34}$$

With the origin of the x-y coordinate system located at the point of launch, as shown in Fig. 6-14, the initial conditions are

$$t = 0 \begin{vmatrix} x = 0 \\ \dot{x} = 440 \text{ ft/sec} \\ y = 0 \\ \dot{y} = 0 \end{vmatrix}$$

The objective of our analysis will be to determine: 1) the data necessary to plot the x-t, y-t, $\dot{x}$-t, $\dot{y}$-t, and V-t curves for a paratrooper launched horizontally with a velocity of 300 mph, and 2) the optimum time for opening the parachute after a period of free fall (the time when the velocity of the paratrooper is minimum).

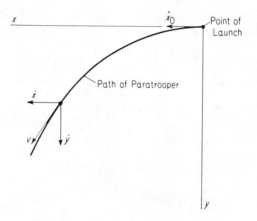

FIG. 6-14. Trajectory of paratrooper.

In applying Euler's self-starting modified method to the simultaneous solution of Eqs. 6-33 and 6-34 for values of $\dot{x}$ and $\dot{y}$, the reader should realize that we are, in effect, solving the following 2 *first-order* differential equations

$$\dot{v}_x = -\frac{g}{V_t^2}\sqrt{v_x^2 + v_y^2}\,v_x \tag{6-35}$$

and

$$\dot{v}_y = g - \frac{g}{V_t^2}\sqrt{v_x^2 + v_y^2}\,v_y \tag{6-36}$$

for V_x and V_y, where the reduction was accomplished by the relations

$$v_x = \dot{x} \qquad v_y = \dot{y}$$
$$\dot{v}_x = \ddot{x} \qquad \dot{v}_y = \ddot{y}$$

However, in applying the predictor-corrector equations (Eq. 6-23), we shall use the notation of Eqs. 6-33 and 6-34. After obtaining the desired values of $\dot{x}$ and $\dot{y}$ in each step, we shall use these values with the trapezoid rule to solve the equations

$$\frac{dx}{dt} = \dot{x} \tag{6-37}$$

and

$$\frac{dy}{dt} = \dot{y} \tag{6-38}$$

to obtain values of the displacements x and y. Since x and y do not appear in explicit form in Eqs. 6-33 and 6-34, their solutions need not be obtained simultaneously with those of Eqs. 6-37 and 6-38. However, these equations will be solved simultaneously in the computer solution accompanying this example, to avoid the necessity of storing the calculated $\dot{x}$ and $\dot{y}$ values in memory for subsequent use in obtaining the desired x and y values.

The predictor-corrector equations, in a form applicable to the solution of Eqs. 6-33 and 6-34 for values of $\dot{x}$ and $\dot{y}$, are

$$P(\dot{x}_{i+1}) = \dot{x}_i + \ddot{x}_i(\Delta t) \tag{a}$$

$$C(\dot{x}_{i+1}) = \dot{x}_i + \left[\frac{\ddot{x}_i + P(\ddot{x}_{i+1})}{2}\right]\Delta t \tag{b}$$

$$P(\dot{y}_{i+1}) = \dot{y}_i + \ddot{y}_i(\Delta t) \tag{c}$$

$$C(\dot{y}_{i+1}) = \dot{y}_i + \left[\frac{\ddot{y}_i + P(\ddot{y}_{i+1})}{2}\right]\Delta t \tag{d}$$

$(6\text{-}39)$

The equations for solving the x and y values by the trapezoid rule are

$$x_{i+1} = x_i + \left(\frac{\dot{x}_i + \dot{x}_{i+1}}{2}\right)\Delta t$$

$$y_{i+1} = y_i + \left(\frac{\dot{y}_i + \dot{y}_{i+1}}{2}\right)\Delta t$$

$(6\text{-}40)$

The initial conditions supply us with values of x, y, $\dot{x}$, and $\dot{y}$ for $t = 0$, and we can determine values of $\ddot{x}$ and $\ddot{y}$ when $t = 0$ by substituting appropriate values in Eqs. 6-33 and 6-34. We next obtain predicted values of $\dot{x}_1$ and $\dot{y}_1$, using the predictor equations (Eq. 6-39a and c). In obtaining these predicted values, the true areas under the curves of $\ddot{x}$ and $\ddot{y}$ are approximated by the *rectangular crosshatched* areas shown in Fig. 6-15a and d. The predicted values $P(\dot{x}_1)$ and $P(\dot{y}_1)$ are shown in Fig. 6-15b and e. We next substitute $P(\dot{x}_1)$ and $P(\dot{y}_1)$ into Eqs. 6-33 and 6-34 to

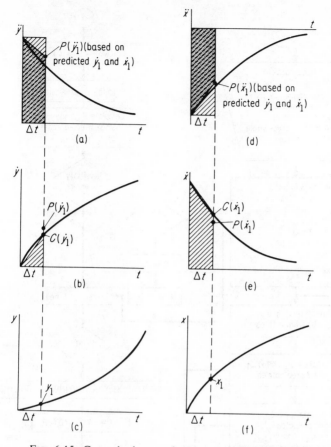

FIG. 6-15. General shape of dynamic-characteristic curves for the paratrooper of Example 6-2.

obtain approximate values of $\ddot{x}_1$ and $\ddot{y}_1$, which are shown as $P(\ddot{x}_1)$ and $P(\ddot{y}_1)$ in Fig. 6-15a and d. Then, using the corrector equations (Eq. 6-39b and d), corrected values of $\dot{x}_1$ and $\dot{y}_1$ are obtained. These values, designated as $C(\dot{x}_1)$ and $C(\dot{y}_1)$, are shown in Fig. 6-15b and e. The corrector equation approximates the true areas under the $\ddot{x}$ and $\ddot{y}$ curves by the *shaded trapezoidal* areas shown in Fig. 6-15a and d. The corrected values of $\dot{x}_1$ and $\dot{y}_1$ are next substituted into Eqs. 6-33 and 6-34 to obtain improved values of $\ddot{x}_1$ and $\ddot{y}_1$ which are, in turn, used in Eq. 6-39b and d to obtain still better values of $\dot{x}_1$ and $\dot{y}_1$. The process continues until successive values of $\dot{x}_1$ and $\dot{y}_1$, respectively, vary by less than some preassigned epsilon value specifying the accuracy desired. At this point we proceed with the determination of the values of x_1 and y_1, using Eq. 6-40,

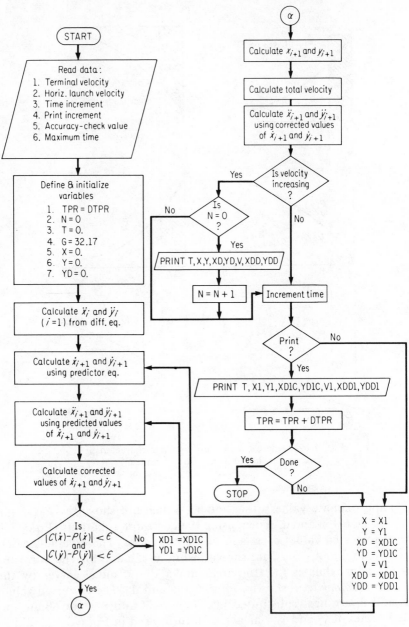

FIG. 6-16. Flow chart for Example 6-2.

which approximates the true area under the $\dot{x}$ and $\dot{y}$ curves by the cross-hatched areas shown in Fig. 6-15b and e.

In the computer program, shown later, the total velocity of the paratrooper is calculated at each step and compared with the velocity at the previous station to determine the lowest velocity calculated. As stated at the beginning of the problem, the time at which the lowest velocity is reached is considered the optimum parachute-opening time.

The flow chart is shown in Fig. 6-16. The variable names and the quantities which they represent in the **FORTRAN** program are as follows:

Variable Name	Quantity	Value Used in Problem
TERM	Terminal velocity, ft/sec	160
XD	Velocity in x direction $\dot{x}_i$, ft/sec	440 (initial)
DELT	Time increment Δt, sec	0.1
DTPR	Print increment Δt_{print}, sec	0.5
EPSI	Accuracy-check value, ft/sec	0.0001
TMAX	Maximum time value, sec	20
TPR	Time at which a print occurs, sec	
N	Fixed-point variable used in program control	
T	Time, sec	
G	Acceleration of gravity, ft/sec^2	32.17
X	Displacement in x direction, ft	
Y	Displacement in y direction, ft	
YD	Vertical component of velocity, $\dot{y}_i$, ft/sec	
V	Total velocity, ft/sec	
XDD	Acceleration in x direction $\ddot{x}_i$, ft/sec^2	
YDD	Acceleration in y direction $\ddot{y}_i$, ft/sec^2	
XD1	Velocity in x direction 1 station ahead of t_i, $\dot{x}_{i+1}$, ft/sec	
YD1	Velocity in y direction 1 station ahead of t_i, $\dot{y}_{i+1}$, ft/sec	
V1	Total velocity 1 station ahead of t_i, ft/sec	
XDD1	Acceleration in x direction 1 station ahead of t_i, $\ddot{x}_{i+1}$, ft/sec^2	
YDD1	Acceleration in y direction 1 station ahead of t_i, $\ddot{y}_{i+1}$, ft/sec^2	
YD1C	Corrected value of y_{i+1}, ft/sec	
DIFXD	Difference in successive calculated values of $\dot{x}_{i+1}$ at a particular station, ft/sec	

		Value Used
Variable Name	*Quantity*	*in Problem*
DIFYD	Difference in successive calculated values of $\dot{y}_{i+1}$ at a particular station, ft/sec	
X1	Displacement in x direction 1 station ahead of t_i, x_{i+1}, ft	
Y1	Displacement in y direction 1 station ahead of t_i, y_{i+1}, ft	

The FORTRAN program follows.

```
C    DYNAMIC CHARACTERISTICS OF FREE FALL OF A PARATROOPER
     READ 1, TERM,XD,DELT,DTPR,EPSI,TMAX
  1  FORMAT  (2F4.0,2F3.2,F5.4,F3.0)
     PRINT 2,XD
  2  FORMAT (24HHORIZONTAL LAUNCH VEL. = ,F7.2,9H FT./SEC.//)
     PRINT 3
  3  FORMAT(2X,1HT,6X,1HX,7X,1HY,6X,2HVX,6X,2HVY,6X,1HV,7X,
                                          2HAX,6X,2HAY/)
     TPR  = DTPR
     N  =  0
     T  =  0.
     G  =  32.17
     X  =  0.
     Y  =  0.
     YD  =  0.
     V  =  XD
     XDD  =  −G/TERM**2*V*XD
     YDD  =  G−G/TERM**2*V*YD
  4  XD1  =  XD+XDD*DELT
     YD1  =  YD+YDD*DELT
  5  V1  =  SQRT(XD1**2+YD1**2)
     XDD1  =  −G/TERM**2*V1*XD1
     YDD1  =  G−G/TERM**2*V1*YD1
     XD1C  =  XD+(XDD+XDD1)/2.*DELT
     YD1C  =  YD+(YDD+YDD1)/2.*DELT
     DIFXD  =  XD1C−XD1
     DIFYD  =  YD1C−YD1
     IF(ABS(DIFXD)−EPSI)6,7,7
  6  IF(ABS(DIFYD)−EPSI)8,7,7
  7  XD1  =  XD1C
     YD1  =  YD1C
     GO TO 5
  8  X1  =  X+(XD+XD1C)/2.*DELT
```

```
    Y1  =  Y+(YD+YD1C)/2.*DELT
    V1  =  SQRT(XD1C**2+YD1C**2)
    XDD1  =  -G/TERM**2*V1*XD1C
    YDD1  =  G-G/TERM**2*V1*YD1C
    IF(V1-V)12,12,9
  9 IF(N)12,10,12
 10 PRINT  11,T,X,Y,XD,YD,V,XDD,YDD
 11 FORMAT(F5.1,2F8.1,4F8.2,F7.2)
    N  =  N+1
 12 T  =  T+DELT
    IF(T-TPR)16,13,16
 13 PRINT  14,T,X1,Y1,XD1C,YD1C,V1,XDD1,YDD1
    TPR  =  TPR  +  DTPR
 14 FORMAT(F5.1,2F8.1,4F8.2,F7.2)
    IF(T-TMAX)16,15,15
 15 STOP
 16 X  =  X1
    Y  =  Y1
    XD  =  XD1C
    YD  =  YD1C
    V  =  V1
    XDD  =  XDD1
    YDD  =  YDD1
    GO TO 4
    END
```

The results of the computer calculations are shown in the following printout, where the column headings VX and VY denote the velocity components XD and YD, respectively. The acceleration components specified for printout in the source program are not shown.

HORIZONTAL LAUNCH VEL. = 440.00 FT./SEC.

T	X	Y	VX	VY	V
.5	194.2	3.7	344.59	14.34	344.89
1.0	350.2	13.9	283.10	26.44	284.33
1.5	480.4	29.9	240.05	37.28	242.92
2.0	592.1	51.1	208.08	47.33	213.39
2.5	689.7	77.1	183.26	56.81	191.86
3.0	776.2	107.8	163.29	65.83	176.06
3.5	853.6	142.9	146.75	74.42	164.54
4.0	923.4	182.2	132.69	82.60	156.30
4.5	986.6	225.4	120.51	90.36	150.62

T	X	Y	VX	VY	V
5.0	1044.1	272.5	109.76	97.66	146.92
5.5	1096.6	323.0	100.16	104.49	144.74
6.0	1144.5	376.9	91.48	110.82	143.70
6.4	1179.8	422.1	85.11	115.52	143.49
6.5	1188.2	433.7	83.59	116.64	143.50
7.0	1228.2	493.4	76.38	121.95	143.90
7.5	1264.7	555.6	69.76	126.76	144.69
8.0	1298.0	620.1	63.67	131.08	145.73
8.5	1328.4	686.6	58.08	134.93	146.90
9.0	1356.2	755.0	52.94	138.35	148.13
9.5	1381.5	824.9	48.21	141.36	149.36
10.0	1404.5	896.3	43.88	144.00	150.54
10.5	1425.4	968.9	39.90	146.30	151.64
11.0	1444.4	1042.5	36.26	148.30	152.67
11.5	1461.7	1117.1	32.94	150.03	153.60
12.0	1477.4	1192.5	29.90	151.52	154.44
12.5	1491.7	1268.6	27.13	152.80	155.19
13.0	1504.6	1345.3	24.60	153.90	155.85
13.5	1516.3	1422.5	22.30	154.83	156.43
14.0	1526.9	1500.1	20.21	155.63	156.94
14.5	1536.6	1578.1	18.31	156.31	157.38
15.0	1545.3	1656.4	16.58	156.89	157.77
15.5	1553.2	1735.0	15.01	157.38	158.10
16.0	1560.3	1813.8	13.59	157.80	158.38
16.5	1566.8	1892.8	12.30	158.15	158.63
17.0	1572.7	1971.9	11.14	158.44	158.83
17.5	1578.0	2051.2	10.08	158.69	159.01
18.0	1582.8	2130.6	9.12	158.90	159.16
18.5	1587.1	2210.1	8.25	159.08	159.29
19.0	1591.0	2289.7	7.46	159.23	159.40
19.5	1594.6	2369.3	6.75	159.35	159.50
20.0	1597.8	2449.0	6.11	159.46	159.58

STOP 0000

The computer results show that a minimum velocity of 143.49 ft/sec is reached when $t = 6.4$ sec, which indicates the optimum time to open the parachute. The velocity data are plotted in Fig. 6-17.

The Non-self-starting Modification. For purposes of easily estimating the per-step truncation error in the corrector equation,

$$P(y_{i+1}) = y_{i-1} + 2y_i'(\Delta x) \qquad \text{6-23(a')}$$

is sometimes used as a predictor equation in place of Eq. 6-23(a). (See Sec. 6-9 for a discussion of error estimation.) However, when this substi-

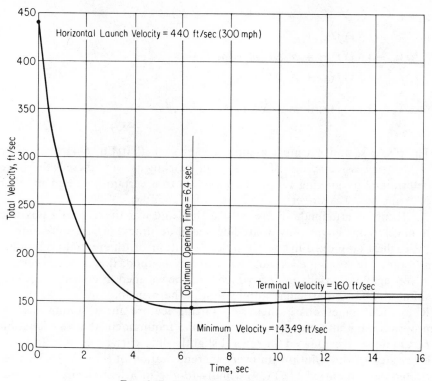

FIG. 6-17. Total velocity of paratrooper.

tution is made, the convenient self-starting feature of the previously described modification of Euler's method is lost. In addition to the usual initial value of y required for solving a first order differential equation, one additional value of y must be known to get the method started. Integration by this method is usually started by applying Eq. 6-23(a) and (b) for the first step only and then using Eq. 6-23(a') in place of Eq. 6-23(a) for subsequent steps.

Equation 6-23(a') approximates the area in two strips under the y' curve, each of width Δx, with a rectangle of width $2(\Delta x)$ and height y_i'.

6-5. Runge-Kutta Methods

A Runge-Kutta method is one which employs a recurrence formula of the form

$$y_{i+1} = y_i + a_1 k_1 + a_2 k_2 + a_3 k_3 + \cdots + a_n k_n \qquad (6\text{-}41)$$

to calculate successive values of the dependent variable y of the differential equation

$$\frac{dy}{dx} = y' = f(x, y) \qquad (6\text{-}42)$$

where

$$k_1 = (\Delta x) f(x_i, y_i)$$
$$k_2 = (\Delta x) f(x_i + p_1 \Delta x, y_i + q_{11} k_1)$$
$$k_3 = (\Delta x) f(x_i + p_2 \Delta x, y_i + q_{21} k_1 + q_{22} k_2) \qquad (6\text{-}43)$$
$$\cdots \cdots$$
$$k_n = (\Delta x) f(x_i + p_{n-1} \Delta x, y_i + q_{n-1,1} k_1$$
$$+ q_{n-1,2} k_2 + \cdots + q_{n-1,n-1} k_{n-1})$$

The a's, p's, and q's must assume values such that Eq. 6-41 accurately yields successive values of y. As will be shown later, these values are determined by making Eq. 6-41 equivalent to a certain specified number of terms of a Taylor-series expansion of y about x_i.

Runge-Kutta methods are self-starting, and it is theoretically possible to develop one having any desired degree of accuracy. These were among the earliest employed in the numerical solution of differential equations, and they are still widely used. As with any method, they possess certain advantages and disadvantages which must be weighed in considering their suitability for a particular application. The principal advantage of the Runge-Kutta methods is their self-starting feature and resulting ease of programming, and one disadvantage is the requirement that the function $f(x, y)$ must be evaluated for several slightly different values of x and y in every step of the solution (in every incrementation of x by Δx). This re-peated determination of $f(x, y)$ usually results in a less efficient method, with respect to computing time, than do other methods, of comparable accuracy, in which previously determined values of the dependent variable are used in subsequent steps. (Hamming's method and Milne's method are examples of the latter type. They are discussed in later portions of this chapter.) Another disadvantage is that it is more difficult to estimate the per-step error for higher-order Runge-Kutta solutions than for solutions obtained by some other commonly used methods.

Before illustrating the general procedure for developing a Runge-Kutta method, let us review 1) the definition of a *total differential* and 2) the expansion of a function of 2 variables in a *Taylor series*, since both will be pertinent to the development.

1. If $y' = f(x, y)$, the total differential dy' is

$$dy' = \frac{\partial f}{\partial x} dx + \frac{\partial f}{\partial y} dy$$

Upon dividing by dx, we obtain

$$\frac{dy'}{dx} = \frac{\partial f}{\partial x} + \frac{\partial f}{\partial y} \frac{dy}{dx} \qquad (6\text{-}44)$$

Differentiating again with respect to x yields

$$\frac{d^2y'}{dx^2} = \frac{\partial\left(\dfrac{\partial f}{\partial x} + \dfrac{\partial f}{\partial y}\dfrac{dy}{dx}\right)}{\partial x} + \frac{\partial\left(\dfrac{\partial f}{\partial x} + \dfrac{\partial f}{\partial y}\dfrac{dy}{dx}\right)}{\partial y}\left(\frac{dy}{dx}\right) \qquad (6\text{-}45)$$

Higher derivatives of y' may be determined in a similar manner.

2. Consider some general function of 2 variables such as $z = f(x, y)$. Such a function may be expanded about a point x_i, y_i in a Taylor series for functions of 2 variables, as follows:

$$z(x_i + h, y_i + j) = f(x_i, y_i) + h\left[\frac{\partial f}{\partial x}(x_i, y_i)\right] + j\left[\frac{\partial f}{\partial y}(x_i, y_i)\right]$$

$$+ \frac{1}{2!}\left\{h^2\left[\frac{\partial^2 f}{\partial x^2}(x_i, y_i)\right] + 2hj\left[\frac{\partial^2 f}{\partial x\,\partial y}(x_i, y_i)\right] + j^2\left[\frac{\partial^2 f}{\partial y^2}(x_i, y_i)\right]\right\} + \cdots$$

$$(6\text{-}46)$$

where h and j are increments of x and y, respectively.

We are now ready to proceed with the development of a *second-order* Runge-Kutta method ($n = 2$ in Eq. 6-41). Equation 6-41 becomes

$$y_{i+1} = y_i + a_1 k_1 + a_2 k_2 \qquad (6\text{-}47)$$

in which

$$\left. \begin{array}{l} k_1 = (\Delta x)f(x_i, y_i) \\ k_2 = (\Delta x)f(x_i + p_1 \Delta x, y_i + q_{11} k_1) \end{array} \right\} \qquad (6\text{-}48)$$

Our problem is to determine values for a_1, a_2, p_1, and q_{11}, so that Eq. 6-47 yields an accurate value of y_{i+1}. A graphical interpretation of the k functions is illustrated in Fig. 6-18. The crosshatched area represents k_1, and k_2 is represented by the shaded area. (There would be similar rectangular areas for each k function of Eq. 6-41 for higher-order Runge-Kutta equations.) For the second-order method being discussed, Eq. 6-41 could be written as

$$y_{i+1} = y_i + a_1 \text{ (crosshatched area)} + a_2 \text{ (shaded area)}$$

It should be evident that the size of the shaded area representing k_2 depends upon the values determined for p_1 and q_{11}.

We shall determine values for a_1, a_2, p_1, and q_{11} by making Eq. 6-47 equivalent to a truncated Taylor-series expansion of y about x_i. As the first step, let us expand y_{i+1} about x_i. We obtain

$$y_{i+1} = y_i + (\Delta x)y_i' + \frac{(\Delta x)^2}{2!}y_i'' + \cdots \qquad (6\text{-}49)$$

Remembering that the given differential equation is $y' = f(x, y)$, we write

$$y_i' = f(x_i, y_i) \qquad (6\text{-}50)$$

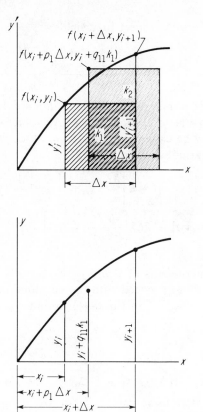

FIG. 6-18. Graphical interpretation of k functions.

From Eq. 6-44 it can be seen that

$$y_i'' = \frac{\partial f}{\partial x}(x_i, y_i) + \left[\frac{\partial f}{\partial y}(x_i, y_i)\right]\left[f(x_i, y_i)\right] \qquad (6\text{-}51)$$

Substituting Eqs. 6-50 and 6-51 into Eq. 6-49, we obtain the expansion in the following form:

$$y_{i+1} = y_i + (\Delta x)f(x_i, y_i)$$

$$+ \frac{(\Delta x)^2}{2!}\left\{\frac{\partial f}{\partial x}(x_i, y_i) + \left[\frac{\partial f}{\partial y}(x_i, y_i)\right]\left[f(x_i, y_i)\right]\right\} + \frac{(\Delta x)^3}{3!}\left\{\cdots\right\} + \cdots$$

$$(6\text{-}52)$$

Looking at Eqs. 6-47, 6-48, and 6-52, we see that k_2 must be expressed in terms of $f(x_i, y_i)$, $\partial f/\partial x(x_i, y_i)$, and $\partial f/\partial y(x_i, y_i)$ if Eqs. 6-47 and 6-52 are to contain similar terms. This can be accomplished by expanding k_2

in a Taylor series for functions of 2 variables about x_i, y_i. Using the first 3 terms of Eq. 6-46 and realizing that $h = p_1 \Delta x$ and $j = q_{11} k_1$ (see Eq. 6-48), we may write

$$k_2 = \Delta x \left\{ f(x_i, y_i) + p_1 \Delta x \left[\frac{\partial f}{\partial x}(x_i, y_i) \right] + q_{11} k_1 \left[\frac{\partial f}{\partial y}(x_i, y_i) \right] \right\} \qquad (6\text{-}53)$$

Substituting the first of Eq. 6-48 and Eq. 6-53 into Eq. 6-47, we obtain

$$y_{i+1} = y_i + a_1(\Delta x) f(x_i, y_i) + a_2(\Delta x) f(x_i, y_i)$$

$$+ a_2(\Delta x)^2 \left\{ p_1 \frac{\partial f}{\partial x}(x_i, y_i) + q_{11} \left[\frac{\partial f}{\partial y}(x_i, y_i) \right] \left[f(x_i, y_i) \right] \right\} \qquad (6\text{-}54)$$

Equating coefficients of similar terms in Eqs. 6-52 and 6-54, we obtain the following 3 independent equations:

$$a_1 + a_2 = 1$$
$$a_2 p_1 = \tfrac{1}{2} \qquad (6\text{-}55)$$
$$a_2 q_{11} = \tfrac{1}{2}$$

which contain 4 unknowns. By arbitrarily assigning a value to 1 unknown and then solving for the other 3, we can obtain as many different sets of values as we desire and, in turn, as many different sets of Eqs. 6-47 and 6-48 as desired.

A solution obtained by the use of Eq. 6-47 in a step-by-step integration will have a per-step truncation error of order $(\Delta x)^3$, since terms containing $(\Delta x)^3$ and higher powers of Δx were neglected in the development. Thus, this is known as a *second-order* Runge-Kutta method.

If a particular second-order method is defined by letting $a_1 = \tfrac{1}{2}$ in Eq. 6-55, then

$$a_2 = \tfrac{1}{2}$$
$$p_1 = 1$$
$$q_{11} = 1$$

Equations 6-47 and 6-48 then become

$$y_{i+1} = y_i + \tfrac{1}{2}(k_1 + k_2) \qquad \text{(a)}$$

with
$$\qquad (6\text{-}56)$$
$$k_1 = (\Delta x) f(x_i, y_i)$$
$$k_2 = (\Delta x) f(x_i + \Delta x, y_i + k_1) \qquad \text{(b)}$$

This set of equations may be used to solve first-order differential equations with an accuracy comparable to that of Euler's modified methods. In fact, if Eq. 6-56b is substituted into Eq. 6-56a, the resulting equation

$$y_{i+1} = y_i + \tfrac{1}{2}\{(\Delta x) f(x_i, y_i)$$
$$+ (\Delta x) f[x_i + \Delta x, y_i + (\Delta x) f(x_i, y_i)]\} \qquad (6\text{-}57)$$

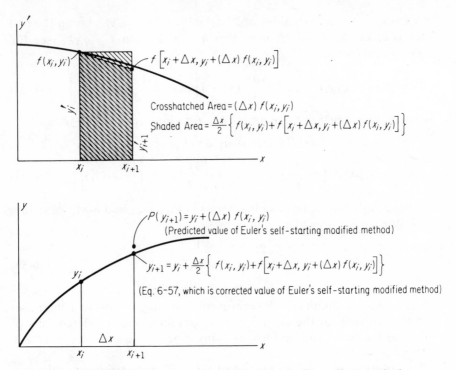

FIG. 6-19. Graphical representation of a second-order Runge-Kutta method.

is exactly equivalent to Euler's self-starting modified method with the iteration at each step omitted. This may be verified by examining the graphical representation of the equation in Fig. 6-19.

Because the second-order Runge Kutta method has only the order of accuracy of Euler's modified methods, let us consider Runge-Kutta methods with higher orders of accuracy. Since the development of such methods rapidly increases in complexity with an increase in accuracy, and since the general procedure has just been demonstrated for a second-order method, the developments will not be given for higher orders. For example, in developing a third-order method, all Taylor-series terms containing $(\Delta x)^3$ must be retained; in developing a fourth-order method, all $(\Delta x)^4$ terms must be retained, and so forth.

If $n = 3$, in Eq. 6-41, and a procedure similar to the one previously outlined is followed, the equating of coefficients of terms containing Δx, $(\Delta x)^2$, and $(\Delta x)^3$ will yield a set of equations with 6 constraints on the parameters. With 8 parameters involved, 2 of them can be assigned values arbitrarily. With a particular choice of values for 2 such parameters, the following *third-order* Runge-Kutta formula can be obtained:

$$y_{i+1} = y_i + \tfrac{1}{6}(k_1 + 4k_2 + k_3) \tag{6-58}$$

in which

$$k_1 = (\Delta x)f(x_i, y_i)$$

$$k_2 = (\Delta x)f\left(x_i + \frac{\Delta x}{2}, y_i + \frac{k_1}{2}\right)$$

$$k_3 = (\Delta x)f(x_i + \Delta x, y_i - k_1 + 2k_2)$$

(6-59)

Since terms containing $(\Delta x)^4$ are neglected, the error is said to be of order $(\Delta x)^4$.

A well-known *fourth-order* Runge-Kutta method, resulting from taking n equal to 4 in Eq. 6-41, equating terms through and including those containing $(\Delta x)^4$, and selecting a particular set of 2 arbitrary parameter values, is expressed as follows:[3]

$$y_{i+1} = y_i + \tfrac{1}{6}(k_1 + 2k_2 + 2k_3 + k_4) \qquad (6\text{-}60)$$

in which

$$k_1 = (\Delta x)f(x_i, y_i)$$

$$k_2 = (\Delta x)f\left(x_i + \frac{\Delta x}{2}, y_i + \frac{k_1}{2}\right)$$

$$k_3 = (\Delta x)f\left(x_i + \frac{\Delta x}{2}, y_i + \frac{k_2}{2}\right)$$

$$k_4 = (\Delta x)f(x_i + \Delta x, y_i + k_3)$$

(6-61)

In this method the per-step error is of order $(\Delta x)^5$.

Having discussed the general method of developing Runge-Kutta formulas and having shown several specific different-order Runge-Kutta equations, let us illustrate the use of the third-order method in solving a first-order differential equation.

EXAMPLE 6-3

The circuit shown in Fig. 6-20 contains a source of emf, an inductance, and a resistor, the magnitude of the latter varying with its tempera-

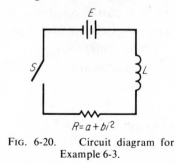

FIG. 6-20.   Circuit diagram for
Example 6-3.

[3]The interested reader will find a complete derivation in *Mathematical Methods for Digital Computers*. Anthony Ralston and Herbert S. Wilf, eds. New York: John Wiley & Sons, Inc., 1960.

ture. Since the temperature of the resistor increases with increasing current in the circuit, the resistance is a function of both temperature and current. In the range of current flow i for this problem, the resistance can be expressed as $R = a + bi^2$. Switch S is closed at time $t = 0$, and the current flow is desired as a function of time for $t > 0$.

Applying Kirchhoff's voltage law (the algebraic sum of all voltage changes around a closed circuit is equal to zero) to the circuit loop, the following differential equation is obtained:

$$E - L\frac{di}{dt} - (a + bi^2)i = 0 \qquad (6\text{-}62)$$

Equation 6-62 may be rearranged algebraically so that

$$\frac{di}{dt} = \frac{E}{L} - \frac{b}{L}i^3 - \frac{a}{L}i \qquad \text{(when } t = 0, i = 0) \qquad (6\text{-}63)$$

Let us now write a **FORTRAN** program for determining $i(t)$, using Eqs. 6-58 and 6-59. The program will be kept general, so that various parameter values may be used for investigating different circuit combinations. We shall assume that the parameter values for this particular example are

$$E = 200 \text{ volts}$$
$$L = 3 \text{ henries}$$
$$a = 100 \text{ ohms}$$
$$b = 50 \text{ ohms/amp}^2$$

The **FORTRAN** names used and the quantities which they represent are as follows:

FORTRAN *Name*	*Quantity*	*Numerical Values Used as Data*
AMP	Current, amps	Initially zero
A	Constant part of resistance, ohms	100
B	Coefficient of i^2 in resistance expression, ohms/amp^2	50
HENRY	Inductance, henries	3
E	Emf, volts	200
C	B/henry	
D	A/henry	
AK1, AK2, AK3	k_1, k_2, and k_3	
AMPI	Incremented values of current used in calculating k's[4]	

[4]Since the independent variable t does not appear explicitly in Eq. 6-63, it is not necessary to provide incremented values of time to calculate k values within each step.

T	Time, sec	
TPR	Print time, sec	
DELT	Increment of time, sec	0.001
DTPR	Increment of print time, sec	0.002
TMAX	Maximum time, sec	0.05

The flow chart for the problem is shown in Fig. 6-21. The IBM 1620 FORTRAN program, written from the outline provided by the flow chart, is as follows:[5]

```
  PRINT 1
1 FORMAT(42HCURRENT IN A RESISTANCE – INDUCTANCE CIRCUIT//)
  PRINT 2
2 FORMAT(3X,4HTIME,3X,7HCURRENT/)
  READ 3,T,DELT,DTPR,AMP,E,HENRY,A,B,TMAX
3 FORMAT(F3.1,2F5.3,F3.1,F5.1,F3.1,2F5.1,F4.2)
  TPR = DTPR
  C = B/HENRY
  D = A/HENRY
4 AK1 = DELT*(E/HENRY – C*AMP**3 – D*AMP)
  AMPI = AMP + AK1/2.
  AK2 = DELT*(E/HENRY – C*AMPI**3 – D*AMPI)
  AMPI = AMP – AK1 + 2.*AK2
  AK3 = DELT*(E/HENRY – C*AMPI**3 – D*AMPI)
  AMP = AMP + (AK1 + 4.*AK2 + AK3)/6.
  T = T + DELT
  IF(T – TPR)4,5,5
5 PRINT 6,T,AMP
6 FORMAT(F7.3,F10.4)
  TPR = TPR + DTPR
  IF(T – TMAX)4,7,7
7 STOP
  END
```

The data output obtained from the computer solution is

CURRENT IN A RESISTANCE – INDUCTANCE CIRCUIT

TIME	CURRENT
.002	.1289
.004	.2493
.006	.3613
.008	.4646

[5]A simpler program can be written, using FORTRAN II or IV, by making use of the arithmetic statement function discussed in Chapter 2 (see Example 6-4).

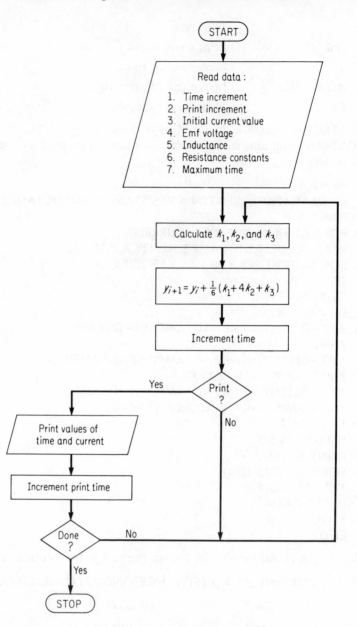

FIG. 6-21. Flow chart for Example 6-3.

.010	.5593
.012	.6451
.014	.7220
.016	.7904
.018	.8505
.020	.9028
.022	.9480
.024	.9865
.026	1.0193
.028	1.0469
.030	1.0701
.032	1.0894
.034	1.1055
.036	1.1188
.038	1.1297
.040	1.1388
.042	1.1462
.044	1.1523
.046	1.1573
.048	1.1614
.050	1.1647

STOP

The data are represented graphically by the curve of Fig. 6-22, illustrating the current buildup in the circuit with time.

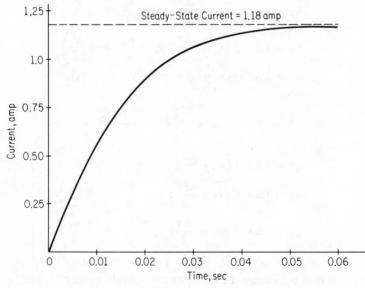

FIG. 6-22. Graphical display of data for Example 6-3.

6-6. Solution of Simultaneous Ordinary Differential Equations by Runge-Kutta Methods

It is frequently necessary to solve sets of simultaneous first-order differential equations in analyzing engineering systems.　Such equations occur most frequently, perhaps, in obtaining solutions of higher-order differential equations which are transformed to sets of first-order differential equations as part of the solution process.　Runge-Kutta methods are well suited for the solution of such equations, and their application will be discussed here.

Let us first consider the solution of 2 simultaneous first-order differential equations of the form

$$\frac{dy}{dx} = f[x, y(x), u(x)]$$

$$\frac{du}{dx} = F[x, y(x), u(x)] \tag{6-64}$$

where the initial values ($y = y_0$, $u = u_0$, when $x = x_0$) are known. Runge-Kutta formulas can be used to solve Eq. 6-64.　Using the fourth-order method already described (Eqs. 6-60 and 6-61), for example, the following *sets* of equations would be used:

$$y_{i+1} = y_i + \tfrac{1}{6}(k_1 + 2k_2 + 2k_3 + k_4) \tag{6-65}$$

where

$$\left.\begin{aligned}
k_1 &= (\Delta x) f(x_i, y_i, u_i) \\
k_2 &= (\Delta x) f\left(x_i + \frac{\Delta x}{2}, y_i + \frac{k_1}{2}, u_i + \frac{q_1}{2}\right) \\
k_3 &= (\Delta x) f\left(x_i + \frac{\Delta x}{2}, y_i + \frac{k_2}{2}, u_i + \frac{q_2}{2}\right) \\
k_4 &= (\Delta x) f(x_i + \Delta x, y_i + k_3, u_i + q_3)
\end{aligned}\right\} \tag{6-66}$$

and

$$u_{i+1} = u_i + \tfrac{1}{6}(q_1 + 2q_2 + 2q_3 + q_4) \tag{6-67}$$

where

$$\left.\begin{aligned}
q_1 &= (\Delta x) F(x_i, y_i, u_i) \\
q_2 &= (\Delta x) F\left(x_i + \frac{\Delta x}{2}, y_i + \frac{k_1}{2}, u_i + \frac{q_1}{2}\right) \\
q_3 &= (\Delta x) F\left(x_i + \frac{\Delta x}{2}, y_i + \frac{k_2}{2}, u_i + \frac{q_2}{2}\right) \\
q_4 &= (\Delta x) F(x_i + \Delta x, y_i + k_3, u_i + q_3)
\end{aligned}\right\} \tag{6-68}$$

The solution begins by substituting the initial values of y and u, which must be known, into the given differential equations to obtain initial values of the functions f and F. Values of k_1 and q_1 are next obtained by multiplying the initial values of f and F, respectively, by Δx, as indicated in Eqs. 6-66 and 6-68. With values of k_1 and q_1 known, k_2 and q_2 are next evaluated, then k_3 and q_3, and finally k_4 and q_4. Then the recurrence formulas (Eqs. 6-65 and 6-67) are used to obtain values of y and u at $x = x_i + \Delta x$ (y_{i+1} and u_{i+1}). These new values of y and u are then used as beginning values in starting the procedure (just described) over again, to obtain values of y_{i+2} and u_{i+2} at $x = x_i + 2\Delta x$, and so on, until the desired range of integration has been covered.

Any number of simultaneous first-order differential equations may be solved by merely using a set of equations such as those shown for each dependent variable appearing in the set of simultaneous differential equations.

An nth-order differential equation can be solved by transforming the equation to a set of n simultaneous first-order differential equations and applying n Runge-Kutta formulas, as discussed in the preceding paragraphs. The procedure can be simplified by combining equations, as will be shown in the following paragraphs.

Consider the second-order differential equation

$$\frac{d^2x}{dt^2} = f\left(t, x, \frac{dx}{dt}\right) \qquad (6\text{-}69)$$

Letting $v = dx/dt$, Eq. 6-69 can be transformed to the 2 first-order differential equations

$$\left.\begin{array}{l} \dfrac{dv}{dt} = f(t, x, v) \\[2mm] \dfrac{dx}{dt} = v \end{array}\right\} \qquad (6\text{-}70)$$

Referring to Eqs. 6-65 through 6-68, the following 2 fourth-order Runge-Kutta formulas could be used to solve Eq. 6-70:

$$v_{i+1} = v_i + \tfrac{1}{6}(k_1 + 2k_2 + 2k_3 + k_4) \qquad (6\text{-}71)$$

where

$$\left.\begin{array}{l} k_1 = (\Delta t)f(t_i, x_i, v_i) \\[2mm] k_2 = (\Delta t)f\left(t_i + \dfrac{\Delta t}{2}, x_i + \dfrac{q_1}{2}, v_i + \dfrac{k_1}{2}\right) \\[2mm] k_3 = (\Delta t)f\left(t_i + \dfrac{\Delta t}{2}, x_i + \dfrac{q_2}{2}, v_i + \dfrac{k_2}{2}\right) \\[2mm] k_4 = (\Delta t)f(t_i + \Delta t, x_i + q_3, v_i + k_3) \end{array}\right\} \qquad (6\text{-}72)$$

and

$$x_{i+1} = x_i + \tfrac{1}{6}(q_1 + 2q_2 + 2q_3 + q_4) \qquad (6\text{-}73)$$

where

$$q_1 = (\Delta t) F(v_i) \qquad\qquad = (\Delta t)(v_i)$$

$$q_2 = (\Delta t) F\left(v_i + \frac{k_1}{2}\right) = (\Delta t)\left(v_i + \frac{k_1}{2}\right)$$

$$q_3 = (\Delta t) F\left(v_i + \frac{k_2}{2}\right) = (\Delta t)\left(v_i + \frac{k_2}{2}\right) \qquad (6\text{-}74)$$

$$q_4 = (\Delta t) F(v_i + k_3) \quad = (\Delta t)(v_i + k_3)$$

However, we may obtain a more compact set of equations by substituting the expressions for the q's into both the expressions for the k's and the recurrence formula of Eq. 6-73. Performing these substitutions yields

$$x_{i+1} = x_i + (\Delta t) v_i + \frac{\Delta t}{6}(k_1 + k_2 + k_3)$$

$$(6\text{-}75)$$

$$v_{i+1} = v_i + \frac{1}{6}(k_1 + 2k_2 + 2k_3 + k_4)$$

where

$$k_1 = (\Delta t) f(t_i, x_i, v_i)$$

$$k_2 = (\Delta t) f\left[t_i + \frac{(\Delta t)}{2}, x_i + \frac{(\Delta t)}{2} v_i, v_i + \frac{k_1}{2}\right]$$

$$k_3 = (\Delta t) f\left[t_i + \frac{(\Delta t)}{2}, x_i + \frac{(\Delta t)}{2} v_i + \frac{(\Delta t)}{4} k_1, v_i + \frac{k_2}{2}\right] \qquad (6\text{-}76)$$

$$k_4 = (\Delta t) f\left[t_i + \Delta t, x_i + (\Delta t) v_i + \frac{(\Delta t)}{2} k_2, v_i + k_3\right]$$

EXAMPLE 6-4

To illustrate the application of Eqs. 6-75 and 6-76 in solving a second-order differential equation, consider the vibrating system shown in Fig. 6-23a. A unit mass is attached to a spring having a spring constant of

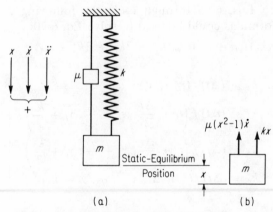

FIG. 6-23. System of Example 6-4.

1 lb/ft, and a damping device that exerts a force on the mass which depends upon both the displacement and the velocity of the mass. The damping force may be expressed mathematically as

$$F_d = \mu(x^2 - 1)\dot{x} \qquad (6\text{-}77)$$

where μ is a damping coefficient. It is desired to obtain x-t and $\dot{x}$-t curves for studying the displacement and velocity characteristics of the system.

A free-body diagram of the mass is shown in Fig. 6-23b. The gravity force acting on such a system is customarily not shown on the free body, since the amplitude of vibration x is measured from the static-equilibrium position of the mass, in which position the gravity force is equal to the spring force, and these forces cancel from the resulting differential equation.

Noting the positive direction assumed for x, $\dot{x}$, and $\ddot{x}$, as shown in the figure, and the positive displacement used in determining the free-body diagram, the application of Newton's second law yields

$$-kx - \mu(x^2 - 1)\dot{x} = m\ddot{x}$$

or, more simply,

$$\ddot{x} + \mu(x^2 - 1)\dot{x} + x = 0 \qquad (6\text{-}78)$$

since $m = k = 1$.

Equation 6-78 is a classical nonlinear differential equation known as *Van der Pol's* equation. Although the mechanical system from which Eq. 6-78 was derived is a hypothetical one, this equation does actually represent the behavior of a certain type of electronic oscillator.[6]

The reader who is familiar with vibration theory will recognize that if $|x| > 1$, the second term of Eq. 6-78 is a *positive-damping* term which represents a loss of energy from the system. Conversely, if $|x| < 1$ this term is a *negative-damping* term which represents an addition of energy to the system. Thus, if we were initially to displace the mass less than 1 ft and then release it, the resulting vibrations would increase in amplitude until they reached some magnitude exceeding 1 ft, at which time energy would be removed from the system during the portion of each cycle in which $|x| > 1$. The buildup in amplitude would thus be limited, and it would seem reasonable to expect the amplitude of vibration to reach some stable state after some interval of time.

To program Eq. 6-78 for solution on the computer, we note that

$$\dot{x} = \frac{dx}{dt}$$

so that

$$\ddot{x} = \frac{d\dot{x}}{dt}$$

$$\left.\begin{array}{c}\\\\\\\\\end{array}\right\} \qquad (6\text{-}79)$$

---

[6]Minorsky, N. *Introduction to Nonlinear Mechanics.* Ann Arbor, Mich.: J. W. Edwards, Publisher, Inc., 1947, p. 293.

Utilizing these relationships, Eq. 6-78 may be transformed to the first-order differential equations

$$\frac{d\dot{x}}{dt} = -\mu(x^2 - 1)\dot{x} - x \qquad \text{(a)}$$

$$\frac{dx}{dt} = \dot{x} \qquad \qquad \text{(b)}$$

(6-80)

Referring to Eqs. 6-75 and 6-76, and noting that the variable t does not appear explicitly in Eq. 6-80, we may write the fourth-order Runge-Kutta formulas

$$x_{i+1} = x_i + (\Delta t)\dot{x}_i + \frac{\Delta t}{6}(k_1 + k_2 + k_3)$$

$$\dot{x}_{i+1} = \dot{x}_i + \frac{1}{6}(k_1 + 2k_2 + 2k_3 + k_4)$$

(6-81)

where

$$k_1 = (\Delta t)f(x_i, \dot{x}_i)$$

$$k_2 = (\Delta t)f\left[x_i + \frac{(\Delta t)}{2}\dot{x}_i, \dot{x}_i + \frac{k_1}{2}\right]$$

$$k_3 = (\Delta t)f\left[x_i + \frac{(\Delta t)}{2}\dot{x}_i + \frac{(\Delta t)}{4}k_1, \dot{x}_i + \frac{k_2}{2}\right]$$

$$k_4 = (\Delta t)f\left[x_i + (\Delta t)\dot{x}_i + \frac{(\Delta t)}{2}k_2, \dot{x}_i + k_3\right]$$

(6-82)

The numerical solution begins with the substitution of the initial values of x and $\dot{x}$ into Eq. 6-80a to obtain a value of this function for use in determining k_1. The successive k values are then determined for use in the recurrence formulas shown to obtain values of x_{i+1} and $\dot{x}_{i+1}$. The latter values obtained are then used in Eqs. 6-80a and 6-82 to obtain new k values for substitution into Eq. 6-81 to obtain values of x_{i+2} and $\dot{x}_{i+2}$, and so on. An outline of the procedure is shown in the flow chart of Fig. 6-24. The initial values used are

$$t = 0 \left|\begin{array}{l} x = 0.75 \text{ ft} \\ \dot{x} = 0 \end{array}\right.$$

The FORTRAN variable names used in the source program and the quantities which they represent are as follows:

FORTRAN Name	Quantity	Values Used in Problem
COEFF	Damping coefficient, lb-sec/ft^3	4.0
X	Displacement of mass from static-equilibrium position, ft	$x_0 = 0.75$
XD	Velocity of mass, ft/sec	$\dot{x}_0 = 0.0$
DELTMS	Time increment, msec	50.
DTPR	Print increment, msec	100.

TMAX	Time interval for which solution is desired, msec	20000.
TMS	Time, msec	
TPR	Time at which printout is to occur, sec	
XDD	Acceleration of mass, ft/sec^2	
DELT	Time increment, sec	
T	Time, sec	
AK1, AK2, AK3, AK4	Quantities k_1, k_2, k_3, and k_4 of Runge-Kutta recurrence formulas	

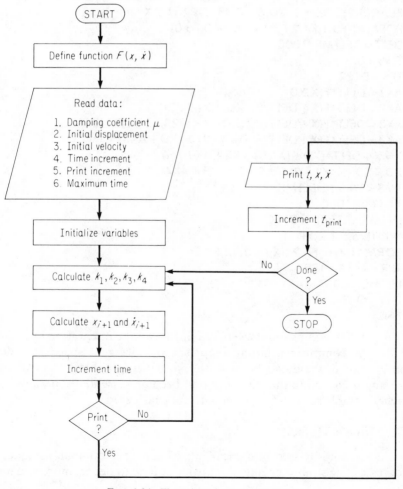

FIG. 6-24. Flow chart for Example 6-4.

The FORTRAN IV computer program used to implement the procedures outlined by the flow chart is shown below. Since this program is to be run on a pure binary computer, the time increment is chosen in milliseconds (msec). With this unit of time, the time increment is a whole number which can be expressed *exactly* in pure binary form. A time increment such as 0.05 sec, for example, cannot be expressed exactly in pure binary form, and, consequently, 20 such increments will not add up exactly to 1.0 sec. When using a *pure binary computer*, the time, the print time, and their increments should be expressed in *whole numbers* to assure printouts at exactly the print times desired.

```
  F(X,XD)= −COEFF*(X*X−1.)*XD−X
  WRITE(6,1)
1 FORMAT(1H1,26H   TIME     DISPL   VELOCITY/)
  READ(5,2)COEFF,X,XD,DELTMS,DTPR,TMAX
2 FORMAT(F3.1,F4.2,F3.1,F3.0,F4.0,F6.0)
  DELT=DELTMS/1000.
  TMS=0.
  TPR=DTPR
3 AK1=DELT*F(X,XD)
  AK2=DELT*F(X+DELT/2.*XD,XD+AK1/2.)
  AK3=DELT*F(X+DELT/2.*(XD+AK1/2.),XD+AK2/2.)
  AK4=DELT*F(X+DELT*(XD+AK2/2.),XD+AK3)
  X=X+DELT*(XD+(AK1+AK2+AK3)/6.)
  XD=XD+(AK1+2.*AK2+2.*AK3+AK4)/6.
  TMS=TMS+DELTMS
  T=TMS/1000.
  IF(TMS.LT.TPR) GO TO 3
4 WRITE(6,5)T,X,XD
5 FORMAT(1H ,F6.2,3X,F6.3,4X,F7.3)
  TPR=TPR+DTPR
  IF(TMS .EQ. TMAX) STOP
  GO TO 3
  END
```

Since 200 data printouts were obtained over the integration interval of 20 sec, the computer printout is not shown, owing to space considerations. Instead, the data obtained are plotted in graphical form in Figs. 6-25 and 6-26. Note that the vibration becomes essentially periodic and reaches a stable state in the 20-sec interval considered.

6-7. Milne's Method

As the step-by-step numerical integration of a differential equation progresses, the solution being obtained may tend to depart more and more

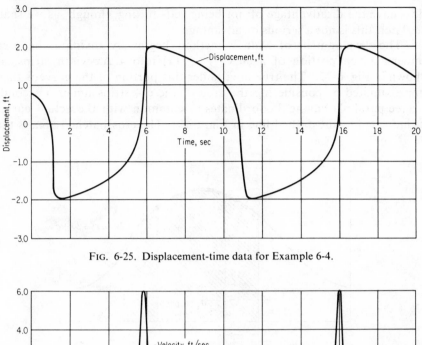

FIG. 6-25. Displacement-time data for Example 6-4.

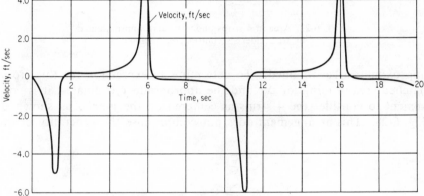

FIG. 6-26. Velocity-time data for Example 6-4.

from the true answer, owing to cumulative *per-step* error. If the solution must be obtained by using a relatively large number of steps, it is very important that the per-step error be kept small. The per-step error, using Euler's method, is of order $(\Delta x)^2$. Euler's modified methods have a per-step error of order $(\Delta x)^3$. It can be shown that Milne's method has a per-step error of order $(\Delta x)^5$. Thus, Milne's method is considerably more accurate than either Euler's method or Euler's modified methods, when a relatively large number of steps is involved. However, Milne's method does have the disadvantage of not being self-starting, though, as we shall see later, this is not a serious disadvantage.

The development of Milne's method begins by dividing the area under a given portion of a curve $y = f(x)$ into 4 Δx-width strips, as shown in Fig. 6-27. The true area under this portion of the curve is then approximated by considering the area of these 4 strips under a second-degree parabola having 3 coordinates in common with the actual curve, as indicated by the dashed line in Fig. 6-27. The crosshatched area is the

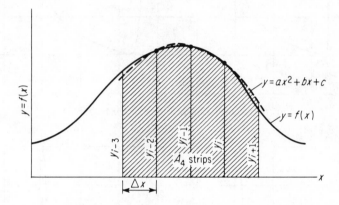

FIG. 6-27. Area in 4 strips under a curve approximated by area under a second-degree parabola.

approximate area obtained. To determine an expression for this cross-hatched area in terms of Δx and the appropriate y ordinates, it is convenient to consider the 4 strips as centered on the y axis, as shown in Fig. 6-28. This arrangement does not compromise the generality of the

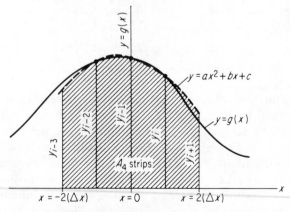

FIG. 6-28. Area of 4 strips centered on y axis.

results obtained, and it has the advantage of simplifying the intermediate expressions involved in determining the desired form of the expression for the area of 4 such strips. The crosshatched area of Fig. 6-28 is given by

$$A_{4\,\text{strips}} = \int_{-2(\Delta x)}^{2(\Delta x)} (ax^2 + bx + c)\,dx \qquad (6\text{-}83)$$

Integrating Eq. 6-83 and substituting the limits gives

$$A_{4\,\text{strips}} = \frac{16}{3}\,a(\Delta x)^3 + 4c(\Delta x) \qquad (6\text{-}84)$$

The constants a and c are determined in the manner explained on p. 286. The appropriate expressions are

$$a = \frac{y_i - 2y_{i-1} + y_{i-2}}{2(\Delta x)^2}$$

$$c = y_{i-1} \qquad (6\text{-}85)$$

Substituting Eq. 6-85 into Eq. 6-84 yields, for the area of the 4 strips in terms of Δx and the y ordinates shown,

$$A_{4\,\text{strips}} = \frac{4}{3}\,(\Delta x)[2y_i - y_{i-1} + 2y_{i-2}] \qquad (6\text{-}86)$$

This expression will be used later as part of the predictor equation.

Let us consider the application of Milne's method in integrating a first-order differential equation of the form

$$y' = f(x, y) \qquad (6\text{-}87)$$

where the value of y is known for $x = 0$. This technique consists, basically, of obtaining approximate values of y by the use of a *predictor* equation and then correcting these values by the iterative use of a corrector equation. Milne's predictor equation

$$P(y_{i+1}) = y_{i-3} + \frac{4}{3}\,(\Delta x)[2y_i' - y_{i-1}' + 2y_{i-2}'] \qquad (6\text{-}88)$$

utilizes the area of 4 strips under a parabolic approximation of a curve (see Eq. 6-86) to provide a predicted value for the successive y ordinates. Milne's *corrector* equation

$$C(y_{i+1}) = y_{i-1} + \frac{\Delta x}{3}\,[y_{i-1}' + 4y_i' + P(y_{i+1}')] \qquad (6\text{-}89)$$

provides corrected y values by using Simpson's rule for determining the area of 2 strips under a curve (see p. 286).

Assuming that the resulting y and y' curves of Eq. 6-87 have the general form of the curves shown in Fig. 6-29, the first step is to obtain a predicted value of y_4. Utilizing Eq. 6-88 with $i = 3$,

$$P(y_4) = y_0 + \frac{4}{3}\,(\Delta x)[2y_3' - y_2' + 2y_1'] \qquad (6\text{-}90)$$

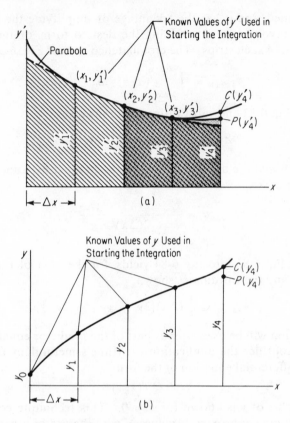

FIG. 6-29. Graphical illustration of integration
by Milne's method.

The predicted value obtained is then substituted into the given differential equation (Eq. 6-87) to obtain a predicted value of y_4', which is designated as $P(y_4')$. This value is then used in Eq. 6-89 to obtain a corrected value of y_4 as

$$C(y_4) = y_2 + \frac{\Delta x}{3} [y_2' + 4y_3' + P(y_4')] \qquad (6\text{-}91)$$

The 3 steps just outlined are the first steps in the application of Milne's method. However, inspection of Eqs. 6-90 and 6-91 reveals that, before $P(y_4)$ and $C(y_4)$ can be obtained, starting values must be determined, in some manner, for y_1', y_2', y_3', and y_2. Furthermore, in stepping forward to obtain values of $P(y_5)$ and $C(y_5)$, starting values must also be known for y_1 and y_3.

The required starting values of y can be determined by the use of the following Taylor-series expansions:

$$y_1 = y_0 + y_0'(\Delta x) + \frac{y_0''(\Delta x)^2}{2!} + \frac{y_0'''(\Delta x)^3}{3!} + \cdots$$

$$y_2 = y_0 + y_0'[2(\Delta x)] + \frac{y_0''[2(\Delta x)]^2}{2!} + \frac{y_0'''[2(\Delta x)]^3}{3!} + \cdots \qquad (6\text{-}92)$$

$$y_3 = y_0 + y_0'[3(\Delta x)] + \frac{y_0''[3(\Delta x)]^2}{2!} + \frac{y_0'''[3(\Delta x)]^3}{3!} + \cdots$$

The numerical values of each of the derivatives, y_0', y_0'', y_0''', and so on, which are required to evaluate Eq. 6-92, are obtained by substituting $x = 0$ and $y = y_0$ into Eq. 6-87 and its derivatives y'', y''', and so forth. Having determined y_1, y_2, and y_3 from Eq. 6-92, the required values of y_1', y_2', and y_3' are next obtained by substituting the corresponding x and y values into Eq. 6-87. The number of terms used in each Taylor series should include terms up to and including $(\Delta x)^4$ or the last term which yields a numerical value compatible with the digit capacity allowed by the compiler being used, whichever number of terms is the least.

Another way of starting Milne's method is to determine the required value of each of the ordinates y_1, y_2, and y_3 by the use of a Runge-Kutta formula. A value of each of the ordinates y_1', y_2', and y_3' may then be obtained, as before, by substituting the appropriate x and y values into Eq. 6-87. The fourth-order Runge-Kutta formula[7] frequently used is

$$y_{i+1} = y_i + \frac{1}{6}(k_1 + 2k_2 + 2k_3 + k_4) \qquad (6\text{-}93)$$

where the respective k values are determined by substituting appropriate values into Eq. 6-87, as follows:

$$k_1 = (\Delta x)f(x_i, y_i)$$

$$k_2 = (\Delta x)f\left(x_i + \frac{\Delta x}{2}, y_i + \frac{k_1}{2}\right)$$

$$k_3 = (\Delta x)f\left(x_i + \frac{\Delta x}{2}, y_i + \frac{k_2}{2}\right)$$

$$k_4 = (\Delta x)f(x_i + \Delta x, y_i + k_3)$$

The solution of Eq. 6-87 could be obtained in its entirety using only the Runge-Kutta method, and with the same degree of accuracy as Milne's method, since both have a per-step error of the order of $(\Delta x)^5$. However, Milne's method is considered to be more efficient (less machine time) than the Runge-Kutta method, and estimation of the per-step error is easier using Milne's method (see Sec. 6-9). It is often used for these reasons, even though the Runge-Kutta method has the advantage of being self-starting. Because the Runge-Kutta method is self-starting and has the

[7] See Sec. 6-5.

same degree of accuracy as Milne's method, it is frequently used to start the latter method, as just described. In using either the Taylor series or the Runge-Kutta method for starting Milne's procedure, the required starting values may be obtained manually or by using a desk calculator. However, if it is desired to use the computer to obtain the starting values so that the program is self-contained, it is generally easier to use the Runge-Kutta method, since higher derivatives of the given differential equation are not required by this method. If the derivatives of the given differential equation become increasingly complex with each successive differentiation, the Runge-Kutta procedure should be utilized for obtaining starting values, whether done manually, by calculator, or by computer.

With the starting procedure established, the following equations provide an outline of the subsequent steps involved.

(Predictor)
$$P(y_{i+1}) = y_{i-3} + \frac{4}{3}(\Delta x)[2y_i' - y_{i-1}' + 2y_{i-2}'] \quad \text{(a)}$$

(Differential equation)
$$P(y_{i+1}') = f[x_{i+1}, P(y_{i+1})] \quad \text{(b)}$$

(Corrector)
$$C(y_{i+1}) = y_{i-1} + \frac{\Delta x}{3}[y_{i-1}' + 4y_i' + P(y_{i+1}')] \quad \text{(c)} \quad \text{(6-94)}$$

(Differential equation)
$$C(y_{i+1}') = f[x_{i+1}, C(y_{i+1})] \quad \text{(d)}$$

(Iterating corrector)
$$C(y_{i+1}) = y_{i-1} + \frac{\Delta x}{3}[y_{i-1}' + 4y_i' + C(y_{i+1}')] \quad \text{(e)}$$

where Eq. 6-94b and d indicate the forms in which the given differential equation is used in the correcting process. Assuming that the starting values (shown in Fig. 6-29) have been determined, the first step is to obtain a predicted value of y_4, using Eq. 6-94a. This equation predicts the value of y_4 by adding the value of y_0 to the value of the crosshatched area shown under the parabola in Fig. 6-29a. Since this area is indicated as less than the true area, $P(y_4)$ will be smaller than the true value of y_4, as shown in Fig. 6-29b. The next step is to substitute $x_4 = 4\Delta x$ and $P(y_4)$ into the given differential equation, as indicated by Eq. 6-94b to obtain a predicted value of y_4', which is shown as $P(y_4')$ in Fig. 6-29a. This predicted value of y_4' is then used in the corrector equation (Eq. 6-94c) to obtain a *corrected* value of y_4, which is shown as $C(y_4)$ in Fig. 6-29b. This corrected value of y_4 is obtained as the sum of y_2 and the shaded area under the curve in Fig. 6-29a, which area is found from Simpson's rule for the area of 2 strips (p. 286). The corrected value of

y_4 is next substituted into Eq. 6-94d to obtain an improved value of y_4', which is shown as $C(y_4')$ in Fig. 6-29a. The latter value is then used in Eq. 6-94e to obtain a further improved value of y_4, which is, in turn, substituted back into Eq. 6-94d to obtain a further improved value of y_4', and so on. The iteration process involving Eq. 6-94d and e then continues until successive values of y_4 differ by less than the value of some desired epsilon. With y_4 determined to the desired accuracy, the method steps forward 1 Δx increment, and the above process is repeated to obtain y_5, and so on. In programming the problem, it is not actually necessary to write Eq. 6-94e as a separate **FORTRAN** statement, since the program can be written so that Eq. 6-94c performs the function of Eq. 6-94e in the iteration process of each step.

EXAMPLE 6-5

A small rocket having an initial weight of 3000 lb, including 2400 lb of fuel, is fired vertically upward. The rocket burns fuel at a constant rate of 40 lb/sec, which provides a thrust of 7000 lb. Instruments are carried by the rocket to record data from which acceleration-time, velocity-time, and displacement-time curves can be obtained.

We wish to provide a theoretical analysis of the rocket flight which will yield data enabling us to plot the same curves obtained from the data recorded by the rocket instruments. A comparison of these sets of data then can check the validity of the mathematical model used in the theoretical analysis, since the model is conditioned by certain necessary simplifying assumptions, as follows: 1) The drag force is proportional to the square of the velocity ($D = Kv^2$), and 2) the coefficient of aerodynamic resistance K has an average value of 0.008 lb-sec^2/ft^2.

A free-body diagram of the rocket appears in Fig. 6-30. The forces acting on the rocket are

T = thrust force, 7000 lb

W = total weight of rocket, fuel, and equipment at time t, (3000 − 40t)

D = drag, 0.008$\dot{y}^2$ lb

Assuming y to be positive upward, as shown in the figure, we use Newton's second law to obtain the second-order nonlinear differential equation

$$\ddot{y} = \frac{gT}{W} - g - \frac{K\dot{y}^2 g}{W} \qquad (6\text{-}95)$$

which has variable coefficients. The initial conditions of the problem are

$$t = 0 \left|\begin{array}{l} y = 0 \\ \dot{y} = 0 \end{array}\right.$$

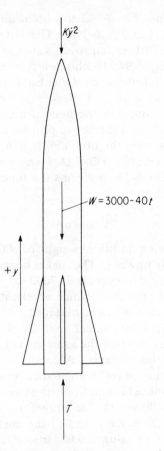

$K\ddot{y}^2$

$W = 3000 - 40t$

$+y$

T

FIG. 6-30. Free-body diagram of
rocket of Example 6-5.

The solution of Eq. 6-95 will illustrate the application of Milne's method for obtaining the solution of a second-order differential equation. The required starting values of y, $\dot{y}$, and $\ddot{y}$, shown below, were obtained from the initial conditions, Taylor-series expansions, and the use of Eq. 6-95 by the procedure outlined in the preceding discussion.

$y_0 = 0.0$ ft	$\dot{y}_0 = 0.0$ ft/sec	
$y_1 = 0.2146$ ft	$\dot{y}_1 = 4.294$ ft/sec	$\ddot{y}_1 = 42.99$ ft/sec^2
$y_2 = 0.8591$ ft	$\dot{y}_2 = 8.598$ ft/sec	$\ddot{y}_2 = 43.08$ ft/sec^2
$y_3 = 1.935$ ft	$\dot{y}_3 = 12.911$ ft/sec	$\ddot{y}_3 = 43.18$ ft/sec^2

In obtaining these values, a value of $\Delta t = 0.1$ was used, and the highest derivative used in the Taylor-series expansions was y''''.

Remember that if the computer program is to be run a number of times, using different data in each run, the calculation of the starting values should be included in the program, so that their calculation becomes part of the computing process. As mentioned previously, the Runge-Kutta equation is more easily programmed for the calculation of starting values than are Taylor-series expansions. The Runge-Kutta formula (Eq. 6-93) can be used to determine starting values for the solution of a first-order differential equation. However, in applying the Runge-Kutta method to the solution of a second-order differential equation of the form $y'' = f(x, y, y')$, as in this example, 2 formulas are required as discussed in Sec. 6-6. Although many variations of Runge-Kutta formulas exist, the following (see p. 352) will be found suitable for the determination of the required starting values:

$$y_{i+1} = y_i + (\Delta x) y_i' + \frac{(\Delta x)}{6} [k_1 + k_2 + k_3]$$

$$y_{i+1}' = y_i' + \frac{1}{6} [k_1 + 2k_2 + 2k_3 + k_4]$$

where

$$k_1 = (\Delta x) f [x_i, y_i, y_i']$$

$$k_2 = (\Delta x) f \left[x_i + \frac{(\Delta x)}{2}, y_i + \frac{(\Delta x)}{2} y_i', y_i' + \frac{k_1}{2} \right]$$

$$k_3 = (\Delta x) f \left[x_i + \frac{(\Delta x)}{2}, y_i + \frac{(\Delta x)}{2} y_i' + \frac{(\Delta x)}{4} k_1, y_i' + \frac{k_2}{2} \right]$$

$$k_4 = (\Delta x) f \left[x_i + (\Delta x), y_i + (\Delta x) y_i' + \frac{(\Delta x)}{2} k_2, y_i' + k_3 \right]$$

As in the formula given for solving first-order differential equations, the error in the above formulas is of order $(\Delta x)^5$.

We shall make use of Eq. 6-94 in the following form:

(Predictor)

$$P(\dot{y}_{i+1}) = \dot{y}_{i-3} + \frac{4}{3} (\Delta t)(2\ddot{y}_i - \ddot{y}_{i-1} + 2\ddot{y}_{i-2}] \qquad \text{(a)}$$

(Differential equation)

$$P(\ddot{y}_{i+1}) = f[t_{i+1}, P(\dot{y}_{i+1})] \qquad \text{(b)}$$

(Corrector)

$$C(\dot{y}_{i+1}) = \dot{y}_{i-1} + \frac{\Delta t}{3} [\ddot{y}_{i-1} + 4\ddot{y}_i + P(\ddot{y}_{i+1})] \qquad \text{(c)} \quad \text{(6-96)}$$

(Differential equation)

$$C(\ddot{y}_{i+1}) = f[t_{i+1}, C(\dot{y}_{i+1})] \qquad \text{(d)}$$

(Iterating corrector)

$$C(\dot{y}_{i+1}) = \dot{y}_{i-1} + \frac{\Delta t}{3} [\ddot{y}_{i-1} + 4\ddot{y}_i + C(\ddot{y}_{i+1})] \qquad \text{(e)}$$

The dynamic-characteristics curves of the rocket for t near zero are sketched in Fig. 6-31. A predicted value of $\dot{y}_4$ is the first value obtained. It is determined from Eq. 6-96a, with $i = 3$, as

$$P(\dot{y}_4) = \dot{y}_0 + \frac{4}{3}(\Delta t)[2\ddot{y}_3 - \ddot{y}_2 + 2\ddot{y}_1]$$

where the second term on the right side is the crosshatched area under the parabola in Fig. 6-31a. A predicted value of $\ddot{y}_4$ is next obtained by substituting $t_4 = 4\Delta t$ and the predicted value of $\dot{y}_4$ into Eq. 6-95, as indicated by Eq. 6-96b. This predicted value of $\ddot{y}_4$ is then substituted into Eq. 6-96c to obtain a corrected value of $\dot{y}_4$. The second term on the right side of

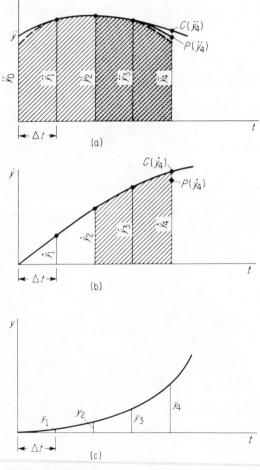

FIG. 6-31. General characteristic curves for rocket of Example 6-5.

Eq. 6-96c is the shaded area shown in Fig. 6-31a. The corrected value $C(\dot{y}_4)$ is next substituted, along with $t_4 = 4\Delta t$, into Eq. 6-95 to obtain a corrected value of $\ddot{y}_4$, as indicated by Eq. 6-96d. This corrected value of $\ddot{y}_4$ is then substituted into Eq. 6-96e to obtain a further improved value of $\dot{y}_4$. This value is then substituted into Eq. 6-95 to obtain a further improved value of $\ddot{y}_4$, which is, in turn, substituted back into Eq. 6-96e to obtain an even-more-accurate value of $\dot{y}_4$. The iterative process involving Eq. 6-96d and e continues until successive values of $\dot{y}_4$ vary by less than some value epsilon chosen to specify the accuracy desired. In programming the problem, it is not actually necessary to write Eq. 6-96e as a separate **FORTRAN** statement, since the program can be written so that Eq. 6-96c performs the function of Eq. 6-96e in the iteration process of each step (see the **FORTRAN** program of this example).

Since the given differential equation (Eq. 6-95) does not contain y in explicit form, it is not necessary to calculate a value of y_4 until $\dot{y}_4$ has been determined with the accuracy desired.[8] The value of y_4 is then calculated, using Milne's corrector equation (Simpson's rule), as

$$y_4 = y_2 + \frac{\Delta t}{3}[\dot{y}_2 + 4\dot{y}_3 + \dot{y}_4]$$

where the second term on the right is the crosshatched area shown in Fig. 6-31b. After obtaining y_4, we move forward 1 step and repeat the process to determine values of $\dot{y}_5$ and y_5, and so on. This is continued until a time is reached corresponding to burnout (60 sec).

The flow chart for programming this problem is given in Fig. 6-32. The variable names, quantities, and values are as follows:

Variable Name	Quantity	Value
W1	Total initial weight of rocket, lb	3000
WF	Initial weight of fuel, lb	2400
TH	Thrust, lb	7000
FR	Fuel-consumption rate, lb/sec	40
DK	Coefficient of aerodynamic resistance, lb-sec^2/ft^2	0.008
G	Acceleration of gravity, ft/sec^2	32.17
DELT	Time increment, sec	0.1
DTPR	Print increment, sec	2.0
EPSI	Accuracy-check value, ft/sec	0.0001
Y	Displacement value at station $i - 3$, ft	(Initial)0.0000

[8]See p. 372 for a brief discussion of the procedure for using Milne's method when y appears in explicit form in the differential equation.

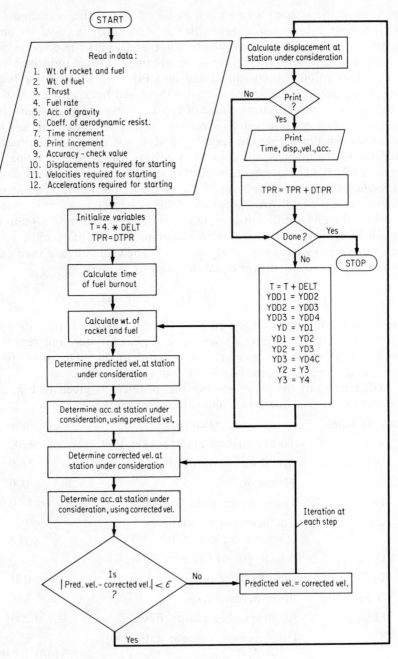

FIG. 6-32. Flow chart for Example 6-5.

Variable Name	Quantity	Value
Y1	Displacement at station $i - 2$, ft	(Initial) 0.2146
Y2	Displacement at station $i - 1$, ft	(Initial) 0.8591
Y3	Displacement at station i, ft	(Initial) 1.9350
YD	Velocity value at station $i - 3$, ft/sec	(Initial) 0.0000
YD1	Velocity at station $i - 2$, ft/sec	(Initial) 4.294
YD2	Velocity at station $i - 1$, ft/sec	(Initial) 8.598
YD3	Velocity at station i, ft/sec	(Initial) 12.911
YDD1	Acceleration at station $i - 2$, ft/sec^2	(Initial) 42.99
YDD2	Acceleration at station $i - 1$, ft/sec^2	(Initial) 43.08
YDD3	Acceleration at station i, ft/sec^2	(Initial) 43.18
T	Time, sec	
TMAX	Time at burnout, sec	60
TPR	Time at which printout occurs, sec	
W	Weight of rocket, fuel, and equipment at time t, lb	
YD4P	Predicted value of velocity, ft/sec	
YDD4	Acceleration of rocket, ft/sec^2	
YD4C	Corrected value of velocity, ft/sec	
Y4	Displacement at station $i + 1$, ft	

The **FORTRAN IV** program follows. Note that all parts of Eq. 6-96 do not appear explicitly in the program. Since Eq. 6-96c is used only once in a particular sequence and is then replaced by Eq. 6-96e, the program utilizes statement **6** to fulfill the function of both Eqs. 6-96c and e.

```
C       DYNAMIC CHARACTERISTICS OF A ROCKET
C       NUMERICAL INTEGRATION BY MILNE METHOD
        READ(5,1)W1,WF,TH,FR,G,DK,DELT,DTPR,EPSI
      1 FORMAT (11F5.0)
        READ(5,1)Y,Y1,Y2,Y3,YD,YD1,YD2,YD3,YDD1,YDD2,YDD3
        WRITE(6,2)
      2 FORMAT(1H1,5X,1HW,8X,1HF,7X,2HTH,7X,1HR,7X,1HG,7X,
                      1HK,5X,2HDT,4X,3HDTP,5X,3HEPS/)
        WRITE(6,3)W1,WF,TH,FR,G,DK,DELT,DTPR,EPSI
      3 FORMAT(2F9.1,F8.0,2F8.2,F8.4,2F6.2,F9.5///)
        WRITE(6,4)
```

```
  4 FORMAT(7H     TIME,6X,6HDISPL.,6X,4HVEL.,7X,4HACC./)
    T = 4.*DELT
    TMAX = WF/FR
    TPR = DTPR
  5 W = W1−FR*T
    YD4P = YD+4./3.*(2.*YDD1−YDD2+2.*YDD3)*DELT
    YDD4 = G*TH/W − G −DK*G/W*(YD4P**2)
  6 YD4C = YD2 + DELT/3.*(YDD2+4.*YDD3+YDD4)
    YDD4 = G*TH/W − G − DK*G/W*(YD4C**2)
    IF(ABS(YD4C−YD4P)−EPSI)8,8,7
  7 YD4P = YD4C
    GO TO 6
  8 Y4 = Y2 + DELT/3.*(YD2+4.*YD3+YD4C)
    IF(T−TPR)11,9,9
  9 WRITE(6,10)T,Y4,YD4C,YDD4
 10 FORMAT(1H ,F7.2,F12.2,F11.2,F10.2)
    TPR = TPR + DTPR
 11 IF(T−TMAX)13,12,12
 12 STOP
 13 T = T+DELT
    YDD1 = YDD2
    YDD2 = YDD3
    YDD3 = YDD4
    YD = YD1
    YD1 = YD2
    YD2 = YD3
    YD3 = YD4C
    Y2 = Y3
    Y3 = Y4
    GO TO 5
    END
```

The computer printout is shown in tabular form. The desired dynamic-characteristic curves, as plotted from the data printout, are given in Fig. 6-33. These curves are available for comparison with the corresponding curves obtained from the instruments carried by the rocket.

W	F	TH	R	G	K
3000.0	2400.0	7000.	40.00	32.17	.0080
DT	DTP	EPS			
.10	2.00	.00010			

TIME	DISPL.	VEL.	ACC.
2.00	86.91	87.38	44.27
4.00	350.49	176.20	44.30

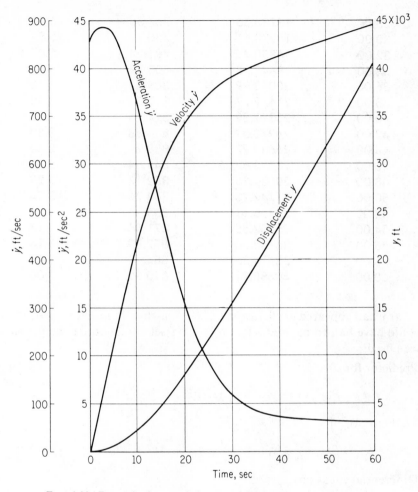

FIG. 6-33. Dynamic-characteristic curves of the rocket of Example 6-5.

6.00	790.82	263.67	42.93
8.00	1402.48	347.09	40.28
10.00	2174.95	424.15	36.63
12.00	3093.74	493.20	32.34
14.00	4141.85	553.38	27.82
16.00	5301.27	604.55	23.39
18.00	6554.38	647.19	19.31
20.00	7884.94	682.17	15.75
22.00	9278.68	710.58	12.75
24.00	10723.64	733.57	10.32
26.00	12210.09	752.24	8.42

28.00	13730.36	767.55	6.96
30.00	15278.61	780.33	5.87
32.00	16850.45	791.24	5.07
34.00	18442.68	800.79	4.50
36.00	20052.99	809.38	4.10
38.00	21679.77	817.30	3.82
40.00	23321.89	824.75	3.63
42.00	24978.57	831.88	3.50
44.00	26649.27	838.79	3.40
46.00	28333.62	845.54	3.34
48.00	30031.35	852.17	3.28
50.00	31742.23	858.70	3.24
52.00	33466.11	865.16	3.21
54.00	35202.85	871.56	3.17
56.00	36952.30	877.89	3.14
58.00	38714.36	884.17	3.11
60.00	40488.91	890.39	3.08

If y had appeared explicitly in Eq. 6-95, a slightly modified procedure would have had to be used. The following set of equations would have been used:

(Predictor for $\dot{y}$)

$$P(\dot{y}_{i+1}) = \dot{y}_{i-3} + \frac{4}{3}(\Delta t)[2\ddot{y}_i - \ddot{y}_{i-1} + 2\ddot{y}_{i-2}] \quad \text{(a)}$$

(Predictor for y)

$$P(y_{i+1}) = y_{i-1} + \frac{\Delta t}{3}[\dot{y}_{i-1} + 4\dot{y}_i + P(\dot{y}_{i+1})] \quad \text{(b)}$$

(Differential equation)

$$P(\ddot{y}_{i+1}) = f[t_{i+1}, P(y_{i+1}), P(\dot{y}_{i+1})] \quad \text{(c)}$$

(Corrector for $\dot{y}$)

$$C(\dot{y}_{i+1}) = \dot{y}_{i-1} + \frac{\Delta t}{3}[\ddot{y}_{i-1} + 4\ddot{y}_i + P(\ddot{y}_{i+1})] \quad \text{(d)} \quad \text{(6-97)}$$

(Iterating corrector for y)

$$C(y_{i+1}) = y_{i-1} + \frac{\Delta t}{3}[\dot{y}_{i-1} + 4\dot{y}_i + C(\dot{y}_{i+1})] \quad \text{(e)}$$

(Differential Equation)

$$C(\ddot{y}_{i+1}) = f[t_{i+1}, C(y_{i+1}), C(\dot{y}_{i+1})] \quad \text{(f)}$$

(Iterating corrector for $\dot{y}$)

$$C(\dot{y}_{i+1}) = \dot{y}_{i-1} + \frac{\Delta t}{3}[\ddot{y}_{i-1} + 4\ddot{y}_i + C(\ddot{y}_{i+1})] \quad \text{(g)}$$

The procedure would be the same as explained before, except that parts b and e of Eq. 6-97 would be introduced into the sequence. Equation 6-97b would provide a predicted value of y to substitute into the given differential equation, along with the appropriate value of time and the predicted $\dot{y}$ value, to obtain a predicted value for $\ddot{y}$. Equation 6-97e would provide a corrected value of y to be used in the iteration process involving Eq. 6-97e, f, and g. The iteration process would provide increasingly improved values of $\dot{y}$ and y until the desired accuracy was obtained. In programming the problem, it would not actually have been necessary to write Eq. 6-97g as a separate **FORTRAN** statement, since Eq. 6-97d could be programmed to perform the function of Eq. 6-97g in the iteration process of each step.

6-8. Hamming's Method

The various numerical methods for solving differential equations discussed thus far in this chapter have had different per-step errors, varying from order $(\Delta x)^2$ for Euler's method to order $(\Delta x)^5$ for Milne's method and the fourth-order Runge-Kutta method. The per-step error of a method is often referred to as a *local* error since it is an error introduced by the step in the integrating procedure. Roundoff error is also considered as a local error since it too is an error introduced by the step. However, the *total* error existing in the solution during any particular step (the difference between the true value at that point and the numerically calculated value) depends not only upon the magnitude of the local errors introduced by that step but also upon the propagation characteristics of local errors introduced in preceding steps, for local errors may tend to grow during subsequent steps, and, when a great many steps are involved in an integration, the total error may be appreciable.

In problems where the range of integration is considerable, the numerical method employed must be *stable* and/or *relatively stable* to obtain an accurate solution.[9] A numerical method is defined as stable if, in the process of integrating a differential equation such as

$$y' = f(x, y) \qquad (6\text{-}98)$$

where $\partial f/\partial y < 0$, the difference between the true solution and the numerical solution (the total error) tends to *decrease* in magnitude as the integration progresses. The stability of a method is not defined when considering the integration of a differential equation such as Eq. 6-98 where $\partial f/\partial y > 0$. The solution of such an equation will increase in an exponential manner, and the total error will generally increase in the same way. In solving

[9] Hamming, Richard W. *Numerical Methods for Scientists and Engineers.* New York: McGraw-Hill Book Company, 1962, p. 191. Ralston, Anthony, and Wilf, Herberts, eds. *Mathematical Methods for Digital Computers.* New York: John Wiley & Sons, Inc., 1960, p. 103.

such a differential equation over an extended range of integration, a method should be used which is *relatively stable*. A method is defined as relatively stable if the *rate of growth* of the total error during the process of integration is *less* than that of the solution. This may be expressed mathematically by stating that if the solution has the general form of

$$y = Ae^x$$

then the total error caused by the numerical method must be of the general form of

$$\epsilon = Be^{mx}$$

with $m < 1$ for the method to be considered relatively stable.

The relative stability of a method is also important when used to solve a differential equation such as Eq. 6-98 for which $\partial f/\partial y < 0$ if the solution approaches zero asymptotically, for, if an accurate solution is desired involving a value of y very close to zero, the *rate of diminution* of the total error must be *greater* than that of the solution. Expressed mathematically, if the solution has the form of

$$y = Ae^{-x}$$

then the total error caused by the method must be of the general form of

$$\epsilon = Be^{-mx}$$

with $m > 1$ for the method to be considered relatively stable.

Figure 6-33, accompanying the rocket problem of Example 6-5, provides the data necessary to plot a curve of $d\dot{y}/dt$ versus $\dot{y}$, as shown in Fig. 6-34. It can be seen, from this latter figure, that $\partial f/\partial\dot{y} < 0$ for most

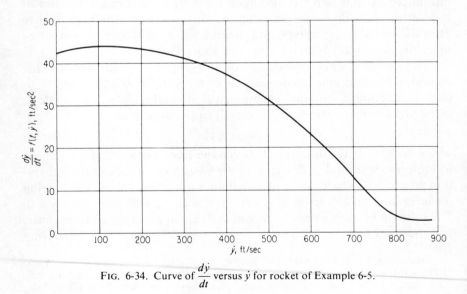

FIG. 6-34. Curve of $\dfrac{d\dot{y}}{dt}$ versus $\dot{y}$ for rocket of Example 6-5.

of the range of $\dot{y}$ under consideration. Therefore, if a stable numerical method is used to integrate

$$\frac{d\dot{y}}{dt} = f(\dot{y}, t)$$

there should be no danger of the total error growing to serious proportions, even though the integration might involve a large number of steps over an extended range of integration.

The curve of $\dot{y}$ versus y for the same problem is shown in Fig. 6-35. In this instance it can be seen that $\partial f / \partial y > 0$. Therefore, in the integration of

$$\dot{y} = f(y, t)$$

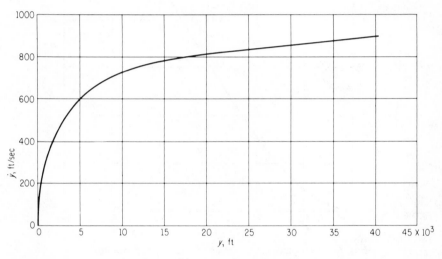

FIG. 6-35. Curve of $\dot{y}$ versus y for rocket of Example 6-5.

the stability of the method employed is not defined, as discussed previously. The solution y increases with time in a general exponential manner, as shown in Fig. 6-36. Here, the use of a relatively stable method will ensure that the rate of growth of the total error is no greater than the rate of growth of the solution, even though both grow in an exponential manner.

The propagation of errors during an integration is not a serious obstacle in the solution of many practical engineering problems. Since we are often not interested in solutions requiring extended ranges of integration, the use of relatively small Δx values will provide sufficiently accurate answers, regardless of the stability or relative-stability characteristics of the numerical method employed. For example, the solutions provided by Milne's method (which is neither stable nor relatively stable) in Example 6-5 agree very closely with the corresponding solutions

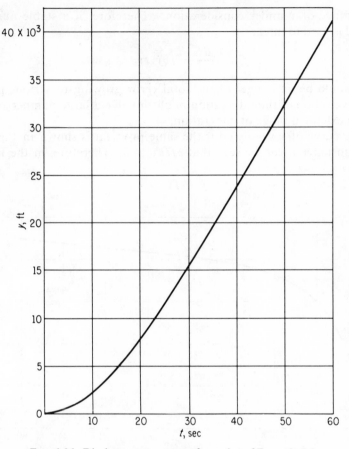

Fig. 6-36. Displacement y versus t for rocket of Example 6-5.

provided by Hamming's method (which is both stable and relatively stable) in Example 6-6 which appears later in this section. However, if solutions were desired over a much longer range of integration than is required in these examples, Milne's method would not provide the same degree of accuracy as would Hamming's method, because Milne's method is unstable, and the total error would grow to proportions capable of introducing serious error during the latter stages of the integration; the discrepancy between the solutions would become more and more pronounced as the range of integration was arbitrarily extended. In certain types of equations, such as Van der Pol's equation, for example, instability leads to serious errors in the solution, even over a relatively short range of integration (see Prob. 6-13).]

   Hamming's method, as mentioned above, is both stable and relatively stable. This method uses the same predictor equation as does Milne's method; that is,

$$P(y_{i+1}) = y_{i-3} + \frac{4(\Delta x)}{3}[2y_i' - y_{i-1}' + 2y_{i-2}'] \qquad (6\text{-}99)$$

where $P(y_{i+1})$, as before, indicates a predicted value of y_{i+1}. To derive Hamming's corrector equation, a generalized corrector equation of the form shown below is considered:

$$y_{i+1} = a_i y_i + a_{i-1} y_{i-1} + a_{i-2} y_{i-2} + (\Delta x)(b_{i+1} y_{i+1}' + b_i y_i' + b_{i-1} y_{i-1}') \qquad (6\text{-}100)$$

If appropriate Taylor-series expansions for y_{i-2}, y_{i-1}, y_{i+1}, y_{i-1}', and y_{i+1}' are substituted into Eq. 6-100, the following equation is obtained:

$$\left[y_i + y_i'(\Delta x) + \frac{y_i''(\Delta x)^2}{2!} + \frac{y_i'''(\Delta x)^3}{3!} + \frac{y_i''''(\Delta x)^4}{4!} + \cdots \right]$$

$$= a_i y_i + a_{i-1}\left[y_i + y_i'(-\Delta x) + \frac{y_i''(-\Delta x)^2}{2!} + \frac{y_i'''(-\Delta x)^3}{3!} \right.$$

$$\left. + \frac{y_i''''(-\Delta x)^4}{4!} + \cdots \right] + a_{i-2}\left[y_i + y_i'(-2\Delta x) \right.$$

$$\left. + \frac{y_i''(-2\Delta x)^2}{2!} + \frac{y_i'''(-2\Delta x)^3}{3!} + \frac{y_i''''(-2\Delta x)^4}{4!} + \cdots \right]$$

$$+ (\Delta x)b_{i+1}\left[y_i' + y_i''(\Delta x) + \frac{y_i'''(\Delta x)^2}{2!} + \frac{y_i''''(\Delta x)^3}{3!} + \cdots \right]$$

$$+ (\Delta x)b_i y_i' + (\Delta x)b_{i-1}\left[y_i' + y_i''(-\Delta x) \right.$$

$$\left. + \frac{y_i'''(-\Delta x)^2}{2!} + \frac{y_i''''(-\Delta x)^3}{3!} + \cdots \right] \qquad (6\text{-}101)$$

where the bracketed terms are the series expansions. Equating coefficients of y_i, y_i', y_i'', y_i''', and y_i'''', respectively, on each side of Eq. 6-101 yields the following relationships:

$$
\begin{array}{lllll}
a_i + & a_{i-1} + & a_{i-2} & = 1 & \text{(a)} \\[4pt]
- & a_{i-1} - 2a_{i-2} + & b_{i+1} + b_i + & b_{i-1} = 1 & \text{(b)} \\[4pt]
+ & \frac{1}{2}a_{i-1} + 2a_{i-2} + & b_{i+1} & - b_{i-1} = \frac{1}{2} & \text{(c)} \\[4pt]
- & \frac{1}{6}a_{i-1} - \frac{4}{3}a_{i-2} + \frac{1}{2}b_{i+1} & + \frac{1}{2}b_{i-1} = \frac{1}{6} & \text{(d)} \\[4pt]
+ & \frac{1}{24}a_{i-1} + \frac{2}{3}a_{i-2} + \frac{1}{6}b_{i+1} & - \frac{1}{6}b_{i-1} = \frac{1}{24} & \text{(e)}
\end{array}
\qquad (6\text{-}102)
$$

The 5 equations shown above contain 6 unknowns. A sixth equation necessary for determining the 6 unknowns could be obtained by adding 1 additional term to each of the Taylor-series expansions used in obtaining Eq. 6-102 and equating the coefficients of y_i'''''. However, Hamming[10] found that the use of $a_{i-1} = 0$ led to a corrector equation that was both stable and relatively stable when certain conditions were imposed upon the magnitude of Δx. Using a value of $a_{i-1} = 0$, the parts of Eq. 6-102 can be solved simultaneously to yield the following values:

$$a_i = \frac{9}{8} \qquad b_{i+1} = \frac{3}{8}$$

$$a_{i-2} = -\frac{1}{8} \qquad b_i = \frac{3}{4}$$

$$b_{i-1} = -\frac{3}{8}$$

Substituting these values into Eq. 6-100 yields Hamming's corrector equation

$$C(y_{i+1}) = \frac{1}{8}\left\{9y_i - y_{i-2} + 3(\Delta x)[P(y_{i+1}') + 2y_i' - y_{i-1}']\right\} \qquad (6\text{-}103)$$

where $C(y_{i+1})$ denotes a corrected value of y_{i+1}. Hamming's corrector equation is both stable and relatively stable for solving differential equations with $\partial f/\partial y < 0$ when

$$(\Delta x) < \frac{0.75}{\left|\dfrac{\partial f}{\partial y}\right|}$$

and the corrector equation is used to iterate to convergence. The corrector equation is relatively stable for solving differential equations in which $\partial f/\partial y > 0$ when

$$(\Delta x) < \frac{0.4}{\dfrac{\partial f}{\partial y}}$$

and the corrector equation is used to iterate to convergence. To keep the per-step error small, Δx would normally be less than either of the Δx values specified above. The per-step error of Hamming's method is of order $(\Delta x)^5$ which is of the same order as Milne's method.

One form of Hamming's method consists of using Eq. 6-99 as a predictor equation and then using the given differential equation in conjunction with Hamming's corrector equation (Eq. 6-103) to iterate to convergence, as was done in Milne's method. An alternate procedure, suggested by Hamming, saves iteration time on the computer. A study of the truncation errors of Eqs. 6-99 and 6-103 indicates that most of the error in the predicted value of y_{i+1} can be eliminated by the use of the following

[10]Hamming, Richard W. "Stable Predictor-Corrector Methods for Ordinary Differential Equations," *J. Assoc. Computing Machinery*, Vol. 6, No. 1 (1959), pp. 37–47.

modifier equation:

$$M(y_{i+1}) = P(y_{i+1}) - \frac{112}{121}[P(y_i) - C(y_i)] \qquad (6\text{-}104)$$

where $M(y_{i+1})$ indicates a modified value of y_{i+1} and the other symbols indicate predicted and corrected values, as before. This modified value of y_{i+1} is next substituted into the given differential equation to obtain a modified value of y'_{i+1} which is designated as $M(y'_{i+1})$. This modified value is then used in the corrector equation

$$C(y_{i+1}) = \frac{1}{8}\left\{9y_i - y_{i-2} + 3(\Delta x)[M(y'_{i+1}) + 2y'_i - y'_{i-1}]\right\} \qquad (6\text{-}105)$$

to obtain a corrected value of y_{i+1}, as shown. The study made of the truncation errors of Eqs. 6-99 and 6-103 also reveals that most of the error in the corrected value of y_{i+1} can be eliminated by using the equation

$$F(y_{i+1}) = C(y_{i+1}) + \frac{9}{121}[P(y_{i+1}) - C(y_{i+1})] \qquad (6\text{-}106)$$

where $F(y_{i+1})$ indicates the final value of y_{i+1}. Thus, in place of iterating the corrector equation to convergence at each step, Eqs. 6-99, 6-104, 6-105, and 6-106 are used just once (in that sequence) for each step. These equations are grouped here for the sake of convenience and are shown in the order in which they are used:

(Predictor)

$$P(y_{i+1}) = y_{i-3} + \frac{4(\Delta x)}{3}[2y'_i - y'_{i-1} + 2y'_{i-2}]$$

(Modifier)

$$M(y_{i+1}) = P(y_{i+1}) - \frac{112}{121}[P(y_i) - C(y_i)] \qquad (6\text{-}107)$$

(Corrector)

$$C(y_{i+1}) = \frac{1}{8}\left\{9y_i - y_{i-2} + 3(\Delta x)[M(y'_{i+1}) + 2y'_i - y'_{i-1}]\right\}$$

(Final value)

$$F(y_{i+1}) = C(y_{i+1}) + \frac{9}{121}[P(y_{i+1}) - C(y_{i+1})]$$

When the procedure involving Eq. 6-107 is employed instead of the iteration procedure, a different condition must be imposed upon the magnitude of Δx to ensure stability and relative stability. In this case (with $\partial f/\partial y < 0$) the condition is

$$(\Delta x) < \frac{0.65}{\left|\dfrac{\partial f}{\partial y}\right|}$$

Hamming's method, as well as other predictor-corrector methods, can be further refined to save machine time by varying the magnitude of Δx during the progress of the integration. A change in the magnitude of Δx is dictated by the relationship existing between the magnitudes of the predicted and corrected values of y_{i+1} calculated. If $[P(y_{i+1}) - C(y_{i+1})]$ is less than some prescribed value, Δx is doubled; if the same expression is larger than some other prescribed value, Δx is halved. For a further discussion of adjusting step size, based on a truncation-error analysis at each step, see Sec. 6-9.

EXAMPLE 6-6

Let us use Hamming's method, to solve the rocket problem of Example 6-5. The reader should reread the first three paragraphs of Example 6-5 for a discussion of the problem and the assumptions involved in deriving the following differential equation of motion of the rocket:

$$\ddot{y} = \frac{gT}{W} - g - \frac{K\dot{y}^2 g}{W} \tag{6-108}$$

where

y = displacement of rocket, ft

$\dot{y}$ = velocity of rocket, ft/sec

$\ddot{y}$ = acceleration of rocket, ft/sec^2

T = thrust force, 7000 lb

W = total weight of rocket, fuel, and equipment at time t, $(3000 - 40t)$ lb

K = coefficient of aerodynamic resistance, 0.008 lb-sec^2/ft^2

g = acceleration of gravity, 32.17 ft/sec^2

The initial conditions of the problem, as before, are

$$t = 0 \begin{vmatrix} y = 0 \\ \dot{y} = 0 \end{vmatrix}$$

The same starting values used in solving the problem by Milne's method are required here. They are repeated for convenience:

$y_0 = 0.0$ ft　　　$\dot{y}_0 = 0.0$ ft/sec

$y_1 = 0.2146$ ft　　　$\dot{y}_1 = 4.294$ ft/sec　　　$\ddot{y}_1 = 42.99$ ft/sec^2

$y_2 = 0.8591$ ft　　　$\dot{y}_2 = 8.598$ ft/sec　　　$\ddot{y}_2 = 43.08$ ft/sec^2

$y_3 = 1.935$ ft　　　$\dot{y}_3 = 12.911$ ft/sec　　　$\ddot{y}_3 = 43.18$ ft/sec^2

In using Hamming's noniterative method to solve a second-order differential equation such as Eq. 6-108 in which y is not present in explicit form, we use Eq. 6-107 in the following form:

(Predictor)
$$P(\dot{y}_{i+1}) = \dot{y}_{i-3} + \frac{4(\Delta t)}{3} [2\ddot{y}_i - \ddot{y}_{i-1} + 2\ddot{y}_{i-2}] \tag{a}$$

(Modifier)
$$M(\dot{y}_{i+1}) = P(\dot{y}_{i+1}) - \frac{112}{121} [P(\dot{y}_i) - C(\dot{y}_i)] \tag{b}$$

(Differential equation)
$$M(\ddot{y}_{i+1}) = f[t_{i+1}, M(\dot{y}_{i+1})] \tag{c}$$

(Corrector)   (6-109)
$$C(\dot{y}_{i+1}) = \frac{1}{8} \left\{ 9\dot{y}_i - \dot{y}_{i-2} + 3(\Delta t)[M(\ddot{y}_{i+1}) + 2\ddot{y}_i - \ddot{y}_{i-1}] \right\} \tag{d}$$

(Final value of $\dot{y}$)
$$F(\dot{y}_{i+1}) = C(\dot{y}_{i+1}) + \frac{9}{121} [P(\dot{y}_{i+1}) - C(\dot{y}_{i+1})] \tag{e}$$

(Final value of $\ddot{y}$)
$$F(\ddot{y}_{i+1}) = f[t_{i+1}, F(\dot{y}_{i+1})] \tag{f}$$

where Eq. 6-109c indicates the substitution of the modified value of $\dot{y}_{i+1}$ and the corresponding time value into the given differential equation to obtain the modified value of $\ddot{y}_{i+1}$ required in Eq. 6-109d. Since y does not appear explicitly in the differential equation being solved, y_{i+1} values are not required in determining $M(\ddot{y}_{i+1})$ values. Thus, final $\dot{y}_{i+1}$ values can be obtained without determining the corresponding y_{i+1} values. If displacement values are desired, they may be determined from Hamming's corrector equation as the final step in each cycle of calculation. This equation is

$$y_{i+1} = \frac{1}{8} \left\{ 9y_i - y_{i-2} + 3(\Delta t)[F(\dot{y}_{i+1}) + 2\dot{y}_i - \dot{y}_{i-1}] \right\} \tag{6-110}$$

where the final value of $\dot{y}_{i+1}$ is used in place of the modified value to obtain the most accurate value of y_{i+1} possible. It may be noted, in the program which follows, that in the *first cycle* of Eq. 6-109 the starting value of $\dot{y}_i$ is used for both $P(\dot{y}_i)$ and $C(\dot{y}_i)$ in Eq. 6-109b.

If the differential equation to be solved contains y in explicit form, Eqs. 6-109 and 6-110 are not sufficient for obtaining a solution. A brief discussion of this case, with the necessary equations, is given at the conclusion of this example.

A computer solution of Eq. 6-108 designed to yield the data necessary to plot curves of the displacement, velocity, and acceleration of the rocket is outlined in the flow chart shown in Fig. 6-37. Note that the previously determined starting values are read in as data and that Hamming's method utilizing Eqs. 6-109 and 6-110 is the method programmed. The variable names used in the program are as follows:

FORTRAN *Name*	*Quantity*	*Value Used*
W1	Initial weight of rocket, fuel, and equipment	3000 lb

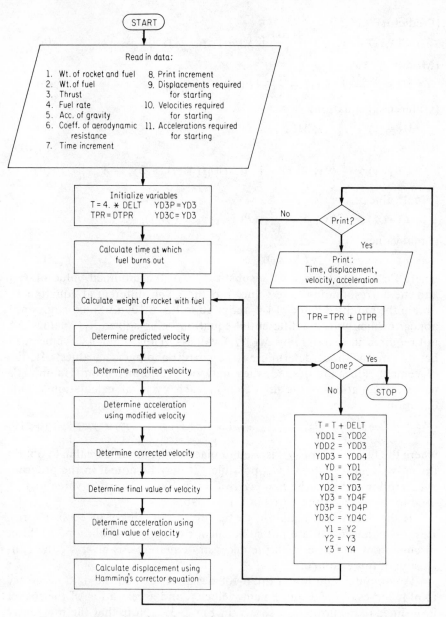

FIG. 6-37. Flow chart for solution of rocket problem by Hamming's method.

FORTRAN *Name*	*Quantity*	*Value Used*
WF	Initial weight of fuel	2400 lb
TH	Thrust	7000 lb
FR	Rate of fuel consumption	40 lb/sec
G	Acceleration of gravity	32.17 ft/sec^2
DK	Coefficient of aerodynamic resistance	0.008 lb-sec^2/ft^2
DELT	Time increment	0.1 sec
DTPR	Print increment	2.0 sec
Y,Y1,Y2,Y3	Successive values of displacement	(See starting values)
YD, YD1,YD2,YD3	Successive values of velocity	(See starting values)
YDD1,YDD2,YDD3	Successive values of acceleration	(See starting values)
T	Time, sec	
TMAX	Time at which fuel burnout occurs	
TPR	Time at which printout occurs, sec	
YD4P	Predicted value of $\dot{y}$ at time considered, ft/sec	
YD4M	Modified value of $\dot{y}$ at time considered, ft/sec	
W	Weight of rocket, fuel, and equipment at time t, lb	
YD4C	Corrected value of $\dot{y}$ at time considered, ft/sec	
YD4F	Final value of $\dot{y}$ at time considered, ft/sec	
YDD4	Acceleration at time considered, ft/sec^2	
Y4	Displacement at time considered, ft	
YD3P	Predicted value of $\dot{y}$ 1 time increment preceding time considered, ft/sec	
YD3C	Corrected value of $\dot{y}$ 1 time increment preceding time considered, ft/sec	

The computer program used is as follows:

```
C     DYNAMIC CHARACTERISTICS OF A ROCKET
C     NUMERICAL INTEGRATION BY HAMMING METHOD
      READ(5,1)W1,WF,TH,FR,G,DK,DELT,DTPR
    1 FORMAT(11F5.0)
      READ(5,1)Y,Y1,Y2,Y3,YD,YD1,YD2,YD3,YDD1,YDD2,YDD3
      WRITE(6,2)
    2 FORMAT(1H1,5X,1HW,8X,1HF,7X,2HTH,7X,1HR,7X,1HG,7X,
                                      1HK,5X,2HDT,4X,3HDTP/)
      WRITE(6,3)W1,WF,TH,FR,G,DK,DELT,DTPR
    3 FORMAT(2F9.1,F8.0,2F8.2,F8.4,2F6.2///)
      WRITE(6,4)
    4 FORMAT(7H     TIME,6X,6HDISPL.,6X,4HVEL.,7X,4HACC./)
      T = 4.*DELT
      TMAX = WF/FR
      TPR = DTPR
      YD3P = YD3
      YD3C = YD3
    5 W = W1-FR*T
      YD4P=YD+4./3.*(2.*YDD1-YDD2+2.*YDD3)*DELT
      YD4M=YD4P-112./121.*(YD3P-YD3C)
      YDD4=G*TH/W-G-DK*G/W*(YD4M**2)
      YD4C=.125*(9.*YD3-YD1+3.*DELT*(YDD4+2.*YDD3-YDD2))
      YD4F=YD4C+9./121.*(YD4P-YD4C)
      YDD4=G*TH/W-G-DK*G/W*(YD4F**2)
      Y4=.125*(9.*Y3-Y1+3.*DELT*(YD4F+2.*YD3-YD2))
      IF(T-TPR)8,6,6
    6 WRITE(6,7)T,Y4,YD4F,YDD4
    7 FORMAT(1H ,F7.2,F12.2,F11.2,F10.2)
      TPR = TPR + DTPR
    8 IF(T-TMAX)10,9,9
    9 STOP
   10 T=T+DELT
      YDD1=YDD2
      YDD2=YDD3
      YDD3=YDD4
      YD=YD1
      YD1=YD2
      YD2=YD3
      YD3=YD4F
      YD3P=YD4P
      YD3C=YD4C
      Y1=Y2
```

        Y2 = Y3
        Y3 = Y4
        GO TO 5
        END

The computer results are shown in the following tabular form:

W	F	TH	R	G	K	DT	DTP
3000.0	2400.0	7000.	40.00	32.17	.0080	.10	2.00

TIME	DISPL.	VEL.	ACC.
2.00	86.91	87.38	44.27
4.00	350.49	176.20	44.30
6.00	790.82	263.67	42.93
8.00	1402.48	347.09	40.28
10.00	2174.94	424.15	36.63
12.00	3093.73	493.20	32.34
14.00	4141.83	553.38	27.82
16.00	5301.25	604.55	23.39
18.00	6554.36	647.19	19.31
20.00	7884.91	682.16	15.75
22.00	9278.65	710.57	12.75
24.00	10723.60	733.57	10.32
26.00	12210.04	752.24	8.42
28.00	13730.30	767.55	6.96
30.00	15278.53	780.33	5.87
32.00	16850.34	791.24	5.07
34.00	18442.54	800.79	4.50
36.00	20052.82	809.38	4.10
38.00	21679.57	817.30	3.82
40.00	23321.67	824.75	3.63
42.00	24978.33	831.88	3.50
44.00	26649.01	838.79	3.40
46.00	28333.33	845.54	3.34
48.00	30031.04	852.16	3.29
50.00	31741.89	858.70	3.24
52.00	33465.74	865.16	3.21
54.00	35202.45	871.56	3.18
56.00	36951.88	877.89	3.15
58.00	38713.92	884.16	3.12
60.00	40488.45	890.38	3.09

A comparison of the results shown with those obtained by Milne's method in Example 6-5 reveals that they are nearly identical. As explained previously, the results obtained by these methods are very similar when the range of integration required is not extended and the stability or relative stability of the numerical method employed is not a critical factor in obtaining an accurate solution.

As stated before, Eq. 6-109 must be modified to obtain the solution of a second-order differential equation if y appears in explicit form in the equation. The following equations, shown in correct sequence, would then be applicable:

(Predictor for $\dot{y}$)

$$P(\dot{y}_{i+1}) = \dot{y}_{i-3} + \frac{4(\Delta t)}{3} [2\ddot{y}_i - \ddot{y}_{i-1} + 2\ddot{y}_{i-2}] \qquad (a)$$

(Modifier for $\dot{y}$)

$$M(\dot{y}_{i+1}) = P(\dot{y}_{i+1}) - \frac{112}{121} [P(\dot{y}_i) - C(\dot{y}_i)] \qquad (b)$$

(Predictor for y)

$$P(y_{i+1}) = \frac{1}{8} \left\{ 9y_i - y_{i-2} + 3(\Delta t)[M(\dot{y}_{i+1}) + 2\dot{y}_i - \dot{y}_{i-1}] \right\} \qquad (c)$$

(Differential equation) $(6\text{-}111)$

$$M(\ddot{y}_{i+1}) = f[t_{i+1}, P(y_{i+1}), M(\dot{y}_{i+1})] \qquad (d)$$

(Corrector for $\dot{y}$)

$$C(\dot{y}_{i+1}) = \frac{1}{8} \left\{ 9\dot{y}_i - \dot{y}_{i-2} + 3(\Delta t)[M(\ddot{y}_{i+1}) + 2\ddot{y}_i - \ddot{y}_{i-1}] \right\} \qquad (e)$$

(Final value of $\dot{y}$)

$$F(\dot{y}_{i+1}) = C(\dot{y}_{i+1}) + \frac{9}{121} [P(\dot{y}_{i+1}) - C(\dot{y}_{i+1})] \qquad (f)$$

(Final value of y)

$$F(y_{i+1}) = \frac{1}{8} \left\{ 9y_i - y_{i-2} + 3(\Delta t)[F(\dot{y}_{i+1}) + 2\dot{y}_i - \dot{y}_{i-1}] \right\} \qquad (g)$$

(Final value of $\ddot{y}$)

$$F(\ddot{y}_{i+1}) = f[t_{i+1}, F(y_{i+1}), F(\dot{y}_{i+1})] \qquad (h)$$

Note that Eq. 6-111c, which is used as a predictor equation for y_{i+1}, is Hamming's corrector equation. An equation of the form of Eq. 6-111a could be used to obtain this predicted value, but, since $M(\dot{y}_{i+1})$ is known at this point, Eq. 6-111c can be used to obtain a better predicted value. Equation 6-111c provides a y_{i+1} value to substitute into the given differential equation in obtaining a modified value of $\ddot{y}_{i+1}$, as indicated by Eq. 6-111d. The final value of y_{i+1} is again determined by Hamming's corrector equation, as discussed in explaining Eq. 6-110.

6-9. Error Analysis of Numerical Methods for Solving Differential Equations

The use of numerical methods for solving differential equations generally yields "solutions" which differ from the true solutions. The difference between the numerical solution and the true solution, at any given step, is known as the *total* error at that step. If the numerical solution is to be of practical value, the total error obviously must be kept within reasonable limits over the desired solution interval. The primary purpose of error analysis is to provide a means of controlling this error. The total error at any step results from the following conditions:

1. A roundoff error is introduced in the integration process at a given step by performing the arithmetic operations of that step with numerical values having a limited number of significant digits. This is known as *per-step roundoff error.*

2. A truncation error is introduced in the integration process at a given step by the use of approximate formulas in the calculations of that step. For example, the corrector formula of Euler's modified method has a truncation error of order $(\Delta x)^3$, which means that series terms containing $(\Delta x)^3$ and higher powers are neglected in using a trapezoidal area to approximate the true area of 1 strip under the curve of the function being integrated. This is known as *per-step truncation error.*

3. An error is present at a given step because of errors introduced in preceding steps.

With perhaps 8 significant digits used in the calculations, the roundoff error introduced at each step for any of the integration methods we have discussed is very small. However, if an *unstable* method is used and if the integration involves a large number of steps, the cumulative effect of the per-step roundoff errors and their magnification in calculating subsequent steps can lead to serious total error. The use of double-precision arithmetic, which is possible on most computers, is an effective means of controlling total error due to roundoff.

Obviously, the truncation error at each step is minimum in methods which employ formulas having truncation errors of high order. This error can be reduced, in any method, by reducing the step size. However, in reducing the per-step truncation error by decreasing the step size, a limit is reached at which further reduction in step size increases the total number of steps to a point where roundoff error becomes dominant, and the total error will increase with further reduction in step size. As with roundoff error, the cumulative effect of small per-step truncation errors and their magnification in calculating subsequent steps can lead to serious total error. The use of a *stable* method such as Hamming's, under certain conditions, ensures that an error introduced at a particular step will not be magnified in subsequent ones. Although unstable methods give no such guarantee, we have seen that they can be used quite satisfactorily if an excessive number of steps is not required.

Since the total error in a numerical-integration process depends on the step size used, the analyst is faced with the problem of selecting a step size to maintain the total error less than some specified bound. On the other hand, there is no point in making the solution more accurate than the data justify by choosing too small a step size, since this unnecessarily uses expensive machine time. Furthermore, as previously stated, there is a limit to the increase in accuracy which can be obtained by decreasing the step size, owing to the presence of roundoff error. On what basis, then, can the step size be selected? To answer this question let us further examine, with respect to step size, the effect of each of the per-step errors discussed on the total error.

Roundoff error is generally present to some degree in each step of a numerical-integration process. Since its magnitude in each step depends primarily upon the digital capacity of the computer being used, the per-step roundoff error is essentially independent of the step size used. The total error due to roundoff increases with the number of steps.

Truncation error also appears in each step of the numerical process. Unlike roundoff error, the per-step truncation error is a function of the step size, since it varies as the order of error, $(\Delta x)^n$, of the method being used. Thus, the only means of controlling the overall per-step error of a method at a given step is by controlling the truncation error at that step. The total error is decreased as the per-step truncation error is decreased up to the point where the increasing number of steps and the presence of roundoff error causes an increase in the total error. Thus, the total error can be kept to a minimum by maintaining the per-step truncation error within some appropriate limiting values or bounds. However, bounds are not always selected on the basis of optimum accuracy; they may be chosen to minimize the machine time required for a solution. This would be true in a case where the optimum accuracy would exceed the justifiable accuracy, as previously mentioned.

In initially selecting a step size for a method, the per-step truncation error, which, it is felt, can be tolerated with respect to the number of steps anticipated in the process, is defined by a set of limiting values as discussed in the preceding paragraph. The best possible estimate is then made of the general magnitude of the derivative function appearing in the truncation-error term of the method, and a step size is calculating to make the per-step truncation error fall within the defined limits. After some experience with different methods for various types of problems, the initial step size can usually be selected with little difficulty.

If the derivative in the truncation-error term of a method is of high order, an estimate of its value may be difficult to determine, and the initial step size chosen may need to be adjusted on the basis of results obtained in the numerical process. A truncation-error analysis can often be made at each step of a numerical process, and the results can be used to adjust the step size at that point, if necessary, for subsequent calculations. Such per-step truncation-error analyses will be discussed subsequently for each of the integration methods considered in this chapter.

Euler's Method.   Euler's formula is simply a truncated Taylor series in which terms containing $(\Delta x)^2$ and higher powers are neglected.   The Taylor series for y_{i+1} expanded about x_i with the Lagrangian form of the remainder is

$$y_{i+1} = y_i + y_i'h + \frac{y''(\xi)h^2}{2}, \quad \begin{Bmatrix} x_i < \xi < x_{i+1} \\ h = \Delta x \end{Bmatrix} \tag{6-112}$$

The last term of Eq. 6-112 is the *truncation-error term* of Euler's method. Assuming that y'' is fairly constant over the ith-step interval, so that the higher-derivative terms are negligible, an estimate of the truncation error E_T in the ith step can be obtained from

$$E_T \cong \frac{y_i''h^2}{2} \tag{6-113}$$

where y'' is evaluated at $\xi = x_i$. If a truncation-error analysis is made at each step, Eq. 6-113 may be used to estimate the truncation error at each step for comparison with some selected set of limiting values. If the estimate exceeds the bound of the maximum specified error, the step size can be reduced and the numerical process continued. On the other hand, if the estimate is smaller than the minimum limit, the step size can be increased and the numerical process continued. In either case the final value of y, calculated by using the old step size, is used as the initial value of y for the subsequent interval of integration using the new step size.

Our *estimate* of the per-step truncation error of Euler's method (a first-order method) was obtained from the remainder term of a Taylor series expressed in Lagrangian form. Estimates of the per-step truncation error of other methods can be determined from similar Taylor-series remainder terms, as will be seen subsequently. In Euler's method the remainder term appears as a matter of course, since Euler's formula is a truncated Taylor series. However, in many integration methods the pertinent formulas are not in Taylor-series form, and must be placed in such form to obtain an estimate of their per-step truncation errors. Such transformations will be illustrated later.

We recall that the per-step truncation error of Euler's method, given by Eq. 6-113, is only an *estimate* of the *true* per-step truncation error. By definition, the true truncation error of the ith step of an integration method is the truncation error that would appear in calculating the ith step *if* the solution were exact up to the ith step. With this definition, the per-step truncation error for the ith step of an rth-order method can be expressed as

$$E_T = \frac{y^{r+1}(\xi)h^{r+1}}{(r + 1)!}, \quad x_i < \xi < x_{i+1}$$

where y^{r+1} is the $(r + 1)$th derivative of y.

In an instance in which the differentiation of

$$y' = f(x, y) \tag{6-114}$$

to obtain y'' for use in estimating the per-step truncation error of Euler's method leads to a rather complicated function, a more practical approach can be made by using a constant step size h to obtain a solution, and then obtaining another solution using a smaller step size, say $h/2$. If the 2 solutions yield results which are in good agreement throughout—to 4 figures, for example—it is fairly safe to assume that both are reasonably accurate to 4 figures, and that the one with the smaller step size has greater than 4-figure accuracy. If the 2 solutions are not in good agreement throughout, one using a still smaller step size should be obtained for comparison with the solution obtained with the next higher step size, and so forth. If the initial step size chosen happened to be too small, so that roundoff error dominated, it would be necessary to follow the above procedure, but increase the step size each time. The programmer who does not wish to complicate his program by incorporating a variable step size over the range of integration will find the procedure just discussed a practical means of checking the accuracy of a solution obtained by any of the integration methods described in this chapter.

Euler's Modified Methods. The corrector equation of Euler's modified methods is based upon approximating the area of 1 incremental strip, under the graph of the function being integrated, by the area in a trapezoidal strip of the same incremental width.

To investigate the error introduced by such an approximation, let us assume that we are integrating the differential equation

$$y' = g[x, y(x)] \tag{6-115}$$

with the initial condition of $y = 0$ at $x = a$. Since y is a function of x, y' is actually some unknown function of x alone, which we shall call $f(x)$. We shall assume that the graphs of $f(x)$ and y appear as shown in Fig. 6-38.

We can obtain an estimate of the per-step truncation error of the corrector equation by determining an exact expression for the area in the strip between x_i and x_{i+1} (the crosshatched area in Fig. 6-38) and then comparing this expression with the expression approximating the exact area (the shaded trapezoidal area in the figure) used in Euler's modified methods.

The area under the graph of $f(x)$ from $x = a$ to any x value is a function of x and is equal to the y value at that value of x. That is,

$$y(x) = \int_a^x f(x)\, dx$$

from which

$$y_i' = f_i$$
$$y_i'' = f_i' \tag{6-116}$$
$$\vdots \qquad \vdots$$

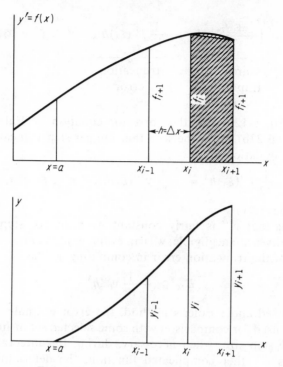

FIG. 6-38. Assumed curves for y and $f(x)$.

Now let us write the Taylor-series expansion for y_{i+1} expanded about x_i with the Lagrangian form of the remainder. It is

$$y_{i+1} = y_i + y_i'h + \frac{y_i''h^2}{2!} + \frac{y'''(\xi_1)h^3}{3!}, \qquad x_i < \xi_1 < x_{i+1} \qquad (6\text{-}117)$$

Combining Eqs. 6-116 and 6-117, we can express the exact (crosshatched) area as

$$(y_{i+1} - y_i) = f_i h + \frac{f_i'h^2}{2!} + \frac{f''(\xi_1)h^3}{3!} \qquad (6\text{-}118)$$

The Taylor series for f_{i+1} expanded about x_i is

$$f_{i+1} = f_i + f_i'h + \frac{f''(\xi_2)h^2}{2}, \qquad x_i < \xi_2 < x_{i+1}$$

from which

$$f_i'h = f_{i+1} - f_i - \frac{f''(\xi_2)h^2}{2!} \qquad (6\text{-}119)$$

Substituting Eq. 6-119 into Eq. 6-118 yields

$$(y_{i+1} - y_i) = f_i h + \frac{\left[f_{i+1} - f_i - \dfrac{f''(\xi_2)h^2}{2!} \right]h}{2!} + \frac{f''(\xi_1)h^3}{3!}$$

or

$$(y_{i+1} - y_i) = \underbrace{\left(\frac{f_i + f_{i+1}}{2}\right)h}_{\substack{\text{area of} \\ \text{trapezoidal} \\ \text{strip}}} - \underbrace{\frac{1}{12}f''(\xi_3)h^3}_{\substack{\text{truncation} \\ \text{error}}}, \quad x_i < \xi_3 < x_{i+1} \qquad (6\text{-}120)$$

Comparing Eq. 6-120 with the corrector equation of Euler's modified methods (Eq. 6-23b), it can be seen that the per-step truncation error of the corrector equation is

$$E_{TC} = -\frac{1}{12}f''(\xi_3)h^3 = -\frac{1}{12}y'''(\xi_3)h^3, \quad x_i < \xi_3 < x_{i+1} \qquad (6\text{-}121)$$

and is of order $(\Delta x)^3$.

Assuming that y''' is fairly constant over the ith step so that the higher derivatives are negligible, we can evaluate y''' at $\xi_3 = x_i$ and obtain an estimate of the truncation error in computing y_{i+1} as

$$E_{TC} \cong -\frac{1}{12}y_i'''h^3 \qquad (6\text{-}122)$$

As discussed under Euler's method, the error estimate given by Eq. 6-122 can be used for comparison with some selected set of limiting values to adjust the step size, when necessary, during the integration process.

If y''' is a rather complicated function, the determination of the truncation error at each step may become quite cumbersome if one uses the method just described. One alternative method of obtaining a solution having some desired degree of accuracy is to run separate solutions, each with a different step size, and compare the solutions obtained, decreasing (or possibly increasing) the step size at each run until consecutive solutions are in good agreement.

Another alternative is to base adjustment of the step size on a truncation-error estimate by Richardson's method,[11] in which 2 solutions, each with a different step size, are run simultaneously. A truncation-error estimate is obtained at each step in terms of the two y values obtained at that step. To develop this way of estimating the per-step truncation error for an rth-order method, consider that

$C_1(h)^{r+1}$ = the per-step truncation error in an rth-order method (a method having a per-step truncation error of order $r + 1$) using a step size of h

$C_2\left(\dfrac{h}{2}\right)^{r+1}$ = the per-step truncation error in the same rth-order method using a step size of $h/2$[12]

[11]Richardson, L. F., and Gaunt, J. A. "The Deferred Approach to the Limit," *Trans. Roy. Soc. London*, Vol. 226A (1927), p. 300.

[12] $C_1 = \dfrac{y^{r+1}(\xi_1)}{(r + 1)!} \quad C_2 = \dfrac{y^{r+1}(\xi_2)}{(r + 1)!} \quad \begin{aligned} x_i &< \xi_1 < x_{i+1} \\ x_i &< \xi_2 < x_{i+\frac{1}{2}} \end{aligned}$

$y^{(1)}$ = the y value obtained at x_{i+1} using a step size of h in step-ping forward from x_i

$y^{(2)}$ = the y value obtained at x_{i+1} using 2 steps of size $h/2$ in stepping forward from x_i

Y = the true value of y at x_{i+1}

Isolating the truncation error of the step from the effects of previous error in the solution, in accordance with the definition given for per-step truncation error, and assuming that roundoff error in the step calcula-tions is negligible, we can write

$$Y - y^{(1)} = C_1(h)^{r+1} \tag{6-123}$$

$$Y - y^{(2)} \simeq 2C_2\left(\frac{h}{2}\right)^{r+1} \tag{6-124}$$

If the derivative y^{r+1} is fairly constant over the interval h, we may assume that $C_1 \simeq C_2$. Subtracting Eq. 6-124 from Eq. 6-123 yields

$$\frac{y^{(2)} - y^{(1)}}{2^r - 1} \simeq 2C_2\left(\frac{h}{2}\right)^{r+1} \tag{6-125}$$

Comparing Eqs. 6-125 and 6-124, it can be seen that the approximate truncation error in obtaining y at x_{i+1}, using 2 steps of size $h/2$ in stepping forward from x_i is given by

$$E_T \simeq \frac{y^{(2)} - y^{(1)}}{2^r - 1} \tag{6-126}$$

For Euler's modified methods ($r = 2$), Eq. 6-126 becomes

$$E_T \simeq \frac{y^{(2)} - y^{(1)}}{3} \tag{6-127}$$

An estimate of the per-step truncation error in the corrector equation of some predictor-corrector methods can also be determined, at each step, in terms of the predicted y value and the final corrected y value. When both the predictor equation and the corrector equation of a method have the same order of truncation error, it is relatively easy to obtain a truncation-error estimate at each step, in such terms, since the estimate can essentially be obtained as the by-product of calculations required in the predictor-corrector process.

In case of Euler's self-starting modified method, the predictor equa-tion has a truncation error of order $(\Delta x)^2$ (Eq. 6-113) whereas the corrector equation has a truncation error of order $(\Delta x)^3$ (Eq. 6-121). A truncation-error estimate at each step in terms of the predicted y value and final corrected y value is not possible. When an error estimate is to be made at each step in terms of these quantities, Euler's non-self-starting modified method should be used since, as we shall see, the predictor and corrector equations have truncation errors of the same order.

As described in Sec. 6-4, Euler's non-self-starting modified method uses the following equations:

(Predictor)
$$P(y_{i+1}) = y_{i-1} + 2y_i'h \qquad \text{(a)}$$

(Differential equation)
$$P(y_{i+1}') = f[x_{i+1}, P(y_{i+1})] \qquad \text{(b)} \qquad \text{(6-128)}$$

(Corrector)
$$C(y_{i+1}) = y_i + \frac{h}{2}[y_i' + P(y_{i+1}')] \qquad \text{(c)}$$

We shall next develop the technique for estimating the per-step truncation error of this method in terms of the predicted and final corrected values of y at each step. Examining first the per-step truncation error in the predictor equation, we expand y_{i+1} in a Taylor series about x_i to obtain

$$y_{i+1} = y_i + y_i'h + \frac{y_i''h^2}{2!} + \frac{y'''(\xi_1)h^3}{3!}, \quad x_i < \xi_1 < x_{i+1} \qquad (6\text{-}129)$$

Similarly, expanding y_{i-1} about x_i yields

$$y_{i-1} = y_i - y_i'h + \frac{y_i''h^2}{2!} - \frac{y'''(\xi_2)h^3}{3!}, \quad x_{i-1} < \xi_2 < x_i \qquad (6\text{-}130)$$

Subtracting Eq. 6-130 from Eq. 6-129 gives

$$y_{i+1} - y_{i-1} = 2y_i'h + \frac{2y'''(\xi_3)h^3}{3!}, \quad x_{i-1} < \xi_3 < x_{i+1} \qquad (6\text{-}131)$$

Comparing Eq. 6-131 with Eq. 6-128a, we can write Eq. 6-131 as

$$\underbrace{y_{i+1} = y_{i-1} + 2y_i'h}_{\substack{\text{predictor} \\ \text{equation}}} + \underbrace{\frac{2y'''(\xi_3)h^3}{3!}}_{\substack{\text{truncation} \\ \text{error}}} \qquad (6\text{-}132)$$

to see that the per-step truncation error of the predictor equation

$$E_{TP} = \frac{y'''(\xi_3)h^3}{3} \qquad (6\text{-}133)$$

is of order $(\Delta x)^3$. This is of the same order as the per-step truncation error of the corrector equation given by Eq. 6-121.

Knowing the per-step truncation errors of both the predictor and the corrector equations, consider that

$P\left(\dfrac{1}{y}\right)$ = the predicted y value obtained at x_{i+1} in the integration process in the first and only application of the predictor equation at that step

$C\left(\dfrac{n}{y}\right)$ = the corrected y value obtained at x_{i+1} in the nth (final) application of the corrector equation at that step

Y = the true value of y at x_{i+1}

Isolating the truncation error of the ith step from the effects of previous errors, in accordance with the definition given of per-step truncation error, and assuming that roundoff error is negligible in the calculations of the step, we can write

$$\text{(Predictor)} \qquad Y = P\binom{1}{y} + \frac{1}{3}y'''(\xi_3)h^3, \qquad x_{i-1} < \xi_3 < x_{i+1} \qquad \text{(6-134)}$$

$$\text{(Corrector)} \qquad Y = C\binom{n}{y} - \frac{1}{12}y'''(\eta)h^3, \qquad x_i < \eta < x_{i+1} \qquad \text{(6-135)}$$

Subtracting Eq. 6-134 from Eq. 6-135, we obtain

$$0 = C\binom{n}{y} - P\binom{1}{y} - \frac{5}{12}y'''(\eta_1)h^3, \qquad x_{i-1} < \eta_1 < x_{i+1} \qquad \text{(6-136)}$$

Comparing Eqs. 6-136 and 6-121, we can write an estimate of the per-step truncation error of the corrector equation, in terms of the predicted y value and the final corrected y value, as

$$E_{TC} \cong -\frac{1}{5}\left[C\binom{n}{y} - P\binom{1}{y}\right] \qquad \text{(6-137)}$$

Milne's Method.   This method is also a predictor-corrector type, and we shall be interested in a means of estimating its per-step truncation error. To investigate this error, let us again assume that we are integrating the differential equation

$$y' = g[x, y(x)] \qquad \text{(6-138)}$$

with the initial condition of $y = 0$ at $x = a$. Since y is a function of x, y' is actually some unknown function of x alone, which we shall call $f(x)$. We shall further assume that the graphs of $f(x)$ and y appear in the general form given in Fig. 6-39.

In Milne's method the approximate area under the $f(x)$ curve from x_{i-3} to x_{i+1} (the shaded area of Fig. 6-39) is added to y_{i-3} to obtain a predicted value of y_{i+1}. To determine an estimate of the per-step truncation error in the predictor equation, we obtain an exact expression for the area in the 4 strips (the crosshatched area in Fig. 6-39) and compare this expression with the expression for the approximate area used in the predictor equation.

The area under the graph of $f(x)$ from $x = a$ to any x value in Fig. 6-39 is a function of x and is equal to the value of y at the x value. That is,

$$y(x) = \int_a^x f(x)\,dx$$

from which

$$y_i' = f_i$$
$$y_i'' = f_i'$$
$$\vdots \qquad \vdots \qquad \text{(6-139)}$$

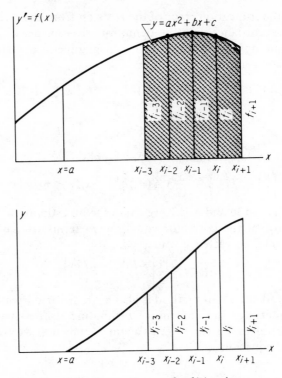

FIG. 6-39. Assumed curves for $f(x)$ and y.

To determine an exact expression for the area of the 4 strips shown in Fig. 6-39, we first expand y_{i+1} in a Taylor series about x_{i-1}. This expansion is

$$y_{i+1} = y_{i-1} + y'_{i-1}(2h) + \frac{y''_{i-1}(2h)^2}{2!} + \frac{y'''_{i-1}(2h)^3}{3!} + \frac{y^{IV}_{i-1}(2h)^4}{4!} + \frac{y^{V}(\xi_1)(2h)^5}{5!}$$

or

$$y_{i+1} - y_{i-1} = 2y'_{i-1}h + 2y''_{i-1}h^2 + \frac{4}{3}y'''_{i-1}h^3 + \frac{2}{3}y^{IV}_{i-1}h^4 + \frac{4}{15}y^{V}(\xi_1)h^5,$$

$$x_{i-1} < \xi_1 < x_{i+1} \qquad (6\text{-}140)$$

Similarly, expanding y_{i-3} about x_{i-1} yields

$$y_{i-3} - y_{i-1} = -2y'_{i-1}h + 2y''_{i-1}h^2 - \frac{4}{3}y'''_{i-1}h^3 + \frac{2}{3}y^{IV}_{i-1}h^4 - \frac{4}{15}y^{V}(\xi_2)h^5,$$

$$x_{i-3} < \xi_2 < x_{i+1} \qquad (6\text{-}141)$$

Subtracting Eq. 6-141 from Eq. 6-140 yields

$$y_{i+1} - y_{i-3} = 4y'_{i-1}h + \frac{8}{3}y'''_{i-1}h^3 + \frac{8}{15}y^{V}(\xi_3)h^5, \qquad (6\text{-}142)$$

$$x_{i-3} < \xi_3 < x_{i+1}$$

which is an exact expression for the area of the 4 strips composing the crosshatched area of Fig. 6-39.

Substituting the relationships of Eq. 6-139 into Eq. 6-142, we can express the exact area as

$$y_{i+1} - y_{i-3} = 4f_{i-1}h + \frac{8}{3}f''_{i-1}h^3 + \frac{8}{15}f^{IV}(\xi_3)h^5, \qquad (6\text{-}143)$$

$$x_{i-3} < \xi_3 < x_{i+1}$$

To put Eq. 6-143 in a form in which we can compare it with Milne's predictor equation, we must express $f''_{i-1}h^2$ in terms of f_i, f_{i-1}, and f_{i-2}. Using a Taylor series, we expand f_i and f_{i-2} about x_{i-1} as

$$f_i = f_{i-1} + f'_{i-1}h + \frac{f''_{i-1}h^2}{2!} + \frac{f'''_{i-1}h^3}{3!} + \frac{f^{IV}(\xi_4)h^4}{4!}, \qquad (6\text{-}144)$$

$$x_{i-1} < \xi_4 < x_i$$

and

$$f_{i-2} = f_{i-1} - f'_{i-1}h + \frac{f''_{i-1}h^2}{2!} - \frac{f'''_{i-1}h^3}{3!} + \frac{f^{IV}(\xi_5)h^4}{4!}, \qquad (6\text{-}145)$$

$$x_{i-2} < \xi_5 < x_{i-1}$$

Adding Eqs. 6-144 and 6-145 gives

$$f_i + f_{i-2} = 2f_{i-1} + f''_{i-1}h^2 + \frac{1}{12}f^{IV}(\xi_6)h^4$$

from which

$$f''_{i-1}h^2 = (f_i - 2f_{i-1} + f_{i-2}) - \frac{1}{12}f^{IV}(\xi_6)h^4, \quad x_{i-2} < \xi_6 < x_i \qquad (6\text{-}146)$$

Then, substituting Eq. 6-146 into Eq. 6-143, we obtain

$$y_{i+1} - y_{i-3} = \underbrace{\frac{4h}{3}(2f_i - f_{i-1} + 2f_{i-2})}_{\substack{\text{Milne's predictor} \\ \text{equation}}} + \underbrace{\frac{14}{45}f^{IV}(\xi_7)h^5}_{\substack{\text{truncation} \\ \text{error}}}, \qquad (6\text{-}147)$$

$$x_{i-3} < \xi_7 < x_{i+1}$$

Equation 6-147 reveals that the per-step truncation error of Milne's predictor equation is given by

$$E_{TP} = \frac{14}{45}f^{IV}(\eta)h^5 = \frac{14}{45}y^V(\eta)h^5, \quad x_{i-3} < \eta < x_{i+1} \qquad (6\text{-}148)$$

Let us next obtain an expression for the per-step truncation error of Milne's corrector equation. The procedure will be to obtain an exact expression for the crosshatched area included in the 2 incremental strips (Fig. 6-40), and then to compare this expression with Milne's corrector equation which defines the area under the second-degree parabola shown as a dashed line.

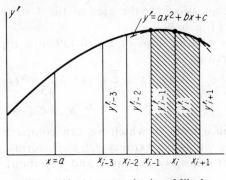

FIG. 6-40. Area used in Milne's corrector equation.

Expanding y_{i+1} and y_{i-1} about x_i in a Taylor series, we obtain

$$y_{i+1} - y_i = y_i'h + \frac{y_i''h^2}{2} + \frac{1}{6}y_i'''h_3 + \frac{1}{24}y_i^{IV}h^4 + \frac{1}{120}y^V(\xi_1)h^5,$$

$$x_i < \xi_1 < x_{i+1} \qquad (6\text{-}149)$$

and

$$y_{i-1} - y_i = -y_i'h + \frac{y_i''h^2}{2} - \frac{1}{6}y_i'''h^3 + \frac{1}{24}y_i^{IV}h^4 - \frac{1}{120}y^V(\xi_2)h^5,$$

$$x_{i-1} < \xi_2 < x_i \qquad (6\text{-}150)$$

Subtracting Eq. 6-150 from Eq. 6-149 yields

$$y_{i+1} - y_{i-1} = 2y_i'h + \frac{1}{3}y_i'''h^3 + \frac{1}{60}y^V(\xi_3)h^5, \qquad (6\text{-}151)$$

$$x_{i-1} < \xi_3 < x_{i+1}$$

Substituting the expressions of Eq. 6-139 into Eq. 6-151 gives

$$y_{i+1} - y_{i-1} = 2f_ih + \frac{1}{3}f_i''h^3 + \frac{1}{60}f^{IV}(\xi_3)h^5 \qquad (6\text{-}152)$$

Then, substituting Eq. 6-146 (with 1 added to each subscript) into Eq. 6-152, we finally obtain

$$\underbrace{y_{i+1} - y_{i-1} = \frac{h}{3}(f_{i+1} + 4f_i + f_{i-1})}_{\substack{\text{Milne's corrector} \\ \text{equation}}} - \underbrace{\frac{1}{90}f^{IV}(\xi_4)h^5}_{\substack{\text{truncation} \\ \text{error}}}, \qquad (6\text{-}153)$$

$$x_{i-1} < \xi_4 < x_{i+1}$$

where f_{i+1} corresponds to $P(y_{i+1}')$ in Eq. 6-89. Equation 6-153 reveals that the per-step truncation error of Milne's corrector equation is

$$E_{TC} = -\frac{1}{90}f^{IV}(\eta)h^5 = -\frac{1}{90}y^V(\eta)h^5, \qquad x_{i-1} < \eta < x_{i+1} \qquad (6\text{-}154)$$

An estimate of the per-step truncation error of Milne's corrector equation can be obtained in terms of the predicted and corrected y values at a step from

$$E_{TC} \cong -\frac{1}{29} \left[C\binom{n}{y} - P\binom{1}{y} \right] \qquad (6\text{-}155)$$

where

$P\binom{1}{y}$ = the predicted value of y at x_{i+1}

$C\binom{n}{y}$ = the corrected value of y obtained in the nth (final) iteration at x_{i+1}

Equation 6-155 is developed in a manner similar to that of Eq. 6-137, as discussed under the error analysis of Euler's modified methods.

Runge-Kutta Methods. One of the disadvantages of the higher-order Runge-Kutta methods mentioned earlier is the difficulty encountered in estimating the per-step truncation error. An expression for the approximate per-step truncation error is given by Romonelli, but it is difficult to apply.[13] Richardson's method (p. 392) is, perhaps, the most practical one available. Richardson's expression for the fourth-order Runge-Kutta method (Eq. 6-126 with $r = 4$) is

$$E_T \cong \frac{y^{(2)} - y^{(1)}}{15} \qquad (6\text{-}156)$$

Collatz has suggested that, in using the fourth-order method, the step size used may be based upon the relationship

$$\left| \frac{k_2 - k_3}{k_1 - k_2} \right|$$

where the expressions for the k's are as given by Eq. 6-61.[14] When this quantity exceeds a few hundredths, the step size should be decreased accordingly.

The engineer who is unfamiliar with the intricacies of error analysis will find that a practical method of ensuring the use of a suitable step size in a Runge-Kutta method is to run several trial solutions, with different step sizes in each one, until consecutive solutions are obtained in which the results are in good agreement throughout. (This procedure was discussed in this section in regard to the error analysis of Euler's method.)

Hamming's Method. The predictor equation used in Hamming's method is the same as the predictor equation of Milne's method, so the per-step truncation error in a predicted value is given by

[13] Ralston, Anthony and Wilf, Herbert S., eds. *Mathematical Methods for Digital Computers.* New York: John Wiley & Sons, Inc., 1960, p. 116.

[14] Collatz, L. *Numerische Behandlung von Differentialgleichungen.* Berlin: Springer-Verlag, 1950, p. 34.

$$E_{TP} = \frac{14}{45} f^{IV}(\eta)h^5 = \frac{14}{45} y^V(\eta)h^5, \qquad x_{i-3} < \eta < x_{i+1} \qquad (6\text{-}157)$$

as developed earlier (Eq. 6-148).

To obtain the per-step truncation error of Hamming's corrector equation, let us return for a moment to the development of Hamming's method in Sec. 6-8, and read particularly the text from Eqs. 6-100 to 6-103. From that discussion it can be seen that the left and right sides of Eq. 6-101 have been made equal by the a and b values determined from Eq. 6-102 (with $a_{i-1} = 0$). It can also be seen that the left side of Eq. 6-101 is only an approximate expression for y_{i+1}, since y_{i+1} is expressed as a truncated Taylor series. If we add the remaining Taylor-series terms of the expansion of y_{i+1} (in a Lagrangian-remainder form) to both sides of Eq. 6-101 and insert Hamming's a and b values, we can obtain an expression for the *true* value of y_{i+1} as

$$
\begin{aligned}
(y_{i+1})_{\text{true}} &= \left[y_i + y_i'h + \frac{y_i''h^2}{2!} + \frac{y_i'''h^3}{3!} + \frac{y_i^{IV}h^4}{4!} + \frac{y^V(\xi_1)h^5}{5!} \right] \\
&= \frac{9}{8} y_i - \frac{1}{8}\left[y_i + y_i'(-2h) + \frac{y_i''(-2h)^2}{2!} + \frac{y_i'''(-2h)^3}{3!} + \frac{y_i^{IV}(-2h)^4}{4!} \right] \\
&\quad + \frac{3h}{8}\left[y_i' + y_i''h + \frac{y_i'''h^2}{2!} + \frac{y_i^{IV}h^3}{3!} \right] + \frac{3h}{4} y_i' \\
&\quad - \frac{3h}{8}\left[y_i' + y_i''(-h) + \frac{y_i'''(-h)^2}{2!} + \frac{y_i^{IV}(-h)^3}{3!} \right] + \frac{y^V(\xi_1)h^5}{5!}
\end{aligned}
$$
$$(6\text{-}158)$$

Now let us examine the expression for y_{i+1} which is obtained by using Hamming's corrector equation (Eq. 6-103). Considering only the truncation error of the step by assuming the solution to be correct up to the step considered, all the y and y' values shown on the right side of the equation will be *true* values. Therefore, substituting a complete Taylor series (in Lagrangian-remainder form) for y_{i-2}, y_{i-1}', and y_{i+1}' in Eq. 6-103, we obtain

$$
\begin{aligned}
(y_{i+1})_{\text{Hamming}} &= \frac{9}{8} y_i - \frac{1}{8}\left[y_i + y_i'(-2h) + \frac{y_i''(-2h)^2}{2!} + \frac{y_i'''(-2h)^3}{3!} \right. \\
&\qquad\qquad\qquad\qquad \left. + \frac{y_i^{IV}(-2h)^4}{4!} + \frac{y^V(\xi_2)(-2h)^5}{5!} \right] \\
&\quad + \frac{3h}{8}\left[y_i' + y_i''h + \frac{y_i'''h^2}{2!} + \frac{y_i^{IV}h^3}{3!} + \frac{y^V(\xi_3)h^4}{4!} \right] + \frac{3h}{4} y_i' \\
&\quad - \frac{3h}{8}\left[y_i' + y_i''(-h) + \frac{y_i'''(-h)^2}{2!} + \frac{y_i^{IV}(-h)^3}{3!} + \frac{y^V(\xi_4)(-h)^4}{4!} \right]
\end{aligned}
$$
$$(6\text{-}159)$$

Comparing the expression for the true value of y_{i+1} (given by Eq. 6-158) with the expression for y_{i+1} from Hamming's corrector equation (given by Eq. 6-159), it is apparent that Hamming's corrector equation does not yield a true value of y_{i+1}. The difference between these expressions is the per-step truncation error of Hamming's corrector equation. Subtracting Eq. 6-159 from Eq. 6-158, we obtain

$$E_{TC} = (y_{i+1})_{\text{true}} - (y_{i+1})_{\text{Hamming}}$$

$$= \frac{1}{8} \frac{y^V(\xi_2)(-2h)^5}{5!} - \frac{3}{8} \frac{y^V(\xi_3)h^5}{4!} + \frac{3}{8} \frac{y^V(\xi_4)h^5}{4!} + \frac{y^V(\xi_1)h^5}{5!} \tag{6-160}$$

which reduces to

$$E_{TC} = -\frac{1}{40} y^V(\eta)h^5, \qquad x_{i-2} < \eta < x_{i+1} \tag{6-161}$$

Thus, Hamming's corrector equation for a true value of y_{i+1} may be written as

$$y_{i+1} = \frac{1}{8}\left[9y_i - y_{i-2} + 3h(y'_{i+1} + 2y'_i - y'_{i-1})\right] - \frac{1}{40} y^V(\eta)h^5 \tag{6-162}$$

As discussed before, an estimate of the per-step truncation error can be obtained from Eq. 6-161 by assuming that y^V is fairly constant over the interval and evaluating the truncation-error term at $\eta = x_i$, although the estimate is generally not made in this manner, owing to the difficulty of obtaining y^V.

A more practical approach can be made by obtaining an estimate of the per-step truncation error in terms of the predicted and corrected values of y at each step. Consider that

$P\left(\dfrac{1}{y}\right)$ = the predicted value of y obtained at x_{i+1} in the integration process

$C\left(\dfrac{n}{y}\right)$ = the corrected value of y obtained at x_{i+1} in the nth (final) iteration at that step

Y = the true value of y at x_{i+1}

Isolating the truncation error of the ith step from the effects of previous errors, in accordance with the definition given for per-step truncation error, and assuming that roundoff error in the calculations of the step is negligible, we can write

$$Y = P\left(\frac{1}{y}\right) + \frac{14}{45} y^V(\eta_1)h^5, \qquad x_{i-3} < \eta_1 < x_{i+1} \tag{6-163}$$

$$Y = C\left(\frac{n}{y}\right) - \frac{1}{40} y^V(\eta_2)h^5, \qquad x_{i-2} < \eta_2 < x_{i+1} \tag{6-164}$$

subtracting Eq. 6-163 from Eq. 6-164 yields

$$0 = C\binom{n}{y} - P\binom{1}{y} - \frac{121}{360} y^V(\eta_3)h^5, \qquad x_{i-3} < \eta_3 < x_{i+1}$$

or

$$C\binom{n}{y} - P\binom{1}{y} = \left(\frac{121}{9}\right)\left(\frac{1}{40}\right) y^V(\eta_3)h^5 \qquad (6\text{-}165)$$

Comparing Eqs. 6-161 and 6-165, it can be seen that an estimate of the per-step truncation error, in the final application of Hamming's corrector equation, is

$$E_{TC} \cong -\frac{9}{121}\left[C\binom{n}{y} - P\binom{1}{y}\right] \qquad (6\text{-}166)$$

6-10. Selecting a Numerical-Integration Method

Having discussed several different numerical methods of integrating differential equations and the error analysis of each of these methods, we are now in a position to compare the methods from the standpoint of selecting the best one for a particular application.

1. When it is obvious that the range of integration of a problem is relatively short, relatively small step sizes can be used without excessive computing time, and there is little reason to analyze the truncation error at each step, or to complicate the solution by using one of the more accurate methods. Stability is also unlikely to be a problem over a short range of integration, so a simple self-starting method such as Euler's should be satisfactory.

2. When it is obvious that the range of integration of a problem is long enough to involve a large number of steps, as in a vibration problem where the motion is to be studied over a substantial number of oscillations, a method having a small per-step truncation error (such as Milne's or Hamming's) should be used in order to minimize the cumulative error. A per-step truncation-error analysis could be made at each step to minimize the computing time required, while at the same time attaining the desired accuracy, by controlling the step size. If stability is also a problem, Hamming's method should be used in preference to Milne's. Starting values, in either case, could be determined by using a fourth-order Runge-Kutta method.

3. When a small per-step truncation error is desired, and computing time is not important enough to require a per-step truncation-error analysis, the fourth-order Runge-Kutta method is a convenient one to use. It is self-starting, stability is usually not a problem, and the equations are easy to program.

4. When a problem involves some intermediate range of integration wherein the accumulation of error and computing time must be con-

sidered, but neither is a critical factor, Euler's self-starting modified method or a third-order Runge-Kutta method should prove satisfactory. If a per-step error estimate is desired for purposes of controlling step size, the non-self-starting modification of Euler's method should be used.

There are many numerical methods, other than those covered in this chapter, for solving differential equations, including techniques especially fitted for certain types or orders of differential equations. However, one of the methods described here should be suitable for most engineering problems of the initial-value type.

Problems

6-1. Utilizing the relationship from elementary beam theory that

$$EI \frac{d^2 y}{dx^2} = M$$

write the moment equation for the beam shown in the accompanying figure and write a program for determining the elastic curve of the beam.

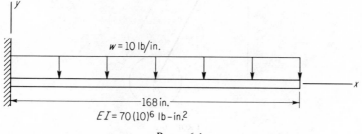

PROB. 6-1

6-2. Utilizing the relationship from elementary beam theory that

$$EI \frac{d^2 y}{dx^2} = M$$

write the necessary moment equations and a program for determining the elastic curve of the beam.

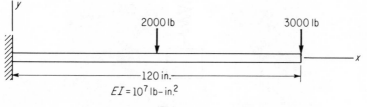

PROB. 6-2

6-3. Neglecting the mass of the slender rod, the differential equation of motion of the pendulum shown in the accompanying figure is

$$\ddot{\theta} + \frac{g}{l} \sin \theta = 0$$

Using the initial values

$$t = 0 \left| \begin{array}{l} \theta = \pi/4 \\ \dot{\theta} = 0 \end{array} \right.$$

write a program for determining the θ-t curve for 1 period of oscillation for each of the following rod lengths: 40 in., 30 in., and 10 in. (frequency $\cong \sqrt{g/4l\pi^2}$).

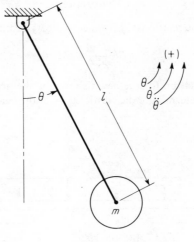

PROB. 6-3

6-4. The differential equation of motion of the spring-and-mass system shown is

$$\ddot{x} + p^2 x = 0$$

PROB. 6-4

where $p^2 = k/m$. If the weight of the mass is 10 lb, the spring constant $k = 1.5$ lb/in., and the initial values are

$$t = 0 \begin{vmatrix} x = 5 \text{ in.} \\ \dot{x} = 0 \end{vmatrix}$$

write a program for determining the x-t curve for 1 cycle of motion (frequency $= p/2\pi$).

6-5. The differential equation of motion of the viscously damped spring-and-mass system shown in the accompanying figure is

$$\ddot{x} + 2n\dot{x} + p^2 x = 0$$

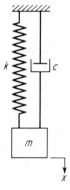

PROB. 6-5

where $p^2 = k/m$, and $2n = c/m$. If the weight of the block is 15 lb, the spring constant $k = 2$ lb/in., and the initial values are

$$t = 0 \begin{vmatrix} x = 5 \text{ in.} \\ \dot{x} = 0 \end{vmatrix}$$

a) write a program for determining the x-t and $\dot{x}$-t curves for 3 cycles of motion for each of the following damping ratios: $n/p = 0.05$, 0.10, 0.25, and 1.0 (frequency $= \sqrt{p^2 - n^2}/2\pi$). b) Modify the program written for part a) so that only the peak values of motion (the amplitude of each successive half cycle) are printed out as data.

6-6. A narrow ring of radius $R = 0.1$ m has a positive charge of $q = 8.00(10)^{-18}$ coulomb uniformly distributed over its circumference. The resultant electric-field strength at a distance x from the ring along the axis shown in the accompanying figure is given by

$$E = \frac{q \cos \alpha}{4\pi \epsilon_0 s^2}$$

where s and α are as defined in the figure. If $\epsilon_0 = 8.85(10)^{-12}$ coulomb^2/Newton m^2, determine the differential equation of motion of an electron released from rest at a position x_0 along the axis of the ring.

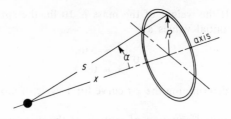

PROB. 6-6

Write a **FORTRAN** program for determining the x-t and $\dot{x}$-t curves for 1 cycle of motion of the electron, using Euler's method. The mass of an electron is approximately $9.11(10)^{-31}$ kg, and the charge on an electron is $1.6(10)^{-19}$ coulomb. The electron is released from rest at a distance $x_0 = 0.2$ m from the plane of the ring.

6-7. An "infinitely long straight wire" has a uniform positive charge of $\lambda = 2.56(10)^{-17}$ coulomb/m. The resultant electric-field strength at a point a distance r from the wire is given by

$$E = \frac{\lambda}{2\pi\epsilon_0 r}$$

where $\epsilon_0 = 8.85(10)^{-12}$ coulomb^2/Newton m^2. The charge on an electron is $1.6(10)^{-19}$ coulomb. Determine the differential equation of motion of an electron released from rest near the wire.

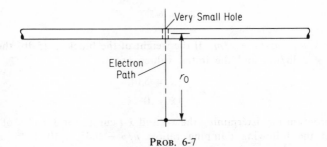

PROB. 6-7

Write a **FORTRAN** program for determining the r-t and $\dot{r}$-t curves for 1 cycle of motion of the electron, using Euler's method. The electron is released from rest at a distance $r_0 = 0.1$ m from the wire. Assume that there is a very small hole in the wire through which the electron can pass. The mass of an electron is approximately $9.11(10)^{-31}$ kg.

6-8. The permanent magnet A exerts a force on the weight W that is inversely proportional to the square of the distance x between the mass center of W and the mass center of the magnet. If the coefficient of friction between W and the flat surface is f, show that the differential equation of motion of W is

$$\frac{d^2x}{dt^2} + \frac{k}{mx^2} - fg = 0$$

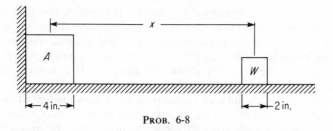

PROB. 6-8

Write a **FORTRAN** program for obtaining the acceleration $\ddot{x}$, the velocity $\dot{x}$, and the displacement x in terms of time t. Consider that the weight W is released from rest with an initial value of $x_0 = 12$ in. As additional data, it is given that $k/m = 7,200$ in.^{3}/sec^2, $f = 0.1$, and $g = 386$ in./sec^2. It is suggested that the solution be obtained by using Euler's method.

6-9. A particle of mass m is released from rest at the edge of a hemispherical bowl, as shown in the accompanying figure, and slides down the inside surface of

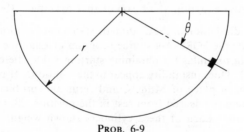

PROB. 6-9

the bowl. If the coefficient of friction between the particle and the surface of the bowl is f, determine the differential *equations* of motion of the particle in the tangential direction. Note that since friction always opposes motion, different equations define the motion when $\dot{\theta}$ is positive and when $\dot{\theta}$ is negative.

Write a **FORTRAN** program for determining the θ-t and $\dot{\theta}$-t curves for the period of time necessary for the particle to return to rest on the side from which it was released. Draw the θ-t and $\dot{\theta}$-t curves for a bowl with $r = 1.0$ ft and $f = 0.20$. Use Euler's self-starting modified method.

6-10. The accompanying figure shows a projectile of weight W in motion in a coordinate system whose origin is at the point from which the projectile was

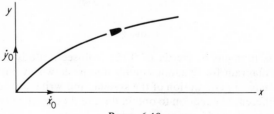

PROB. 6-10

fired. Assuming that the acceleration of gravity is constant and that the air resistance is proportional to the square of the *total* velocity, derive the differential equations of motion for the projectile (in the x and y directions) and write a FORTRAN program for determing the x-t, y-t, $\dot{x}$-t, $\dot{y}$-t, $\ddot{x}$-t and $\ddot{y}$-t curves from the time of firing until the projectile strikes the ground. Use Euler's self-starting modified method.

6-11. Section 6-7 includes an explanation of Milne's method of numerically integrating ordinary differential equations. Also included is a discussion concerned with using the fourth-order Runge-Kutta method to obtain starting values for the numerical process, by means of the computer. In Example 6-5 a program is shown in which the starting values were precalculated manually and entered into the program as data input.

Revise the program shown by adding the program steps necessary to have the computer calculate the necessary starting values for the problem, in Example 6-5, by using the appropriate Runge-Kutta formulas.

6-12. Rewrite the FORTRAN source program of Example 6-3 to use an arithmetic statement function (if available in the compiler being used) for the function $f(i)$ of the differential equation $\dfrac{di}{dt} = f(i)$ of that example. (See Chapter 2 and Example 6-4 for a discussion of the arithmetic statement function.)

6-13. Rewrite the FORTRAN source program of Example 6-4, using fourth-order Runge-Kutta formulas for obtaining starting values before switching over to Milne's method. Does instability appear in the solution? If so, use Hamming's corrector equation in place of Milne's, and rerun the problem.

6-14. A system is released from rest in the position shown in part a) of the accompanying figure. Each of the 2 cylinders shown weighs 32.2 lb and has a

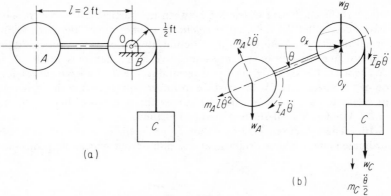

Prob. 6-14

centroidal mass moment of inertia of 0.125 ft-lb-sec^2. Body C weighs 16.1 lb. The free-body diagram for dynamic equilibrium is shown in part b. Determine the differential equation of motion of the system, and write a program for solving the resulting differential equation to obtain $\dot{\theta}$-t and θ-t curves over a 2-sec interval after the system is released from rest.

6-15.   The circuit shown in the accompanying figure consists of a coil wound around an iron core, a resistance R, a switch SW, and a voltage source E.   The magnetization curve may be obtained from the equation

$$Ni = 0.5\phi + 0.003\phi^3$$

where

N = number of turns of coil
ϕ = flux in the core, kilolines
i = current, amp

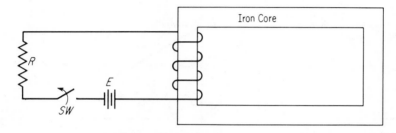

PROB. 6-15

From Kirchhoff's law, the impressed voltage E is

$$E = Ri + L\frac{di}{dt} = Ri + N\frac{d\phi}{dt}(10)^{-5}$$

where

L = self-inductance, henries
R = resistance, ohms
t = time, sec

If $N = 100$ turns and $R = 500$ ohms, show that the differential equation for the flux is

$$\frac{d\phi}{dT} = E - 2.5\phi - 0.015\phi^3$$

where T is in *milliseconds*.   Determine solutions of this differential equation for a) $E = 20$ volts and b) $E = 40$ volts.

6-16.   In the accompanying figure a rocket is anchored to a very rigid abutment by an elastic supporting structure of stiffness k lb/ft.   The pertinent data for a static firing test are as follows:

m_0 = initial mass = 100 slugs
t_0 = burnout time = 100 sec
m_{bo} = mass at burnout = $0.1\,m_0$ = 10 slugs
m' = constant rate at which fuel is burned = 0.9 slug/sec
u = velocity of jet stream relative to rocket = 8000 ft/sec
T = constant thrust = $m'u$ = 7200 lb
m = mass of rocket for $0 \leq t \leq 100$ sec

Considering that the thrust T reaches its maximum value in a few milliseconds, the differential equation of motion of the rocket is $m\ddot{x} + kx = T$ where $m =$

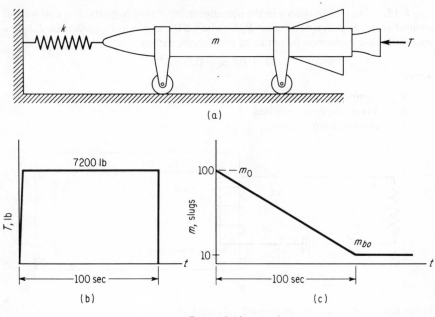

(a)

(b)   (c)

PROB. 6-16

$m_0 - m't$. Thus, the mathematical model of the system is a differential equation with a variable coefficient.

Program the equation to the computer and determine a) the maximum acceleration $\ddot{x}$ and b) the maximum displacement x for k/m_0 equal to 2000, 4000, 6000, 8000, and 10,000.

6-17. The decay of the unstable isotope Te^{135}, with atomic weight of 135, results in the chemical-kinetics process

$$(Te^{135})^{k_1} \rightarrow (I^{135})^{k_2} \rightarrow (Xe^{135})^{k_3} \rightarrow (Cs^{135})^{k_4} \rightarrow Ba$$

where

Element	Half-life
Te = tellurium	2 min
I = iodine	6.7 hr
Xe = xenon	9.2 hr
Cs = cesium	$2(10)^4$ years
Ba = barium	Stable

The set of simultaneous equations representing the transformations of the unstable isotopes to an end result of stable barium are

$$\frac{d(Te)}{dt} = -k_1(Te)$$

$$\frac{d(I)}{dt} = k_1(Te) - k_2(I)$$

$$\frac{d(\text{Xe})}{dt} = k_2(\text{I}) - k_3(\text{Xe})$$

$$\frac{d(\text{Cs})}{dt} = k_3(\text{Xe}) - k_4(\text{Cs})$$

$$\frac{d(\text{Ba})}{dt} = k_4(\text{Cs})$$

The reaction rate k for each unstable isotope can be determined from its half-life, as shown following for the isotope tellurium:

$$\int_1^{\frac{1}{2}} \frac{d(\text{Te})}{\text{Te}} = -k_1 \int_0^{120 \text{ sec}} dt$$

Write a computer program for determining the amount of each element present a) at 5-sec intervals for the first 2 min, b) at 1000-sec intervals for the next 9 hr, and c) at $(10)^{10}$-sec intervals for the next 100 intervals. (HINT: Use the Runge-Kutta method and change the time increments for the different time intervals given above.)

6-18. The accompanying figure shows the earth with mass m_e, the moon with mass m_m, and a satellite with mass m. The satellite is small compared to the earth and the moon ($m \ll m_e$, $m \ll m_m$). The three masses are assumed to attract each other according to the inverse square law, but the influence of the satellite on the motion of the earth and the moon is considered to be negligible. The analysis of such a system is referred to as the restricted three-body problem.

The earth and the moon revolve about their common center of mass, which is located inside the earth as shown in the figure. The distance D between the mass center of the earth and that of the moon is assumed to be constant. The motion of the satellite is such that it lies in the plane of revolution of the earth and the moon.

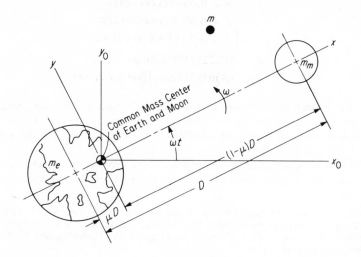

PROB. 6-18

The x_0-y_0 coordinate system shown is nonrotating, and its acceleration is assumed as negligible (Newton's second law is valid in this reference frame). Transforming the equation of motion of the satellite in the x_0 direction in the nonrotating set of axes to the rotating x-y coordinate system results in two equations of motion in the latter coordinate system. If the distance D between the mass centers of the earth and moon is chosen as unity, and the unit of time is chosen such that the angular velocity ω of the rotating x-y reference frame is unity ($\tau = 2\pi$), the equations of motion of the satellite in terms of the x-y coordinate system are

$$\ddot{x} = x + 2\dot{y} - \mu' \frac{x + \mu}{[(x + \mu)^2 + y^2]^{3/2}} - \mu \frac{x - \mu'}{[(x - \mu')^2 + y^2]^{3/2}}$$

$$\ddot{y} = y - 2\dot{x} - \mu' \frac{y}{[(x + \mu)^2 + y^2]^{3/2}} - \mu \frac{y}{[(x - \mu')^2 + y^2]^{3/2}}$$

where

$$\mu = \frac{m_m}{m_e + m_m}$$

$$\mu' = 1 - \mu$$

These equations may be solved numerically to obtain the x and y coordinates of the satellite for various values of the independent variable time. It is known that closed periodic orbits exist in the rotating x-y coordinate system.

Write a **FORTRAN** program for solving these equations simultaneously, using the fourth-order Runge-Kutta method. Using the following initial conditions and parameters, determine the path of the satellite in the x-y system:[15]

$$t = 0 \quad \begin{vmatrix} x = 0.9940000000000000 \\ y = 0.0000000000000000 \\ \dot{x} = 0.0000000000000000 \\ \dot{y} = -2.1138987966945027 \end{vmatrix}$$

$$\mu = 0.0122774710000000$$
$$\tau = 5.4367954392601900 \text{ time units}$$

Use the radius of curvature of the satellite's path in the x-y system to control the time increment in the computer program. If $\rho < 0.1$, use $\Delta t = 0.0001$; if $0.1 \leq \rho < 0.7$, use $\Delta t = 0.001$; if $0.7 \leq \rho < 2.0$, use $\Delta t = 0.005$; and if $\rho \geq 2.0$, use $\Delta t = 0.01$.

6-19. Using the computer program written for Prob. 6-18, and the following initial conditions and parameters, determine the path of the satellite in the ro-

[15]These initial conditions result in a closed periodic orbit. See NASA Contractor Report CR-61139, "Study of the Methods for the Numerical Solution of Ordinary Differential Equations," prepared by O. B. Francis, Jr., et al for the NASA-George C. Marshall Space Flight Center, June 7, 1966.

tating x-y coordinate system:

$$t = 0 \begin{vmatrix} x & = & 0.9940000000000000 \\ y & = & 0.0000000000000000 \\ \dot{x} & = & 0.0000000000000000 \\ \dot{y} & = & -2.0317326295573368 \end{vmatrix}$$

$$\mu = 0.0122774710000000$$

$$\tau = 11.1243403372660851 \text{ time units}$$

Use the same time increments as suggested in Prob. 6-18.

chapter 7

Ordinary Differential Equations; Boundary-Value Problems

7-1. Introduction

Problems in which the conditions to be satisfied by the solution or its derivatives are given at the point where the integration is to begin are usually referred to as *initial-value* problems, as explained in Chapter 6. We shall now consider problems in which conditions are specified at both ends of the interval over which the integration is to occur. Ones of this type are known as *boundary-value* problems. Since these involve a minimum of 2 boundary conditions, we shall obviously be considering differential equations of the second order or higher.

The numerical solution of boundary-value problems is somewhat more difficult than that of initial-value problems. Two elementary methods are used to solve engineering problems of this type: one consists of a trial-and-error procedure; the other requires the simultaneous solution of a set of algebraic equations.

7-2. Trial-and-Error Method

A trial-and-error method can be used to solve both linear and nonlinear differential equations of the second order or higher. The technique involves the assumption or approximate calculation of the initial values of the problem which are unknown. This, in effect, reduces the problem to an initial-value problem for which trial solutions can be obtained by using one of the integration methods discussed in Chapter 6. After a trial solution is obtained, the known boundary values at the end of the integration interval are compared with the corresponding values provided by the trial solution. If the solution values at this point do not agree with the known boundary values, new initial-condition values must be approxi-

414

mated and another trial solution made. This procedure continues until a trial solution is obtained which satisfies the known final boundary values.

It should be apparent that if it becomes necessary to approximate several different initial values, the number of trial solutions required could become very large. For this reason the trial-and-error approach is usually applied only to the solution of problems in which just one initial value is unknown. For example, if we consider the equation

$$y'' = f(x, y, y') \tag{7-1}$$

with the boundary conditions

$$x = a \left| \begin{array}{l} y = y_a \\ y' = ? \end{array} \right. \qquad x = b \left| \begin{array}{l} y = y_b \end{array} \right.$$

we can assume a value for y' at $x = a$ and integrate as we normally would to obtain the solution of a second-order initial-value problem, using a method applicable to that type of problem. If the value of y at $x = b$, provided by the trial solution, is larger than the known boundary value at this point, a new initial value of y' is chosen which is smaller than the original approximate value used, and another trial solution is made. If the resulting value of y at $x = b$ is smaller than y_b, a larger initial value is chosen for y', and another trial solution is made. This procedure continues until a solution is obtained in which the calculated value of y at $x = b$ is approximately equal to the boundary value at that point, within some prescribed limit of accuracy.

In general, the relationship between a change in the approximate initial value of y' and the resulting change in the final value of y obtained from the trial solution is not a linear one. However, linear interpolation is often used to determine the adjustments necessary in the approximate initial values used. In this procedure successive approximate values of y_a' and the corresponding values of y obtained at $x = b$ are used along with the known boundary value of y at $x = b$ to correct the value of y_a' for a subsequent trial solution. Linear interpolation is used in the example which follows.

EXAMPLE 7-1

Let us consider the problem of dissipating heat in space. In many engineering applications, heat must be dissipated from bodies. We are all aware of common examples of heat dissipation—from combustion engines, air-conditioning units, bearing surfaces, and so on. Often, heat is dissipated from a body by the simultaneous action of conductive and convective heat transfer to a fluid medium surrounding the body, and by thermal radiation. The dissipation of heat from a body deep in outer space is limited to thermal radiation, because of the negligible amount of atmosphere encountered there. Therefore, the thermal-radiation charac- teristics of materials and the geometries of radiating surfaces become very important in considering heat dissipation in such an environment.

In the power plant of a space station, for example, heat must be dis- sipated to maintain the plant at a normal operating temperature. If a working fluid is utilized to transfer heat from the power plant through coolant tubes which are exposed to surrounding space, and is then re- cycled through the power plant, the fluid must lose some heat during the cycle. Assuming that the material composing the coolant tubes is an ex- cellent conductor, the amount of heat dissipated from the space station will depend primarily on the thermal-radiation characteristics of the tubing. Since the rate of heat transfer by thermal radiation is a function, among others, of the area of the radiating surface, the addition of area to the coolant tubing, in the form of numerous small fins, facilitates heat dissipation and reduces the amount of tubing required. Figure 7-1 is a simplified sketch of a section of coolant tubing with several such fins attached.

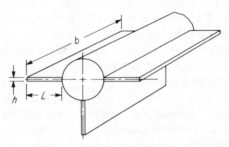

FIG. 7-1. Heat-dissipating system.

We shall be concerned with analyzing temperature distribution along fins with various geometries. With a constant operating temperature for the power plant, the problem is one of *steady* heat flow with the system in thermal equilibrium. Since the dissipation of heat by the fin being con- sidered involves both conduction along the fin and radiation from the fin surface, a brief review of the basic principles of each type of heat transfer is in order, before proceeding to the development of the differential equa- tion defining the temperature distribution along such a fin.

Conduction.   Fourier's law of conduction states that the instantane- ous rate of heat flow is proportional to the area A through which the heat flows at right angles, and to the temperature gradient along the flow axis. It is formulated as

$$\frac{\partial Q}{\partial \phi} = -kA \frac{\partial T}{\partial x} \tag{7-2}$$

where ϕ is time, A is area, $\partial T/\partial x$ is the temperature gradient and is negative when heat flow is in the positive x direction, and k is a proportionality factor which is a function of the physical properties of the conductor and is referred to as the *thermal conductivity* of the conductor. Since the temperature at any given location in a conductor does not vary with time for steady-state conduction, it follows that the temperature gradient and, consequently, the rate of heat flow are likewise independent of time. Hence the instantaneous rate of heat flow $\partial Q/\partial\phi$ becomes a constant rate of heat flow and is usually designated as q_c. Equation 7-2 then becomes, for steady heat flow,

$$q_c = -kA\frac{dT}{dx} \tag{7-3}$$

Equation 7-3, with the appropriate parameter values, will define the rate of heat transfer by conduction along the fin to be considered in our analysis.

Thermal Radiation. When a body is heated, radiant energy is emitted by the body at a rate and of a quality dependent on the temperature of the body. The *emissive power* W of a surface actually varies not only with the temperature but also with the roughness of the surface and, if the surface is metal, with the degree of surface oxidation. The quality of radiation is measured by its distribution in the spectrum, and is a function of the wavelength of emission and the temperature at which emission occurs. A surface which emits radiant energy will also absorb incident radiation. The fraction of the total incident radiation present which a surface is capable of absorbing is called the *absorptivity* of the surface; it is designated by α.

Consider two small surfaces, of area A_1 and A_2, in a large enclosure which is perfectly insulated from any external heat transfer. When the surfaces reach a state of thermal equilibrium, they will emit radiation at the respective rates $A_1 W_1$ and $A_2 W_2$ throughout the portion of the hemisphere above each element of surface. If the incident radiation impinging on the surfaces, owing to the radiation of the enclosure, is designated as I, and the surfaces have respective absorptivities of α_1 and α_2, they will absorb the incident radiation in that proportion, and an energy balance will show that

$$\alpha_1 I A_1 = A_1 W_1 \quad \text{and} \quad \alpha_2 I A_2 = A_2 W_2 \tag{7-4}$$

from which

$$\frac{W_1}{\alpha_1} = \frac{W_2}{\alpha_2} = \frac{W_3}{\alpha_3} = \cdots \frac{W_n}{\alpha_n} \tag{7-5}$$

The above generalization—that, at thermal equilibrium, the ratio of the emissive power of a surface to its absorptivity is the same for all bodies— is known as Kirchhoff's law. Since α is the fraction of incident radiation absorbed and cannot exceed unity, Eq. 7-4 shows that an upper limit exists on the emissive power of a body. This upper limit is usually denoted as W_B, and any surface having this upper-limiting emissive power is called a *perfect radiator*. Since such a surface must also have perfect absorptivity (α = unity), it will have zero reflectivity, and is thus commonly referred to as a *black body*.

The ratio of the emissive power of an actual surface (commonly called a *gray body*) to that of a black body is called the *emissivity* of the surface and is denoted by ϵ. Since the emissivity of an actual body is, in general, $W_n = W_B \epsilon_n$, Eq. 7-5 may be rewritten as

$$\frac{W_B \epsilon_1}{\alpha_1} = \frac{W_B \epsilon_2}{\alpha_2} = \frac{W_B \epsilon_3}{\alpha_3} = \cdots = \frac{W_B}{\alpha_B} \tag{7-6}$$

where W_B/α_B is the ratio for a black body. Since α_B is unity for a black body, Eq. 7-6 may be reduced to

$$\frac{\epsilon_1}{\alpha_1} = \frac{\epsilon_2}{\alpha_2} = \frac{\epsilon_3}{\alpha_3} = \cdots = \text{unity} \tag{7-7}$$

Thus, Kirchhoff's law may be restated to say that, at thermal equilibrium, the emissivity and absorptivity of a body are the same. Actually, this law is valid only when the body is receiving radiation from surroundings at its own temperature, since the emissivity of a body at temperature T_1 is not the same as its absorptivity when it is absorbing radiation from some other body at temperature T_2. However, owing to the high values of emissivity of most surfaces which are of engineering importance, and because of the small change of their emissivities with temperature, the emissivity and absorptivity of a body may be considered equal without introducing serious error. The emissivity value normally used is the value associated with the higher temperature.

Other factors involved in the transfer of heat by thermal radiation include the shape and relative positions of the heat-interchanging surfaces. Although the *intensity of radiation* of black bodies is independent of these factors, this is not true for actual bodies. For the latter, the intensity varies with the angle between the normals to the two surfaces. Two values of emissivity are therefore usually considered—*hemispherical* emissivity and *normal* emissivity. For nonmetals, the hemispherical emissivity is substantially the same as the normal emissivity. Fortunately, for most surfaces used in engineering, the values of normal emissivity may be used for hemispherical-emission conditions without introducing appreciable error.

The preceding discussion is a good example of the rational idealization which occurs in correlating physical phenomena with representative mathematical models.

Since the total emissive power of a black body depends only on its temperature, the second law of thermodynamics may be utilized to prove a proportionality between emissive power and the fourth power of the absolute temperature. This relation, the Stephan-Boltzmann law, is

$$W_B = \sigma T^4 \qquad (7\text{-}8)$$

where σ is the Stefan-Boltzmann constant.

The net rate of loss of energy by radiation from a body at temperature T_1 in black surroundings at temperature T_2 is given by

$$q_r = \sigma A_r(\epsilon_1 T_1^4 - \alpha_{1,2} T_2^4) \qquad (7\text{-}9)$$

where A_r is the area of the radiating surface, ϵ_1 is the emissivity of the radiating body at temperature T_1, and T_1 and T_2 are the temperatures of the radiating and receiving bodies, respectively, measured in degrees Rankine (°R). The subscripts of the absorptivity factor $\alpha_{1,2}$ refer to the value of the absorptivity with different emitter and receiver temperatures T_1 and T_2. Referring to the previous discussion of the relationship between ϵ_1 and $\alpha_{1,2}$ for engineering applications, we may rewrite Eq. 7-9 as

$$q_r = \sigma A_r \epsilon_1 (T_1^4 - T_2^4) \qquad (7\text{-}10)$$

since $\epsilon_1 \cong \alpha_{1,2}$.

With the preceding information as a background, let us consider the development of the differential equation defining the thermal-equilibrium state of one of the fins of Fig. 7-1. Such a fin is shown in Fig. 7-2, with the geometry defined. The parameters with which we shall be concerned are as follows:

T_1 = absolute Fahrenheit temperature at any position along the fin, °R

T_2 = absolute Fahrenheit temperature of surrounding space, 0°R

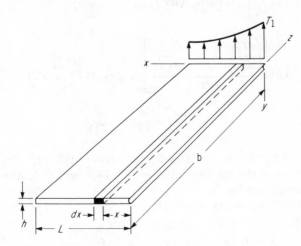

FIG. 7-2. Geometry of radiating fin.

σ = Stefan-Boltzmann constant, $0.173(10)^{-8}$ Btu/(ft)^2(hr)($^\circ$R)^4
ϵ_1 = emissivity of fin, 0.8
b = width of fin in z direction, 0.5 ft
h = thickness of fin, $0.005 \leq h \leq 0.01$ ft
k = thermal conductivity of fin, 25 Btu/(hr)(ft)($^\circ$R)
$T_1)_0$ = constant temperature of fin at root end ($x = 0$), 2000°R
L = length of fin, 0.25 ft

Since the root end of the fin, $x = 0$, is exposed to a constant heat source such that its temperature is a constant 2000°R, the fin will be in thermal equilibrium when the net heat loss per hour due to radiation is equal to the heat per hour flowing into the fin from the coolant tube to which the fin is attached. Since a temperature gradient must exist in order that heat can be conducted along the fin, the temperature T_1 will be different at each x coordinate along the fin. Because the radiation of heat is a function of the temperature T_1 of the radiating surface, the radiation of each differential area along the fin in the x direction will be different. With the fin as a whole in thermal equilibrium, each element of the fin must also be in thermal equilibrium. Therefore, the difference between the amount of heat flowing into and out of each differential element (per unit of time) must equal the heat dissipated (per unit of time) by the radiating surfaces of the element. Referring to Fig. 7-2, an element is selected which has a cross-sectional area bh, an effective radiating surface of $2b\,dx$, and a length of dx. Neglecting any radiation from the very small perimetrical surfaces of the fin and the curvature of the root area of the fin, we may write, from Eqs. 7-3 and 7-10,

$$\left[-kbh\left(\frac{dT_1}{dx}\right)_x\right] - \left[-kbh\left(\frac{dT_1}{dx}\right)_{x+dx}\right] = \sigma\epsilon_1(2b\,dx)(T_1^4 - T_2^4)$$

from which

$$kbh\left[\frac{\left(\frac{dT_1}{dx}\right)_{x+dx} - \left(\frac{dT_1}{dx}\right)_x}{dx}\right] = 2\sigma\epsilon_1 b(T_1^4 - T_2^4)$$

or

$$\frac{d^2 T_1}{dx^2} = \frac{2\sigma\epsilon_1}{kh}(T_1^4 - T_2^4) \qquad (7\text{-}11)$$

Equation 7-11 is the differential equation defining the thermal-equilibrium state of the fin, the solution of which will yield the temperature distribution along the fin.

The pertinent boundary values are

$$x = 0 \left|\begin{array}{l} T_1 = 2000^\circ\text{R} \\ \dfrac{dT_1}{dx} = ? \end{array}\right. \qquad x = L \left|\dfrac{dT_1}{dx} = 0\right. \qquad (7\text{-}12)$$

To illustrate the trial-and-error solution of Eq. 7-11, we shall use Euler's self-starting modified method which was discussed in Sec. 6-4. The equations outlining this method are as follows:

(Predictor for T')

$$P(T'_{i+1}) = T'_i + T''_i(\Delta x) \tag{a}$$

(Predictor for T)

$$P(T_{i+1}) = T_i + \left[\frac{T'_i + P(T'_{i+1})}{2}\right](\Delta x) \tag{b}$$

(Differential equation)

$$P(T''_{i+1}) = f[P(T_{i+1})] \tag{c}$$

$$(7\text{-}13)$$

(Corrector for T')

$$C(T'_{i+1}) = T'_i + \left[\frac{T''_i + P(T''_{i+1})}{2}\right](\Delta x) \tag{d}$$

(Corrector for T)

$$C(T_{i+1}) = T_i + \left[\frac{T'_i + C(T'_{i+1})}{2}\right](\Delta x) \tag{e}$$

(Differential equation)

$$C(T''_{i+1}) = f[C(T_{i+1})] \tag{f}$$

where $P(T'_{i+1})$, $C(T'_{i+1})$, and $P(T_{i+1})$, $C(T_{i+1})$ are predicted and corrected values of the temperature gradients and temperatures, respectively. Note that T_1 is designated merely as T in Eq. 7-13 to facilitate the subscripting used. The symbols $P(T''_{i+1})$ and $C(T''_{i+1})$ indicate predicted and corrected values of T''_{i+1}) which are obtained by substituting the appropriate T values into the given differential equation as indicated by Eq. 7-13c and f.

Inspection of Eq. 7-13a reveals that, although we can determine the initial value of T''_i by substituting the initial value of T into the given differential equation, we cannot start the numerical integrating process until we have obtained an initial value of T'_i. We may arbitrarily assume some value for this initial T', but, if this assumed value is excessively in error, the resulting temperature and temperature-gradient values calculated will be so large that they will probably exceed the maximum allowable number size of the compiler being used. In a problem of this type, in which the solution is very sensitive with respect to the initial value, several attempts might be necessary to get the trial solutions started on the computer.

The correct value of the initial temperature gradient which must be determined in the process of solving Eq. 7-11 by trial and error can be obtained quite rapidly by the use of the *linear-interpolation* formula

$$(T'_c)_0 = \frac{(T'_A)_F(T'_B)_0 - (T'_A)_0(T'_B)_F}{(T'_A)_F - (T'_B)_F} \tag{7-14}$$

where $(T_A')_0$ and $(T_B')_0$ are approximate values of the true initial temperature gradient, $(T_A')_F$ and $(T_B')_F$ are corresponding final temperature-gradient values obtained from trial solutions using $(T_A')_0$ and $(T_B')_0$, respectively, and $(T_c')_0$ is a corrected approximation of the true initial temperature gradient T_0'. Equation 7-14 is based upon the assumption of a linear relationship existing between the approximate initial values of T' and the resulting final T' values obtained by the use of these approximate initial values in a trial solution. Such a relationship is indicated by the straight line AB in Fig. 7-3. Equation 7-14 is easily derived by

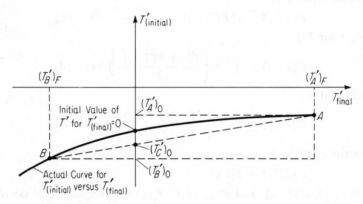

FIG. 7-3. Graphical representation of the linear-interpolation formula.

solving for $(T_c')_0$ from the relationship

$$\frac{(T_A')_0 - (T_c')_0}{(T_A')_F - 0} = \frac{(T_A')_0 - (T_B')_0}{(T_A')_F - (T_B')_F}$$

which is established from the similar triangles shown in Fig. 7-3.

The linear-interpolation formula is used in conjunction with Eq. 7-13 in obtaining a trial-and-error solution of Eq. 7-11, as follows:

1. Two initial values of T', $(T_A')_0$, and $(T_B')_0$ are estimated as accurately as possible from a physical consideration of the system.

2. Equation 7-13 is then used to integrate over the desired interval $(x = 0$ to $x = L)$, using the value estimated for $(T_A')_0$ as the starting value of T_i' in Eq. 7-13a. The final value of T' obtained by this trial integration is designated as $(T_A')_F$.

3. Step 2 is repeated, using the value estimated for $(T_B')_0$ as the starting value of T_i' in Eq. 7-13a. The final value of T' obtained by this trial integration is designated as $(T_B')_F$.

4. The calculated $(T_A')_F$ and $(T_B')_F$ values from steps 2 and 3 are then substituted into Eq. 7-14, along with the estimated $(T_A')_0$ and $(T_B')_0$ values

from step 1, to obtain an improved approximation of the true initial T' value. This improved value is designated as $(T'_c)_0$.

5. Another trial integration is then made with Eq. 7-13, using the value obtained for $(T'_c)_0$ in step 4 as the starting value of T'_i in Eq. 7-13a. This integration yields an improved final value of T'.

6. The improved final value of T' obtained in step 5 and the value of $(T'_c)_0$ used in obtaining it are next substituted into Eq. 7-14 as new values of $(T'_B)_F$ and $(T'_B)_0$, respectively. The old values of $(T'_B)_F$ and $(T'_B)_0$ become the new values of $(T'_A)_F$ and $(T'_A)_0$, respectively. The solution of Eq. 7-14 then yields a further improved approximation of the initial temperature gradient $(T'_c)_0$, which is, in turn, used for the starting value of T'_i in Eq. 7-13a to initiate another trial integration as in step 5. Steps 5 and 6 are then repeated, checking each final temperature gradient calculated against the true value (zero in this case), until the final T' value obtained from Eq. 7-13d varies from zero by less than some prescribed value used to specify the accuracy desired.

In discussing the use of Euler's self-starting modified method in Sec. 6-4, the numerical process ended by iterating, using the corrector equations and the given differential equation (Eq. 7-13d, e, and f, in this case) until successive values of the desired variables varied by less than some prescribed value defining the accuracy desired. However, in this problem in which the complete integration may have to be performed many times because of the trial-and-error nature of the method, we shall make a small sacrifice in accuracy to save computing time by not iterating at each numerical step.

The flow chart for the solution of this example is shown in Fig. 7-4. The variable names associated with the problem quantities in the computer program are as follows:

FORTRAN *Name*	*Quantity*	*Value Used in Problem*
TAPI	First value of initial temperature gradient, $°R/ft$ (starting value shown)	$-15,000$
TBPI	Second value of initial temperature gradient, $°R/ft$ (starting value shown)	$-18,000$
EMISS	Emissivity of fin	0.8
C	Thermal conductivity of fin, $Btu/(hr)(ft)(°R)$	25
EL	Length of fin, ft	0.25
H	Thickness of fin, ft	0.005
DELTX	Increment of distance along fin length, ft	0.005
TI	Known temperature of fin at $x = 0$, $°R$	2000
EPSI	Accuracy-check value for final temperature gradient, $°R/ft$	1

FORTRAN *Name*	*Quantity*	*Value Used in Problem*
XPR	x value at which a printout occurs, ft	
DXPR	Increments of x used for printout, ft	0.01
X	Variable distance along fin, ft	
SIG	Stefan-Boltzman constant, Btu/(ft)^2(hr) (°R)^4	$0.173(10)^{-8}$
N	Constant used in controlling flow of program	
T	Temperature at points along fin length, °R	
T1	Temperature 1 station in advance of that at which temperature is T, °R	
TP	Temperature gradient at points along fin length, °R/ft	
TP1	Temperature gradient 1 station in advance of that at which gradient is TP, °R/ft	
TDP	Second derivative of temperature with respect to x, (T''), °R/ft^2	
TDP1	Second derivative of temperature, with respect to x, 1 station in advance of that at which TDP applies, °R/ft^2	
TAPF	A calculated value of final temperature gradient (at $x = L$) from a trial integration, °R/ft	
TBPF	A calculated value of final temperature gradient (at $x = L$) obtained from trial integration immediately following trial integration in which TAPF was obtained, °R/ft	

The **FORTRAN IV** source program used to implement the flow chart is as follows:

```
1 FORMAT(2F7.0,3F4.0,3F5.0,2F3.0)
2 FORMAT(1H ,E14.8,6X,E14.8)
3 FORMAT(1H ,F8.0,F9.0,F5.1,F7.1,F7.2,F8.3,F8.3,F9.0,F7.1,F7.3)
  READ(5,1)TAPI,TBPI,EMISS,C,EL,H,DELTX,TI,EPSI,EXPR
  WRITE(6,3)TAPI,TBPI,EMISS,C,EL,H,DELTX,TI,EPSI,DXPR
  WRITE(6,4)
4 FORMAT(13H    FINAL TEMP,7X,15HFINAL TEMP GRAD,7X,
                              16HNEW INITIAL GRAD)
  XPR = DXPR
```

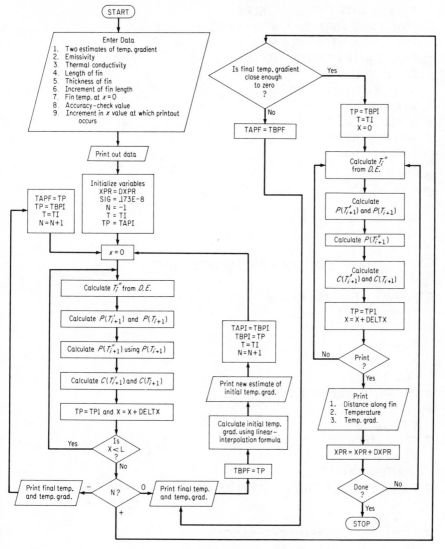

FIG. 7-4. Flow chart for Example 7-1.

```
   SIG = .173E−8
   N = −1
   T = TI
   TP = TAPI
25 X = 0.
 5 TDP = 2.*SIG*EMISS*T**4/(C*H)
   TP1 = TP+TDP*DELTX
```

```
      T1  =  T+(TP+TP1)/2.*DELTX
      TDP1  =  2.*SIG*EMISS*T1**4/(C*H)
      TP1  =  TP+(TDP+TDP1)/2.*DELTX
      T  =  T+(TP+TP1)/2.*DELTX
      TP  =  TP1
      X  =  X+DELTX
      IF(X−EL)5,6,6
    6 IF(N)7,8,10
    7 WRITE(6,2)T,TP
      TAPF  =  TP
      TP  =  TBPI
      T  =  TI
      N  =  N+1
      GO TO 25
    8 WRITE(6,2)T,TP
      TBPF  =  TP
      TP  =  (TAPF*TBPI−TAPI*TBPF)/(TAPF−TBPF)
      WRITE(6,9)TP
    9 FORMAT(1H ,43X,F11.2)
      TAPI  =  TBPI
      TBPI  =  TP
      T  =  TI
      N  =  N+1
      GO TO 25
   10 IF(ABS(TP)−EPSI)12,12,11
   11 TAPF  =  TBPF
      GO TO 8
   12 TP  =  TBPI
      T  =  TI
      WRITE(6,13)
   13 FORMAT(1H0,15HDISPL ALONG FIN,6X,11HTEMPERATURE,
                                   7X,13HTEMP GRADIENT)
      X  =  0.
   14 TDP  =  2.*SIG*EMISS*T**4/(C*H)
      TP1  =  TP+TDP*DELTX
      T1  =  T+(TP+TP1)/2.*DELTX
      TDP1=2.*SIG*EMISS*T1**4/(C*H)
      TP1  =  TP+(TDP+TDP1)/2.*DELTX
      T  =  T+(TP+TP1)/2.*DELTX
      TP  =  TP1
      X  =  X+DELTX
      IF(X−XPR)14,15,15
   15 WRITE(6,16)X,T,TP
```

```
16 FORMAT(1H ,4X,F6.3,13X,F7.0,13X,F9.0)
   XPR = XPR+DXPR
   IF(X−EL)14,17,17
17 STOP
   END
```

A graphical plot of the results given by the computer printout (to follow) is shown in Fig. 7-5, along with similar curves for two other fin thick-
nesses for which the tabular data are not shown.

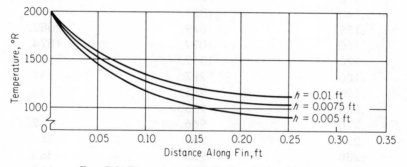

FIG. 7-5. Temperature distribution along radiating fin.

```
−15000.    −18000.    .8    25.0    .25    .005    .005    2000.
                                                    1.0    .010
```

FINAL TEMP	FINAL TEMP GRAD	NEW INITIAL GRAD
.60302201E+04	.26553654E+06	
.19052288E+02	−.63297317E+04	−17930.15
.57635010E+02	−.61289124E+04	−15798.43
.20406807E+04	.16719907E+05	−17358.34
.40161923E+03	−.41881807E+04	−17045.87
.61893295E+03	−.27452166E+04	−16451.39
.11340128E+04	.18675951E+04	−16692.08
.90448434E+03	−.43966777E+03	−16646.21
.94560655E+03	−.59436120E+02	−16639.04
.95213390E+03	.21741000E+01	−16639.29

DISPL ALONG FIN	TEMPERATURE	TEMP GRADIENT
.010	1849.	−13597.
.020	1725.	−11336.
.030	1620.	−9601.
.040	1531.	−8233.

DISPL ALONG FIN	TEMPERATURE	TEMP GRADIENT
.050	1455.	−7132.
.060	1388.	−6227.
.070	1329.	−5471.
.080	1278.	−4830.
.090	1232.	−4280.
.100	1192.	−3801.
.110	1156.	−3379.
.120	1124.	−3004.
.130	1096.	−2667.
.140	1071.	−2362.
.150	1049.	−2082.
.160	1029.	−1824.
.170	1012.	−1583.
.180	997.	−1357.
.190	985.	−1143.
.200	975.	−939.
.210	966.	−742.
.220	960.	−551.
.230	955.	−365.
.240	952.	−182.
.250	951.	.

STOP 00000

7-3. Simultaneous-Equation Method

We shall now examine a method of solving ordinary differential equations of the boundary-value type which involves the solution of simultaneous algebraic equations. In this process, the differential equation to be solved is first put into finite-difference form. If the interval over which the integration is desired is then divided into equal increments, the finite-difference equation used to approximate the given differential equation must be satisfied at *each* of the stations dividing the interval. The finite-difference equation has the form of an algebraic equation at each station, and if n stations are used we obtain a set of $n - 2$ algebraic equations which can be solved simultaneously to obtain a desired solution. Such a set of equations can be solved by any of the applicable methods discussed in Chapter 4.

This approach to the solution of boundary-value problems is usually reserved for linear differential equations, since the resulting algebraic equations are also linear and are more easily solved than those resulting from nonlinear differential equations. The procedure involved is illustrated by the following example.

Example 7-2

Let us determine the elastic curve of the nonuniform shaft described in Fig. 7-6a.[1] From mechanics of materials, we know that the equation defining the elastic curve (the deflection of the beam at any point) can be obtained by 2 successive integrations beginning with the integration of the differential equation

$$\frac{d^2y}{dx^2} = \frac{M}{EI} \tag{7-15}$$

where

y = beam deflection at any point, in.
x = variable distance along the beam, in.
M = internal beam moment at any point along the beam, lb-in.
E = modulus of elasticity, lb/in.^{2}
I = area moment of inertia of beam cross section, in.^{4}

In general, the expression M/EI is a function of the variable distance x along the beam. When this relationship can be easily expressed by a

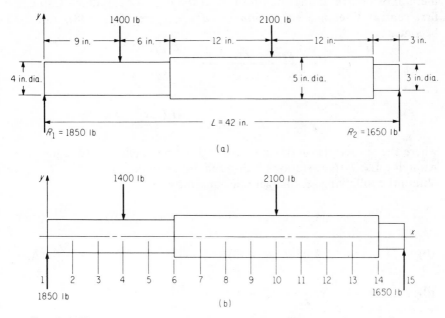

FIG. 7-6. Simply supported beam of Example 7-2. a) Beam loading and dimensions of shaft. b) Stations along beam.

[1] Creech, Merl D., Ammons, Robert L., and McPherson, James I. "Deflections of Complex Beams," *Prod. Eng.*, Aug. 14, 1961, pp. 47–49.

single continuous expression over the length of the beam (the desired range of integration), the *double-integration* method, mentioned above, provides a convenient means of analytically determining the elastic curve of the beam. However, when M/EI cannot be represented by a single elementary function over the desired range of x, an analytical solution becomes somewhat involved. For example, the determination of an analytical solution yielding the elastic curve of the shaft in Fig. 7-6a, by the double-integration method, would require the solution of 5 differential equations, since 5 different expressions would be required to define M/EI over the length of the shaft, because of the abrupt changes in cross section and the loading shown. The double integration required would thus involve 10 equations and 10 attendant constants of integration. Although a solution could be obtained, the process would be rather tedious. The *moment-area* method or *Castigliano's* method could also be used but would be equally tedious for solving a beam or shaft problem of this type.

The reduction of Eq. 7-15 to finite-difference form, with the resulting set of simultaneous linear algebraic equations, provides a convenient method of programming the problem to the digital computer. Using the first central-difference expression for d^2y/dx^2 (see Eq. 5-38), Eq. 7-15 becomes

$$\frac{y_{i+1} - 2y_i + y_{i-1}}{(\Delta x)^2} = \frac{M_i}{EI_i}$$

or

$$y_{i+1} - 2y_i + y_{i-1} = \frac{M_i(\Delta x)^2}{EI_i} \qquad (7\text{-}16)$$

where the subscripts on M and I remind us that each is a function of x. Applying Eq. 7-16 at stations 2 through 14, as indicated by Fig. 7-6b, we obtain the following set of algebraic equations:

$$y_1 - 2y_2 + y_3 + (0)y_4 + \cdots \qquad \cdots + (0)y_{15} = \frac{M_2}{EI_2}(\Delta x)^2$$

$$(0)y_1 + y_2 - 2y_3 + y_4 + (0)y_5 + \cdots \qquad \cdots + (0)y_{15} = \frac{M_3}{EI_3}(\Delta x)^2$$

$$(0)y_1 + (0)y_2 + y_3 - 2y_4 + y_5 + (0)y_6 + \cdots + (0)y_{15} = \frac{M_4}{EI_4}(\Delta x)^2$$

$$\vdots \qquad\qquad\qquad\qquad\qquad\qquad\qquad \vdots$$

$$(0)y_1 + (0)y_2 + \cdots \qquad \cdots + (0)y_{12} + y_{13} - 2y_{14} + y_{15} = \frac{M_{14}}{EI_{14}}(\Delta x)^2$$

$$(7\text{-}17)$$

This set of 13 linear algebraic equations contains the 15 deflection terms y_1 through y_{15}. However, since $y_1 = y_{15} = 0$ as known boundary values, Eq. 7-17 constitutes a set of 13 independent equations containing 13 unknowns, the simultaneous solution of which will yield unique solutions for the desired deflections.

The value of M and I at each station must be available as data for solving Eq. 7-17. The computation of these values can either be incorporated in the computer program or be determined manually beforehand and introduced into the computer program as data input, as is done in this example. The following values were determined, using an E value of $30(10)^6$ lb/in.^{2} for the modulus of elasticity of the steel. It should be noted that the I values, at the stations where the cross section changes, are obtained by averaging the I values of the abutting sections.

Station	M_i (lb-in.)	I_i (in.^{4})	$\dfrac{M_i}{EI_i}(\Delta x)^2$ (in.)
1	0	12.57	0.0
2	5,550	12.57	0.0001325
3	11,100	12.57	0.0002649
4	16,650	12.57	0.0003974
5	18,000	12.57	0.0004296
6	19,350	21.63	0.0002684
7	20,700	30.68	0.0002024
8	22,050	30.68	0.0002156
9	23,400	30.68	0.0002288
10	24,750	30.68	0.0002420
11	19,800	30.68	0.0001936
12	14,850	30.68	0.0001452
13	9,900	30.68	0.0000968
14	4,950	17.33	0.0000857
15	0	3.98	0.0

The computer program shown in Example 4-2, which was used to solve a set of linear simultaneous algebraic equations by the *Gauss-Jordan elimination method*, is used here for the solution of Eq. 7-17.

The computer printout of the solution is as follows:

DEFLECTIONS IN INCHES OF A STEEL SHAFT AT 3 INCH INCREMENTS
SOLUTION OF SIMULTANEOUS EQUATIONS BY ELIMINATION
$-.16560550E\text{-}02$
$-.31796106E\text{-}02$
$-.44382662E\text{-}02$
$-.52995222E\text{-}02$
$-.57311787E\text{-}02$

−.58944351E-02
−.58552921E-02
−.56005494E-02
−.51170072E-02
−.43914653E-02
−.34723236E-02
−.24079821E-02
−.12468410E-02
STOP 00000

A graphical representation of the same results is shown in Fig. 7-7.

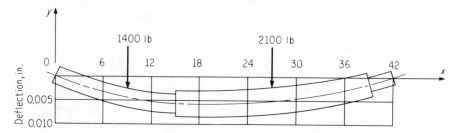

FIG. 7-7. Graphical representation of the deflection of the steel shaft of Example 7-2.

The displacement shown at station 10, $y_{10} = 0.005117$ in., compares with a value of 0.005196 in. for the same station obtained by the use of Castigliano's method.[2] It can be seen that the accuracy obtained with the finite-difference method, using just 15 stations, is sufficient for most practical problems. Increasing the number of stations will increase the accuracy of the solution, but the use of an excessive number of stations with the elimination method can lead to a loss in accuracy owing to the large number of calculations introduced in solving the many more simultaneous equations (see p. 188). The authors have solved problems of this type, using a large number of stations, by the Gauss-Seidel iteration method discussed in Sec. 4-6. However, convergence is generally relatively slow, and considerable computing time is thus involved. For many practical boundary-value problems the number of stations can be kept small and an elimination method employed, as was done in this example, to obtain solutions quickly with sufficient accuracy.

The procedure used to solve Eq. 7-15 in this example is said to be of the *third order*. This means that such a method is capable of yielding exact results if $y(x)$ is a polynomial of the third degree or less. For the shaft used in this example, an analytical solution will show that the dis-

[2] *Ibid.*

placements can be expressed by 5 different third-degree polynomials, each applicable to a particular segment of the shaft. However, exact results are not obtained by a third-order numerical method unless $y(x)$ can be expressed over the entire interval of integration with a single polynomial of the third degree or less.

For problems in which $y(x)$ is known to be a polynomial of degree higher than 3, more accurate results can be expected if a numerical procedure of higher order than 3 is used. Methods, known as *fifth-* and *seventh-order* methods, have been developed for use with problems of this type.[3] However, in most engineering problems the degree of accuracy required in the solutions does not warrant the use of higher-order procedures, and the third-order method, illustrated in this example, can be used to obtain the desired solutions.

7-4. Eigenvalue Problems

Numerous physical systems lead to homogeneous differential equations in which the parameters of the system must have particular values before a solution, which must satisfy certain boundary conditions at the end of the interval of integration, can be obtained. The required parameter values appear in the *characteristic values* or *eigenvalues.*

To illustrate the general nature of eigenvalue problems associated with differential equations, let us consider a slender column of length l subjected to an axial load P, as shown in Fig. 7-8. From beam theory

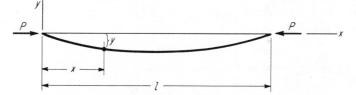

FIG. 7-8. Slender column subjected to an axial load P.

the basic relationship between the curvature d^2y/dx^2 and the internal moment M for the axes shown is

$$\frac{d^2y}{dx^2} = \frac{M}{EI}$$

(7-18)

where

  y = deflection at any point, in.
  x = variable distance along column, in.
  E = modulus of elasticity, lb/in.^{2}
  I = area moment of inertia of column cross section, in.^{4}

[3]Hildebrand, F. B. *Introduction to Numerical Analysis.* New York: McGraw-Hill Book Company, 1956.

Since y is negative for the configuration shown, and, by convention, the bending moment at any section is positive for this configuration, the bending moment M must be equal to $-Py$. With $M = -Py$, Eq. 7-18 becomes

$$\frac{d^2y}{dx^2} + \frac{P}{EI}y = 0 \tag{7-19}$$

or

$$\frac{d^2y}{dx^2} + \lambda y = 0 \tag{7-19a}$$

where $\lambda = \dfrac{P}{EI}$.

The solution of Eq. 7-19a is

$$y = A \cos \sqrt{\lambda}x + B \sin \sqrt{\lambda}x \tag{7-20}$$

where A and B are constants. Equation 7-20 is easily verified as being a solution by substituting it and its second derivative into Eq. 7-19a.

The *known* boundary conditions for the column are

$$y\,|_{x=0} = y\,|_{x=l} = 0 \tag{7-21}$$

Since the slope dy/dx is not known at $x = 0$, only 1 *initial* condition is known, and therefore, 1 constant, A or B, will be indeterminate. The parameter $\lambda = \dfrac{P}{EI}$ must have certain values to satisfy the condition that $y = 0$ at $x = l$. The required values of λ necessary to satisfy this condition are eigenvalues. To determine these values of λ, let us now consider the boundary conditions given in Eq. 7-21. Using $y = 0$ at $x = 0$, we find, from Eq. 7-20, that

$$A = 0 \tag{7-22}$$

Similarly, using $y = 0$ at $x = l$, we find that

$$B \sin \sqrt{\lambda}l = 0 \tag{7-23}$$

Since B cannot equal zero for a nontrivial solution, Eq. 7-23 can be satisfied only if

$$l\sqrt{\lambda} = n\pi \qquad n = 1, 2, 3, \ldots$$

Thus, the *eigenvalues* are

$$\lambda = \frac{n^2\pi^2}{l^2} = \frac{P}{EI} \qquad n = 1, 2, 3, \ldots \tag{7-24}$$

The configurations of the column for the first 3 eigenvalues, determined by substituting the eigenvalues into Eq. 7-20 with $A = 0$, are shown in Fig. 7-9.

The values of P which satisfy Eq. 7-24, for a given value of EI, are known as the *buckling* or *critical* loads. From a practical point of view,

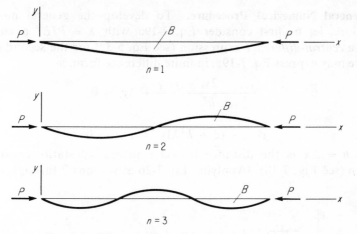

FIG. 7-9. Column configurations for first 3 eigenvalues.

the smallest value of P is of primary importance, since the configurations associated with the larger values of P cannot generally be obtained without failure first occurring under the action of the lowest value of P. The eigenvalue associated with the smallest buckling load is obtained with $n = 1$, so the smallest buckling load is

$$P_{cr} = \frac{\pi^2 EI}{l^2} \qquad (7\text{-}25)$$

If EI is not a constant but is some function of x, then the solution of Eq. 7-19, given by Eq. 7-20, is not applicable. In most cases in which such a differential equation contains variable coefficients, analytical solutions cannot be obtained, and it becomes necessary to resort to some numerical procedure for finding the eigenvalues.

The remainder of this chapter will be devoted to the discussion of a finite-difference method for obtaining the solution of homogeneous differential equations such as that given by Eq. 7-19. Such a differential equation can be readily expressed in general finite-difference form as a homogeneous algebraic equation. The application of this general equation for a set of values of the independent variable (at uniformly spaced stations along the column) yields a *set* of homogeneous algebraic equations. The eigenvalues of the set are approximations of the eigenvalues of the differential equation.

Two methods (previously discussed in Chapter 4 for determining eigenvalues of sets of homogeneous algebraic equations), the polynomial method and the iteration method, will be applied in the solution of the algebraic equations resulting from the finite-difference form of the differential equations.

General Numerical Procedure.   To develop the general numerical procedure, let us first consider Eq. 7-19a with $\lambda = P/EI$ a constant. Using a *central-difference* expression (see Eq. 5-32) for the second derivative, we may express Eq. 7-19a, in finite difference form, as

$$\frac{y_{i+1} - 2y_i + y_{i-1}}{h^2} + \lambda y_i = 0$$

or as

$$y_{i-1} - (2 - h^2\lambda)y_i + y_{i+1} = 0 \qquad (7\text{-}26)$$

where $h = \Delta x$ is the distance between successive stations along the column (see Fig. 7-10). Applying Eq. 7-26 at stations 2 through n along

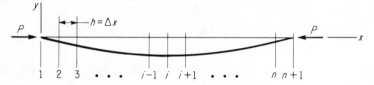

FIG. 7-10. Stations along column (n increments).

the column, we can write the system of homogeneous algebraic equations

$$
\begin{aligned}
y_1^0 - (2 - h^2\lambda)y_2 \quad &+ y_3 \quad + (0)y_4 + \cdots\cdots\cdots + (0)y_n = 0 \\
y_2 - (2 - h^2\lambda)y_3 \quad &+ y_4 + (0)y_5 + \cdots\cdots + (0)y_n = 0 \\
y_3 - (2 - h^2\lambda)y_4 + \; &y_5 + (0)y_6 + \cdots + (0)y_n = 0 \\
\cdots\cdots\cdots\cdots&\cdots\cdots\cdots\cdots\cdots\cdots\cdots\cdots \\
y_{n-1} - (2 - h^2\lambda)&y_n + y_{n+1}^0 = 0 \\
&(7\text{-}27)
\end{aligned}
$$

With n increments along the column, Eq. 7-27 yields $n - 1$ equations, the solution of which involves the expansion of an $n - 1$ by $n - 1$ determinant. From Sec. 4-7 we know that the expansion of the determinant yields an $n - 1$-degree polynomial in λ, the roots of which are eigenvalues. Since we used only a finite number of stations along the column, the $n - 1$ eigenvalues obtained will be only approximations of the true eigenvalues of the column. Fortunately, the lowest root or eigenvalue, which, in this problem, is the most important, is the most accurately approximated root value obtained. Improved approximations of all the eigenvalues determined can be obtained by increasing the number of increments. To illustrate, let us first take $h = \dfrac{l}{2}$ and obtain a first approximation of λ_1. The exact value of λ_1 was found to be $9.87/l^2$ (see Eq. 7-24). With $h = \dfrac{l}{2}$ (only 3 stations), and using the boundary conditions

$y_1 = y_3 = 0$, we can write, from Eq. 7-27,

$$0 - \left[2 - \left(\frac{l}{2}\right)^2 \lambda\right] y_2 + 0 = 0 \tag{7-28}$$

Thus, Eq. 7-28 shows that the approximation of λ_1 obtained for $h = \dfrac{l}{2}$ is

$$\lambda_1 = \frac{8}{l^2}$$

To obtain an improved approximation, let us use 3 increments (4 stations) so that $h = l/3$. From Eq. 7-27

$$\left.\begin{aligned}
\left[2 - \left(\frac{l}{3}\right)^2 \lambda\right] y_2 - y_3 = 0 \\
-y_2 + \left[2 - \left(\frac{l}{3}\right)^2 \lambda\right] y_3 = 0
\end{aligned}\right\} \tag{7-29}$$

Setting the determinant $|\mathbf{D}|$ of the coefficients of the y's equal to zero gives

$$|\mathbf{D}| = \begin{vmatrix} \left[2 - \left(\frac{l}{3}\right)^2 \lambda\right] & -1 \\ -1 & \left[2 - \left(\frac{l}{3}\right)^2 \lambda\right] \end{vmatrix} = 0$$

Expanding the determinant and simplifying yields the quadratic

$$\lambda^2 - \frac{36}{l^2}\lambda + \frac{243}{l^4} = 0$$

which has the roots

$$\lambda_1 = \frac{9}{l^2} \quad \text{and} \quad \lambda_2 = \frac{27}{l^2}$$

Thus, the approximation $\lambda_1 = 9/l^2$ is considerably closer to the exact value of $9.87/l^2$ than the approximation $8/l^2$ which was obtained by using only 2 increments. The value $\lambda_2 = 27/l^2$ is an approximation of the second eigenvalue which has the exact value $4(9.87)/l^2$ (see Eq. 7-24). It should now be apparent that the use of 4 increments ($h = l/4$) would yield a still-better approximation of λ_1 and λ_2 as well as a rough approximation of λ_3.

In general, a very good approximation of the smallest eigenvalue can be obtained by using a reasonable number of increments, say 10, for example. However, fairly accurate approximations of the higher eigenvalues are obtained only by using a large number of increments. Therefore, unless higher eigenvalues are desired, the required number of increments depends upon the desired accuracy of the approximation of λ_1 (the smallest eigenvalue).

One procedure for qualitatively evaluating the convergence of the approximation of λ_1 to the true value is to compute λ_1 by using successively larger numbers of increments. As the value of λ_1 converges to the true value, an increase in the number of increments will cause very little change in successively computed values of λ_1.

Polynomial Method.   Let us consider a column having a variable cross section. If the cross section of the column is not uniform, then the coefficient P/EI in the differential equation (see Eq. 7-19) is a variable, since the moment of inertia of the cross section varies along the column.

Denoting the value of I at station i as I_i, Eq. 7-26 becomes

$$y_{i-1} - \left(2 - h^2 \frac{P}{EI_i}\right) y_i + y_{i+1} = 0 \qquad (7\text{-}30)$$

Since the eigenvalues must appear as constants in each of the simultaneous equations resulting from Eq. 7-30, they must be defined in terms of the moment of inertia at some particular station. For example, if we relate the eigenvalues to the moment of inertia at station 1, we write

$$\frac{P}{EI_i} = \left(\frac{I_1}{I_i}\right) \frac{P}{EI_1} = \alpha_i \lambda \qquad (7\text{-}31)$$

where the variable coefficient $\alpha_i = I_1/I_i$ and $\lambda = P/EI_1$.

Using Eq. 7-30 and the notation of Eq. 7-31, we can write the system of the simultaneous equations as

$$y_1^0 - (2 - h^2\alpha_2\lambda)y_2 + y_3 + (0)y_4 + \cdots + (0)y_n = 0$$
$$y_2 - (2 - h^2\alpha_3\lambda)y_3 + y_4 + (0)y_5 + \cdots + (0)y_n = 0$$
$$y_3 - (2 - h^2\alpha_4\lambda)y_4 + y_5 + (0)y_6 + \cdots + (0)y_n = 0 \qquad (7\text{-}32)$$
$$\cdots\cdots\cdots\cdots\cdots\cdots\cdots\cdots\cdots\cdots\cdots\cdots$$
$$y_{n-1} - (2 - h^2\alpha_n\lambda)y_n + y_{n+1}^0 = 0$$

Dividing these equations through by the negatives of $h^2\alpha_2, h^2\alpha_3, \ldots, h^2\alpha_n$, respectively, we can express the determinant of the coefficient matrix in the form $|\mathbf{A} - \lambda\mathbf{I}|$ which is suitable for obtaining the characteristic polynomial by the Faddeev-Leverrier method discussed in Chapter 4. The resulting determinant is

$$|\mathbf{D}| = \begin{vmatrix} \left(\dfrac{2}{h^2\alpha_2} - \lambda\right) & -\dfrac{1}{h^2\alpha_2} & 0 & 0 & 0 \\ & \left(\dfrac{2}{h^2\alpha_3} - \lambda\right) & -\dfrac{1}{h^2\alpha_3} & 0 & 0 \\ & & \left(\dfrac{2}{h^2\alpha_4} - \lambda\right) & -\dfrac{1}{h^2\alpha_4} & 0 \\ & \cdots & \cdots & & \\ 0 & 0 & 0 & -\dfrac{1}{h^2\alpha_n} & \left(\dfrac{2}{h^2\alpha_n} - \lambda\right) \end{vmatrix} = 0$$

$$(7\text{-}33)$$

With n increments along the column, the expansion of this $n - 1$ by $n - 1$ determinant yields an $n - 1$ degree polynomial in λ. The *smallest* root λ_1 of the polynomial will be a close approximation of the smallest value of P/EI_1. The buckling load may then be determined from

$$\lambda_1 = \frac{P}{EI_1} \tag{7-34}$$

In considering columns of variable cross section with uniform thickness (see Fig. 7-11), the equation

$$I = I_1 \left(\frac{x'}{a}\right)^m \qquad x' \le a + \frac{l}{2} \tag{7-35}$$

might be used to define the moment of inertia of the column about a centroidal axis perpendicular to the xy plane at any cross section of the

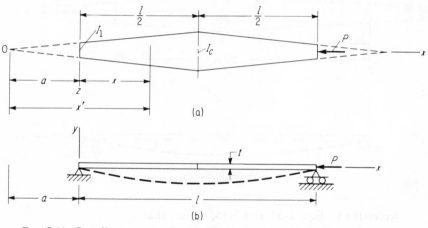

(a)

(b)

FIG. 7-11. Coordinate system for simply supported column of variable cross section.

column, where

x = distance along column (independent variable)

$x' = a + x$ (as shown in Fig. 7-11)

I = moment of inertia about centroidal axis perpendicular to xy plane (plane of bending) anywhere along column

I_1 = moment of inertia about centroidal axis perpendicular to plane of bending at $x' = a$

By using different values for the parameter a and the exponent m, Eq. 7-35 may be used for expressing the moment of inertia at any section of many differently shaped columns of uniform thickness. (For the column shown in Fig. 7-11, $m = 1$.)[4]

[4]Timoshenko, S. P., and Gere, J. M. *Theory of Elastic Stability*. New York: McGraw-Hill Book Company, 1961.

EXAMPLE 7-3

Let us consider the column shown in Fig. 7-12. This column has a uniform thickness and a cross section which varies as shown. The shape of this parabolic column is defined by choosing

$$a = 206.19 \text{ in.}$$

$$m = 2$$

$$I_c = 1.0 \text{ in.}^4$$

Since the column of Fig. 7-12 is symmetrical about $x = l/2$, the values of I, computed from Eq. 7-35 for the stations in the region of $0 < x < l/2$, may also be used for corresponding stations in the region of $x > l/2$.

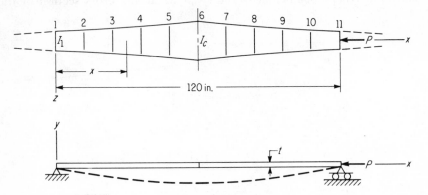

FIG. 7-12. Column of Example 7-3.

Referring to Eqs. 7-31 and 7-35, we see that

$$\alpha_i = \frac{I_1}{I_i} = \left(\frac{a}{x_i'}\right)^m$$

or

$$\alpha_i = \left(\frac{a}{a + x_i}\right)^m \tag{7-36}$$

With α_i defined by Eq. 7-36 and dividing the column into 10 increments so that h is defined, we can see (from Eq. 7-33) that we are ready to write a program for calculating the elements of the matrix **A** in the determinant of Eq. 7-33, $|\mathbf{A} - \lambda \mathbf{I}| = 0$. We will need to do no further programming, since these elements will then be used as data for the program developed in Chapter 4 for generating the characteristic polynomial coefficients by the Faddeev-Leverrier method. The roots of the characteristic polynomial will then be determined by Graeffe's method, using the computer program developed in Chapter 3.

The reader will recall that the latter program was written only to obtain the Graeffe table, from which the roots of the polynomial were calculated by slide rule. This procedure was used for polynomials which might have both real and complex roots, since a computer program for determining the roots of a polynomial having both types of roots is very complex. If it is known that all the roots of a polynomial are real (all the eigenvalues of the column problem are real, for example, since they correspond to the critical loads), a complete Graeffe program can easily be written which will utilize the data calculated for the Graeffe table to determine the roots of the polynomial. If such a program were written for this problem, both it and the program for finding the coefficients of the characteristic polynomial could be written as subroutine subprograms of a main program for determining the eigenvalues of a tapered column. However, since the use of subprograms is not possible with some smaller computers, the separate programs developed previously are used, as described in the preceding paragraph.

The procedure for generating the elements of the matrix for which we wish to determine the eigenvalues is outlined in the flow chart of Fig. 7-13. Note that an even number of column increments should always be used, since there is a whole number of increments in each half of the column. The elements of the matrix are calculated and then printed out by columns for visual inspection, and they also are punched out as data for the program concerned with generating the characteristic polynomial coefficients.

The FORTRAN names used in the program, the quantities they represent, and the data values used in this example are as follows:

FORTRAN Name	Quantity	Data Values Used in Problem
N	Number of increments into which column is divided for finite-difference representation of the differential equation $$\frac{d^2 y}{dx^2} = \frac{M}{EI}$$	10
M	Exponent m of Eq. 7-36 (The exponent describes the column shape)	2
EL	Length of column, in.	120.
AY	Distance from point of zero column width (if column were extended to $x' = 0$) to actual end of column, in.	206.19

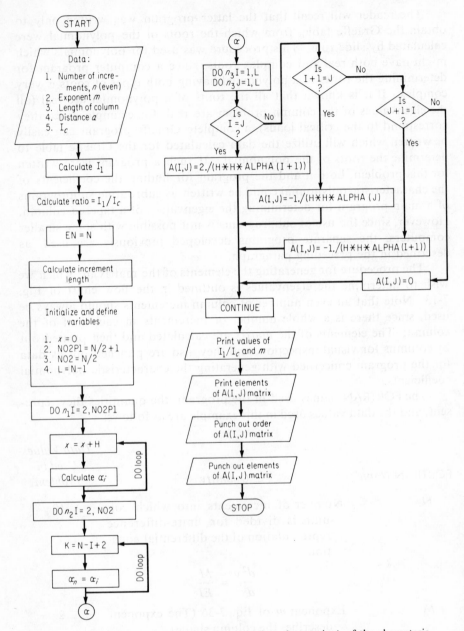

FIG. 7-13. Flow chart for the program to generate the matrix **A** of the characteristic polynomial $|\mathbf{A} - \lambda\mathbf{I}| = 0$ for the tapered-column problem.

FORTRAN *Name*	*Quantity*	*Data Values Used in Problem*
EYEC	I_c, the moment of inertia of the cross section of midpoint of column, in.[4]	1.0
EYE1	I_1, the moment of inertia of the cross section at end of column, in.[4]	
RATIO	I_1/I_c	
EN	Floating-point (real) name for number of increments n in column	
H	$h(h = \Delta x)$	
X	Variable distance x along the axis of column measured from column end	
NO2P1	$\dfrac{n}{2} + 1$	
ALPHA(I)	$\alpha_i = \left(\dfrac{a}{a + x_i}\right)^m$	
NO2	$n/2$	
K	Quantity $(n - i + 2)$, where $i = 2, 3, \ldots, n/2$	
L	Order of the **A** matrix, equal to $(n - 1)$	
A(I,J)	Elements of the matrix for which we want the eigenvalues λ	

The IBM 1620 FORTRAN source program, written to implement the flow chart shown in Fig. 7-13, is as follows:

```
DIMENSION ALPHA(16),A(15,15)
2 FORMAT (I5)
3 FORMAT (E14.0)
4 FORMAT (8HI1/IC = F6.4,6X,3HM= ,I2//)
5 FORMAT (29HCOEFFICIENT MATRIX BY COLUMNS/)
6 FORMAT (E14.8)
7 FORMAT (1H /)
  ACCEPT TAPE 2,N,M
  ACCEPT TAPE 3,EL,AY,EYEC
  EYE1 = EYEC*(AY/(EL/2.+AY))**M
  RATIO = EYE1/EYEC
  EN = N
  H = EL/EN
  X = 0.
  NO2P1 = N/2+1
  NO2 = N/2
  L = N−1
```

```
   DO8I = 2,NO2P1
   X = X+H
 8 ALPHA(I) = (AY/(AY + X))**M
   DO9I = 2,NO2
   K = N-I+2
 9 ALPHA(K) = ALPHA(I)
   DO16J = 1,L
   DO16I = 1,L
   IF(I-J)10,13,10
10 IF(I+1-J)11,14,11
11 IF(J+1-I)12,15,12
12 A(I,J) = 0.
   GO TO 16
13 A(I,J) = 2./(H**2*ALPHA(I+1))
   GO TO 16
14 A(I,J) = -1./(H**2*ALPHA(J))
   GO TO 16
15 A(I,J) = -1./(H**2*ALPHA(I+1))
16 CONTINUE
   PRINT 4,RATIO,M
   PRINT 5
   DO 18J = 1,L
   DO 17I = 1,L
17 PRINT 6,A(I,J)
18 PRINT 7
   PUNCH TAPE 2,L
   DO 19J = 1,L
   DO 19I = 1,L
19 PUNCH TAPE 6,A(I,J)
   STOP
   END
```

The following computer printout gives the elements of the matrix **A** for which we must determine the eigenvalues:

```
   I1/IC = .6000     M= 2
COEFFICIENT MATRIX BY COLUMNS
           .15552563E-01            -.77762819E-02
          -.86551625E-02             .17310325E-01
           .00000000E-99            -.95810861E-02
           .00000000E-99             .00000000E-99
           .00000000E-99             .00000000E-99
           .00000000E-99             .00000000E-99
           .00000000E-99             .00000000E-99
           .00000000E-99             .00000000E-99
           .00000000E-99             .00000000E-99
```

.00000000E−99
−.86551625E−02
.19162172E−01
−.10554052E−01
.00000000E−99
.00000000E−99
.00000000E−99
.00000000E−99
.00000000E−99

.00000000E−99
.00000000E−99
.00000000E−99
.00000000E−99
.00000000E−99
−.10554052E−01
.19162172E−01
−.86551625E−02
.00000000E−99

.00000000E−99
.00000000E−99
−.95810861E−02
.21108104E−01
−.11574061E−01
.00000000E−99
.00000000E−99
.00000000E−99
.00000000E−99

.00000000E−99
.00000000E−99
.00000000E−99
.00000000E−99
.00000000E−99
.00000000E−99
−.95810861E−02
.17310325E−01
−.77762819E−02

.00000000E−99
.00000000E−99
.00000000E−99
−.10554052E−01
.23148122E−01
−.10554052E−01
.00000000E−99
.00000000E−99
.00000000E−99

.00000000E−99
.00000000E−99
.00000000E−99
.00000000E−99
.00000000E−99
.00000000E−99
.00000000E−99
−.86551625E−02
.15552563E−01

.00000000E−99
.00000000E−99
.00000000E−99
.00000000E−99
−.11574061E−01
.21108104E−01
−.95810861E−02
.00000000E−99
.00000000E−99

Using the punched tape, from the program just discussed, as data for the program to determine the characteristic polynomial coefficients by the Faddeev-Leverrier method (see Chapter 4), we obtain the following computer output:

THE CHARACTERISTIC POLYNOMIAL COEFFICIENTS
P(1) THROUGH P(N) ARE,

$$
\begin{array}{r}
.16941444E-00 \\
-.11981431E-01 \\
.45951526E-03 \\
-.10387507E-04 \\
.14079792E-06 \\
-.11128907E-08 \\
.47381384E-11 \\
-.91692431E-14 \\
.53611237E-17
\end{array}
$$

STOP 0000

These coefficients are substituted into Eq. 4-98 to obtain the characteristic polynomial where Eq. 4-98 is of the form

$$\lambda^9 - p_1\lambda^8 - p_2\lambda^7 \cdots p_8\lambda - p_9 = 0 \qquad (7\text{-}37)$$

Because of the minus signs associated with all terms but the first in Eq. 7-37, the coefficients used in the program for determining the Graeffe table must be opposite in sign to those printed out above, since the program for Graeffe's method is based upon all plus signs in the characteristic polynomial. Using the characteristic-polynomial coefficients of opposite sign as input data to the program developed in Chapter 3 yields the Graeffe table shown in the following computer printout:

COEFFICIENTS OF POLYNOMIAL	SCALED COEFFICIENTS M= 1
$-.16941444E+00$	$-.14057949E+02$
$.11981431E-01$	$.82499589E+02$
$-.45951526E-03$	$-.26255155E+03$
$.10387507E-04$	$.49249014E+03$
$-.14079792E-06$	$-.55392888E+03$
$.11128907E-08$	$.36331375E+03$
$-.47381384E-11$	$-.12835376E+03$
$.91692431E-14$	$.20611325E+02$
$-.53611237E-17$	$-.99999953E-00$

SCALE FACTOR=   .12051149E-01

DERIVED COEFFICIENTS

ITER. NO. 1   M = 2

.32626760E+02
.40928988E+03
.25204315E+04
.80556626E+04
.13006540E+05
.95758200E+04
.26057890E+04
.16811932E+03
.99999906E−00

ITER. NO. 4   M = 16

.30678406E+09
.44638421E+16
.51568075E+22
.22135626E+27
.15020014E+30
.24857766E+30
.13652034E+27
.27478998E+18
.99999248E−00

ITER. NO. 2   M = 4

.24592570E+03
.19162505E+05
.58794346E+06
.69983852E+07
.27888810E+08
.26615316E+08
.35963887E+07
.23052532E+05
.99999812E−00

ITER. NO. 5   M = 32

.85188775E+17
.16762276E+32
.24616557E+44
.47449489E+53
.22450034E+59
.61749843E+59
.18637667E+53
.75509533E+35
.99998496E−00

ITER. NO. 3   M = 8

.22154439E+05
.92017550E+08
.91128250E+11
.17201573E+14
.40948533E+15
.50809970E+15
.11706966E+14
.52422647E+09
.99999624E−00

ITER. NO. 6   M = 64

.72236028E+34
.27677979E+63
.60438415E+87
.15101906E+36
.91759000E+96
.00000000E−99
.99999067E+99
.57016895E+70
.99996992E−00

From the table it is apparent that each of the last derived coefficients (m = 64) is approaching the square of the corresponding preceding coefficient and that we have a regular relationship for all coefficients. We recall, from our discussion of Graeffe's method in Chapter 3, that if all the derived coefficients form a regular relationship (derived coefficients are essentially the square of the corresponding preceding coefficients), then all the roots of the polynomial will be real and distinct. This should be expected for the column problem.

The eigenvalues can be quickly obtained from the table of derived coefficients by the use of Eq. 3-39. Thus, to find the *smallest* eigenvalue, we use

$$r_n = \left(\frac{b_n}{b_{n-1}}\right)^{1/m} \qquad \text{or} \qquad \log r_n = \frac{1}{m} \log\left(\frac{b_n}{b_{n-1}}\right)$$

where the largest subscript of r ($n = 9$) refers to the *smallest* root so that $r_9 = \lambda_1$. Hence, from the table of derived coefficients, for $m = 64$, we write for the *scaled* polynomial

$$\log_e r_9 = \frac{1}{64} \log\left[\frac{.99996992}{(.57016895) 10^{70}}\right]$$

$$= -2.5092$$

$$r_9 = 0.08144 \text{ (smallest root of scaled polynomial)}$$

To obtain the actual root we multiply the scaled root by the scale factor. Hence,

$$r_9 \text{ (actual root)} = 0.08144 (0.01205) = 0.000981 \text{ in.}^{-2}$$

Thus, we write for the *smallest* eigenvalue

$$\lambda_1 = \frac{P_{cr}}{EI_1} = 0.000981 \text{ in.}^{-2}$$

For our particular problem $I_c = 1.0$ and $I_1/I_c = 0.6$, as given by the computer printout of the coefficient matrix. Hence, $I_1 = 0.6$. For a steel column in which $E = 30 \times 10^6$ psi, the critical or buckling load is

$$P_{cr} = (0.000981)(30 \times 10^6)(0.6)$$

$$= 17,700 \text{ lb}$$

The smallest eigenvalues for tapered columns of the form described by Eq. 7-35 have been determined analytically by Timoshenko.[5] He tabulates values of the dimensionless factor f in the formula

$$P_{cr} = \frac{fEI_c}{l^2}$$

for different values of I_1/I_c and the exponent m (see Eq. 7-35). For $I_1/I_c = 0.6$ and $m = 2$ (the values used in this example), Timoshenko gives $f = 8.51$. The numerical solution by the polynomial method yields

$$f = \frac{Pl^2}{EI_c} = \frac{P}{EI_1}\left(\frac{I_1}{I_c}\right)l^2 = (0.000981)(0.6)(120)^2$$

$$= 8.49$$

Thus, the numerical solution is well within the limits of engineering accuracy. Furthermore, it has the advantage of being applicable to any kind of variation of cross section. In addition, approximations to the higher eigenvalues—and thus higher buckling loads—may also be ob-

[5] *Ibid.*

tained from the polynomial method. For example, referring to the table of derived coefficients for $m = 32$, the second eigenvalue (next to the smallest) is determined as follows:

$$\log r_8 = \frac{1}{32} \log \frac{b_8}{b_7}$$

$$= \frac{1}{32} \log \frac{0.75509533 \times 10^{35}}{0.18637667 \times 10^{53}}$$

$$r_8 = 0.2863 \text{ (root of scaled polynomial)}$$

$$r_8 \text{ (actual root)} = (0.2863)(0.01205) = 0.003450$$

Hence,

$$\lambda_2 = r_8 = \frac{P_{cr}}{EI_1} = 0.003450 \text{ in.}^{-2}$$

For a steel column ($E = 30 \times 10^6$), the critical load corresponding to λ_2 is

$$P_{cr} = (0.003450)(30 \times 10^6)(0.6)$$

$$= 62,100 \text{ lb}$$

The general configuration of the column corresponding to λ_2 is shown in Fig. 7-14.

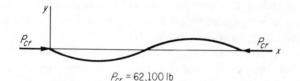

$$P_{cr} = 62,100 \text{ lb}$$

FIG. 7-14. General configuration of tapered column corresponding to $\lambda_2 = 0.003450$.

As previously discussed, the polynomial method results in the best approximation of the smallest eigenvalue. Therefore, we know that the approximation of $\lambda_2 = 0.003450$ is slightly less accurate than the approximation $\lambda_1 = 0.000981$.

Using the program of Sec. 4-9 for finding the linearly independent eigenvectors associated with an eigenvalue of a matrix **A,** we find that there is just 1 eigenvector associated with each eigenvalue in this problem.

The components of the eigenvector associated with $\lambda_1 = 0.000981$ are determined as

THE LINEARLY INDEPENDENT EIGENVECTORS ARE,

$$-.34046267E-00$$
$$-.63797499E-00$$

$$-.86317753E-00$$
$$-.10000000E\ 01$$
$$-.10446372E\ 01$$
$$-.10007326E\ 01$$
$$-.86380994E-00$$
$$-.63844242E-00$$
$$-.34071211E-00$$

and the components of the eigenvector associated with $\lambda_2 = 0.003450$ are found to be

THE LINEARLY INDEPENDENT EIGENVECTORS ARE,

$$-.11184325E\ 01$$
$$-.17406649E\ 01$$
$$-.16712231E\ 01$$
$$-.10000000E\ 01$$
$$.00000000E-99$$
$$.99678635E-00$$
$$.16696227E\ 01$$
$$.17412541E\ 01$$
$$.11188112E\ 01$$

In this problem the components of the eigenvectors are beam deflections, and it is apparent that these eigenvectors conform to the first 2 modes of bending, as shown in Fig. 7-9.

Iteration Method.   In Chapter 4 an iteration method, known as the power method, was developed for use in solving eigenvalue problems. This was found to be a convenient method to use when only the smallest and/or largest eigenvalues of a matrix are desired, since the procedure is rather direct and the associated eigenvectors are obtained along with the eigenvalues.

This method may also be used for solving eigenvalue problems associated with differential equations of the type discussed in the introductory paragraphs of this section.   Its use is illustrated in the example which follows.

EXAMPLE 7-4

Let us again consider the column of Fig. 7-12, which was analyzed in Example 7-3. This column has a uniform thickness, and a variable cross section for which the moment of inertia varies according to Eq. 7-35. A set of n simultaneous equations describing such a column with a variable cross section is given by Eq. 7-32. Dividing these equations through by $h^2\alpha_2, h^2\alpha_3, \ldots, h^2\alpha_n$, respectively, we obtain the equations in a matrix form, suitable for the iteration method, as

$$
\begin{bmatrix}
\left(\dfrac{2}{h^2\alpha_2} - \lambda\right) & -\dfrac{1}{h^2\alpha_2} & 0 & 0 & 0 \\[2ex]
 & \left(\dfrac{2}{h^2\alpha_3} - \lambda\right) & -\dfrac{1}{h^2\alpha_3} & 0 & 0 \\[2ex]
 & \dfrac{1}{h^2\alpha_4} & \left(\dfrac{2}{h^2\alpha_4} - \lambda\right) & -\dfrac{1}{h^2\alpha_4} & 0 \\[2ex]
\hdotsfor{5} \\[1ex]
0 & 0 & 0 & -\dfrac{1}{h^2\alpha_n} & \left(\dfrac{2}{h^2\alpha_n} - \lambda\right)
\end{bmatrix}
\begin{Bmatrix}
y_2 \\[1ex] y_3 \\[1ex] y_4 \\[1ex] \cdot \\[1ex] y_n
\end{Bmatrix} = \mathbf{0}
$$

The above may be written more compactly as

$$[\mathbf{A} - \lambda \mathbf{I}]\mathbf{Y} = \mathbf{0} \tag{7-38}$$

and we see that the equations are in the form for which the program in Sec. 4-10 was written for determining the smallest eigenvalue of the matrix $\mathbf{A}$.

The computer output resulting from the application of this program to the column problem of Example 7-3 is

SMALLEST EIGENVALUE IS .97964253E−03

THE ASSOCIATED EIGENVECTOR COMPONENTS ARE

.10000000E 01
.18740216E 01
.25359309E 01
.29385476E 01
.30684042E 01
.29385480E 01
.25359312E 01
.18740221E 01
.10000002E 01

STOP 0000

The smallest eigenvalue is found to be 0.000980 in.$^{-2}$, to 3 significant figures, as compared to 0.000981 in.$^{-2}$ obtained by the polynomial method. Thus, the critical load for the column is found to be 17,650 lb, as compared to 17,700 lb when using the polynomial method. This small difference is insignificant from an engineering standpoint.

Problems

7-1. Example 7-1 is concerned with the digital-computer solution of the radiating-fin problem. The following differential equation, derived in Example

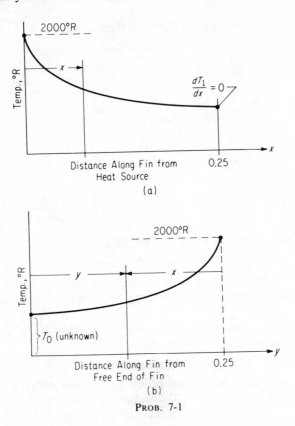

Distance Along Fin from   0.25
Heat Source
(a)

Distance Along Fin from   0.25
Free End of Fin
(b)

PROB. 7-1

7-1, refers to the coordinate system shown in part a) of the accompanying figure:

$$\frac{d^2 T_1}{dx^2} = \frac{2\sigma\epsilon_1}{kh} T_1^4$$

where the pertinent initial and final boundary conditions are

$$x = 0 \quad \begin{vmatrix} T_1 = 2{,}000°\text{R} \\ \dfrac{dT_1}{dx} = ? \end{vmatrix} \quad x = L \quad \begin{vmatrix} \dfrac{dT_1}{dx} = 0 \end{vmatrix}$$

The use of a different set of coordinate axes, such as shown in part b) of the figure, with the new independent variable y, results in a new differential equation

$$\frac{d^2 T_1}{dy^2} = \frac{2\sigma\epsilon_1}{kh} T_1^4$$

which describes the system.

Considering T_1 as a function of y, determine the pertinent initial and final boundary conditions required to obtain a numerical solution by the trial-and-error approach discussed in Sec. 7-2.

Write a **FORTRAN** program for solving the differential equation associated with the new set of axes so that the temperature distribution along the fin may be determined. Using the program written and the data given in Example 7-1, obtain a computer solution of the temperature distribution along the fin.

7-2. The simply supported beam of the accompanying figure is subjected to a uniformly distributed lateral load of $q = 20$ lb/in. and an axial load P. The

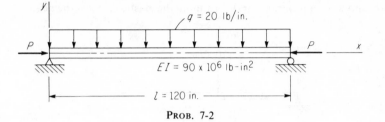

$q = 20$ lb/in.

P P x

$EI = 90 \times 10^6$ lb-in.²

$l = 120$ in.

PROB. 7-2

differential equation of the beam is

$$EI \frac{d^2y}{dx^2} = -Py + \frac{ql}{2} x - \frac{q}{2} x^2$$

where

E = modulus of elasticity of beam
I = moment of inertia of beam cross section

Since the beam is simply supported, the y deflection of the beam is zero at $x = 0$ and $x = l$, and the slope (dy/dx) of the beam is unknown at both $x = 0$ and $x = l$.

Write a **FORTRAN** program for determining the deflections which define the elastic curve of the beam for various axial loads P. Include in the program the steps necessary to obtain the information required to plot the maximum deflection of the beam for each lateral load P as a function of P.

Using the program written, obtain computer solutions for axial loads of 10,000 lb, 20,000 lb, 30,000 lb, and 40,000 lb applied along with the lateral loading specified above. Is the maximum deflection of the beam a linear function of the axial loads P applied?

7-3. The analytical solution of the differential equation of the beam shown in the figure accompanying Prob. 7-2 is

$$y = \frac{qEI}{P^2} \left[(1 - \cos kx) + \left(\frac{\cos kl - 1}{\sin kl} \right) \right] \sin kx + \frac{ql}{2P} x - \frac{q}{2P} x^2$$

where

$$k^2 = \frac{P}{EI}$$

Write a **FORTRAN** program for evaluating the analytical solution shown. Using the program written and the values of E, I, l, q, and P given in Prob. 7-2, determine the deflections defining the elastic curve of the beam for each value of P.

If Prob. 7-2 has been worked prior to working this problem, select a Δx increment corresponding to that used in Prob. 7-2 and compare the solutions obtained in the two problems at various points along the beam.

7-4.   Utilizing the relationship from elementary beam theory,

$$EI \frac{d^2 y}{dx^2} = M$$

write the necessary moment equations for the beam shown in the accompanying figure, and write a program for determining the elastic curve of the beam.

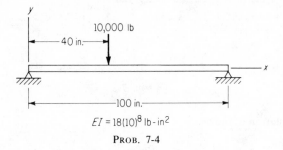

$$EI = 18(10)^8 \text{ lb-in}^2$$

Prob. 7-4

7-5.   Utilizing the relationship from elementary beam theory,

$$EI \frac{d^2 y}{dx^2} = M$$

write the necessary moment equations for the beam shown in the accompanying figure, and write a program for determining the elastic curve of the beam.

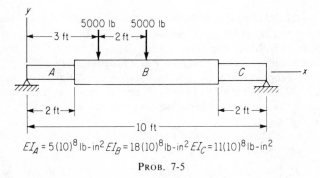

$$EI_A = 5(10)^8 \text{ lb-in}^2 \quad EI_B = 18(10)^8 \text{ lb-in}^2 \quad EI_C = 11(10)^8 \text{ lb-in}^2$$

Prob. 7-5

7-6. The beam shown in part a) of the accompanying figure is fixed at A and pinned at B and is thus statically indeterminate. However, looking at the free-body diagram of the beam in part b), we can take moments about an axis through B and obtain the following relationship between the moment at the fixed end and the reaction there:

$$\frac{M_A}{100} + 5000 = R_A$$

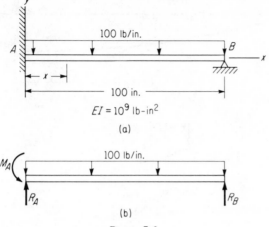

100 lb/in.

$EI = 10^9$ lb-in^2

(a)

100 lb/in.

(b)

PROB. 7-6

Utilizing the relationship from elementary beam theory,

$$EI \frac{d^2 y}{dx^2} = M$$

write the moment equation of the beam, in terms of M_A, and write a program for determining the elastic curve of the beam, the moment at the fixed end, and the vertical reactions at each end.

7-7. The differential equation for a flexible cable is

$$\frac{d^2 y}{dx^2} = -\frac{w(x)}{H} \tag{1}$$

where y is the vertical displacement, $w(x)$ is the load per unit length, and the constant H is the horizontal component of the tension T in the cable. The differential equation is readily derived by setting the summation of forces in the x and y directions equal to zero for a differential segment, as shown in the accompanying illustration. That is,

$$T_1 \sin \theta_1 - T_2 \sin \theta_2 = w(x)\,dx \tag{2}$$

$$H = T_1 \cos \theta_1 = T_2 \cos \theta_2 \quad \text{(a constant)} \tag{3}$$

Eliminating T_1 and T_2 from the first equation gives

$$H(\tan \theta_1 - \tan \theta_2) = w(x)\,dx \tag{4}$$

where $\tan \theta_1 = \left. \dfrac{dy}{dx} \right)_x$ and $\tan \theta_2 = \left. \dfrac{dy}{dx} \right)_{x+dx}$. Since

$$\frac{\left. \dfrac{dy}{dx} \right)_x - \left. \dfrac{dy}{dx} \right)_{x+dx}}{dx} = -\frac{d^2 y}{dx^2}$$

Eq. 4 yields the differential equation, Eq. 1.

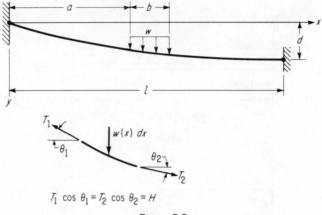

$$T_1 \cos \theta_1 = T_2 \cos \theta_2 = H$$

PROB. 7-7

Write a **FORTRAN** program for obtaining, by the trial-and-error method, the y displacements of the cable shown in the accompanying illustration. The right end is anchored a distance d below the left end. The pertinent data are as follows:

$$l = 200 \text{ ft} \qquad d = 10 \text{ ft} \qquad a = 100 \text{ ft}$$
$$b = 10 \text{ ft} \qquad H = 10{,}000 \text{ lb} \qquad w = 20 \text{ lb/ft}$$

7-8. Referring to Prob. 7-7, write a **FORTRAN** program for obtaining, by the finite-difference–simultaneous-equation method, the y displacements of the cable.

7-9. Referring to Prob. 7-7, write a **FORTRAN** program for obtaining the y displacements of the cable and the tension T in the cable at various values of x along the cable. Do not make the assumption that $\sin \theta = \tan \theta = \theta$ for obtaining the values for the tension T.

7-10. The differential equation for the radial displacement u of a point in a thick-walled cylinder is

$$\frac{d^2 u}{d\rho^2} + \frac{1}{\rho} \frac{du}{d\rho} - \frac{u}{\rho^2} = 0$$

The radial displacement of point A to A', as shown in the accompanying illustration, is a result of the tangential and radial strains which may be induced by subjecting the inside and outside boundaries of the cylinder to changes in temperature and/or pressures. The relation between the tangential strain ϵ_t, of a fiber at a distance ρ from the center, and the radial displacement u is $\epsilon_t = u/\rho$. Assuming that the tangential strains ϵ_t have been measured on the inside and outside boundaries of a cylinder subjected to an internal pressure and known temperature changes, write a **FORTRAN** program for obtaining the radial displacements u throughout the cylinder. The tangential strains on the boundaries, as measured with SR-4 strain gauges, are

$$\epsilon_t \big|_{\rho = 2 \text{ in.}} = 1000 \times 10^{-6} \text{ in./in.}$$
$$\epsilon_t \big|_{\rho = 4 \text{ in.}} = 200 \times 10^{-6} \text{ in./in.}$$

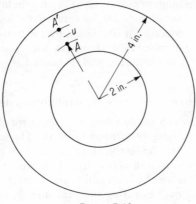

PROB. 7-10

7-11. In Prob. 7-10 the differential equation for the radial displacement u in a thick-walled cylinder was given as

$$\frac{d^2u}{d\rho^2} + \frac{1}{\rho}\frac{du}{d\rho} - \frac{u}{\rho^2} = 0$$

Assume a solution to this differential equation of the form

$$u = \Sigma\alpha_n\rho^n$$

and show that the solution is

$$u = \alpha_1\rho + \frac{\alpha_2}{\rho}$$

where α_1 and α_2 are constants for integration. If a numerical solution has been obtained for Prob. 7-10, compare these results with the analytical solution.

7-12. The deflection z of a circular membrane which is loaded uniformly with a pressure p is described by the differential equation

$$\frac{d^2z}{dr^2} + \frac{1}{r}\frac{dz}{dr} = -\frac{p}{T}$$

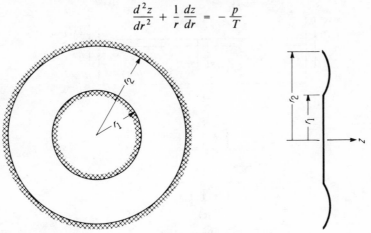

PROB. 7-12

where T is the tension (pounds per linear inch). For a highly stretched membrane, the tension T may be assumed constant for small deflections.

Write a **FORTRAN** program for obtaining, by the trial-and-error method, the deflections of the annular membrane shown in the accompanying illustration. The pertinent data for the membrane, which is fastened at r_1 and r_2, are as follows:

$r_1 = 6$ in. $r_2 = 12$ in.

$T = 100$ lb/in. $p = 5$ psi (uniformly distributed)

7-13.   Fluid flowing in a conduit flows by a thin wire of length l and radius r, as shown in the accompanying illustration (part a). The temperature of the fluid flowing by the wire is U, and the temperatures at the ends of the wire in the walls of the conduit are $u(0) = u_0$ and $u(l) = u_e$, as shown in part b of the figure. Thus, heat flows along the wire by conduction, and from the surface of the wire by convection and conduction. Equating the heat flow q_1 into the element to the heat flow $q_2 + q_3$ from the element, as shown in part c of the figure, the differential equation for the temperature u in the wire is found to be

$$\frac{d^2u}{dx^2} = \frac{2K}{kr} u - \frac{2K}{kr} U$$

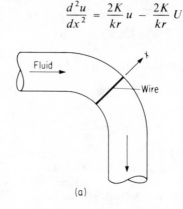

(a)

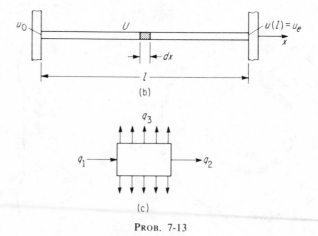

(b)

(c)

PROB. 7-13

where

k = thermal conductivity of wire material

r = radius of wire

K = effective conductance of wire surface for heat transfer by convection and conduction

The conductance K depends to some extent upon the Reynolds number, which is proportional to the velocity of the fluid. Since the wire cuts across the fluid stream at a bend in the conduit, the velocity of the fluid varies along the length of the wire. Considering that the velocity along the wire increases with x, a reasonable assumption for the variation of K along the wire is

$$K = K_0 + cx$$

where c is a constant, and K_0 is the value of K at $x = 0$.

Write a **FORTRAN** program for obtaining, by the finite-difference-simultaneous-equation method, the temperature u along the wire. Use the following data:

$$l = 1 \text{ ft}$$

$$r = 0.01 \text{ ft}$$

$$u_0 = 100°\text{F}$$

$$u_e = 250°\text{F}$$

$$k = 0.035 \text{ Btu}/(\text{sec})(\text{ft})(°\text{F})$$

$$K_0 = 3.8 \text{ Btu}/(\text{sec})(\text{ft}^2)(°\text{F})$$

$$c = 2 \text{ Btu}/(\text{sec})(\text{ft})^3(°\text{F})$$

$$U = 300°\text{F}$$

chapter 8

Partial Differential Equations

8-1. Introduction

We shall now consider the numerical solution of partial differential equations of the general form

$$a \frac{\partial^2 u}{\partial x^2} + b \frac{\partial^2 u}{\partial x \partial y} + c \frac{\partial^2 u}{\partial y^2} = f \qquad (8\text{-}1)$$

where, in general, the coefficients a, b, and c are functions of x and y, and f is a function of x, y, u, $\partial u/\partial x$, and $\partial u/\partial y$. Such equations arise in engineering work involving heat transfer, boundary-layer flow, vibrations, elasticity, and so on. It will not be possible, within the scope of this text, to present a comprehensive coverage of the various numerical methods for solving partial differential equations. However, the material presented will provide an introduction to the subject by illustrating some of the most easily understandable and useful methods. The various forms which Eq. 8-1 may take are classified as *elliptic*, *parabolic*, or *hyperbolic*. The solution of each type will be illustrated by an engineering example.

8-2. Elliptic Partial Differential Equations

Elliptic partial differential equations are found in *equilibrium*-type boundary-value problems. In this kind of problem the differential equation will have coefficients such that

$$b^2 - 4ac < 0$$

where a, b, and c are the coefficients associated with Eq. 8-1.[1] Typical examples of this type of differential equation include Laplace's equation

$$\frac{\partial^2 u}{\partial x^2} + \frac{\partial^2 u}{\partial y^2} = 0 \qquad (8\text{-}2)$$

---

[1]Crandall, Stephen H. *Engineering Analysis.* New York: McGraw-Hill Book Company, 1956, pp. 353 ff.

and Poisson's equation

$$\frac{\partial^2 u}{\partial x^2} + \frac{\partial^2 u}{\partial y^2} = f(x, y) \tag{8-3}$$

where the function $u(x, y)$ must satisfy both the differential equation over a *closed domain* and the boundary conditions on the closed boundary of the domain. A closed solution domain (as opposed to an open-ended domain) is characteristic of elliptic partial differential equations. This is illustrated graphically in Fig. 8-1. The solution domains of parabolic

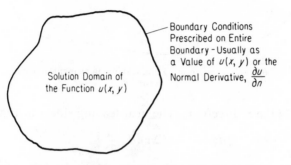

FIG. 8-1. Solution domain of an elliptic partial differential equation.

and hyperbolic differential equations are fundamentally different in nature, as they are open-ended domains.

To illustrate a physical situation in which an elliptic partial differential equation arises, let us consider the problem of determining the temperature distribution in a thin homogeneous rectangular plate, insulated perfectly on both faces, with prescribed boundary conditions maintained along the edges of the plate. It will be assumed that the specific heat and thermal conductivity of the plate material do not vary throughout the plate and that the plate is thin enough to consider the heat flow in a direction normal to the insulated faces as negligible.

Establishing an x-y coordinate system on the plate, as shown in Fig. 8-2, we first consider a small element of the plate with dimensions of Δx and Δy. Such an element is shown greatly exaggerated in size in the figure. The quantity of heat entering side 1 of the element in time dt is given by Fourier's law of heat conduction as

$$dq_1 = -k(\Delta y)(d) \left. \frac{\partial u}{\partial x} \right|_x dt \tag{8-4}$$

where k is the coefficient of thermal conductivity, d is the thickness of the plate, and $\partial u/\partial x \,|_x$ is the average temperature gradient over side 1 of

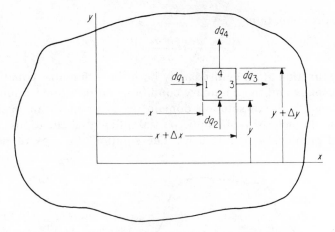

FIG. 8-2. Heat entering and leaving an element of a plate
in time dt.

the element in the x direction. The heat leaving side 3 in time dt is

$$dq_3 = -k(\Delta y)(d) \left. \frac{\partial u}{\partial x} \right|_{x+\Delta x} dt \qquad (8\text{-}5)$$

The *net* heat gain of the element in time dt due to heat flow in the x direction is thus

$$dq_1 - dq_3 = \left[-k(\Delta y)(d) \left. \frac{\partial u}{\partial x} \right|_x + k(\Delta y)(d) \left. \frac{\partial u}{\partial x} \right|_{x+\Delta x} \right] dt$$

or

$$dq_1 - dq_3 = k(\Delta y)(d)(\Delta x) \left[\frac{\left. \frac{\partial u}{\partial x} \right|_{x+\Delta x} - \left. \frac{\partial u}{\partial x} \right|_x}{(\Delta x)} \right] dt \qquad (8\text{-}6)$$

Similarly, the net heat gain in time dt due to heat flow in the y direction is

$$dq_2 - dq_4 = k(\Delta x)(d)(\Delta y) \left[\frac{\left. \frac{\partial u}{\partial y} \right|_{y+\Delta y} - \left. \frac{\partial u}{\partial y} \right|_y}{(\Delta y)} \right] dt \qquad (8\text{-}7)$$

The *total* net heat gain dQ of the element in time dt is found by adding Eqs. 8-6 and 8-7,

$$dQ = k(\Delta x)(\Delta y)(d) \left[\frac{\left. \frac{\partial u}{\partial x} \right|_{x+\Delta x} - \left. \frac{\partial u}{\partial x} \right|_x}{(\Delta x)} + \frac{\left. \frac{\partial u}{\partial y} \right|_{y+\Delta y} - \left. \frac{\partial u}{\partial y} \right|_y}{(\Delta y)} \right] dt \qquad (8\text{-}8)$$

The total net heat gain of the element in time dt may also be expressed as

$$dQ = c(\Delta x)(\Delta y)(d)\rho \frac{\partial u}{\partial t} dt \qquad (8\text{-}9)$$

where c is the specific heat of the plate material, ρ is the weight density, and $\partial u / \partial t$ is the average rate of change of the temperature of the element with respect to time.

Equating Eqs. 8-8 and 8-9 and dividing both sides by $(\Delta x)(\Delta y)(dt)(d)$ gives

$$k \left[\frac{\left. \frac{\partial u}{\partial x} \right|_{x+\Delta x} - \left. \frac{\partial u}{\partial x} \right|_{x}}{(\Delta x)} + \frac{\left. \frac{\partial u}{\partial y} \right|_{y+\Delta y} - \left. \frac{\partial u}{\partial y} \right|_{y}}{(\Delta y)} \right] = c\rho \frac{\partial u}{\partial t} \qquad (8\text{-}10)$$

Letting both (Δx) and (Δy) approach zero and rearranging terms,

$$\frac{\partial u}{\partial t} = \frac{k}{c\rho} \left[\frac{\partial^2 u}{\partial x^2} + \frac{\partial^2 u}{\partial y^2} \right] \qquad (8\text{-}11)$$

Equation 8-11 is the *2-dimensional heat equation.*

If we are interested in the *equilibrium* or *steady-state* condition, we realize that $\partial u / \partial t = 0$, and Eq. 8-11 reduces to

$$\frac{\partial^2 u}{\partial x^2} + \frac{\partial^2 u}{\partial y^2} = 0 \qquad (8\text{-}12)$$

The latter is Laplace's partial differential equation which was mentioned earlier in this section as an example of an elliptic partial differential equation. The temperature $u(x, y)$ throughout the plate must satisfy this equation, as well as the boundary conditions along the entire boundary of the plate when the plate is in thermal equilibrium. Usually, the boundary is either insulated in part, in which case the *normal derivative* of the temperature at the boundary is equal to zero, and/or the temperature is maintained at a specified value over part or all of the boundary.

We shall next develop a numerical method for obtaining the solution of Eq. 8-12. Let us superimpose a lattice or grid with a mesh size of Δx by Δy upon the plate, as shown in Fig. 8-3. The numerical solution

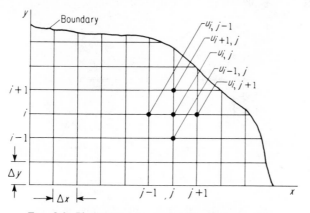

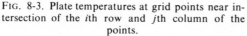

FIG. 8-3. Plate temperatures at grid points near intersection of the *i*th row and *j*th column of the points.

will consist of determining the temperatures at the finitely spaced grid points shown. Figure 8-3 shows the temperatures at the grid points in the neighborhood of the intersection of the ith row and jth column. From Eq. 5-38 we can write *first central-difference* approximations for the second partial derivatives of the temperature with respect to distance, in the x and y directions, as follows:

$$\frac{\partial^2 u}{\partial x^2} = \frac{u_{i,\,j+1} - 2u_{i,\,j} + u_{i,\,j-1}}{(\Delta x)^2} \tag{8-13}$$

$$\frac{\partial^2 u}{\partial y^2} = \frac{u_{i+1,\,j} - 2u_{i,\,j} + u_{i-1,\,j}}{(\Delta y)^2}$$

Substituting these finite-difference expressions into Eq. 8-12,

$$\frac{u_{i,\,j+1} - 2u_{i,\,j} + u_{i,\,j-1}}{(\Delta x)^2} + \frac{u_{i+1,\,j} - 2u_{i,\,j} + u_{i-1,\,j}}{(\Delta y)^2} = 0 \tag{8-14}$$

If we use a square mesh so that $\Delta x = \Delta y = h$, Eq. 8-14 reduces to

$$u_{i,\,j+1} + u_{i,\,j-1} + u_{i+1,\,j} + u_{i-1,\,j} - 4u_{i,\,j} = 0 \tag{8-15}$$

and is referred to as the *Laplacian* difference equation. This equation must hold at every *interior* grid point on the plate.

As mentioned previously, usually the temperatures at the boundary points are known, or the boundary is considered to be perfectly insulated. Insulated boundaries are handled by developing boundary equations. Figure 8-4 shows a *half element* lying on an *insulated* left boundary of the plate. The *net* heat flowing into this element must equal zero when we are considering a steady-state condition for the plate. The quantity of

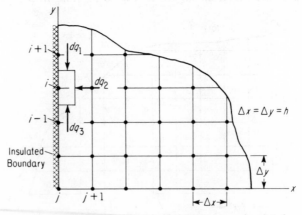

FIG. 8-4. Heat flow into half-element on an insulated left boundary.

heat flowing into the 3 faces of the half element in time dt are given by the following equations:

$$dq_1 = \left(\frac{khd}{2}\right)\frac{\partial u}{\partial y}\bigg|_{i+\frac{1}{2}} dt = \left(\frac{khd}{2}\right)\left(\frac{u_{i+1,j} - u_{i,j}}{h}\right)dt$$

$$dq_2 = (khd)\frac{\partial u}{\partial x}\bigg|_{j+\frac{1}{2}} dt = (khd)\left(\frac{u_{i,j+1} - u_{i,j}}{h}\right)dt \qquad (8\text{-}16)$$

$$dq_3 = -\left(\frac{khd}{2}\right)\frac{\partial u}{\partial y}\bigg|_{i-\frac{1}{2}} dt = -\left(\frac{khd}{2}\right)\left(\frac{u_{i,j} - u_{i-1,j}}{h}\right)dt$$

Substituting Eq. 8-16 into the heat-balance equation for the half element

$$dq_1 + dq_2 + dq_3 = 0$$

yields

(Left) $\qquad\qquad u_{i+1,j} + 2u_{i,j+1} + u_{i-1,j} - 4u_{i,j} = 0 \qquad (8\text{-}17)$

Similarly, the difference equations which apply on the right, upper, and lower *insulated* boundaries of a rectangular plate are

(Right) $\qquad\qquad u_{i+1,j} + 2u_{i,j-1} + u_{i-1,j} - 4u_{i,j} = 0 \qquad (8\text{-}18)$

(Upper) $\qquad\qquad u_{i,j-1} + 2u_{i-1,j} + u_{i,j+1} - 4u_{i,j} = 0 \qquad (8\text{-}19)$

(Lower) $\qquad\qquad u_{i,j-1} + 2u_{i+1,j} + u_{i,j+1} - 4u_{i,j} = 0 \qquad (8\text{-}20)$

Thus, in obtaining a solution for the steady-state heat flow in a rectangular plate, Eq. 8-15 must hold at every *interior* grid point, and Eqs. 8-17 through 8-20 must be satisfied at any appropriate insulated boundaries. (A method for handling irregular or curved boundaries will be discussed on page 471.) Reviewing the pertinent equations, it can be seen that the problem has been reduced to obtaining the simultaneous solution of a set of linear algebraic equations in the unknown grid-point temperatures u, the total number of equations depending upon the extent of the insulated boundaries and the number of grid points used. If the number of grid points required is not too large, the resulting equations may be solved by the *elimination* methods, discussed in Secs. 4-2 and 4-3. Usually, however, a rather large number of grid points is desirable, and the number of equations which must be solved simultaneously becomes too large to solve accurately by the elimination methods. In this case the Gauss-Seidel iteration method (see Sec. 4-6) can be employed to obtain a more accurate solution. (In connection with the solution of elliptic partial differential equations, the Gauss-Seidel method is often referred to as Liebmann's method.) The equations which must be solved are of the type which have a dominant coefficient for a different unknown in each equation. In addition, there are many zero coefficients in each equation (only 4 or 5 unknowns in each equation have nonzero coefficients). The existence of a dominant coefficient in each equation, as mentioned, is a necessary feature for convergence with the equations which are to be solved by the Gauss-Seidel method, and the presence of zero coefficients is a very convenient feature.

Following the procedure outlined for the Gauss-Seidel method in Sec. 4-6, we first arrange each equation in a form convenient for solving for the unknown with the *largest* coefficient in that equation. In the case we are considering, this unknown will always be $u_{i,j}$. For example, from Eq. 8-15 we obtain

$$u_{i,j} = \frac{u_{i,j+1} + u_{i,j-1} + u_{i+1,j} + u_{i-1,j}}{4} \tag{8-21}$$

All unknown temperatures at the grid points are then assigned initial values on the basis of the best estimate available (the better the estimate, the more rapid the convergence to a solution). In calculating $u_{i,j}$ the values of the temperatures on the right side of Eq. 8-21 consist initially of estimated values or known boundary values. However, as soon as an approximate temperature at a grid point is calculated, this calculated value supersedes the estimated value and is used as the temperature at that point until it is, in turn, superseded by a new calculated value. Thus, the latest calculated values of the temperatures we are seeking are always used in calculating newer and better values. The applicable equations are used at points on the plate which are selected in some systematic manner, usually either by rows or by columns. The following example illustrates the procedure. (A discussion of a technique for speeding up convergence follows the example.)

EXAMPLE 8-1

Utilizing the digital computer to perform the calculations required by the Gauss-Seidel method, let us determine the temperature distribution in a square plate which has both faces insulated and also has several portions of the edges insulated, as shown in Fig. 8-5. The upper edge and the upper portions of the left and right edges are held at a constant temperature U_T. The bottom edge is maintained at a constant temperature U_B. A grid having 10 rows and 10 columns of points is superimposed upon the plate, as shown. The left edge is insulated from the bottom up to row $IA = 5$, and the right edge is insulated from the bottom up to row $IB = 8$.

Referring to Eqs. 8-15 through 8-20 and the explanation accompanying Eq. 8-21, we can write the applicable interior and boundary difference equations for this problem as follows:

(Interior)

$$u_{i,j} = \frac{u_{i,j+1} + u_{i,j-1} + u_{i+1,j} + u_{i-1,j}}{4} \tag{a}$$

$$1 < i < 10$$
$$1 < j < 10$$

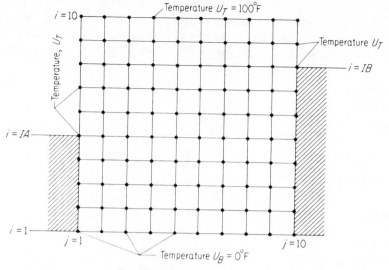

FIG. 8-5. Plate of Example 8-1.

(Insulated portion of left boundary)

$$u_{i,j} = \frac{u_{i+1,j} + 2u_{i,j+1} + u_{i-1,j}}{4} \qquad \text{(b)}$$

$1 < i < IA$
$j = 1$

(Insulated portion of right boundary)

$$u_{i,j} = \frac{u_{i+1,j} + 2u_{i,j-1} + u_{i-1,j}}{4} \qquad \text{(c)} \qquad \text{(8-22)}$$

$1 < i < IB$
$j = 10$

(Boundaries with temperature U_T)

$$u_{i,j} = U_T \qquad \text{(d)}$$

$\begin{aligned} 1 &\le j \le 10 & i &= 10 \\ IA &\le i < 10 & j &= 1 \\ IB &\le i < 10 & j &= 10 \end{aligned}$

(Boundary with temperature U_B)

$$u_{i,j} = U_B \qquad \text{(e)}$$

$1 \le j \le 10$
$i = 1$

Equation 8-22, for all i and j values, must be solved simultaneously to obtain the equilibrium temperature over the plate. The initial temperatures at the grid points where the temperatures are unknown are estimated by assuming a linear temperature gradient between U_B at the bottom of the plate and U_T at the top of the plate. The reader should review the steps outlined for employing the Gauss-Seidel method (see p. 218) before studying the flow chart for this problem (Fig. 8-6). The FORTRAN

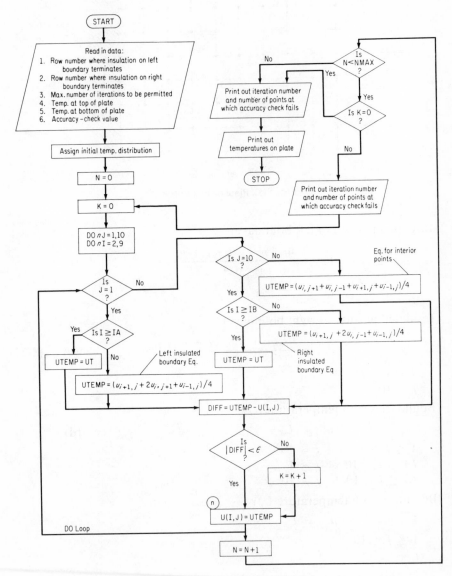

FIG. 8-6. Flow chart for Example 8-1.

names used for this problem and the quantities they represent are as follows:

FORTRAN *Name*	*Quantity*	*Value Used in Problem*
U(I,J)	Temperatures at grid points, °F	
IA	Row at which insulation stops on left boundary	5
IB	Row at which insulation stops on right boundary	8
NMAX	Maximum number of iterations desired	100
UT	Temperature at top of plate and portions of left and right boundaries, °F	100
UB	Temperature at bottom of plate, °F	0
EPSI	Accuracy-check value, °F	0.05
I	Grid row number	
J	Grid column number	
A	Floating-point designation for row number I	
N	Number of iterations completed	
K	Number of grid points at which accuracy check fails	
UTEMP	Temporary name for value of U(I,J), °F	
DIFF	Difference in calculated temperatures at a grid point for 2 successive iterations, °F	

Referring now to the flow chart, it can be seen that 1 iteration is complete when an approximate value has been computed for each grid point whose temperature is sought. In all iterations the *latest* calculated temperature of each of these grid points is used in each equation in which it appears. After each step in the iteration, the computer is instructed to check the difference between successive calculated values for that grid point. At the end of each iteration, the computer is then instructed to print out the number of grid points at which the value of the temperature has changed from the preceding iteration by more than some predetermined value, epsilon, which defines the accuracy desired. At this time the computer is also instructed to print out the number of iterations completed. When the temperature change at *all* grid points between successive iterations is less than or equal to the prescribed-value epsilon, the computer is programmed to print out these temperatures in a tabular array corresponding to the location of the grid points on the plate. The program also has a provision to instruct the computer to print out the temperatures in the form stated if a certain maximum number of iterations is completed before all the grid-point temperatures vary by less than the prescribed-value epsilon. This procedure is incorporated to avoid excessive computing time in case the convergence to a solution is slow. Either printout mentioned terminates the program.

The FORTRAN IV computer program used to implement the flow chart shown is as follows:

```
      DIMENSION  U(10,10)
      READ(5,2)IA,IB,NMAX,UT,UB,EPSI
    2 FORMAT(2I3,I4,2F6.0,F5.2)
      WRITE(6,3)
    3 FORMAT(47H1TEMP DIST IN A PLATE BY GAUSS-SEIDEL
                                           ITERATION//)
      DO 4I=1,10
      DO 4J=1,10
      A=I
    4 U(I,J)=UB+(UT-UB)*(A-1.)/9.
      N=0
    5 K=0
      DO 16J=1,10
      DO 16I=2,9
      IF(J-1)9,6,9
    6 IF(IA-I)7,7,8
    7 UTEMP=UT
      GO TO 14
    8 UTEMP=(U(I+1,J)+2.*U(I,J+1)+U(I-1,J))/4.
      GO TO 14
    9 IF(J-10)13,10,13
   10 IF(I-IB)12,11,11
   11 UTEMP=UT
      GO TO 14
   12 UTEMP=(U(I+1,J)+2.*U(I,J-1)+U(I-1,J))/4.
      GO TO 14
   13 UTEMP=(U(I,J+1)+U(I,J-1)+U(I+1,J)+U(I-1,J))/4.
   14 DIFF=UTEMP-U(I,J)
      IF(ABS(DIFF)-EPSI)16,15,15
   15 K=K+1
   16 U(I,J)=UTEMP
      N=N+1
      IF(N-NMAX)17,20,20
   17 IF(K)18,20,18
```

```
18 WRITE(6,19)N,K
19 FORMAT(7H IT NO.,I4,4H K= ,I4)
   GO TO 5
20 WRITE(6,19)N,K
21 FORMAT(///10F7.2)
   DO 22M=1,10
   I=11−M
22 WRITE(6,21)(U(I,J),J=1,10)
   STOP
   END
```

The computer results are shown in the tabular printout pp. 472 and 473.

In recent years much study has been given to ways for speeding the convergence of iterative methods in solving computational problems. The Gauss-Seidel method is iterative, and it has been studied extensively in this regard. A technique called *overrelaxation* has been found to be extremely profitable in speeding the convergence of the Gauss-Seidel method, when applied to the solution of elliptic partial differential equations (the Liebmann process). In place of Eq. 8-21, the equation

$$(u_{i,j})_{new} = \omega\left(\frac{u_{i,j+1} + u_{i,j-1} + u_{i+1,j} + u_{i-1,j}}{4}\right) + (1 - \omega)(u_{i,j})_{old} \qquad (8\text{-}21a)$$

is used.[2] The parameter ω is known as the *relaxation parameter*. For overrelaxation the value of ω lies between 1 and 2; for *underrelaxation*, between 0 and 1. For the Gauss-Seidel method, overrelaxation must be used to speed up convergence. It should be noted that when $\omega = 1$, Eq. 8-21a reduces to Eq. 8-21.

Forsythe and Wasow show that for a square solution domain with a 45-by-45 mesh (1936 interior points), the optimum value of ω is approximately 1.870.[3] They further point out that, in using optimal relaxation in this case, convergence is approximately 30 times faster than for the usual Liebmann process ($\omega = 1$).

Estimating ω_{opt} is an advanced problem beyond the scope of this text, but, for any given situation, it can be determined experimentally (see Prob. 8-2). The value of $\omega = 1.870$ can be used as a guide in choosing a value of ω for a square solution domain where the number of grid points is "large."

Grid Points Near Irregular Boundaries. Since it is obviously not possible to have a rectangular grid fit the boundaries of an irregular domain, we must be concerned, in such instances, with writing equations

---

[2] Forsythe, George E., and Wasow, Wolfgang R. *Finite Difference Methods for Partial Differential Equations.* New York: John Wiley & Sons, Inc., 1960, p. 247, Eq. 22.4.

[3] *Ibid.*, p. 256.

TEMP DIST IN A PLATE BY GAUSS-SEIDEL ITERATION

IT NO. 1 K= 32
IT NO. 2 K= 39
IT NO. 3 K= 52
IT NO. 4 K= 62
IT NO. 5 K= 65
IT NO. 6 K= 68
IT NO. 7 K= 70
IT NO. 8 K= 70
IT NO. 9 K= 73
IT NO. 10 K= 73
IT NO. 11 K= 73
IT NO. 12 K= 73
IT NO. 13 K= 73
IT NO. 14 K= 71
IT NO. 15 K= 71
IT NO. 16 K= 71
IT NO. 17 K= 71
IT NO. 18 K= 71
IT NO. 19 K= 69
IT NO. 20 K= 68
IT NO. 21 K= 67
IT NO. 22 K= 65
IT NO. 23 K= 62
IT NO. 24 K= 61
IT NO. 25 K= 58
IT NO. 26 K= 56

IT NO. 27 K= 51										
IT NO. 28 K= 46										
IT NO. 29 K= 43										
IT NO. 30 K= 38										
IT NO. 31 K= 37										
IT NO. 32 K= 34										
IT NO. 33 K= 31										
IT NO. 34 K= 24										
IT NO. 35 K= 17										
IT NO. 36 K= 13										
IT NO. 37 K= 3										
IT NO. 38 K= 0										

100.00	100.00	100.00	100.00	100.00	100.00	100.00	100.00	100.00	100.00
100.00	97.66	95.63	94.07	93.02	92.51	92.61	93.56	95.83	100.00
100.00	95.02	90.81	87.64	85.53	84.42	84.39	85.80	89.77	100.00
100.00	91.64	84.97	80.19	77.06	75.30	74.77	75.49	77.48	80.07
100.00	86.62	77.29	71.16	67.27	65.00	63.97	63.95	64.63	65.32
100.00	77.58	66.45	59.95	55.94	53.53	52.25	51.78	51.83	51.99
63.44	57.31	51.05	46.34	43.10	41.01	39.79	39.20	39.00	39.00
39.19	37.22	34.15	31.35	29.20	27.73	26.80	26.30	26.08	26.04
18.93	18.29	17.04	15.76	14.72	13.97	13.48	13.19	13.06	13.03
.00	.00	.00	.00	.00	.00	.00	.00	.00	.00

which are applicable to interior grid points that lie near irregular or curved boundaries.

Consider such a point P in a square mesh, as shown in Fig. 8-7a. Equation 8-15, which was developed earlier for the interior grid points of a square mesh, does not apply at a grid point such as P, since the grid points C and D are not the defined mesh interval h away from point P. The simplest way to obtain an equation defining the temperature at P, when the boundary temperatures are known, is to make use of linear interpolation. Referring to Fig. 8-7b, we see that the interpolation may be

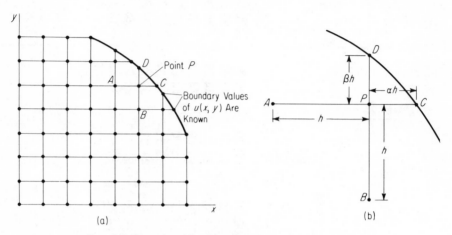

(a)   (b)

FIG. 8-7. Domain with grid points near a curved boundary.

made either between points A and C or between points B and D. An average of these 2 interpolations may also be used. For example, if we linearly interpolate between grid points A and C, we find that

$$u_P = u_A + (u_C - u_A)\left(\frac{h}{h + \alpha h}\right)$$

or

$$u_P = \left(\frac{\alpha}{1 + \alpha}\right)u_A + \left(\frac{1}{1 + \alpha}\right)u_C \qquad (8\text{-}23)$$

Similarly, interpolating between grid points B and D yields

$$u_P = \left(\frac{\beta}{1 + \beta}\right)u_B + \left(\frac{1}{1 + \beta}\right)u_D \qquad (8\text{-}24)$$

An equation such as Eq. 8-23 or 8-24 must be used for each grid point lying close to an irregular boundary.

If the normal derivative of the function $u(x, y)$ is known at the boundary rather than the temperature $u(x, y)$ itself, the problem of hand-

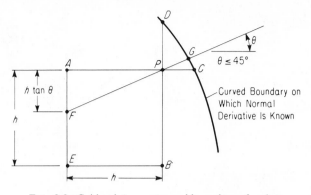

FIG. 8-8. Grid points near curved boundary of a plate
along which the normal derivative is known.

ling irregular boundaries is, in general, more difficult. For example, consider point P near an irregular boundary for which $\partial u / \partial N$ is specified, as
shown in Fig. 8-8. To solve the problem it is necessary to write equations
defining the temperature at all grid points such as P near the boundary.
The value of the normal derivative at G, $\partial u / \partial N \mid_G$, is known and can be
expressed approximately in the following finite-difference form:

$$\left.\frac{\partial u}{\partial N}\right|_G = \frac{u_P - u_F}{\overline{FP}} \qquad (8\text{-}25)$$

When the angle θ is less than 45°, a value of u_F can be obtained by linearly interpolating between the vertically spaced grid points A and E such
that

$$u_F = u_A + (u_E - u_A)\frac{h \tan \theta}{h} \qquad (8\text{-}26)$$

Combining Eqs. 8-25 and 8-26 and expressing the distance $\overline{FP}$ as $h/\cos\theta$,
we obtain

$$u_P = \left.\frac{\partial u}{\partial N}\right|_G \left(\frac{h}{\cos\theta}\right) + u_A(1 - \tan\theta) + u_E \tan\theta \qquad (8\text{-}27)$$

An equation of this type must be used for each grid point close to the
irregular boundary. The value of θ for each such grid point will be determined from the geometry of the irregular boundary.

When the angle θ is greater than 45°, linear interpolation can be used
along a horizontal grid line, such as line EB in Fig. 8-9, to determine an
expression for the temperature at a grid point such as F. Combining the
expression derived from this interpolation with Eq. 8-25 yields the following equation, defining the temperature at grid point P:

$$u_P = \left.\frac{\partial u}{\partial N}\right|_G \left(\frac{h}{\sin\theta}\right) + u_B(1 - \cot\theta) + u_E \cot\theta \qquad (8\text{-}28)$$

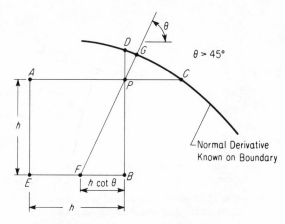

FIG. 8-9. Case where normal derivative makes
an angle greater than 45° with horizontal.

In considering problems with irregular boundaries where the boundary conditions are known normal derivatives, the boundary equations developed previously for rectangular domains (Eqs. 8-17 through 8-20) are obviously not applicable. The equations developed for grid points near irregular boundaries in the preceding paragraphs (Eqs. 8-27 and 8-28), in effect, replace the boundary equations used for rectangular domains. If it is desired to obtain the temperatures at the boundary grid points, they may be calculated by using linear interpolation between the boundary point desired and adjacent grid points whose temperatures were calculated in the solution obtained.

More elaborate (and more accurate) methods have been developed for handling grid points near curved boundaries by the use of 2-dimensional Taylor series.[4] Such methods greatly increase the complexity of computer programming, if there are many such grid points to be considered. The resulting increase in accuracy is usually insignificant in most engineering problems.

For some nonrectangular domains it is possible to use non-Cartesian grids to simplify the solution of the problem. For example, polar coordinates may be used with circular domains and triangular and skew coordinates with appropriately shaped domains.[5] However, a discussion of these methods is beyond the scope of this text.

8-3. Parabolic Partial Differential Equations

Parabolic partial differential equations arise in what are called *propagation* problems. In this type of problem the solution advances outward

---

[4] Crandall, *op. cit.*, pp. 262–264.

[5] Salvadori, M. G., and Baron, M. L. *Numerical Methods in Engineering.* Englewood Cliffs, N.J.: Prentice Hall, Inc., 1961, pp. 237 ff.

indefinitely from known initial values, always satisfying the known boundary conditions as the solution progresses. This *open-ended* type of solution domain is illustrated in Fig. 8-10, where the dependent variable is u and the independent variables are x and t. The solution u must satisfy the partial differential equation throughout the open domain, as well as the initial and boundary conditions.

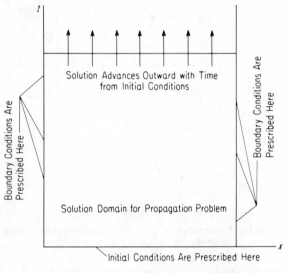

FIG. 8-10. Solution domain for a propagation problem.

The general partial differential equation, as given by Eq. 8-1, is *parabolic* when the coefficients a, b, and c have values such that

$$b^2 - 4ac = 0$$

An example of a parabolic partial differential equation is found in considering the 1-dimensional *transient*-heat-flow problem which is defined by the differential equation

$$\frac{\partial u}{\partial t} = \frac{k}{c\rho} \frac{\partial^2 u}{\partial x^2} \qquad (8\text{-}29)$$

which may be obtained from the 2-dimensional heat equation (Eq. 8-11).

As mentioned previously, the solution $u(x, t)$ propagates with time in a space-time plane, as shown in Fig. 8-10. If we consider a space-time grid, such as the one shown in Fig. 8-11, a solution of Eq. 8-29 will consist of determining the temperature u at each grid point used. To utilize the grid shown, we must put Eq. 8-29 in finite-difference form. Referring to Eqs. 5-38 and 5-40, we find it convenient to substitute a *first*

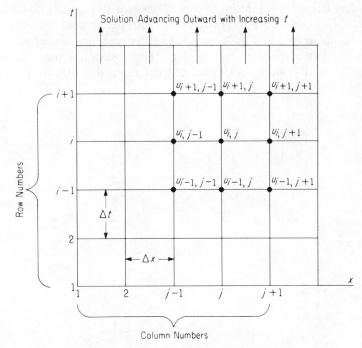

FIG. 8-11. Temperature at grid points in the solution domain near ith row and jth column of points.

forward-difference expression for the first partial such that

$$\frac{\partial u}{\partial t} = \frac{u_{i+1,j} - u_{i,j}}{\Delta t} \tag{8-30}$$

and a *first central-difference* expression for the second partial such that

$$\frac{\partial^2 u}{\partial x^2} = \frac{u_{i,j+1} - 2u_{i,j} + u_{i,j-1}}{(\Delta x)^2} \tag{8-31}$$

Substituting these difference equations into Eq. 8-29,

$$u_{i+1,j} = u_{i,j} + \frac{k}{c\rho} \frac{(\Delta t)}{(\Delta x)^2} (u_{i,j+1} - 2u_{i,j} + u_{i,j-1}) \tag{8-32}$$

It can be seen, from Eq. 8-32, that we can obtain the temperature at a particular grid point with coordinates x and $(t + \Delta t)$ in terms of the temperatures at adjacent grid points $(x - \Delta x)$, and $(x + \Delta x)$ at a time t. Known initial temperatures and boundary temperatures provide the values necessary to start the calculations which then proceed *row* by *row*, the end points of each row satisfying the given boundary conditions, until some final temperature state (with time) is approximately satisfied as the solution approaches a steady state. This row-by-row progression with time, which continues indefinitely, illustrates the open-ended nature of the solution domain of a parabolic-type partial differential equation.

In solving Eq. 8-32, the stability of the solution obtained is of great importance. It can be shown that the solution will be stable and nonoscillatory if[6]

$$\frac{k}{c\rho}\frac{(\Delta t)}{(\Delta x)^2} \leq 0.25$$

The solution obtained will be stable if

$$\frac{k}{c\rho}\frac{(\Delta t)}{(\Delta x)^2} \leq 0.50$$

The following example shows in detail the application of Eq. 8-32.

Example 8-2

The problem is to determine the transient temperature distribution along a slender rod. The rod, which is shown in Fig. 8-12, is made of

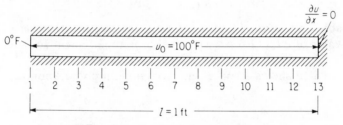

Fig. 8-12. Insulated aluminum bar.

aluminum and is 1 ft long. It is assumed to be perfectly insulated at all boundaries except the left end. The pertinent material properties are

$$k = 0.0370 \text{ Btu/(sec)(ft)(}^\circ\text{F)}$$
$$c = 0.212 \text{ Btu/(lb)(}^\circ\text{F)}$$
$$\rho = 168 \text{ lb/ft}^3$$

and the rod is divided into 12 equal increments by the 13 stations shown.

Initially, the rod is in a state of thermal equilibrium at a temperature of 100°F. The temperature at the uninsulated end is then suddenly reduced to 0°F, at which time the temperature distribution in the rod assumes a transient state. This state exists until a time at which the temperature everywhere in the rod approaches the final equilibrium state of 0°F. The boundary conditions stated mathematically are

$$u(0, t) = 0°\text{F}$$

[6] *Ibid.* p. 261.

$$\frac{\partial u}{\partial x}(l, t) = 0°F/ft$$

and the initial condition is

$$u(x, 0) = 100°F$$

In the preceding discussion it was shown that the 1-dimensional transient-heat-flow equation (Eq. 8-29) can be approximated by the following finite-difference equation:

$$u_{i+1, j} = u_{i, j} + \frac{k}{c\rho} \frac{(\Delta t)}{(\Delta x)^2} [u_{i, j+1} - 2u_{i, j} + u_{i, j-1}] \qquad (8\text{-}33)$$

The given values of k, c and ρ establish a thermal diffusivity ($k/c\rho$) of 0.00104 ft²/sec. With the number of stations shown in Fig. 8-12, the value of Δx is 1/12 ft. Using these values and referring to the stability criterion discussed earlier, which established that

$$\frac{k}{c\rho} \frac{(\Delta t)}{(\Delta x)^2} \leq 0.25$$

for a stable and nonoscillatory solution, we see that the use of a convenient value of $\Delta t = 1.0$ sec will satisfy the requirement for such a solution.

Figure 8-13 shows a space-time grid superimposed upon the solution

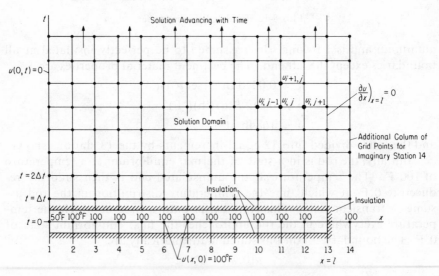

FIG. 8-13. Space-time grid for Example 8-2.

domain. A careful study of the information contained in this figure will give an excellent insight into the numerical procedures required to obtain a solution of the problem. The temperature is known for each station at $t = 0$, as indicated. An *average* value of 50°F is assumed at station 1 for $t = 0$, as shown, since the temperature at this station is discontinuous at $t = 0$, changing very suddenly from 100°F to 0°F when the transient state is introduced. This average value of 50°F is used only in calculating the temperature at the grid point above station 2 in the row corresponding to $t = \Delta t$. In calculating the temperature at all subsequent grid points above station 2, the *boundary* value of 0°F is used for the temperature at the left-boundary grid points. An additional column of grid points corresponding to an *imaginary* station 14 is included in the space-time grid to provide a means of satisfying the boundary condition imposed at the insulated end of the rod. This condition may be expressed, in finite-difference form, as

$$\frac{u_{i,14} - u_{i,12}}{2(\Delta x)} = 0$$

from which

$$u_{i,14} = u_{i,12}$$

Applying Eq. 8-33, the temperature at each grid point from 2 through 13 is determined in the row corresponding to $t = \Delta t$, using the known initial temperatures. The grid point in that row associated with station 14 is then assigned the value calculated for the grid point associated with station 12, thus approximately establishing a zero temperature gradient at station 13. Equation 8-33 is then used again to determine the temperature at grid points 2 through 13 in the next row corresponding to $t = 2\Delta t$, using the grid-temperature values calculated for the *preceding* row. The grid point in this row corresponding to station 14 is then assigned the value calculated for station 12, and the solution advances to the next row, where $t = 3\Delta t$. This procedure is repeated for each subsequent row of grid points until the temperatures at *all* the grid points in a row differ by less than a small predetermined value epsilon from the known final equilibrium temperature of 0°F. Thus, the solution advances outward with time, the number of rows ultimately calculated in the solution depending upon the time rate at which the temperature of the stations approaches the final equilibrium temperature and the temperature limit desired for the solution, as specified by the value of epsilon chosen. Since the temperature at each station along the rod approaches the final equilibrium temperature of 0°F asymptotically in this problem, too small a value of epsilon can result in excessive computing time.

The flow chart for programming this problem for a computer solution

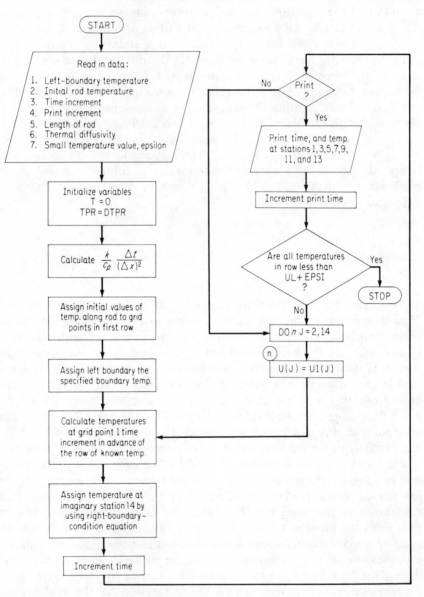

FIG. 8-14. Flow chart for Example 8-2.

is shown in Fig. 8-14. The FORTRAN names and the problem quantities which they represent are:

FORTRAN *Name*	*Quantity*	*Value Used in Problem*
U(J)	Temperature along a row of grid points corresponding to time t, °F	
U1(J)	Temperature along a row of grid points corresponding to time $t + \Delta t$, °F	
UL	Temperature at which left end of rod is held	0°F
UX	Initial temperature along rod	100°F
DELT	Time increment	1 sec
EL	Length of rod	1 ft
TPR	Time at which printout occurs, sec	
DTPR	Print increment	100 sec
THDIF	Thermal diffusivity, $k/c\rho$	0.00104 ft²/sec
B	$\dfrac{k(\Delta t)}{c\rho(\Delta x)^2}$	
EPSI	Small value of temperature selected to terminate program. Program terminates when temperature at each station in row is less than UL + EPSI	0.05°F

The FORTRAN IV computer program used to solve the problem is as follows:

```
      DIMENSION  U(14),U1(14)
      READ(5,2)UL,UX,DELT,DTPR,EL,THDIF,EPSI
    2 FORMAT  (5F4.0,F7.0,F4.0)
      WRITE(6,3)
    3 FORMAT(1H1,14X,27HTRANSIENT  HEAT-FLOW  PROBLEM)
      WRITE(6,4)
    4 FORMAT(1H ,13X,29H(PARABOLIC  PARTIAL  DIFF  EQN.)//)
      WRITE(6,5)
    5 FORMAT(6H   TIME,6X,1H1,5X,1H3,6X,1H5,6X,1H7,6X,1H9,6X,
     2H11,5X,2H13/)
      T=0.
      TPR=DTPR
      B=THDIF*DELT/(EL/12.)**2
      U(1)=(UL+UX)/2.
      DO6J=2,14
```

```
 6  U(J) = UX
    U1(1) = UL
 7  DO 8J = 2,13
 8  U1(J) = U(J) + B*(U(J + 1) − 2.*U(J) + U(J − 1))
    U1(14) = U1(12)
    T = T + DELT
    IF(T − TPR)12,9,9
 9  WRITE(6,10)T,(U1(J),J = 1,13,2)
10  FORMAT(F6.0,7F7.2)
    TPR = TRP + DTPR
    DO 11J = 2,13
    DIFF = U1(J) − (UL + EPSI)
    IF(DIFF)11,12,12
11  CONTINUE
    STOP
12  DO 13J = 2,14
13  U(J) = U1(J)
    U(1) = UL
    GO TO 7
    END
```

The computer results are shown in the following tabular printout:

TRANSIENT HEAT-FLOW PROBLEM
(PARABOLIC PARTIAL DIFF EQN.)

TIME	1	3	5	7	9	11	13
100.	.00	28.51	53.49	72.60	85.26	92.16	94.31
200.	.00	20.02	38.52	54.18	65.99	73.31	75.78
300.	.00	15.28	29.52	41.72	51.06	56.92	58.91
400.	.00	11.80	22.81	32.25	39.50	44.06	45.61
500.	.00	9.13	17.64	24.95	30.56	34.09	35.29
600.	.00	7.06	13.65	19.30	23.64	26.37	27.30
700.	.00	5.46	10.56	14.93	18.29	20.40	21.12
800.	.00	4.23	8.17	11.55	14.15	15.78	16.34
900.	.00	3.27	6.32	8.94	10.95	12.21	12.64
1000.	.00	2.53	4.89	6.91	8.47	9.45	9.78
1100.	.00	1.95	3.78	5.35	6.55	7.31	7.57
1200.	.00	1.51	2.92	4.14	5.07	5.65	5.85
1300.	.00	1.17	2.26	3.20	3.92	4.37	4.53
1400.	.00	.90	1.75	2.47	3.03	3.38	3.50
1500.	.00	.70	1.35	1.91	2.34	2.62	2.71
1600.	.00	.54	1.04	1.48	1.81	2.02	2.09
1700.	.00	.42	.81	1.14	1.40	1.56	1.62
1800.	.00	.32	.62	.88	1.08	1.21	1.25

TIME	1	3	5	7	9	11	13
1900.	.00	.25	.48	.68	.84	.93	.97
2000.	.00	.19	.37	.53	.65	.72	.75
2100.	.00	.15	.29	.41	.50	.56	.58
2200.	.00	.11	.22	.31	.38	.43	.45
2300.	.00	.09	.17	.24	.30	.33	.34
2400.	.00	.06	.13	.19	.23	.26	.26
2500.	.00	.05	.10	.14	.18	.20	.20
2600.	.00	.04	.08	.11	.13	.15	.16
2700.	.00	.03	.06	.08	.10	.12	.12
2800.	.00	.02	.04	.06	.08	.09	.09
2900.	.00	.01	.03	.05	.06	.07	.07
3000.	.00	.01	.02	.04	.05	.05	.05
3100.	.00	.01	.02	.03	.03	.04	.04

The computer printout provides the temperatures at stations 1, 3, 5, 7, 9, 11, and 13 at intervals of 100 sec. The computer printout for stations 3, 5, and 13 is shown in graphical form in Fig. 8-15.

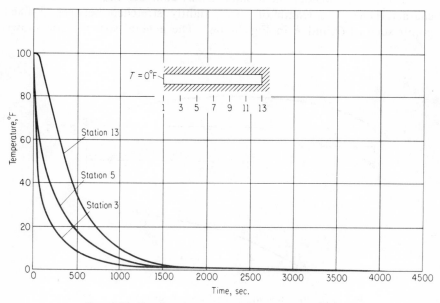

FIG. 8-15. Results of numerical solution of Example 8-2.

8-4. Hyperbolic Partial Differential Equations

The general partial differential equation (Eq. 8-1) is hyperbolic when the coefficients a, b, and c have values such that

$$b^2 - 4ac > 0$$

This type of partial differential equation, like the parabolic type, arises in the solution of so-called *propagation* problems. The solution domain of the hyperbolic differential equation has the same open-ended characteristic encountered in the solution of parabolic differential equations, consisting of a solution which advances outward indefinitely from known initial conditions while always satisfying specified boundary conditions as the solution progresses.

The 1-*dimensional wave equation*

$$\frac{\partial^2 u}{\partial t^2} = a^2 \frac{\partial^2 u}{\partial x^2} \tag{8-34}$$

which is frequently encountered in the areas of physics and engineering, is an example of a hyperbolic partial differential equation. This equation, with appropriate variables and associated physical constants, describes the motion of various types of systems, including the torsional vibrations of cylindrical rods, the longitudinal vibrations of slender rods, the transmission of sound in a column of air, and the transverse vibrations of flexible members in a stressed state.

In the last category mentioned, let us consider the free vibrational characteristics of a length of string tightly stretched between 2 fixed points such as O and E in Fig. 8-16a. The general string shape shown

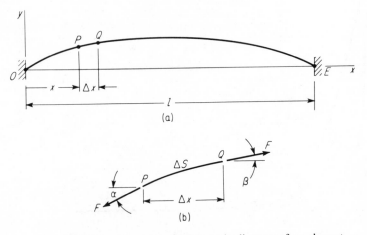

Fig. 8-16. Vibrating string and free-body diagram of an element of the string.

(with greatly exaggerated y displacements) represents 1 vibrational configuration of the string at some instant in time. Figure 8-16b shows an enlarged view of the small Δs length element PQ. In deriving the wave equation for the vibrating string, we shall make use of the following simplifying assumptions in idealizing the mathematical model which results:

1. For small displacements, $\Delta x = \Delta s$.

2. For small displacements, the additional tension introduced in the string due to its displacement is negligible compared to the initial tension introduced in stretching the string between the supporting points O and E; that is, the tension in the string is considered as constant, with a magnitude equal to the initially applied tension F.

3. The gravity force acting upon the string is negligible compared to the tension in the string.

4. The string is flexible enough to consider the bending and shear stresses developed as negligible compared to the tension in the string.

With these assumptions in mind, the forces acting upon the element are shown in Fig. 8-16b. Applying Newton's second law of motion in the y direction

$$F \sin \beta - F \sin \alpha = \frac{w}{g} (\Delta x) \frac{\partial^2 y}{\partial t^2} \qquad (8\text{-}35)$$

where w is the weight per unit length of the string. Since α and β are very small angles, we may use the approximations $\sin \alpha = \tan \alpha$ and $\sin \beta = \tan \beta$ in rewriting Eq. 8-35 as

$$F \tan \beta - F \tan \alpha = \frac{w}{g} (\Delta x) \frac{\partial^2 y}{\partial t^2}$$

Noting that $\tan \alpha$ and $\tan \beta$ represent the respective slopes at the ends of the element, we may write

$$F \left[\frac{\left.\frac{\partial y}{\partial x}\right|_{x+\Delta x} - \left.\frac{\partial y}{\partial x}\right|_x}{(\Delta x)} \right] = \frac{w}{g} \frac{\partial^2 y}{\partial t^2}$$

Letting Δx approach zero and rearranging terms,

$$\frac{\partial^2 y}{\partial t^2} = \frac{Fg}{w} \frac{\partial^2 y}{\partial x^2} \qquad (8\text{-}36)$$

which has the form of Eq. 8-34, where $Fg/w = a^2$.

The solution of Eq. 8-36 exists in a general space-time plane such as the one shown in Fig. 8-17. A numerical solution begins by superimposing a rectangular grid over the solution domain, a portion of which is shown in the figure. The value of the dependent variable y is then determined at all grid points over the desired time interval. The numerical procedure itself begins with the use of the known initial-condition values and proceeds from there in a *row-by-row* progression with time, always satisfying the specified *boundary* conditions as the solution progresses. (This procedure will be discussed more specifically in the next example.)

Equation 8-36 may be expressed, in finite-difference form, by using

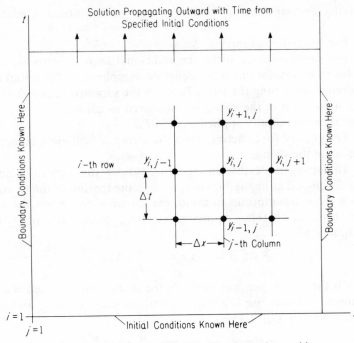

FIG. 8-17. Solution domain for the vibrating-string problem.

the following *first central-difference* approximations (see Eq. 5-38) for the 2 second partial derivatives which appear in the equation:

$$\frac{\partial^2 y}{\partial t^2} = \frac{y_{i+1,j} - 2y_{i,j} + y_{i-1,j}}{(\Delta t)^2}$$

and

$$\frac{\partial^2 y}{\partial x^2} = \frac{y_{i,j+1} - 2y_{i,j} + y_{i,j-1}}{(\Delta x)^2}$$

Substituting these 2 finite-difference expressions into Eq. 8-36 yields

$$\frac{y_{i+1,j} - 2y_{i,j} + y_{i-1,j}}{(\Delta t)^2} = \frac{Fg}{w}\left(\frac{y_{i,j+1} - 2y_{i,j} + y_{i,j-1}}{(\Delta x)^2}\right)$$

from which

$$y_{i+1,j} = 2y_{i,j} - y_{i-1,j} + C[y_{i,j+1} - 2y_{i,j} + y_{i,j-1}] \qquad (8\text{-}37)$$

where

$$C = \frac{Fg}{w}\frac{(\Delta t)^2}{(\Delta x)^2}$$

The value of C is important in considering the numerical solution of a partial differential equation, such as Eq. 8-36. It has been shown that an unstable solution is obtained for the wave equation when $C > 1$, that the solution is stable when $C \leq 1$, and that a theoretically correct solution is obtained when $C = 1$.[7] Furthermore, the accuracy of the solution has been shown to decrease as the value of C decreases further and further below the value of 1.

With the preceding discussion in mind it would seem logical to select values for Δx and Δt such that $C = 1$. However, experience reveals that such a selection often results in an inconvenient value of Δt for use in the numerical procedures involved in obtaining a solution. Therefore, it is desirable to select Δx and Δt values which are convenient for use in the numerical procedure and which, at the same time, yield a value of C which is as large as possible consistent with the stability criterion that $C \leq 1$.

The following example illustrates the numerical solution of a hyperbolic partial differential equation as represented by the 1-dimensional wave equation.

EXAMPLE 8-3

A string 1.5 ft in length, weighing 0.02 lb/ft, is stretched between supports A and B, as shown in Fig. 8-18, so that the string has an initial tension of 6 lb. The string is then plucked at the two-thirds point, yielding

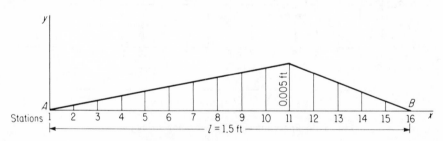

FIG. 8-18. Configuration of string at $t = 0$ for Example 8-3.

the initial configuration shown in the figure. It is desired to determine various intermediate configurations of the string during the first 0.2 sec after the string is released from rest in the configuration shown. To determine the desired configurations we must calculate the y displacements at various points along the string at various time intervals.

Selecting a value of $\Delta x = 0.1$ ft as a convenient interval for determining stations along the length of the string, we find that for

$$C = \frac{Fg}{w} \frac{(\Delta t)^2}{(\Delta x)^2} = 1$$

a value of $\Delta t = 0.00102$ sec must be used. A more convenient value is $\Delta t = 0.001$ sec, the selection of which will yield a value of C only slightly less than 1, which will still assure us of a stable and accurate solution. We next determine that $Fg/w = 9651$ ft^2/sec^2 from the values given for the problem parameters. This latter value, along with the Δx and Δt values selected, is used as input data in the computer program which is shown near the end of this example.

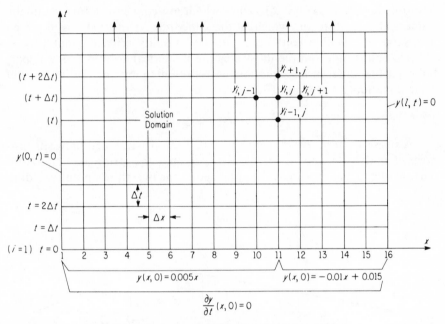

FIG. 8-19. Space-time grid for vibrating-string problem.

We next sketch a space-time grid such as the one in Fig. 8-19. Since the string is released from rest, the initial conditions are

$$y(x, 0) = \left\{ \begin{array}{l} 0.005x \\ -0.01x + 0.015 \end{array} \right\} \quad \begin{array}{l} (0 \le x \le 1.0) \\ (1.0 < x \le 1.5) \end{array}$$

$$\frac{\partial y}{\partial t}(x, 0) = 0$$

The boundary conditions which must be satisfied are

$$y(0, t) = 0$$
$$y(l, t) = 0$$

The second initial condition shown can be expressed in finite-difference form as

$$\frac{y_{i+1, j} - y_{i-1, j}}{2(\Delta t)} = 0$$

from which

$$y_{i+1, j} = y_{i-1, j} \qquad (8\text{-}38)$$

This relationship implies the use of an *imaginary* row of grid points preceding the row identified by $t = 0$ in Fig. 8-19. If we substitute Eq. 8-38 into Eq. 8-37, we obtain the following equation:

$$y_{i+1, j} = y_{i, j} + \frac{C}{2} [y_{i, j+1} - 2y_{i, j} + y_{i, j-1}] \qquad (8\text{-}39)$$

Equation 8-39 is used to calculate the displacements at the grid points in the row corresponding to $t = \Delta t$, since its use yields values which satisfy the initial condition that the string is released from rest.

The first step in the numerical procedure, then, is to calculate the displacements at grid points 2 through 15 in the row corresponding to $t = \Delta t$ by the use of Eq. 8-39, utilizing the known initial displacements to start the calculating process. Equation 8-37 is then employed to calculate the displacements at grid points 2 through 15 for all subsequent rows in a *row-by-row* progression. The grid points in the vicinity of the ith row and the jth column, shown in Fig. 8-19, illustrate the calculating process, the displacement at each grid point under consideration ($y_{i+1, j}$) being calculated from the previously calculated values at the adjacent grid points shown. The number of rows of grid points calculated obviously depends upon the time interval over which a solution is desired. Thus, the computer solution is usually terminated by adding the Δt increments used and specifying a termination when their sum corresponds to the time interval desired.

In writing the computer program it will not be necessary to use a double-subscripted variable name for identifying the displacements at the various grid points, because all the values calculated need not be stored in memory if we specify a printout of the desired displacements as they are calculated. The numerical procedure discussed shows that it is necessary to retain in memory only the displacements of the last 2 rows calculated to furnish sufficient data for the ensuing calculation (see Fig. 8-19). Therefore, we shall use single-subscripted variable names for identifying the grid points in the pertinent rows, as shown in the following list.

FORTRAN *Name*	*Quantity*	*Value Used in Problem*
Y(J) ⎫ Y1(J) ⎬ Y2(J) ⎭	Displacements corresponding to rows of grid points for times t, $t + \Delta t$, and $t + 2\Delta t$, respectively, ft.	
ASQR	$a^2 = Fg/w$	9651 ft^2/sec^2
DELT	Time increment, Δt	0.001 sec
DELX	Increment of string length, Δx	0.1 ft
TPR	Time at which a printout occurs, sec	

		Value Used
FORTRAN *Name*	*Quantity*	*in Problem*
DTPR	Print time increment	0.005 sec
T	Time, sec	
C	$C = \dfrac{Fg}{w}\dfrac{(\Delta t)^2}{(\Delta x)^2}$	
TFIN	Length of time desired for solution interval	0.2 sec

The flow chart for the problem is shown in Fig. 8-20. The FOR-
TRAN IV source program, written from the outline provided by the flow
chart, is as follows:

```
   DIMENSION Y(16),Y1(16),Y2(16)
 2 FORMAT(8F5.0)
   DO 3J=1,16
 3 READ(5,2)Y1(J)
   READ(5,2)ASQR,DELT,DELX,DTPR,TFIN
   TPR=DTPR
   T=DELT
   C=ASQR*DELT**2/DELX**2
   WRITE(6,4)
 4 FORMAT(6H   TIME,3X,47HDISPLACEMENTS AT STATIONS 1,3,5,7,
                                       9,11,13,15,16//)
   Y2(1)=0.
   Y2(16)=0.
   DO 5J=2,15
 5 Y2(J)=Y1(J)+.5*C*(Y1(J+1)-2.*Y1(J)+Y1(J-1))
 6 DO 7J=2,15
   Y(J)=Y1(J)
 7 Y1(J)=Y2(J)
   DO 8J=2,15
 8 Y2(J)=2.*Y1(J)-Y(J)+C*(Y1(J+1)-2.*Y1(J)+Y1(J-1))
   T=T+DELT
   IF(T-TPR)6,9,9
 9 WRITE(6,10)T,(Y2(J),J=1,15,2),Y2(16)
10 FORMAT(F6.4,9F7.4)
   TPR=TPR+DTPR
   IF(T-TFIN)6,11,11
11 STOP
   END
```

It should be noted in the program that the displacements at the grid
points of the row corresponding to $t = \Delta t$ in Fig. 8-19 are calculated in

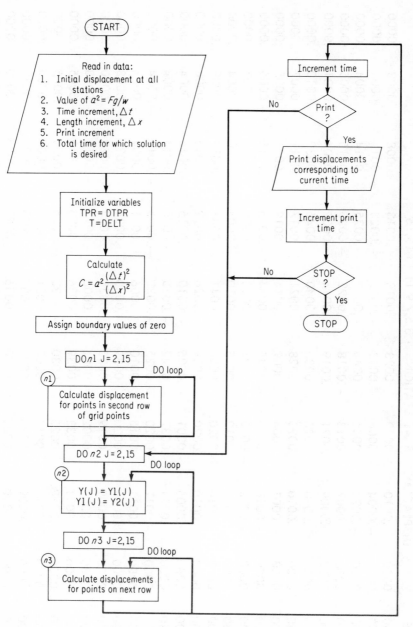

FIG. 8-20. Flow chart for Example 8-3.

DISPLACEMENTS AT STATIONS 1,3,5,7,9,11,13,15,16

TIME	1	3	5	7	9	11	13	15	16
.0050	.0000	.0010	.0020	.0023	.0018	.0013	.0008	.0003	.0000
.0100	.0000	-.0004	-.0008	-.0013	-.0018	-.0023	-.0014	-.0004	.0000
.0150	.0000	-.0020	-.0041	-.0046	-.0035	-.0025	-.0014	-.0004	.0000
.0200	.0000	-.0007	-.0013	-.0018	-.0022	-.0025	-.0015	-.0005	.0000
.0250	.0000	.0009	.0021	.0019	.0014	.0009	.0004	-.0001	.0000
.0300	.0000	.0010	.0020	.0030	.0040	.0046	.0030	.0010	.0000
.0350	.0000	.0010	.0020	.0028	.0021	.0017	.0011	.0007	.0000
.0400	.0000	.0001	-.0004	-.0009	-.0014	-.0019	-.0016	-.0005	.0000
.0450	.0000	-.0018	-.0040	-.0045	-.0034	-.0025	-.0015	-.0005	.0000
.0500	.0000	-.0012	-.0016	-.0021	-.0028	-.0025	-.0015	-.0005	.0000
.0550	.0000	.0009	.0019	.0015	.0010	.0004	.0000	-.0004	.0000
.0600	.0000	.0010	.0020	.0030	.0041	.0041	.0031	.0009	.0000
.0650	.0000	.0010	.0020	.0029	.0026	.0022	.0015	.0008	.0000
.0700	.0000	.0005	-.0001	-.0005	-.0010	-.0015	-.0016	-.0004	.0000
.0750	.0000	-.0021	-.0037	-.0042	-.0035	-.0025	-.0014	-.0004	.0000
.0800	.0000	-.0017	-.0020	-.0025	-.0032	-.0025	-.0014	-.0004	.0000
.0850	.0000	.0011	.0015	.0010	.0006	.0001	-.0004	-.0004	.0000
.0900	.0000	.0009	.0020	.0029	.0040	.0039	.0031	.0008	.0000
.0950	.0000	.0009	.0019	.0030	.0031	.0024	.0022	.0010	.0000
.1000	.0000	.0007	.0002	-.0001	-.0006	-.0011	-.0014	-.0003	.0000
.1050	.0000	-.0021	-.0033	-.0039	-.0036	-.0023	-.0015	-.0005	.0000
.1100	.0000	-.0018	-.0025	-.0030	-.0033	-.0025	-.0015	-.0005	.0000
.1150	.0000	.0011	.0012	.0007	.0001	-.0002	-.0009	-.0004	.0000
.1200	.0000	.0009	.0020	.0031	.0037	.0033	.0028	.0010	.0000
.1250	.0000	.0010	.0020	.0030	.0036	.0027	.0025	.0010	.0000
.1300	.0000	.0009	.0009	.0001	-.0002	-.0006	-.0012	-.0007	.0000

.1350	.0000	−.0004	−.0016	−.0024	−.0035	−.0034	−.0029	−.0019	.0000
.1400	.0000	−.0004	−.0015	−.0026	−.0034	−.0034	−.0029	−.0019	.0000
.1450	.0000	−.0005	−.0012	−.0007	−.0002	.0003	.0008	.0009	.0000
.1500	.0000	.0012	.0023	.0029	.0035	.0031	.0019	.0011	.0000
.1550	.0000	.0009	.0027	.0034	.0038	.0029	.0020	.0010	.0000
.1600	.0000	−.0007	−.0007	−.0003	.0001	.0005	.0013	.0009	.0000
.1650	.0000	−.0004	−.0014	−.0026	−.0033	−.0029	−.0025	−.0019	.0000
.1700	.0000	−.0005	−.0014	−.0024	−.0035	−.0038	−.0033	−.0020	.0000
.1750	.0000	−.0005	−.0013	−.0011	−.0004	−.0001	.0003	.0008	.0000
.1800	.0000	.0012	.0020	.0026	.0030	.0030	.0018	.0010	.0000
.1850	.0000	.0010	.0029	.0040	.0038	.0030	.0020	.0009	.0000
.1900	.0000	−.0005	−.0003	−.0000	.0006	.0010	.0015	.0009	.0000
.1950	.0000	−.0005	−.0013	−.0025	−.0030	−.0027	−.0021	−.0016	.0000
.2000	.0000	−.0005	−.0015	−.0024	−.0034	−.0042	−.0037	−.0019	.0000

the D05J = 2,15 loop using Eq. 8-39, while the displacements at the grid points of subsequent rows are calculated in the D08J = 2,15 loop using Eq. 8-37, but that all grid points in the process of *being calculated* are identified by the Y2(J) designation.

The computer printout of the displacement-time data for the stations selected is shown on pp. 494 and 495.

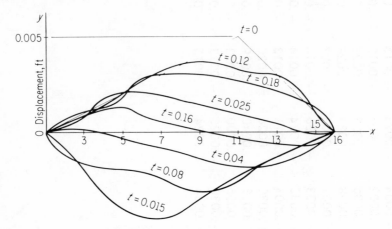

FIG. 8-21. String configurations at different times.

Figure 8-21 shows a sketch of the *approximate* string configurations for the various times indicated with the y displacements greatly exaggerated. Although the graphical plot shown was done manually, plotters are available which will display digital readout in graphical form, plotting from either the computer output or magnetic-tape storage.

The solution shown reveals that the period of vibration of the string is approximately 0.03 sec, since the displacements at each station repeat at approximately this interval. If it were desired to plot the displacement-time curve for a particular station over 1 cycle, a printout increment of 0.001 sec should be used to obtain enough values to plot a reasonably accurate curve.

Problems

8-1. Write a FORTRAN program for determining the temperature distribution over the triangular plate shown in the accompanying figure. The left boundary is insulated up to and including row $I = IA$, and the right diagonal boundary is completely insulated. A temperature of $U = U_B$ is maintained along the bottom edge of the plate, and a temperature of $U = U_L$ is maintained along the uninsulated portion of the left edge.

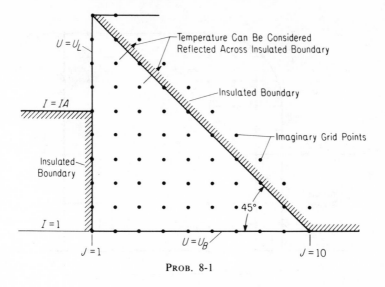

PROB. 8-1

Note that the applicable equation on the insulated diagonal boundary is

$$u_{i,j} = \frac{2u_{i,j-1} + 2u_{i-1,j}}{4}$$

This equation can be obtained by considering an imaginary row of grid points having temperatures which are the reflections of temperatures at points situated perpendicularly across the boundary, as shown in the figure. Such a consideration reveals that

and

$$u_{i-1,j} = u_{i,j+1}$$

$$u_{i,j-1} = u_{i+1,j}$$

These relationships are substituted into the general finite-difference form of the differential equation

$$u_{i,j} = \frac{u_{i,j+1} + u_{i,j-1} + u_{i+1,j} + u_{i-1,j}}{4}$$

to obtain the diagonal-boundary equation given.

8-2. Rewrite the program of Example 8-1 to utilize overrelaxation (Eq. 8-21a in place of Eq. 8-21). Run the problem for a range of values of ω between 1 and 2, and determine an approximate value of ω_{opt} for this example.

8-3. Write a **FORTRAN** program for determining the temperature distribution over the plate shown in the accompanying figure. The left boundary is insulated up to and including row $I = IA$, and the right boundary is completely insulated. A temperature of $U = U_B$ is maintained along the bottom edge of the plate, and a temperature of $U = U_T$ is maintained along the upper edge of the

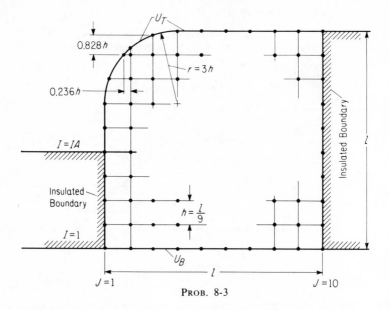

PROB. 8-3

plate and along the upper portion of the left edge, as shown in the figure. Use a grid having a space of $h = l/9$.

8-4. Write a **FORTRAN** program for determining the temperature distribution over the plate shown in the accompanying figure. The left boundary is

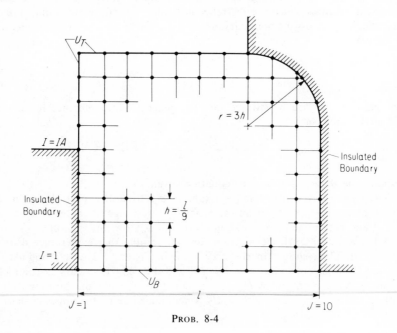

PROB. 8-4

insulated up to and including row $I = IA$, and the right boundary is completely insulated, as shown in the figure. A temperature of $U = U_B$ is maintained along the bottom edge of the plate, and a temperature of $U = U_T$ is maintained along the portions of the left and upper edges, as shown in the figure. Use a grid spacing of $h = l/9$.

8-5. As shown in the accompanying figure, a 6-in.-square tube, with a 2-in.-square hole in the center portion, carries a fluid having a temperature of 300°F. The outside boundary of the tube is 75°F. Write a **FORTRAN** program for obtaining the temperature distribution across the tube. Owing to the symmetry of the temperature distribution, it is necessary to calculate the temperatures over only one fourth of the tube cross section. In using only one fourth of the tube for obtaining the temperature distribution, it is necessary to satisfy the temperature-gradient conditions of $\partial u/\partial x = 0$ at $x = 3$ in. and $\partial u/\partial y = 0$ at $y = 3$ in.

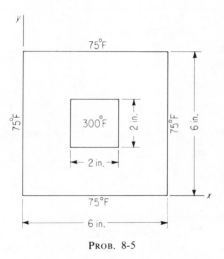

PROB. 8-5

8-6. A 12-in.-square membrane (no bending or shear stresses), with a 4-in.-square hole in the middle, is fastened at the outside and inside boundaries, as shown in the accompanying illustration. If a highly stretched membrane is subjected to a pressure p, the partial differential equation for the deflection w in the z direction is

$$\frac{\partial^2 w}{\partial x^2} + \frac{\partial^2 w}{\partial y^2} = -\frac{p}{T}$$

where T is the tension (pounds per linear inch). For a highly stretched membrane, the tension T may be assumed constant for small deflections.

Utilizing the finite-difference expressions of Eq. 8-13, write a **FORTRAN** program and obtain the deflections w for a membrane in which

$$p = 5 \text{ psi (uniformly distributed)}$$

$$T = 100 \text{ lb/in.}$$

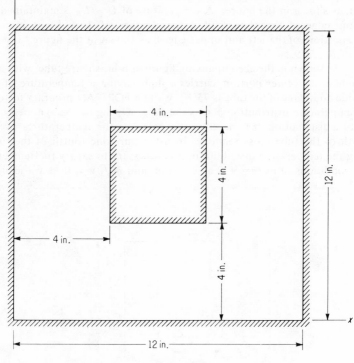

PROB. 8-6

It should be noted that, owing to symmetry, it is necessary to consider only one fourth of the membrane. In calculating the deflection over one fourth of the symmetrical membrane, it is necessary to satisfy the conditions of $\partial w/\partial y = 0$ at $y = 6$ in. and $\partial w/\partial x = 0$ at $x = 6$ in. (This is analogous to an insulated boundary in the temperature-distribution problem discussed in Sec. 8-2.)

8-7. Fluid is flowing through a conduit having a cross section as shown in the accompanying illustration. The partial differential equation for the steady-state velocity ϕ of the fluid is

$$\frac{\partial^2 \phi}{\partial x^2} + \frac{\partial^2 \phi}{\partial y^2} = -\frac{c}{\mu}$$

where c is the absolute value of the pressure gradient in the direction of flow, and μ is the viscosity of the fluid. Noting that the velocity of the fluid is zero on the boundaries, write a **FORTRAN** program for obtaining the velocity distribution of the fluid. In addition to obtaining the velocities of the fluid flow, the program is to include the calculation of the flow rate Q (volume/sec) where

$$Q = \int_A \phi \, dA$$

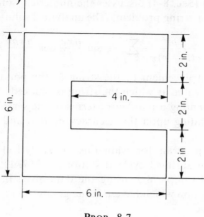

PROB. 8-7

The values for c and μ are as follows:

$$c = 0.02 \text{ lb/in.}^2/\text{in. (constant over the cross section)}$$

$$\mu = 0.25 \times 10^{-6} \text{ lb-sec/in.}^2$$

8-8. Write a FORTRAN program for determining the transient temperatures along a slender rod for which all the data of Example 8-2 (Sec. 8-3) are pertinent except that the temperature applied at the left end of the rod is a function of time, as shown in the accompanying figure. The temperature function is represented by the absolute value of a sine wave with the amplitude and period shown.

Determine your solution up to the approximate time at which the rod reaches a final equilibrium temperature state. (HINT: Compare temperatures at each station at time intervals corresponding to the period of the temperature function applied to the rod.)

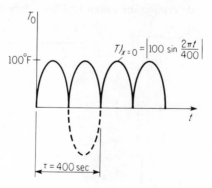

PROB. 8-8

8-9. Example 8-3 (Sec. 8-4) discusses the numerical solution, on the digital computer, of a vibrating-string problem. The analytical solution of this problem is

$$y(x, t) = \frac{2bl^2}{c(l - c)\pi^2} \sum_{n=1}^{\infty} \frac{1}{n^2} \sin \frac{n\pi c}{l} \cos \frac{n\pi a t}{l} \sin \frac{n\pi x}{l}$$

where b is the initial displacement of the string at the point where the string is plucked, and c is the x value at which the string is plucked. The analytical solution is evaluated by summing a number of terms of the series shown, the number of terms summed depending upon the accuracy desired and on the rate of convergence of the series.

Write a **FORTRAN** program for evaluating the analytical solution for the displacements of the string during 1 cycle at stations 3, 5, 7, 11, 13, and 15, as indicated by Fig. 8-18 in Example 8-3, using the data given in that example. Use all terms in each summation which have a value greater than 0.000001 ft. Use Δt increments of 0.0001 sec.

Compare the results obtained with the results given for corresponding stations in the computer printout included in Example 8-3.

8-10. A steel bar has one end fixed, as shown in the accompanying figure. The unrestrained end of the bar is suddenly subjected to a constant force F which is applied as shown in the figure. Sections at various locations along the bar will be displaced longitudinally by the application of such a force, and the displacements $u(x, t)$ at these sections will be functions of both time and location along the bar. Applying Newton's second law to an element of the bar of length dx, determine the partial differential equation describing the displacement of any section along the bar at any time t where

A = cross-sectional area of bar
E = modulus of elasticity of bar
ρ = weight density of bar
l = length of bar

Recall, from strength of materials or theory of elasticity, that the strain in the x direction is given by

$$\epsilon_x = \frac{\partial u}{\partial x}$$

It is left to the reader to determine the initial and boundary conditions.

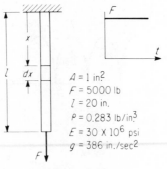

$A = 1$ in.^{2}
$F = 5000$ lb
$l = 20$ in.
$\rho = 0.283$ lb/in.^{3}
$E = 30 \times 10^6$ psi
$g = 386$ in./sec^2

PROB. 8-10

Write a **FORTRAN** program for determining, by a numerical method, the displacements of the bar at equally spaced stations along the bar at equally spaced time intervals over a total time interval equal to at least 1 period of the fundamental mode of vibration of the bar. It can be shown that the fundamental period is given by

$$\tau = \frac{4l}{\sqrt{\dfrac{Eg}{\rho}}}$$

where g is the acceleration of gravity.

Obtain a solution using the values shown in the accompanying figure.

8-11. The analytical solution of Prob. 8-10 is

$$u(x, t) = \frac{8glF}{a^2 \pi^2 \rho A} \sum_{n=1,3,5,\ldots}^{\infty} \frac{(-1)^{(n-1)/2}}{n^2} \sin \frac{n\pi x}{2l} \left(1 - \cos \frac{n\pi at}{2l}\right)$$

where

$$a = \sqrt{\frac{Eg}{\rho}}$$

and the other parameters are as defined in Prob. 8-10 and its accompanying figure.

Write a **FORTRAN** program for evaluating the series expression for $u(x, t)$. Obtain a solution using the values shown in the figure accompanying Prob. 8-10.

If you have obtained a solution of Prob. 8-10, check the correspondence of the two solutions.

8-12. A circular shaft of length l has a rigid disk attached to each end, as shown in the accompanying figure, and is supported by "frictionless" bearings (not shown). When free torsional vibrations are initiated in the shaft, the twisting

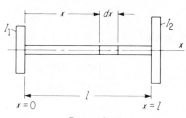

PROB. 8-12

moments on the ends of the element of length dx (shown in the figure) are

$$GJ \frac{\partial \theta}{\partial x} \qquad \text{and} \qquad GJ\left(\frac{\partial \theta}{\partial x} + \frac{\partial^2 \theta}{\partial x^2} dx\right)$$

where

G = modulus of rigidity of shaft, $lb/in.^2$
J = polar moment of inertia of shaft cross section, $in.^4$
ρ = weight density of shaft material, $lb/in.^3$
θ = angle of twist at any cross section, radians

By applying the equation $T = I \dfrac{\partial^2 \theta}{\partial t^2}$ to the element considered as a free body, show that the partial differential equation describing the angular motion of the shaft for any position x at any time t is

$$\frac{\partial^2 \theta}{\partial t^2} = \frac{Gg}{\rho} \frac{\partial^2 \theta}{\partial x^2}$$

When the shaft is released from rest with a specified initial configuration, the initial conditions are given by the equations

$$\theta(x, 0) = f(x)$$

$$\frac{\partial \theta}{\partial t}(x, 0) = 0$$

By considering the disks at the ends of the shaft as free bodies and applying the equation $T = I \frac{\partial^2 \theta}{\partial t^2}$, show that the boundary conditions at the ends of the shaft are given by

$$I_1 \left(\frac{\partial^2 \theta}{\partial t^2}\right)_{x=0} = GJ \left(\frac{\partial \theta}{\partial x}\right)_{x=0}$$

and

$$I_2 \left(\frac{\partial^2 \theta}{\partial t^2}\right)_{x=l} = -GJ \left(\frac{\partial \theta}{\partial x}\right)_{x=l}$$

where I_1 and I_2 are the mass moments of inertia of the disks about the x axis, as indicated on the accompanying figure.

Write a **FORTRAN** program for determining θ for equally spaced increments of x and t over a time interval equal to at least 1 period of the fundamental mode. The period of the fundamental mode is given by

$$\tau = \frac{2\pi l}{\beta a}$$

In the latter equation $a = \sqrt{Gg/\rho}$ and β is the first positive root of the transcendental equation

$$\tan \beta = \frac{(m + n)\beta}{mn\beta^2 - 1}$$

where

$$m = \frac{I_1}{I_o}$$

$$n = \frac{I_2}{I_o}$$

$$I_o = \frac{\rho l J}{g} \quad \text{(mass moment of inertia of shaft about longitudinal axis)}$$

Include in your overall program the steps necessary to determine the fundamental period of the system, and use the value determined as the criterion for stopping the overall program.

As a hint for applying the boundary-condition equations in the solution of the problem, put the boundary equations in difference form by using a first *central-difference* expression for each second derivative and first *forward-* and *backward-*

difference expressions for the respective first derivatives. Use the resulting equations to solve for boundary values of θ as the solution progresses with time.

8-13. Using the program written for Prob. 8-12, determine values of θ for equally spaced x values over a period of time approximately equal to the fundamental period of the system discussed in Prob. 8-12. The shaft is 24 in. long and 2 in. in diameter. The disk on the left end has a mass moment of inertia of 0.25 lb-in.-sec^2, and the disk on the right end has a mass moment of inertia of 0.5 lb-in.-sec^2. The shaft is made of steel such that

$$G = 12(10)^6 \text{ lb/in.}^2$$

$$\rho = 0.286 \text{ lb/in.}^3$$

An initial configuration is given to the shaft by holding the left end fixed and twisting the right end through an angle of 0.04 radian.

Index

507